Stanley Gibbon

COLLECT
Channel Islands
and Isle of Man
STAMPS

A STANLEY GIBBONS CHECKLIST

2005 Edition

STANLEY GIBBONS LTD
London and Ringwood

*By Appointment to
Her Majesty The Queen,
Stanley Gibbons Ltd., London,
Philatelists*

Published by **Stanley Gibbons Publications**
Editorial, Sales Offices and Distribution Centre:
Parkside, Christchurch Road, Ringwood,
Hants BH24 3SH

21st COMBINED EDITION (2005)

ISBN: 0-85259-588-3

© Stanley Gibbons Ltd 2005

Item No. 2855 (05)

Text assembled and printed in Great Britain by
Piggott Black Bear, Cambridge

Introductory Notes

Scope. The listing of **stamps** for Guernsey and Jersey comprises German Occupation issues, the 1958–69 Regionals and the issues of the Independent Postal Administrations from their inception in 1969. Isle of Man sections cover the 1958–71 Regionals and the issues of the Independent Postal Administration from 1973 onwards.

Information is given on:

- Designers and printers
- The different printings for definitives and postage dues
- Distinctive papers
- Such varieties as imperforates and missing colours
- Phosphors
- Cylinder and plate numbers
- Sheet sizes and imprints
- Quantities sold
- Withdrawal and invalidation dates

The 'Notes' on page 1 may be found helpful in further explanation.

The checklist also covers:

- Miniature sheets
- First-day covers
- Presentation packs and Yearbooks
- Gutter pairs
- Stamp booklets
- Stamp sachets (listed, but unpriced)
- Postal stationery commemorative cards and covers

Items outside the scope and therefore *omitted* are: cylinder and plate varieties; non-postage stamps, such as revenues; and other classes of postal stationery.

Layout. Stamps are set out chronologically by date of issue. In the catalogue lists the first numeral is the Stanley Gibbons catalogue number; the black (boldface) numeral alongside is the type number referring to the respective illustration. The denomination and colour of the stamp are then shown. Before February 1971 British currency was:

£1=20s One Pound = twenty shillings *and*
1s=12d One shilling = twelve pence.

Upon decimalisation this became:

£1=100p One pound = one hundred (new) pence

The catalogue list then shows two price columns. The left-hand is for unused stamps and the right-hand for used.

Our method of indicating prices is:

Numerals for pence, e.g. 5 denotes 5p (5 pence). Numerals for pounds and pence, e.g. 4.25 denotes £4.25 (4 pounds and 25 pence). For £100 and above, prices are in whole pounds and so include the £ sign and omit the zeros for pence.

Size of illustrations. To comply with Post Office regulations illustrations of stamps and booklets are three-quarters linear size. Illustrations of watermarks are actual size.

Prices. Prices quoted in this catalogue are our selling prices at the time the book went to press. They are for stamps in fine condition; in issues where condition varies we may ask more for the superb and less for the sub-standard. With unused stamps prices are for unmounted mint (though where not available unmounted, mounted mint stamps are often supplied at a lower price). Used prices are normally for stamps postally used but may be for stamps cancelled-to-order where this practice exists. All prices are subject to change without prior notice and we give no guarantee to supply all stamps priced, since it is not possible to keep every catalogue item perpetually in stock. Commemoratives may, at times, only be available in complete sets. Individual low value stamps sold at 399, Strand are liable to an additional handling charge.

Perforations. The 'perforation' is the number of holes in a length of 2 cm, as measured by the Gibbons *Instanta* gauge. The stamp is viewed against a dark background with the transparent gauge put on top of it. Perforations are quoted to the nearest half. Stamps without perforation are termed 'imperforate'.

Se-tenant combinations. *Se-tenant* means 'joined together'. Some sets include stamps of different design arranged *se-tenant* as blocks or strips and, in mint condition, these are usually collected unsevered as issued. Where such combinations exist, the individual stamps are priced normally as mint and used singles. The set price for mint refers to the unsevered combination plus singles of any other values in the set. The used set price is for single stamps of all values.

First Day Covers. Prices for first day covers are for complete sets used on special covers, the stamps of which bear an official postmark for first day of issue. Where the stamps in a set were issued on different days, prices are for a cover from each day.

Catalogue numbers used. The checklist uses the same catalogue numbers as the Stanley Gibbons *Stamps of the World* catalogue, 2005 edition.

Latest stamps recorded in this edition appeared in December 2004.

Specialist Philatelic Society. Channel Islands Specialists Society. Membership Secretary: Sheila Marshall (SGC), 3 La Marette, Alderney, Channel Islands, GY9 3UQ.

CONTENTS

v

Printings
For definitives and postage due stamps released by the independent Postal Administration we give the dates of the printings as announced, and relate them in the listings to the actual stamps involved. Users will therefore be able to see at a glance how many printings have been made of any particular item.

Cylinder and Plate Numbers
Following the listing of each issue we give the printers' cylinder or plate numbers known to us.

Sheet size
In describing the sheet arrangement we always give the number of stamps across the sheet first. For example, '50 (5×10)' indicates a sheet of fifty stamps in ten horizontal rows of five stamps each.

Paper
Only distinctive types are mentioned. Granite paper can be easily distinguished by the coloured lines in its texture. *Chalky* or *chalk-surfaced* applies to paper which shows a black line when touched with silver.

Perforations
Perforations are normally given to the nearest half and the Instanta gauge is our standard. In this checklist we state if a perforation is by a line (L) or a comb (C) machine. A line machine only perforates one line at a time and consequently it requires two operations to do the horizontal and vertical perforations and where these intersect an irregular-shaped hole often results. A comb machine perforates three sides at a time and therefore produces a single hole at all corner intersections. The differences are easily seen in blocks of four.

The various perforations in this checklist are expressed as follows:

Perf 14:   Perforated alike on all sides.
Perf 14×15: Compound perforation. The first figure refers to top and bottom, the second to left and right sides.

Abbreviations
des = designer, designed
eng = engraver, engraved
litho = lithographed
mm = millimetres
MS = miniature sheet
No. = number
perf = perforated
photo = photogravure
recess = recess-printed
typo = typographed
wmk(d) = watermark(ed)

Channel Islands

C **1** Gathering Vraic   C **2** Islanders gathering Vraic

Third Anniversary of Liberaton

(Des J. R. R. Stobie (1d.), or from drawing by E. Blampied (2½d). Photo Harrison and Sons)

1948 (10 MAY). *Wmk Mult* G VI R. Perf 15×14 (C)
C1	C **1**	1d scarlet	25	30
C2	C **2**	2½d ultramarine	25	30
		First Day Cover		35·00

These stamps were primarily intended for use in the Channel Islands although they were also available at eight head post offices in Great Britain.

Cylinder Nos.: 1d 2; 2½d 4

Sheets: 120 (6×20)

Quantities sold: 1d 5,934,000; 2½d 5,398,000

Guernsey

THE GERMAN OCCUPATION 1940—1945

The first German soldiers to arrive in Guernsey set foot on the island on 30 June 1940 and an official notice appeared in the local newspaper the following day announcing the occupation.

The first evidence of the occupation, philatelically, came towards the end of the year when supplies of Great Britain 1d stamps then in use began to dry up. It was decided that the bisecting of 2d stamps for use as 1d's be allowed and this commenced on 27 December. The decision to print 1d stamps locally had been taken in October, but these were not ready and were eventually issued on 18 February 1941. In the meantime the two currently available 2d stamps, the 1937 definitive and the 1940 Postal Centenary, were bisected and used, as were 2d stamps of the reign of George V which were in collectors' hands. Other values are also known to have been bisected and used, and were allowed to pass through the post in most instances without a postage due charge being made.

When the decision to bisect the 2d stamps was taken the German Commandant in Guernsey decided on adding a swastika to each half of the stamp. This overprint was applied to the Postal Centenary stamp and these were submitted to Berlin for approval, but this proposal was turned down. Another proposal, the overprinting of the 1937 1d with a number of small swastikas, would appear to have been dealt with in a similar way. Examples of both items exist though these are very rare.

As previously mentioned, the locally printed 1d stamps were issued on 18 February 1941. The ½d stamp was released on 7 April 1941 and the 2½d on 12 April 1944. This last stamp was issued in an effort to economise on the use of paper as it was found that sealed letters were franked with two 1d stamps and one ½d or a larger number of ½d's, a gross waste in times of shortage. Many printings of these stamps were made, the most notable being on the French bank-note paper in 1942.

Shades of these issues abound, the more outstanding ones being the bluish green (4th) and olive-green (8th) printings of the ½d, and the pale vermilion (11th) printing of the 1d. During the occupation Guernsey stamps were only valid on mail within the Channel Islands. Letters sent overseas were despatched via the German Feldpost system. The stamps continued to be used after the liberation in 1945 until 13 April 1946.

The Swastika Overprints

1940. *Prepared for use but not issued. Stamps of Great Britain overprinted*

(a) 1937 *definitive overprinted with a number of small swastikas*

Cat No.		Unused
SW1	1d scarlet	£900

(b) 1940 *Postal Centenary issue overprinted with a swastika on each half of the stamp*

SW2	2d orange	£900

Example of bisected 2d Postal Centenary stamp

The Bisects

1940 (27 DEC).

(a) *Stamps of King George V*

Cat. No.			Price on cover
BS1	1912–22	2d orange	£250
BS2	1924–26	2d orange	£250
BS3	1934–36	2d orange	£275

(b) *Stamps of King George VI*

BS4	1937	1d scarlet	£475
BS5	1938	2d orange	40·00
BS6	1940	Stamp Centenary 1d scarlet	£475
BS7	1940	Stamp Centenary 2d orange	32·00
BS8	1940	Stamp Centenary 2½d ultramarine	£750
BS9	1940	Stamp Centenary 3d violet	

Forged postmarks on fake bisects are known from Guernsey Head Post Office ('2 JA 41'), Market Place ('19 FE 41' or '7 AP 41'), St. Sampson ('27 DE 40') and The Vale ('18 FE 41').

The bisects are priced on philatelic cover. Those which were used commercially are worth more, particularly Nos. BS5 and BS7.

Invalidated: 22.2.41 (last postings were postmarked 24.2.41.)

1 Arms of Guernsey

1a Loops

Stamps issued during the German Occupation

(Des E. W. Vaudin. Typo Guernsey Press Co Ltd)

1941–44. *Rouletted*

(a) *White paper. No wmk*

Cat. No.	Type No.		Unused	Used
1	**1**	½d light green (7.4.41)	3·00	1·75
		a. *Emerald-green* (6.41)	3·50	1·50
		b. *Bluish green* (11.41)	30·00	13·00
		c. *Bright green* (2.42)	18·00	9·00
		d. *Dull green* (9.42)	3·00	1·75
		e. *Olive-green* (2.43)	25·00	10·00
		f. *Pale yellowish green* (7.43 and later) (*shades*)	3·00	1·50
		g. *Imperf* (*pair*)	£200	
		h. *Imperf between* (*horizontal pair*)	£700	
		i. *Imperf between* (*vertical pair*)		£800
2		1d scarlet (18.2.41)	2·00	90
		a. *Pale vermilion* (7.43) (*etc*) . .	2·50	90
		b. *Carmine* (1943)	2·00	90
		c. *Imperf* (*pair*)	£150	75·00
		d. *Imperf between* (*horizontal pair*)	£700	
		da. *Imperf vert* (*centre stamp of horizontal strip of 3*)		
		e. *Imperf between* (*vertical pair*)		£800
		f. *Ptd double* (*scarlet shade*) . .	£100	
3		2½d ultramarine (12.4.44)	3·25	4·00
		a. *Pale ultramarine* (7.44)	3·25	5·00
		b. *Imperf* (*pair*)	£500	
		c. *Imperf between* (*horizontal pair*)	£1000	
1		*First Day Cover*		6·00
2		*First Day Cover*		12·00
3		First Day Cover		8·00

(b) *Bluish French bank-note paper. Wmk* **1a** (*sideways*)

4	**1**	½d bright green (11.3.42)	20·00	18·00
5		1d scarlet (9.4.42)	10·00	16·00
4		*First Day Cover*		90·00
5		*First Day Cover*		55·00

The dates for the shades of Nos. 1/3 are the months in which they were printed as indicated on the printer's imprints (see below). Others are issue dates.

Printings and imprint: The various printings can be identified from the sheet imprints as follows:

½d 1st Printing 240M/3/41
2nd Printing 2×120M/6/41
3rd Printing 3×120M/6/41
4th Printing 4×120M/11/41
5th Printing 5×120M/2/42
6th Printing 6×240M/2/42
7th Printing 7×120M/9/42
8th Printing 8×120M/2/43
9th Printing 9×120M/7/43
10th Printing 10×120M/10/43
11th Printing Guernsey Press Co., (*stop and comma*)
12th Printing Guernsey Press Co. (*stop only, margin at bottom 23 to 27 mm*)
13th Printing Guernsey Press Co. (*stop only, margin at bottom 15 mm*)

1d 1st Printing 120M/2/41
2nd Printing 2×120M/2/41
3rd Printing 3×120M/6/41
4th Printing 4×120M/6/41
5th Printing 5×120M/9/41
6th Printing 6×240M/11/41
7th Printing 7×120M/2/42
8th Printing 8×240M/4/42
9th Printing 9×240M/9/42
10th Printing 10×240M/1/43
11th Printing 11×240M/7/43
12th Printing Guernsey Press Co.
13th Printing PRESS TYP.
14th Printing 'PRESS' (*inverted commas unlevel*)
15th Printing 'PRESS' (*inverted commas level, margin at bottom 28 mm*)
16th Printing 'PRESS' (*inverted commas level, margin at bottom 12 mm*)

2½d 1st Printing Guernsey Press Co.,
2nd Printing 'PRESS' (*inverted commas unlevel*)
3rd Printing 'PRESS' (*inverted commas level, margin at bottom 22 mm*)
4th Printing 'PRESS' (*inverted commas level, margin at bottom 15 mm*)

The numbered imprints occur in the left-hand corner, bottom margin on the 1st printing of the 1d, and central, bottom margin on all other printings of all three values.

In the numbered imprints, for example, 2×120M/6/41, the '2' indicates the number of the printing; '120M' denotes the number of stamps printed in thousands, in this case 120,000; and '6/41' denotes the date of the printing, June 1941.

In the first ten printings of the ½d and the first eleven printings of the 1d the printing details are prefixed by the name of the printer, "Guernsey Press Co."

Sheets: 60 (6×10)

Quantities printed: ½d 1,772,160; 1d 2,478,000; 2½d 416,640

Withdrawn and invalidated: 13.4.46

REGIONAL ISSUES

Although specifically issued for regional use, these issues were initially valid for use throughout Great Britain. However, they ceased to be valid in Guernsey and Jersey from 1 October 1969 when these islands each established their own independent postal administration and introduced their own stamps.

DATES OF ISSUE. Conflicting dates of issue have been announced for some of the regional issues, partly explained by the stamps being released on different dates by the Philatelic Bureau in Edinburgh or the Philatelic Counter in London and in the regions. We have adopted the practice of giving the earliest known dates, since once released the stamps could have been used anywhere in the U.K.

INVALIDATION. The regional issues of Guernsey were invalidated for use in Guernsey and Jersey on 1 November 1969 (although Guernsey granted a further extension for British and regional stamps till the end of March 1970). The stamps continued to be valid for use in the rest of the United Kingdom until 29 February 1972. Those still current remained on sale at philatelic sales counters until 30 September 1970.

1b Multiple Crowns

2

3

(Des E. A. Piprell. Portrait by Dorothy Wilding Ltd. Photo Harrison and Sons)

1958–67. *Wmk Type* **1b.** *Perf 15 × 14 (C)*

6	**2**	2½d rose-red (8.6.64)	35	40
7	**3**	3d deep lilac (18.8.58)	30	30
		p. *One centre phosphor band* (24.5.67)	15	20
8		4d ultramarine (7.2.66)	25	30
		p. *Two phosphor bands* (24.10.67)	15	20
6/8p		*Set of 3*	60	70
6		*First Day Cover*		30·00
7		*First Day Cover*		17·00
8		*First Day Cover*		8·00

Cylinder Nos.: 2½d 1, 3; 3d (ord) 4, 5; 3d (phos) 5; 4d (ord) 1; 4d (phos) 1

Sheets: 240 (12×20)

Quantities sold (ordinary only): 2½d 3,485,760; 3d 25,812,360; 4d 4,415,040

Withdrawn: 31.8.66 2½d

Sold out: 6.3.68 3d and 4d (ordinary); 10.68 4d (phosphor); 11.68 3d (phosphor)

1968-69. *No wmk. Chalk-surfaced paper. One centre phosphor band* (*Nos.* 10/11) *or two phosphor bands* (*others*). *Perf* 15×14 (C)

9	**3**	4d pale ultramarine (16.4.68) . .	10	20
10		4d pale ultramarine (4.9.68) . . .	10	15
11		4d bright vermilion (26.2.69) . . .	20	25
12		5d royal blue (4.9.68)	20	30
9/12		*Set of 4*	55	80
10, 12		*First Day Cover*		3·00

No. 9 was not issued in Guernsey until 22 April.

Cylinder Nos. 4d (pale ultramarine) 1; 4d (olive-sepia) 1; 4d (bright vermilion) 1; 5d 1

Sold out: 3.69 4d ultramarine

Withdrawn: 30.9.69 (locally), 30.9.70 (British Philatelic Counters) 4d olive-sepia, 4d bright vermilion and 5d

INDEPENDENT POSTAL ADMINISTRATION

Guernsey established their own independent postal administration on 1 October 1969 and introduced their own stamps.

NO WATERMARK. All the following issues are on unwatermarked paper.

4 Castle Cornet and Edward the Confessor

5 Map and William I

6 Martello Tower and Henry II

7 Arms of Sark and King John

8 Arms of Alderney and Edward III

9 Guernsey Lily and Henry V

10 Arms of Guernsey and Elizabeth I

4

11 Arms of Alderney and Charles II

12 Arms of Sark and George III

13 Arms of Guernsey and Queen Victoria

14 Guernsey Lily and Elizabeth I

15 Martello Tower and King John

16 View of Sark

17 View of Alderney

18 View of Guernsey

Two types of 1d and 1s6d

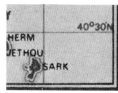

I Latitude inscr '40° 30' N'

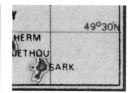

II Corrected to '49° 0' N'

(Des R. Granger Barrett. Photo Harrison (½d to 2s6d), Delrieu (others))

1969 (1 OCT)–**70**. Perf 14 (½d to 2s6d) or 12½ (others), all comb

13	**4**	½d deep magenta and black (a) .	10	10
		a. Thin paper	40	50
14	**5**	1d bright blue and black (I) (a) . .	10	10
		a. *Thin paper* (b)	50	50
14b		1d bright blue and black (*thin paper*) (II) (eg)	30	30
		c. *Booklet stamp with margins (thick paper)* (c)	40	40
15	**6**	1½d yellow-brown and black (a) .	10	10
16	**7**	2d gold, brt red, dp blue & blk (a)	10	10
		a. *Thin paper* (g)	40	40
17	**8**	3d gold, pale greenish yellow, orange-red and black (a) . . .	15	15
		a. *Error. Wmk Block CA* £1200		
		ai. *Wmk inverted* £900		
		b. *Thin paper* (g)	50	50
18	**9**	4d multicoloured (a)	20	25
		a. *Booklet stamp with margins* (c)	40	45
		ab. *Yellow omitted* £250		
		ac. *Emerald (stem) omitted* £110		
19	**10**	5d gold, bright vermilion, bluish violet and black (a) . . .	20	20
		a. *Booklet stamp with margins* (c)	50	50
		b. *Gold (inscription etc.) omitted (booklets)* £500		
20	**11**	6d gold, pale greenish yellow, light bronze-green & black (a)	20	30
		a. *Thin paper* (g)	45	45
21	**12**	9d gold, brt red, crimson & blk (a)	30	30
		a. *Thin paper* (g)	3·00	1·75
22	**13**	1s gold, brt verm, bistre & blk (a) .	30	30
		a. *Thin paper* (g)	1·00	75
23	**5**	1s6d turquoise-grn & blk (I) (a) . .	25	30
		a. *Thin paper* (d)	1·75	3·25
23b		1s6d turquoise-green and black (thin paper) (II) (eg)	2·00	1·75

24	**14**	1s9d multicoloured (*a*)	80	80
		a. Emerald (stem) omitted	£325	
		b. Thin paper (*g*)	2·25	1·90
25	**15**	2s6d brt reddish violet & black (*a*)	3·25	2·75
		a. Thin paper (*g*)	5·50	4·50
26	**16**	5s multicoloured (*a*)	2·50	2·25
27	**17**	10s multicoloured (*a*)	16·00	18·00
		a. Perf 13½×13 (*f*)	35·00	35·00
28	**18**	£1 multicoloured (*a*)	2·25	2·25
		a. Perf 13½ × 13 (*fh*)	2·25	2·25
13/28*a*		*Set of 16*	22·00	26·00
13/28		*First Day Cover*		28·00
13/28		*Presentation Packs (incl. both*		
		1d *and* 1s6d) (3) (9.70)	35·00	
13/25		*Set of 13 Gutter Pairs*		

Thinner paper – see note after Jersey No. 29.

There was no postal need for the ½d and 1½d values as the ½d coin had been withdrawn prior to their issue in anticipation of decimalisation. These values were only on sale at the Philatelic Bureau and at the Crown Agents as well as in the U.S.A.

Type **18** was re-issued as a booklet pane in 2001. See No. 927.

Printings: (*a*) 1.10.69; (*b*) 24.11.69; (*c*) 12.12.69; (*d*) 1.70; (*e*) 4.2.70; (*f*) 4.3.70; (*g*) 18.5.70; (*h*) 7.71

Cylinder Nos.: ½d, 1½d, 2s6d 1A–1A, 1B–1B; 1d (*l*) 1A–1A, 1B–1B, 2A–2A (*b*), 2B–2B; 1d (ll) 2A–2A, 2B–2B, 3A–3A (*g*), 3B–3B; 2d, 3d, 5d, 6d, 9d, 1s 1A, 1B (each ×4); 4d, 1s9d 1A, 1B (each ×5); 1s6d (l) 1A–1A, 1B–1B, 1A–2A (*d*), 1B–2B; 1s6d (ll) 1B–1B, 1A–2A, 1B–2B, 2A–3A (*g*), 2B–3B; 5s to £1 None

Sheets: 60 (2 panes (5×6) most sheets of the 5s, 10s and £1 were divided into two panes before issue

Imprint: Central, bottom margin (½d to 2s6d)

Quantities sold ½d 2,480,000; 1d (Nos. 14/14*b*) 1,560,971; 1½d 980,000; 2d 574,610; 3d 487,199; 4d 2,782,490; 5d 1,393,193; 6d 456,275; 9d 374,975; 1s 435,773; 1s6d (Nos. 23/23*b*) 627,003; 1s9d 255,111; 2s6d 225,732; 5s 165,047; 10s (No. 27) 114,000; 10s (No. 27*a*) 55,200; £1 (No. 28) 120,000; £1 (No. 28*a*) 141,802

Sold out: 8.71 10s (No. 27*a*)

Withdrawn: 6.10.69; ½d, 1½d; 4.2.70, 1d (No. 14); 1s6d (No. 23); others 14.2.72 (except for No. 28*a* which remained on sale with decimal definitives until 31.3.76)

Although officially withdrawn the ½d, 1d (No. 14), 1½d and 1s6d (No. 23) were subsequently included in Presentation Packs, whilst the ½d and 1½d remained on sale at the Philatelic Bureau until 14 February 1972.

Invalidated: 14.2.72 (except £1)

19 Isaac Brock as Colonel

20 Sir Isaac Brock as Major-General

21 Isaac Brock as Ensign

22 Arms and Flags

Birth Centenary of Sir Isaac Brock

(Litho Format)

1969 (1 DEC). Perf 13½×14 (2s6d) or 14×13½ (others), all comb

29	**19**	4d multicoloured	20	20
30	**20**	5d multicoloured	20	20
31	**21**	1s9d multicoloured	90	75
32	**22**	2s6d multicoloured	90	75
29/32		*Set of 4*	2·00	1·70
		First Day Cover		3·25
		Presentation Pack	3·75	
		Set of 4 Gutter Pairs	£150	

Plate Nos. 4d, 2s6d 1A, 1B, 1C, 1D (each ×6); 5d 1A, 1B, 1C, 1D (each ×7); 1s9d 1A, 1B, 1C, 1D (each ×5)

Sheets: 60 (2 panes 5×6) 2s6d; (2 panes 6×5) others

Imprint: Right-hand corner, bottom margin

Quantities sold: 4d 940,956; 5d 732,658; 1s9d 224,157; 2s6d 218,955

Withdrawn: 30.11.70

Invalidated: 14.2.72

23 H.M.S. *L103* (landing craft) entering St. Peter's Harbour

24 H.M.S. *Bulldog* and H.M.S. *Beagle* (destroyers) entering St. Peter Port

25 Brigadier Snow reading the Proclamation

25th Anniversary of Liberation

(Des and photo Courvoisier)

1970 (9 MAY). *Granite paper.* Perf 11½ (C)

33	**23**	4d blue and pale blue	20	20
34	**24**	5d brown-lake and pale grey . . .	30	20
35	**25**	1s6d bistre-brown and buff	1·00	90
33/5		*Set of 3*	1·30	1·10
		First Day Cover		2·40
		Presentation Pack	4·00	

Cylinder Nos.: A1–1, B1–1 (all values)

Sheets: 25 (5×5)

Imprint: Left-hand corner, top margin (4d, 5d); bottom corner, left-hand margin (1s6d)

Quantities sold: 4d 968,873; 5d 817,958; 1s6d 248,532

Withdrawn: 8.5.71

Invalidated: 14.2.72

26 Guernsey 'Toms'

27 Guernsey Cow

28 Guernsey Bull

29 Freesias

Agriculture and Horticulture

(Des and Photo Courvoisier)

1970 (12 AUG). *Granite paper.* Perf 11½ (C)

36	**26**	4d multicoloured	55	20
37	**27**	5d multicoloured	70	20
38	**28**	9d multicoloured	2·75	1·30
39	**29**	1s6d multicoloured	2·75	2·40
36/9		*Set of 4*	6·00	4·00
		First Day Cover		4·50
		Presentation Pack	12·00	

Cylinder Nos.: A1–1–1–1, B1–1–1–1, C1–1–1–1, D1–1–1–1 (all values)

Sheets: 25 (5×5)

Imprint: Central, bottom margin

Quantities sold: 4d 1,082.608; 5d 1,000,000; 9d 237,685; 1s6d 241,816

Withdrawn: 11.8.71

Invalidated: 14.2.72

30 St. Anne's Church, Alderney

31 St. Peter's Church, Guernsey

32 St. Peter's Church, Sark

33 St. Tugual Chapel, Herm

Christmas. Guernsey Churches (1st series)

(Des and photo Courvoisier)

1970 (11 NOV). *Granite paper.* Perf 11 ½ (C)

40	**30**	4d multicoloured	20	10
41	**31**	5d multicoloured	20	10
42	**32**	9d multicoloured	1·00	75
43	**33**	1s6d multicoloured	1·00	1·00
40/3		*Set of 4*	2·00	1·50
		First Day Cover		2·10
		Presentation Pack	4·75	

See also Nos. 63/6.

Cylinder Nos.: A1–1–1–1 or B1–1–1–1 (all values)

Sheets: 50 (5×10) 4d, 5d; (10×5) others

Quantities sold: 4d 815,737; 5d 668.886; 9d 236,833; 1s6d 223,907

Withdrawn: 10.11.71

Invalidated: 14.2.72

34 Martello Tower and King John

Decimal Currency

(Photo Harrison (½p to 10p), Delrieu (others))

1971 (6 JAN)–**73**. *Designs as Type* **4** *etc., but values inscribed in decimal currency as in Type* **34**. *Chalk-surfaced paper.* Perf 14 (½p to 10p) or 13½×13) (others), all comb

44	**4**	½p deep magenta and black (*b*) .	10	15
		a. *Booklet stamp with margins.* *Glazed, ordinary paper*	15	20
		ab. *Ditto. Chalk-surfaced paper (e)*	15	20
45	**5**	1p bright blue and black (ll) (*b*) .	10	10
46	**6**	1½p yellow-brown and black (*b*) .	15	15

7

47	**9**	2p multicoloured (b)	15	15
		a. Booklet stamp with margins.		
		Glazed, ordinary paper	20	20
		ab. Ditto. Chalk-surfaced paper (e)	20	20
		ac. Emerald (stem) omitted £1200		
		b. Glazed, ordinary paper (b) . .	20	20
48	**10**	2½p gold, bright vermilion, bluish violet and black (be) . .	15	10
		a. Bright vermilion omitted . . . £500		
		b. Booklet stamp with margins. Glazed, ordinary paper	20	20
		ba. Ditto. Chalk-surfaced paper (e)	20	20
49	**8**	3p gold, pale greenish yellow, orange-red and black (be) . .	20	20
50	**14**	3½p mult (glazed, ordinary paper) (b)	20	20
51	**7**	4p multicoloured (b)	20	20
52	**5**	5p turquoise-green & black (II) (b)	20	20
53	**11**	6p gold, pale greenish yellow, lt bronze-green and black (b) . .	20	20
54	**13**	7½p gold, brt verm, bistre & blk (b)	35	
55	**12**	9p gold, brt red, crimson & blk (b)	65	
56	**34**	10p bright reddish violet & blk (a)	1·75	1·75
		a. Ordinary paper. Bright reddish violet and deep black (c) . . .	1·25	1·25
57	**16**	20p mult (glazed, ordinary paper) (af)	70	70
		a. Shade* (d)	70	70
58	**17**	50p mult (glazed, ordinary paper) (adg)	1·25	1·25
44/58		Set of 15	5·00	5·25
		First Day Covers (2)		8·00
44/58,28a		Presentation Packs (3) . . . . . 10·00		
44/56		Set of 13 Gutter Pairs . . . . . 14·00		

*No. 57 has the sky in a pale turquoise-blue; on No. 57a it is pale turquoise-green.

Printings: (a) 6.1.71; (b) 15.2.71; (c) 1.9.72; (d) 25.1.73; (e) 2.4.73; (f) 10.74; (g) 7.75

Cylinder Nos.: ½p, 1p, 1½p, 5p, 10p 1A–1A, 1B–1B; 2p, 3½p 1A, 1B (each ×5); 2½p, 3p, 4p, 6p, 7½p, 9p 1A, 1B (each ×4); 20p none; 50p 21–22–23–24. Sheets from ptg (g) have an additional S99 (reversed)

On the 3½p only four '1A' Nos. are shown in the margin, the black '1A' being omitted in error.

Sheets: 50 (2 panes 5×5) ½p to 10p; 30 (5×6) others

Imprint: Central, bottom margin (½p to 10p)

Quantities sold: ½p 980,959; 1p 568,509; 1½p 559,576; 2p 2,512,903; 2½p 4,469,578; 3p 2,245,564; 3½p 317,523; 4p 527,696; 5p 511,742; 6p 346,255; 7½p 322,905; 9p 349,211; 10p 538,153; 20p 630,888; 50p 258,150

Withdrawn: 1.4.75 ½p to 10p (½p, 9p 10p and Presentation Packs sold out by 5.74); 31.3.76 20p, 50p

BAILIWICK OF GUERNSEY

35 Hong Kong 2c of 1862

36 Great Britain 4d of 1855–7

37 Italy 5c of 1862

38 Confederate States 5c of 1862

Thomas De La Rue Commemoration

(Des and recess De La Rue)

1971 (2 JUNE). Perf 14×13½ (C)

59	**35**	2p dull purple to brown-purple*	35	15
60	**36**	2½p carmine-red	35	15
61	**37**	4p deep bluish green	1·10	1·00
62	**38**	7½p deep blue	1·40	1·20
59/62		Set of 4	2·50	2·20
		First Day Cover		3·75
		Presentation Pack	4·50	

*These colours represent the extreme range of shades of this value. The majority of the printing, however, is an intermediate shade.

Plate Nos.: 1A, 1B each

Sheets: 25 (5×5)

Imprint: Central, bottom margin

Quantities sold: 2p 897,742; 2½p 1,404,085; 4p 210,691; 7½p 199,424

Withdrawn: 1.6.72

39 Ebenezer Church, St. Peter Port

40 Church of St. Pierre du Bois

41 St. Joseph's
Church, St. Peter
Port

42 Church of St.
Philippe de
Torteval

Christmas. Guernsey Churches (2nd series)

(Des and photo Courvoisier)

1971 (27 OCT). *Granite paper.* Perf 11½ (C)

63	**39**	2p multicoloured	10	10
64	**40**	2½p multicoloured	10	10
65	**41**	5p multicoloured	1·00	1·00
66	**42**	7½p multicoloured	1·00	1·00
63/6		Set of 4	2·00	2·00
		First Day Cover		2·50
		Presentation Pack	4·25	
		Set of 4 Gutter Pairs . . . . . . 21·00		

Cylinder Nos: A1–1–1–1, B1–1–1–1, C1–1–1–1, D1–1–1–1 (all values)

Sheets: 50 (2 panes 5×5)

Imprint: central, bottom margin (2p, 2½p) or left-hand corner, bottom margin (5p, 7½p)

Quantities sold: 2p 991,155; 2½p 916,004; 5p 223,412; 7½p 215,768

Withdrawn: 26.10.72

43 *Earl of
Chesterfield* (1794)

44 *Dasher* (1827)

45 *Ibex* (1891)

46 *Alberta* (1900)

Mail Packet Boats (1st series)

(Des and photo Courvoisier)

1972 (10 FEB). *Granite paper.* Perf 11 (C)

67	**43**	2p multicoloured	15	10
68	**44**	2½p multicoloured	15	10
69	**45**	7½p multicoloured	40	35
70	**46**	9p multicoloured	50	50
67/70		Set of 4	1·00	95
		First Day Cover		3·00
		Presentation Pack	3·25	

See also Nos. 80/3.

Cylinder Nos.: A1–1–1–1 or B1–1–1–1 (all values)

Sheets: 25 (5×5)

Imprint: Central, bottom margin

Quantities sold: 2p 973,503; 2½p 954,263; 7½p 288,929; 9p 289,340

Withdrawn: 9.2.73

47 Guernsey Bull

World Conference of Guernsey Breeders, Guernsey

(Photo Courvoisier)

1972 (22 MAY). *Granite paper.* Perf 11½ (C)

71	**47**	5p multicoloured	30	30
		First Day Cover*		2·25
		Gutter Pair	5·50	

*Prepared by the Royal Guernsey Agricultural and Horticultural Society.

Cylinder Nos.: A1–1–1–1, B1–1–1–1

Sheets: 50 (2 panes 5×5)

48 Bermuda Buttercup

49 Heath Spotted
Orchid

50 Kaffir Fig   **51** Scarlet Pimpernel

Wild Flowers

(Des and photo Courvoisier)

1972 (24 MAY). *Granite paper.* Perf 11½ (C)

72	**48**	2p multicoloured	. . . .	10	10
73	**49**	2½p multicoloured	. . . .	10	10
74	**50**	7½p multicoloured	. . . .	45	40
75	**51**	9p multicoloured	. . . .	50	50
72/5		*Set of* 4		1·00	90
		First Day Cover			2·25
		Presentation Pack		3·25	
		Set of 4 *Gutter Pairs*		5·00	

Cylinder Nos.: A1–1–1–1, B1–1–1–1, C1–1–1–1, D1–1–1–1 (all values)

Sheets: 50 (2 panes 5×5)

Imprint: 2p, 7½p Central, bottom margin, others left-hand corner, bottom margin

Quantities sold: 2p 1,006,041; 2½p 1,028,826; 7½p 249,471; 9p 244,839

Withdrawn: 23.5.73

52 Angels adoring Christ

53 The Epiphany

54 The Virgin Mary

55 Christ

Royal Silver Wedding and Christmas

(Des and photo Courvoisier)

1972 (20 NOV). *Designs show stained glass windows from Guernsey Churches. Granite paper.* Perf 11½ (C)

76	**52**	2p multicoloured	. . . .	10	10
77	**53**	2½p multicoloured	. . . .	15	10
78	**54**	7½p multicoloured	. . . .	30	25
79	**55**	9p multicoloured	. . . .	35	35
76/9		*Set of* 4		80	70
		First Day Cover			1·10
		Presentation Pack		1·90	
		Set of 4 *Gutter Pairs*		3·00	

Cylinder Nos.: A1–1–1–1, B1–1–1–1 each

Sheets: 50 (2 panes 5×5)

Imprint: Central, bottom margin of each pane

Quantities sold: 2p 878.893; 2½p 1,037,387; 7½p 314,972; 9p 313,367

Sold out: By 31.3.73

56 *St. Julien* (1925)

57 *Isle of Guernsey* (1930)

58 *St. Patrick* (1947)

59 *Sarnia* (1961)

Mail Packet Boats (2nd series)

(Des and photo Courvoisier)

1973 (9 MAR). *Granite paper.* Perf 11½ (C)

80	**56**	2½p multicoloured	. . . .	10	10
81	**57**	3p multicoloured	. . . .	20	20
82	**58**	7½p multicoloured	. . . .	40	40
83	**59**	9p multicoloured	. . . .	45	45
80/3		*Set of 4*		1·10	1·00
		First Day Cover			1·40
		Presentation Pack		2·00	
		Set of 4 Gutter Pairs		4·50	

Cylinder Nos.: All values A1–1–1–1, B1–1–1–1, C1–1–1–1, D1–1–1–1

Sheets: 50 (2 panes 5×5)

Imprint: Central, bottom margin of each pane

Quantities sold: 2½p 947,888; 3p 1,274,699; 7½p 278,998; 9p 263,569

Withdrawn: 8.3.74 (3p and Presentation Pack sold out earlier)

60 Supermarine Sea Eagle

61 Westland Wessex Trimotor

62 De Havilland D.H.89 Dragon Rapide

63 Douglas DC-3

64 Vickers Viscount 800 *Anne Marie*

50th Anniversary of Air Service

(Des and photo Courvoisier)

1973 (4 JULY). *Granite paper.* Perf 11½ (C)

84	**60**	2½p multicoloured	. . . .	10	10
85	**61**	3p multicoloured	. . . .	10	10
86	**62**	5p multicoloured	. . . .	25	25
87	**63**	7½p multicoloured	. . . .	30	30
88	**64**	9p multicoloured	. . . .	40	40
84/8		*Set of 5*		1·00	1·00
		First Day Cover			1·50
		Presentation Pack		2·00	
		Set of 5 Gutter Pairs		3·00	

Cylinder Nos.: A1-1-1-1, B1-1-1-1 each

Sheets: 50 (2 panes (5×5)

Imprint: Central, bottom margin of each pane

Quantities sold: 2½p 918,953; 3p 1,285,890; 5p 313,882; 7½p 294,369; 9p 288,225

Withdrawn: 3.7.74 (5p and Presentation Pack sold our earlier)

65 'The Good Shepherd'

66 Christ at the Well of Samaria

67 St. Dominic

68 Mary and the Child Jesus

Christmas

(Des and photo Courvoisier)

1973 (24 OCT). *Designs show stained glass windows from Guernsey Churches. Granite paper.* Perf 11½ (C)

89	**65**	2½p multicoloured	. . . .	10	10
90	**66**	3p multicoloured	. . . .	10	10

91	**67**	7½p multicoloured	30	30
9?	**60**	20p multicoloured	40	40
89/92		Set of 4	75	75
		First Day Cover		90
		Presentation Pack	1·50	
		Set of 4 Gutter Pairs	2·25	

Cylinder Nos.: A1–1–1–1, B1–1–1–1 each

Sheets: 50 (2 panes 5×5)

Imprint: Central, bottom margin of each pane

Quantities sold: 2½p 1,284,342; 3p 1,285,851; 7½p 367,714; 20p 367,625

Withdrawn: 23.10.74

69 Princess Anne and Capt. Mark Phillips

Royal Wedding

(Des G. Anderson. Photo Courvoisier)

1973 (14 NOV). *Granite paper*. Perf 11½ (C)

93	**69**	25p multicoloured	45	45
		First Day Cover		75
		Presentation Pack	90	
		Gutter Pair	1·50	

Cylinder Nos.: A1–1–1–1, B1–1–1–1

Sheets: 50 (2 panes 5×5)

Imprint: Central, bottom margin of each pane

Quantity sold: 392,767

Withdrawn: 13.11.74

70 *John Lockett*, 1875

71 *Arthur Lionel*, 1912

72 *Euphrosyne Kendal*, 1954

73 *Arun*, 1972

150th Anniversary of Royal National Life-boat Institution

(Des and photo Courvoisier)

1974 (15 JAN). *Granite paper*. Perf 11½ (C)

94	**70**	2½p multicoloured	10	10
95	**71**	3p multicoloured	10	10
96	**72**	8p multicoloured	20	20
97	**73**	10p multicoloured	25	25
94/97		Set of 4	60	60
		First Day Cover		1·00
		Presentation Pack	1·60	
		Set of 4 Gutter Pairs	1·50	

Cylinder Nos.: A1–1–1–1, B1–1–1–1 each

Sheets: 50 (2 panes 5×5)

Imprint: Central, bottom margin of each pane

Quantities sold: 2½p 1,016,058; 3p 1,162,020; 8p 393,660; 10p 393,668

Withdrawn: 14.1.75 (8p, 10p and Presentation Pack sold out earlier)

74 Private, East Regt., 1815   **75** Officer, 2nd North Regt., 1825   **76** Gunner, Guernsey Artillery, 1787

77 Gunner, Guernsey Artillery, 1815   **78** Corporal, Royal Guernsey Artillery, 1868   **79** Field Officer, Royal Guernsey Artillery, 1895

80 Sergeant, 3rd Regt., 1867   **81** Officer, East Regt., 1822   **82** Field Officer, Royal Guernsey Artillery, 1895

83 Colour-
Sergeant of
Grenadiers,
1833

84 Officer, North
Regt., 1832

85 Officer, East
Regt., 1822

86 Field Officer,
Rifle
Company,
1868

87 Private, 4th
West Regt.,
1785

88 Field Officer,
4th West
Regt., 1824

89 Driver, Field Battery,
Royal Guernsey
Artillery, 1848

90 Officer, Field Battery,
Royal Guernsey
Artillery, 1868

91 Cavalry Trooper, Light
Dragoons, 1814

Militia Uniforms

(Photo Courvoisier (½p to 10p), Delrieu (others))

1974 (2 APR)–**78**. *Granite paper* (½p to 10p). Perf 11½ (½p to
10p), 13×13½ (20, 50p) or 13½×13 (£1), all comb

98	**74**	½p multicoloured (*aj*)	10	10
		a. Booklet strip of 8 (98×5 *and*		
		102×3)†	35	
		b. Booklet pane of 16 (98×4,		
		102×6 *and* 103×6)†	75	
99	**75**	1p multicoloured (*aci*)	10	10
		a. Booklet strip of 8 (99×4, 103,		
		105×2 *and* 105a) (8.2.77)† .	55	
		b. Booklet strip of 4 (99, 101×2,		
		and 105a) (7.2.78)†	35	

100	**76**	1½p multicoloured (*a*)	10	10
101	**77**	2p multicoloured (*ak*)	10	10
102	**78**	2½p multicoloured (*a*)	10	10
103	**79**	3p multicoloured (*a*)	10	10
104	**80**	3½p multicoloured (*a*)	10	10
105	**81**	4p multicoloured (*abc*)	10	10
105a	**82**	5p multicoloured (*f*)	15	15
106	**83**	5½p multicoloured (*a*)	10	10
107	**84**	6p multicoloured (*ae*)	10	10
107a	**85**	7p multicoloured (*f*)	25	25
108	**86**	8p multicoloured (*ag*)	15	10
109	**87**	9p multicoloured (*al*)	15	10
110	**88**	10p multicoloured (*ah*)	15	10
111	**89**	20p multicoloured (*d*)	30	40
112	**90**	50p multicoloured (*d*)	90	1·00
113	**91**	£1 multicoloured (*d*)	1·90	1·75
98/113		*Set of* 18	4·50	4·25
		First Day Covers (3)		5·75
		Presentation Packs (3)	5·50	
		Set of 15 *Gutter Pairs* (*Nos.*		
		98/110)	3·50	

†Nos. 98*a/b* come from a special booklet sheet of 88
(8×11), and Nos. 99*a/b* from booklet sheets of 80 (two panes
8×5). These sheets were put on sale in addition to the normal
sheets. The strips and panes have the left-hand selvedge
stuck into booklet covers, except for No. 99*b* which had the
strip loose, and then folded and supplied in plastic wallets.

Printings: (*a*) 2.4.74; (*b*) 10.74; (*c*) 12.74; (*d*) 1.4.75; (*e*) 12.75; (*f*)
29.5.76; (*g*) 7.76; (*h*) 11.76; (*i*) 8.2.77; (*j*) 7.77; (*k*) 12.77; (*l*) 7.2.78.

Plate Nos.: 20p to £1 none; A1–1–1–1–1, B1–1–1–1–1 1½p, 2p, 6p;
A1–1–1–1, B1–1–1–1 others.

Sheets: 20p to £1, 25 (5×5); others, 100 (2 panes 10×5)

Imprint: Central, bottom margin of each page

Quantities sold: ½p 1,173,560; 1p 1,367,828; 1½p 525,248; 2p
1,098,053; 2½p 1,124,091; 3p 1,953,796; 3½p 1,891,493; 4p
3,435,614; 5p 2,920,246; 5½p 634,870; 6p 2,006,983; 7p 3,103,925;
8p 811,418; 9p 717,815; 10p 1,133,141; 20p 788,840; 50p 570,505;
£1 464,428

Withdrawn: 12.2.80 ½p to 20p; 4.2.81 50p, £1

92 Badge of Guernsey
and U.P.U. Emblem

93 Map of Guernsey

94 U.P.U. Building, Berne, and Guernsey Flag

95 'Salles des Etats'

Centenary of Universal Postal Union

(Photo Courvoisier)

1974 (7 JUNE). *Granite paper.* Perf 11½ (C)

114	**92**	2½p multicoloured	. . . .	10	10
115	**93**	3p multicoloured	. . . .	10	10
116	**94**	8p multicoloured	. . . .	20	20
117	**95**	10p multicoloured	. . . .	20	20
114/17		Set of 4	. . . .	50	50
		First Day Cover	. . . .		75
		Presentation Pack	. . . .	90	
		Set of 4 Gutter Pairs	. . . . . .	1·50	

Cylinder Nos.: 2½p, 8p A1–1–1, B1–1–1; 3p A1–1–1–1, B1–1–1–1; 10p A1–1–1–1, B1–1–1–1

Sheets: 50 (2 panes 5×5)

Imprint: Central, bottom margin

Quantities sold: 2½p 1,231,657; 3p 1,839,674; 8p 345,271; 10p 356,501

Withdrawn: 6.6.75

96 'Cradle Rock'

97 'Moulin Huet Bay'

98 'Au Bord de la Mer'   **99** Self-portrait

Renoir Paintings

(Des and photo Delrieu)

1974 (21 SEPT). Perf 13 (C)

118	**96**	3p multicoloured	. . . .	10	10
119	**97**	5½p multicoloured	. . . .	10	10
120	**98**	8p multicoloured	. . . .	25	25
121	**99**	10p multicoloured	. . . .	25	25
118/21		Set of 4	. . . .	60	60
		First Day Cover	. . . .		90
		Presentation Pack	. . . .	1·40	

Sheets: 25 (5×5)

Imprint: Right-hand corner, top margin (3p and 5½p), and bottom corner, right-hand margin (others)

Quantities sold: 3p 670,648; 5p 422,677; 8p 377,615; 10p 391,095

Withdrawn: 20.9.75

100 Guernsey Spleenwort   **101** Sand Quillwort

102 Guernsey Fern   **103** Least Adder's Tongue

Guernsey Ferns

(Des and photo Courvoisier)

1975 (7 JAN). *Granite paper.* Perf 11½ (C)

122	**100**	3½p multicoloured	. . . .	10	10
123	**101**	4p multicoloured	. . . .	10	10

124	**102**	8p multicoloured	. . . .	25	25
125	**103**	10p multicoloured	. . . .	25	25
122/5		Set of 4	. . . .	60	60
		First Day Cover	. . . .		90
		Presentation Pack	. . . .	1·40	
		Set of 4 Gutter Pairs	. . . . . .	1·40	

Cylinder Nos.: 3½p, 4p, 8p each A1–1–1–1, B1–1–1–1, C1–1–1–1, D1–1–1–1; 10p A1–1–1–1–1, B1–1–1–1–1, C1–1–1–1–1, D1–1–1–1–1

Sheets: 50 (2 panes 5×5)

Imprint: Central, bottom margin

Quantities sold: 3½p 1,089,142; 4p 1,370,743; 8p 430,672; 10p 443,636

Withdrawn: 6.1.76

108 Globe and Seal of Bailiwick

109 Globe and Guernsey Flag

104 Victor Hugo House

105 Candie Gardens

110 Globe, Guernsey Flag and Alderney Shield

111 Globe, Guernsey Flag and Sark Shield

106 United Europe Oak, Hauteville

107 Tapestry Room, Hauteville

Christmas

(Des and photo Delrieu)

Victor Hugo's Exile in Guernsey

(Des and photo Courvoisier)

1975 (6 JUNE). *Granite paper.* Perf 11½ (C)

126	**104**	3½p multicoloured	. . . .	10	10
127	**105**	4p multicoloured	. . . .	10	10
128	**106**	8p multicoloured	. . . .	25	25
129	**107**	10p multicoloured	. . . .	25	25
126/9		Set of 4	. . . .	60	60
		First Day Cover	. . . .		80
		Presentation Pack	. . . .	1·75	
MS130		114×143 mm. Nos. 126/9	. . . . . .	65	90
		First Day Cover	. . . .		6·50

Cylinder Nos.: A1–1–1–1, B1–1–1–1 each

Sheets: 50 (5×10) 3½p, 10p; (10×5) others

Imprint: Central, left-hand margin (3½p, 10p) or central, bottom margin (4p, 8p)

Quantities sold: 3½p 810,327; 4p 1,346,628; 8p 377,637; 10p 369,282; miniature sheet 269,217

Withdrawn: 5.6.76

1975 (7 OCT). Perf 13 (C)

131	**108**	4p multicoloured	. . . .	10	10
132	**109**	6p multicoloured	. . . .	10	10
133	**110**	10p multicoloured	. . . .	25	25
134	**111**	12p multicoloured	. . . .	25	25
131/4		Set of 4	. . . .	60	60
		First Day Cover	. . . .		90
		Presentation Pack	. . . .	1·00	

Sheets: 25 (5×5)

Imprint: Central, left-hand margin (4p, 6p); central, bottom margin (10p, 12p)

Quantities sold: 4p 678,619; 6p 667,413; 10p 392,529; 12p 361,548

Withdrawn: 6.10.76

112 Les Hanois

113 Les Casquets

114 Quesnard

115 Point Robert

Lighthouses

(Des and photo Courvoisier)

1976 (10 FEB). *Granite paper*. Perf 11½ (C)

135	**112**	4p multicoloured	10	10
136	**113**	6p multicoloured	10	10
137	**114**	11p multicoloured	20	20
138	**115**	13p multicoloured	25	25
135/8		*Set of 4*	60	60
		First Day Cover		80
		Presentation Pack	1·00	
		Set of 4 Gutter Pairs	1·50	

Cylinder Nos.: A1–1–1–1, B1–1–1–1 each

Sheets: 50 (2 panes 5×5)

Quantities sold: 4p 846,362; 6p 900,899; 11p 366,468; 13p 348,358

Withdrawn: 9.2.77

116 Milk Can

117 Christening Cup

Europa

(Des and photo Courvoisier)

1976 (29 MAY). *Granite paper*. Perf 11½ (C)

139	**116**	10p brown and green	20	20
140	**117**	25p grey and blue	40	35
139/40		*Set of 2*	60	55
		First Day Cover		75
		Presentation Pack	1·00	

Sheets: 9 (3×3)

Quantities sold: 1,185,014 of each

Sold out: 4.6.76

118 Pine Forest, Guernsey

119 Herm and Jethou

120 Grand Greve Bay, Sark

121 Trois Vaux Bay, Alderney

Views

(Des and photo Courvoisier)

1976 (3 AUG). *Granite paper*. Perf 11½ (C)

141	**118**	5p multicoloured	10	10
142	**119**	7p multicoloured	10	10
143	**120**	11p multicoloured	25	25
144	**121**	13p multicoloured	25	25
141/4		*Set of 4*	60	60
		First Day Cover		80
		Presentation Pack	1·00	
		Set of 4 Gutter Pairs	1·50	

Cylinder Nos.: A1–1–1–1, B1–1–1–1 each

Sheets: 50 (2 panes 5×5)

Quantities sold: 5p 661,771; 7p 1,016,350; 11p 349,773; 13p 336,027

Withdrawn: 2.8.77

122 Royal Court House, Guernsey

123 Elizabeth College, Guernsey

124 La Seigneurie, Sark

125 Island Hall, Alderney

Christmas. Buildings

(Des and photo Courvoisier)

1976 (14 OCT). *Granite paper.* Perf 11½ (C)

145	**122**	5p multicoloured	10	10
146	**123**	7p multicoloured	10	10
147	**124**	11p multicoloured	25	25
148	**125**	13p multicoloured	25	25
145/8		*Set of 4*	60	60
		First Day Cover		85
		Presentation Pack	1·00	
		Set of 4 Gutter Pairs	1·50	

Cylinder Nos.: A1–1–1–1, B1–1̃–1–1 each

Sheets: 50 (2 panes 5 × 5)

Imprint: Central, bottom margin

Quantities sold: 5p 1,097,445; 7p 1,051,184; 11p 371,155; 13p 352,347

Withdrawn: 13.10.77

126   Queen Elizabeth II   **127**

Silver Jubilee

(Des R. Granger Barrett. Photo Courvoisier)

1977 (8 FEB). *Granite Paper.* Perf 11½ (C)

149	**126**	7p multicoloured	20	15
150	**127**	35p multicoloured	55	40
149/50		*Set of 2*	65	55
		First Day Cover		70
		Presentation Pack	90	

Cylinder Nos.: 7p A1–1–1–1–1, B1–1–1–1–1; 35p A1–1–1–1–1

Sheets: 25 (5×5)

Imprint: Central, bottom margin

Quantities sold: 7p 1,004,250; 35p 536,971

Withdrawn: 7.2.78

128 Woodland, Talbots Valley

129 Pastureland, Talbots Valley

Europa

(Des and photo Courvoisier)

1977 (17 MAY). *Granite paper.* Perf 11½ (C)

151	**128**	7p multicoloured	15	15
152	**129**	25p multicoloured	45	45
151/2		*Set of 2*	60	60
		First Day Cover		70
		Presentation Pack	90	
		Set of 2 Gutter Pairs	1·40	

Cylinder Nos.: A1–1–1–1, B1–1–1–1 each

Sheets: 50 (2 panes 5×5)

Imprint: Right-hand corner, bottom margin

Quantities sold: 7p 1,371,463; 25p 598,453

Withdrawn: 16.5.78

130 Statue-menhir, Castel

131 Megalithic Tomb, St. Saviour

132 Cist, Tourgis

133 Statue-menhir, St. Martin

Prehistoric Monuments

(Des and photo Courvoisier)

1977 (2 AUG). *Granite paper.* Perf 11½ (C)

153	**130**	5p multicoloured	10	10
154	**131**	7p multicoloured	10	10
155	**132**	11p multicoloured	25	25
156	**133**	13p multicoloured	25	25
153/6		*Set of 4*	60	60
		First Day Cover		75
		Presentation Pack	90	
		Set of 4 Gutter Pairs	1·40	

Cylinder Nos.: A1–1–1–1, B1–1–1–1 each

Sheets: 50 (2 panes 5×5)

Imprint: Central, right-hand margin (5p and 13p); Central, bottom margin (others)

Quantities sold: 5p 747,236; 7p 1,077,714; 11p 390,927; 13p 373,063

Withdrawn: 1.8.78

134 Mobile First Aid Unit

135 Mobile Radar Unit

136 Marine Ambulance *Flying Christine II*

137 Cliff Rescue

Christmas. St. John Ambulance Centenary

(Des P. Slade and M. Horder. Photo Courvoisier)

1977 (25 OCT). *Granite paper.* Perf 11½ (C)

157	**134**	5p multicoloured	10	10
158	**135**	7p multicoloured	10	10
159	**136**	11p multicoloured	25	25
160	**137**	13p multicoloured	25	25
157/60		*Set of 4*	60	60
		First Day Cover		75
		Presentation Pack	90	
		Set of 4 Gutter Pairs	1·40	

Cylinder Nos.: 5p A1–1–1–1, B1–1–1–1; others A1–1–1–1, B1–1–1–1

Sheets: 50 (2 panes 5×5)

Imprint: Right-hand corner, bottom margin (7p and 11p); top, right-hand margin (others)

Quantities sold: 5p 1,218,293; 7p 1,155,448; 11p 406,244; 13p 383,489

Withdrawn: 24.10.78

138 View from Clifton, *c* 1830

18

139 Market Square, St. Peter Port, c 1838

140 Petit-Bo Bay, c 1839

141 The Quay, St. Peter Port, c 1830

Old Guernsey Prints (1st series)

(Des, recess and litho De La Rue)

1978 (7 FEB). Perf 14×13½ (C)

161	**138**	5p black and light stone	10	10
162	**139**	7p black and cream	10	10
163	**140**	11p black and light pink	25	25
164	**141**	13p black and light azure	25	25
161/4		Set of 4	60	60
		First Day Cover		75
		Presentation Pack	90	
		Set of 4 Gutter Pairs	1·40	

See also Nos. 249/52.

Plate Nos.: All values 1A–1A, 1B–1B, 1C–1C, 1D–1D

Sheets: 50 (2 panes 5×5)

Imprint: Left-hand corner, bottom margin

Quantities sold: 5p 858,816; 7p 930,955; 11p 442,009; 13p 338,163

Withdrawn: 6.2.79

142 Prosperity Memorial

143 Victoria Monument

Europa. Monuments

(Des R. Granger Barrett. Litho Questa)

1978 (2 MAY). Perf 14½ (C)

165	**142**	5p multicoloured	10	10
		a. Imperf between stamp and right margin		
166	**143**	7p multicoloured	25	25
165/6		Set of 2	30	30
		First Day Cover		45
		Presentation Pack	55	

Sheets: 20 (5p 5×4; 7p 4×5)

Quantities sold: 5p 2,581,345; 7p 2,370,766

Withdrawn: 1.5.79

144   Queen Elizabeth   **145**

25th Anniversary of Coronation

(Des R. Granger Barrett from bust by Arnold Machin. Photo Courvoisier)

1978 (2 MAY). Granite paper. Perf 11½ (C)

167	**144**	20p black, grey and bright blue	30	45
		First Day Cover		60
		Presentation Pack	60	
		Gutter Pair	90	

Cylinder Nos.: A1–1–1, B1–1–1

Sheets: 50 (2 panes 5×5)

Imprint: Right-hand corner, bottom margin

Quantity sold: 488,466

Withdrawn: 1.5.79

Royal Visit

(Des R. Granger Barrett from bust by Arnold Machin. Photo Courvoisier)

1978 (28 JUNE). Granite paper. Perf 11½ (C)

168	**145**	7p black, grey and bright green	20	20
		First Day Cover		45
		Presentation Pack	50	
		Gutter Pair	40	

Cylinder Nos.: A1–1–1, B1–1–1

Sheets: 50 (2 panes 5×5)

Imprint: Top corner, right-hand margin

Quantity sold: 1,149,768

Withdrawn: 27.6.79

146 Northern Gannet

147 Firecrest

148 Dartford Warbler   **149** Spotted Redshank

152 Holly

153 Mistletoe

Christmas

(Des and photo Courvoisier)

1978 (31 OCT). *Granite paper.* Perf 11½ (C)

173	**150**	5p multicoloured	10	10
174	**151**	7p multicoloured	10	10
175	**152**	11p multicoloured	20	20
176	**153**	13p deep blue-green, grey and greenish yellow	25	25
173/6		*Set of* 4	60	60
		First Day Cover		90
		Presentation Pack	95	
		Set of 4 *Gutter pairs*	1·40	

Cylinder Nos.: 13p A1–1–1, B1–1–1; others A1–1–1–1, B1–1–1–1

Sheets: 50 (2 panes 5×5)

Imprint: 5, 7p central, bottom margin; others central, right-hand margin

Quantities sold: 5p 1,222,140; 7p 1,246,260; 11p 409,168; 13p 372,991

Withdrawn: 30.10.79

Birds

(Des John Waddington Ltd. Photo Courvoisier)

1978 (29 AUG). *Granite paper.* Perf 11½ (C)

169	**146**	5p multicoloured	10	10
170	**147**	7p multicoloured	20	15
171	**148**	11p multicoloured	25	20
172	**149**	13p multicoloured	35	20
169/72		*Set of* 4	80	60
		First Day Cover		75
		Presentation Pack	1·10	
		Set of 4 *Gutter Pairs*	1·50	

Cylinder Nos.: All values A1–1–1–1, B1–1–1–1, C1–1–1–1, D1–1–1–1

Sheets: 50 (2 panes 5×5)

Imprint: Right-hand corner, bottom margin

Quantities sold: 5p 750,011; 7p 924,627; 11p 442,395; 13p 432,106

Withdrawn: 28.8.79

150 Solanum

154 One Double, 1830

155 Two Doubles, 1899

156 Four Doubles, 1902

157 Eight Doubles, 1959

158 Three Pence, 1956

159 Five New Pence, 1968

151 Christmas Rose

160 Fifty New Pence, 1969

161 Ten New Pence, 1970

162 Half New Penny, 1971

163 One New Penny, 1971

164 Two New Pence, 1971

165 Half Penny, 1979

166 One Penny, 1977

167 Two Pence, 1977

168 Five Pence, 1977

169 Ten Pence, 1977

170 Twenty-five Pence, 1972

171 Ten Shillings William I Commem, 1966

172 Silver Jubilee Commemorative Crown, 1977

173 Royal Silver Wedding Commemorative Crown, 1972

174 Seal of the Bailiwick

Coins

(Des R. Reid and Courvoisier (£5). Photo Courvoisier)

1979 (13 FEB)–**83**. *Granite paper.* Perf 11½ (C)

177	**154**	½p multicoloured (a)	10	10
		a. Booklet pane. Nos. 177×2, 178×3, 179×2, 181, 183 and 187 (c)	70	
		b. Booklet pane. Nos. 177×2, 178, 179×2, 183×2, and 187×3 (c)	90	
178	**155**	1p multicoloured (al)	10	10
		a. Booklet strip of 4. Nos. 178×2, 179 and 182	40	
179	**156**	2p multicoloured (a)	10	10
		a. Booklet strip of 5. Nos. 179, 182×2 and 184×2	90	
180	**157**	4p multicoloured (a)	10	10
		a. Booklet pane of 10. Nos. 180 and 184, each ×5 (d) . .	1·25	
		b. Booklet pane of 15. Nos. 180, 184 and 190, each ×5 (d)	2·50	
		c. Booklet pane of 10. Nos. 180×2, 185×3 and 191×5 (k)	1·90	
		d. Booklet pane of 15. Nos. 180, 185 and 191, each ×5 (k)	2·25	
181	**158**	5p grey-black, silver and chestnut (a)	10	10
		a. Grey-black, silver and yellowish brown (f)	30	40
		b. Booklet pane of 10. Nos. 181a×5, 184×4 and 191 (f)	1·75	
		c. Booklet pane of 15. Nos. 181a, 184 and 191, each ×5 (f)	2·25	

182	**159**	6p grey-black, silver and brown-red (a)	15	10
183	**160**	7p grey-black, silver & grn (a) .	15	15
184	**161**	8p grey-blk, silver & brn (agIj) .	15	15
185	**162**	9p multicoloured (a)	15	15
186	**163**	10p mult (green background) (a)	30	25
187		10p mult (orge background (b) .	20	15
188	**164**	11p multicoloured (a)	20	15
189	**165**	11½p multicoloured (b)	20	15
190	**166**	12p multicoloured (a)	20	15
191	**167**	13p multicoloured (ah)	25	20
192	**168**	14p grey-blk, silver & dull bl (a) .	25	20
193	**169**	15p grey-blk, silver & bistre (a) .	25	25
194	**170**	20p grey-black, silver and dull brown (a)	30	30
195	**171**	50p grey-black, orange-red and silver (b)	85	60
196	**172**	£1 grey-black, yellowish green and silver (b)	1·75	1·10
197	**173**	£2 grey-black, new blue and silver (b)	3·75	2·00
198	**174**	£5 multicoloured (e)	7·50	6·50
177/98		Set of 22	15·00	12·00
		First Day Covers (4)		14·00
		Presentation Packs (4) . . . . 18·00		
		Set of 22 Gutter Pairs . . . . 30·00		

Nos. 177a/b, 178a, 179a, 180a/d and 181b/c come from special booklet sheets of 40 (80×5) (Nos. 177a and 178a), 30 (6×5) (Nos. 177b, 180a/b, 180d and 181b/c), 25 (5×5) (No. 179a) or 20 (4×5) (No. 180c). These were put on sale as complete sheets or separated into strips, folded and either affixed by the selvedge to booklet covers or supplied loose in plastic wallets.

The booklet sheets containing Nos. 177a/b show either four (No. 177a) or three (No. 177b) different arrangements of the same stamps.

Printings: (a) 13.2.79; (b) 5.2.80; (c) 6.5.80; (d) 24.2.81; (e) 22.5.81; (f) 2.2.82; (g) 4.82; (h) 5.82; (i) 7.82; (j) 11.82; (k) 14.3.83; (l) 6.83

Cylinder Nos.: 5, 6, 7, 8, 14, 15, 20, 50p, £1, £2 A1–1–1; others A1–1–1–1, B1–1–1–1

Sheets: ½ to 20p 100 (2 panes 10×5); 50p to £5 50 (2 panes 5×5)

Imprint: 50p top corner, left-hand margin; £1, £2 right-hand corner, bottom margin; £5 bottom corner, right-hand margin; others central margin

Quantities sold: ½p 1,285,162; 1p 1,888,850; 2p 1,249,506; 4p 650,195; 5p 1,110,783; 6p 1,678,775; 7p 1,683,430; 8p 3,059,366; 9p 1,952,892; 10p (No. 186) 484,956; 10p (No. 187) 1,751,126; 11p 711,268; 11½p 351,422; 12p 957,197; 13p 1,459,086; 14p 595,744; 15p 677,289; 20p 960,124; 50p 863,760; £1 537,871; £2 375,786

Withdrawn: 4.2.81 10p (No. 186); 22.7.85 (all other values except £5); 31.12.98 £5

175 Pillar Box and Postmark, 1853, Mail Van and Postmark, 1979

176 Telephone, 1897 and Telex Machine, 1979

Europa. Communications

(Des R. Granger Barrett. Photo Courvoisier)

1979 (8 MAY). *Granite paper.* Perf 11½ (C)

201	**175**	6p multicoloured	10	10
202	**176**	8p multicoloured	20	20
201/2		Set of 2	30	30
		First Day Cover		45
		Presentation Pack 55		

Cylinder Nos.: Both values A1–1–1–1, B1–1–1–1

Sheets: 20 (5×4)

Quantities sold: 6p 1,863,564; 8p 2,293,379

Withdrawn: 7.5.80

177 Steam Tram, 1879

178 Electric Tram, 1896

179 Motor Bus, 1911

180 Motor Bus, 1979

184 'Philately'

History of Public Transport

(Photo Courvoisier)

1979 (7 AUG). *Granite paper.* Perf 11½ (C)

203	**177**	6p multicoloured	10	10
204	**178**	8p multicoloured	15	10
205	**179**	11p multicoloured	20	15
206	**180**	13p multicoloured	20	25
203/6		Set of 4	60	55
		First Day Cover		70
		Presentation Pack	1·25	
		Set of 4 Gutter Pairs	1·25	

Cylinder Nos.: 6p A1–1–1–1–1, B1–1–1–1–1; others A1–1–1–1, B1–1–1–1

Sheets: 50 (2 panes 5×5)

Imprint: Central, bottom margin

Quantities sold: 6p 676,046; 8p 981,431; 11p 384,701; 13p 371,882

Withdrawn: 6.8.80

10th Anniversary of Guernsey Postal Administration

(Des R. Granger Barrett. Photo Courvoisier)

1979 (1 OCT). *Granite paper.* Perf 11½ (C)

207	**181**	6p multicoloured	10	10
208	**182**	8p multicoloured	15	10
209	**183**	13p multicoloured	20	15
210	**184**	15p multicoloured	25	25
207/10		Set of 4	65	55
		First Day Cover		80
		Presentation Pack	1·10	
		Set of 4 Gutter Pairs	1·40	
MS211		120×80 mm. Nos. 207/10	80	80
		First Day Cover		1·25

One copy of a pre-release sample as No. 210, but with a face value of 11p, is known. Such stamps were not sold for postal purposes.

Cylinder Nos.: All values A1–1–1–1, B1–1–1–1

Sheets: 50 (2 panes 5×5)

Imprint: Central, bottom margin

Quantities sold: 6p 1,254,914; 8p 1,376,682; 13p 389,524; 15p 386,234; miniature sheet 398,443

Withdrawn: 30.9.80

181 Bureau and Postal Headquarters

182 'Mails and Telegrams'

183 'Parcels'

185 Major-General Le Merchant

186 Admiral Lord De Saumarez

Europa. Personalities

(Des and photo Courvoisier)

1980 (6 MAY). *Granite paper.* Perf 11½ (C)

212	**185**	10p multicoloured	15	15
213	**186**	13½p multicoloured	30	25
212/13		Set of 2	45	40
		First Day Cover		70
		Presentation Pack	80	

Cylinder Nos.: Both values A1–1–1–1, B1–1–1–1, C1–1–1–1, D1–1–1–1

Sheets: 20 (5×4)

Quantities sold: 10p 2,794,871; 13½p 1,715,880

Withdrawn: 5.5.81

187 Policewoman with Lost Child

188 Police Motorcyclist escorting Lorry

189 Police Dog-handler

60th Anniversary of Guernsey Police Force

(Litho John Waddington Ltd)

1980 (6 MAY). Perf 13½×14 (C)

214	**187**	7p multicoloured	15	15
215	**188**	15p multicoloured	25	25
216	**189**	17½p multicoloured	30	25
214/16		Set of 3	65	60
		First Day Cover		85
		Presentation Pack	1·00	
		Set of 3 Gutter Pairs	1·40	

Plate Nos: All values 1A, 1B, 1C, 1D (each ×4)

Sheets: 50 (2 panes 5×5)

Imprint: Central, bottom margin

Quantities sold: 7p 907,714; 15p 352,802; 17½p 337,551

Withdrawn: 5.5.81

190

191

192

193

T **190/3** show Golden Guernsey Goats.

Golden Guernsey Goats

(Des P. Lambert. Photo Delrieu)

1980 (5 Aug). Perf 13 (C)

217	**190**	7p multicoloured	10	10
218	**191**	10p multicoloured	20	15
219	**192**	15p multicoloured	25	20
220	**193**	17½p multicoloured	40	35
217/20		Set of 4	85	80
		First Day Cover		95
		Presentation Pack	1·25	
		Set of 4 Gutter Pairs	1·75	

Cylinder Nos.: 7p 598–599–600–601–602–603; 10p 578–580–581–583; 15p 605–606–607–608–609–610; 17½p 621–622–623–624–625–626

Sheets: 50 (2 panes 5×5)

Imprint: Bottom margin

Quantities sold: 7p 779,424; 10p 931,214; 15p 364,917; 17½p 329,133

Withdrawn: 4.4.81

194 'Sark Cottage'

195 'Moulin Huet'

196 'Boats at Sea'

197 'Cow Lane'

198 'Peter le Lievre'

Christmas. Peter le Lievre Paintings

(Photo Courvoisier)

1980 (15 NOV). *Granite paper*. Perf 11½ (C)
221	**194**	7p multicoloured	15	10
222	**195**	10p multicoloured	20	15
223	**196**	13½p multicoloured	25	20
224	**197**	15p multicoloured	25	25
225	**198**	17½p multicoloured	40	35
221/5		*Set of 5*	1·10	95
		First Day Cover		1·40
		Presentation Pack	1·50	
		Stamp-cards (set of 5)	1·60	3·25
		Set of 5 Gutter Pairs	2·50	

Cylinder Nos.: All values A1–1–1–1, B1–1–1–1

Sheets: 50 (2 panes 5×5)

Imprint: 15, 17½p top corner, right-hand margin; others right-hand corner, bottom margin

Quantities sold: 7p 1,199,280; 10p 1,159,622; 13½p 397,812; 15p 432,182; 17½p 359,116

Withdrawn: 14.11.81

199 *Polyommatus icarus*

200 *Vanessa atalanta*

201 *Aglais urticae*

202 *Lasiommata megera*

Butterflies

(Photo Harrison)

1981 (24 FEB). Perf 14 (C)
226	**199**	8p multicoloured	15	15
227	**200**	12p multicoloured	20	20
228	**201**	22p multicoloured	35	35
229	**202**	25p multicoloured	40	40
226/9		*Set of 4*	1·00	1·00
		First Day Cover		2·25
		Presentation Pack	1·75	
		Set of 4 Gutter Pairs	2·25	

Cylinder Nos.: All values 1A, 1B (each ×5)

Sheets: 50 (2 panes 5×5)

Imprint: Right-hand corner, bottom margin

Quantities sold: 8p 986,229; 12p 971,801; 22p 438,478; 25p 438,575

Withdrawn: 23.2.82

203 Sailors paying respect to 'Le Petit Bonhomme Andriou' (rock resembling head of a man)

204 Fairies and Guernsey Lily

Europa. Folklore

(Des C. Abbott. Litho Questa)

1981 (22 MAY). Perf 14½ (C)
230	**203**	12p gold, red-brown & cinnamon	25	15
231	**204**	18p gold, indigo and azure	30	30
230/1		*Set of 2*	55	45
		First Day Cover		65
		Presentation Pack	80	
		Set of 2 Gutter Pairs	1·10	

Plate Nos.: 12p 1B, 1F, 1G, 1H (each ×3); 18p 1B, 1D, 1F, 1G, 1H (each ×3)

Sheets: 20 (2 panes 5×2)

Imprint: Central, left-hand margin

Quantities sold: 12p 2,516,514; 18p 1,937,023

Withdrawn: 21.5.82

8ᵖ GUERNSEY

8ᵖ GUERNSEY

8ᵖ GUERNSEY

205 Prince Charles

206 Prince Charles and Lady Diana Spencer

207 Lady Diana

25ᵖ GUERNSEY BAILIWICK 25ᵖ

208 Royal Family

Royal Wedding

(Des C. Abbott. Litho Questa)

1981 (29 JULY). Perf 14½ (C)

232	**205**	8p multicoloured	15	10
		a. Strip of 3. Nos. 232/4	75	75
233	**206**	8p multicoloured	15	10
234	**207**	8p multicoloured	15	10
235	**205**	12p multicoloured	25	25
		a. Strip of 3. Nos. 235/7	1·10	1·10
236	**206**	12p multicoloured	25	25
237	**207**	12p multicoloured	25	25
238	**208**	25p multicoloured	65	60
232/8		Set of 7	2·00	1·60
		First Day Cover		3·25
		Presentation Pack	3·25	
		Stamp-cards (set of 7)	2·00	8·50
MS239		104×127 mm. Nos. 232/8. P 14 (C)	3·00	2·75
		First Day Cover		4·25

Plate Nos.: 8p 1A, 1C (each ×6); 12p 1B (×6); 25p 1A (×6)

Sheets: 8p, 12p 60 (6×10) each value in *se-tenant* strips of 3 across sheet, 25p 30 (3×10)

Imprint: Bottom corner, right-hand side margin

Quantities sold: 8p 2,115,103; 12p 2,235,005; 25p 510,608; miniature sheet 432,743

Withdrawn: 28.7.82

209 Sark Launch

210 Britten Norman 'short nose' Trislander Airplane

211 Hydrofoil

212 Herm Catamaran

213 *Sea Trent* (coaster)

Inter-island Transport

(Des and photo Courvoisier)

1881 (25 AUG). *Granite paper.* Perf 11½ (C)

240	**209**	8p multicoloured	15	15
241	**210**	12p multicoloured	25	20
242	**211**	18p multicoloured	30	30
243	**212**	22p multicoloured	45	45
244	**213**	25p multicoloured	55	55
240/4		Set of 5	1·50	1·50
		First Day Cover		1·75
		Presentation Pack	2·00	
		Set of 5 Gutter Pairs	3·00	

Cylinder Nos.: All values A1–1–1–1, B1–1–1–1

Sheets: 50 (2 panes 5×5)

Imprint: Right-hand corner, bottom margin

Quantities sold: 8p 790,215; 12p 785,488; 18p 457,763; 22p 469,315; 25p 466,112

Withdrawn: 24.8.82

214 Rifle Shooting

215 Riding

216 Swimming

217 Circuit Construction

International Year for Disabled Persons

(Des P. le Vasseur. Litho Questa)

1981 (17 NOV). Perf 14½ (C)

245	**214**	8p multicoloured	15	10
246	**215**	12p multicoloured	25	20
247	**216**	22p multicoloured	45	35
248	**217**	25p multicoloured	55	40
245/8		Set of 4	1·25	95
		First Day Cover		1·10
		Presentation Pack	1·60	
		Set of 4 Gutter Pairs	2·50	

Plate Nos.: All values 1A, 1B, 1C, 1D, 1E, 1F, 1G, 1H (each ×4)

Sheets: 50 (2 panes 5×5)

Imprint: Foot of right-hand margin on each pane

Quantities sold: 8p 912,908; 12p 910,614; 22p 280,882; 25p 287,725

Withdrawn: 16.11.82

218 Jethou

219 Fermain Bay

220 The Terres

221 St. Peter Port

Old Guernsey Prints (2nd series)

(Des, recess and litho De La Rue)

1982 (2 FEB). Perf 14×13½ (C)

249	**218**	8p black and pale blue	15	15
250	**219**	12p black & pale turquoise-grn	25	20
251	**220**	22p black and pale yellow-brown	40	40
252	**221**	25p black and pale rose-lilac	50	50
249/52		Set of 4	1·10	1·10
		First Day Cover		1·40
		Presentation Pack	1·60	
		Set of 4 Gutter Pairs	2·25	

Plate Nos.: All values 1A–1A, 1B–1B, 1C–1C, 1D–1D

Sheets: 50 (2 panes 5×5)

Imprint: Left-hand corner, bottom margin

Quantities sold: 8p 350,198; 12p 346,515; 22p 346,661; 25p 244,669

Withdrawn: 1.2.83

222 Sir Edgar MacCulloch (founder-president) and Guille-Allès Library, St. Peter Port

223 Norman Invasion Fleet crossing English Channel, 1066 ('history')'

224 H.M.S. *Crescent*, 1793 ('history')

225 Dragonfly ('entomology')

226 Common Snipe caught for Ringing ('ornithology')

227 Samian Bowl 160–200 A.D. ('archaeology')

Centenary of La Société Guernesiaise

(Des G. Drummond. Photo Courvoisier)

1982 (28 APR). Granito paper. Perf 11½ (C)

253	**222**	8p multicoloured	....	15	15
254	**223**	13p multicoloured	....	30	15
255	**224**	20p multicoloured	....	40	25
256	**225**	24p multicoloured	....	50	40
257	**226**	26p multicoloured	....	60	50
258	**227**	29p multicoloured	....	65	55
253/8		Set of 6	....	2·30	1·75
		First Day Cover	....		2·00
		First Day Cover (Nos. 254/5)			2·00
		Presentation Pack	....	2·50	
		Presentation Pack (Nos. 254/5)			1·75
		Stamp-cards (set of 6)	.....	2·00	4·00

The 13p and 20p (Nos. 254/5) also include the Europa C.E.P.T. emblem in the designs.

Cylinder Nos.: 24p A1–1–1–1, B1–1–1–1, C1–1–1–1, D1–1–1–1; others A1–1–1–1–1, B1–1–1–1–1, C1–1–1–1–1, D1–1–1–1–1

Sheets: 20 (5×4)

Quantities sold: 8p 921,095; 13p 2,820,311; 20p 1,491,351; 24p 315,735; 26p 309,919; 29p 298,761

Withdrawn: 27.4.83

228 Sea Scouts

229 Scouts

230 Cub Scouts

231 Air Scouts

75th Anniversary of Boy Scout Movement

(Des W.L.G. Creative Services Ltd. Litho Questa)

1982 (13 JULY). Perf 14½×14 (C)

259	**228**	8p multicoloured	....	15	25
260	**229**	13p multicoloured	....	30	25
261	**230**	26p multicoloured	....	55	80
262	**231**	29p multicoloured	....	65	1·10
259/62		Set of 4	....	1·50	2·10
		First Day Cover	....		2·25
		Presentation Pack	,,......	2·00	
		Set of 4 Gutter Pairs	....	3·00	

Plate Nos.: 8p 1A, 1B, 1C, 1D (each ×6); others 1A, 1B, 1C, 1D (each ×7)

Sheets: 50 (2 panes 5×5)

Imprint: Bottom corner, right-hand margin

Quantities sold: 8p 796,018; 13p 930,924; 26p 237,958; 29p 233,204

Withdrawn: 12.7.83

232 Midnight Mass   **233** Exchanging Gifts

234 Christmas Meal   **235** Exchanging Cards

236 Queen's Christmas Message

Christmas

(Des Lynette Hammant. Photo Harrison)

1982 (12 OCT). Perf 14½ (C)

263	**232**	8p multicoloured	....	15	15
		a. Black (Queen's head, value and inscr) omitted	....		
264	**233**	13p multicoloured	....	25	15
265	**234**	24p multicoloured	....	50	45
266	**235**	26p multicoloured	....	55	50
267	**236**	29p multicoloured	....	65	55
263/7		Set of 5	....	1·90	1·60
		First Day Cover	....		2·00
		Presentation Pack	....	2·40	
		Set of 5 Gutter Pairs	......	4·00	

Cylinder Nos.: All values 1A, 1B (each ×5)

Sheets: 50 (2 panes 5×5)

Imprint: Right-hand corner, bottom margin

Quantities sold: 8p 944,560; 13p 927,844; 24p 227,145; 26p 249,110; 29p 232,323

Withdrawn: 11.10.83

237 Flute Player and Boats

238 Cymbal Player and Tug 'o' war

239 Trumpet Player and Bible Class

240 Drummer and Cadets marching

241 Boys' Brigade Band

Centenary of Boys' Brigade

(Des Sally Stiff. Photo Harrison)

1983 (18 JAN). Perf 14 (*C*)

268	**237**	8p multicoloured	. . . .	15	10
269	**238**	13p multicoloured	. . . .	25	20
270	**239**	24p multicoloured	. . . .	40	40
271	**240**	26p multicoloured	. . . .	55	50
272	**241**	29p multicoloured	. . . .	65	55
268/72		Set of 5	. . . .	1·75	1·60
		First Day Cover	. . . .		1·90
		Presentation Pack	. . . .	2·25	
		Set of 5 Gutter Pairs	. . . . . .	3·50	

Cylinder Nos.: All values 1A, 1B (each ×5)

Sheets: 50 (2 panes 5×5)

Imprint: Bottom margin, right-hand corner

Quantities sold: 8p 671,921; 13p 538,257; 24p 223,069; 26p 234,482; 29p 214,723

Withdrawn: 17.1.84

242 Building Albert Pier Extension, 1850s

243 St. Peter Port Harbour, 1983

244 St. Peter Port, 1680

245 Artist's Impression of Future Development Scheme

Europa. Development of St. Peter Port Harbour

(Des C. Abbott. Photo Courvoisier)

1983 (14 MAR). *Granite paper.* Perf 11½ (*C*)

273	**242**	13p multicoloured	. . . .	20	15
		a. Horiz pair. Nos. 273/4	. . . . .	1·00	70
274	**243**	13p multicoloured	. . . .	20	15
275	**244**	20p multicoloured	. . . .	30	30
		a. Horiz pair. Nos. 275/6	. . . . .	1·25	1·00
276	**245**	20p multicoloured	. . . .	30	30
273/6		Set of 4	. . . .	2·00	80
		First Day Cover	. . . .		1·60
		Presentation Pack	. . . .	2·25	

Cylinder Nos.: Both values A1–1–1–1–1, B1–1–1–1–1

Sheets: 20 (4×5). The two designs of each value were printed together, *se-tenant*, in horizontal pairs throughout

Quantities sold: 13p 1,884,714; 20p 1,676,250

Withdrawn: 13.3.84

246 'View at Guernsey'

247 'Children on the Seashore'

248 'Marine, Guernesey'

249 'La Baie du Moulin Huet à travers les Arbres'

250 'Brouillard à Guernesey'

Centenary of Renoir's visit to Guernsey

(Des and photo Courvoisier)

1983 (6 SEPT). *Granite paper.* Perf 11×11½ (13p) or 11½ (others), all comb

277	**246**	9p multicoloured	20	15
278	**247**	13p multicoloured	25	25
279	**248**	26p multicoloured	55	50
280	**249**	28p multicoloured	85	80
281	**250**	31p multicoloured	1·00	90
277/81		*Set of 5*	2·50	2·40
		First Day Cover		3·00
		Presentation Pack	3·25	
		Stamp-cards (set of 5)	1·50	4·00
		Set of 5 Gutter Pairs	5·00	

Cylinder Nos.: 13p A1–1–1–1–1, B1–1–1–1–1, C1–1–1–1–1, D1–1–1–1–1; others A1–1–1–1–1, B1–1–1–1–1

Sheets: 40 (2 panes 4 × 5)

Quantities sold: 9p 547,148; 13p 757,838; 26p 185,045; 28p 219,830; 31p 305,219

Withdrawn: 5.9.84

251 Launching *Star of the West*, 1869, and Capt. J. Lenfestey

252 Leaving St. Peter Port

253 Off Rio Grande Bar

254 Off St. Lucia

255 Map of 1879–80 Voyage

Guernsey Shipping (1st series). Star of the West (brigantine)

(Des R. Granger Barrett. Litho Quensta)

1983 (15 NOV). Perf 14 (C)

282	**251**	9p multicoloured	20	70
283	**252**	13p multicoloured	25	15
284	**253**	26p multicoloured	50	50
285	**254**	28p multicoloured	80	75
286	**255**	31p multicoloured	85	80
282/6		*Set of 5*	2·40	2·10
		First Day Cover		2·40
		Presentation Pack	3·25	
		Set of 5 Gutter Pairs	4·75	

See also Nos. 415/19.

Plate Nos.: 26p, 31p 1C, 1D (each ×5); others 1A, 1B (each ×5)

Sheets: 50 (2 panes 5×5)

Imprint: Bottom corner, right-hand margin

Quantities sold: 9p 706,809; 13p 974,736; 26p 236,974; 28p 216,279; 31p 218,647

Withdrawn: 14.11.84

256 Dame of Sark as Young Woman

257 German Occupation, 1940–45

258 Royal Visit, 1957

259 Chief Pleas

260 Dame of Sark Rose

Birth Centenary of Sibyl Hathaway, Dame of Sark

(Des Jennifer Toombs. Litho Questa)

1984 (7 FEB). Perf 14½ (C)

287	**256**	9p multicoloured	20	20
288	**257**	13p multicoloured	30	15
289	**258**	26p multicoloured	70	55

290	**259**	28p multicoloured	. . . .	75	70
291	**260**	31p multicoloured	. . . .	80	75
287/91		Set of 5	. . . .	2·50	2·10
		First Day Cover	. . . .		2·50
		Presentation Pack	. . . .	3·00	
		Set of 5 Gutter Pairs	. . . . . .	5·00	

Plate Nos.: 13p 1A, 1B, 1C, 1D (each ×5); others 1A, 1B, 1C, 1D, (each ×7)

Sheets: 50 (2 panes 5×5)

Imprint: Bottom margin, right-hand corner

Quantities sold: 9p 637,566; 13p 836,270; 26p 315,561; 28p 293,716; 31p 270,742

Withdrawn: 6.2.85

261 C.E.P.T. 25th Anniversary Logo

Europa

(Des J. Larrivière. Litho Questa)

1984 (10 APR). Perf 15×14½ (C)

292	**261**	13p cobalt, dull ultramarine & blk	25	15
293		20½p emerald, deep dull grn & blk	55	50
292/3		Set of 2	75	60
		First Day Cover		1·25
		Presentation Pack	1·50	

Plate Nos.: Both values 1A, 1B (each ×3)

Sheets: 20 (4×5)

Imprint: Bottom corner, right-hand margin

Quantities sold: 13p 1,680,033; 20½p 903,972

Withdrawn: 9.4.85

262 The Royal Court and St. George's Flag

263 Castle Cornet and Union Flag

Links with the Commonwealth

(Des C. Abbott. Litho Questa)

1984 (10 APR.) Perf 14×14½ (C)

294	**262**	9p multicoloured	. . . .	20	15
295	**263**	31p multicoloured	. . . .	85	85
294/5		Set of 2	. . . .	1·00	95
		First Day Cover	. . . .		1·25
		Presentation Pack	. . . .	1·50	

Plate Nos.: Both values 1A, 1B, 1C, 1D (each ×6)

Sheets: 20 (4×5)

Imprint: Bottom corner, right-hand margin

Quantities sold: 9p 1,419,845, 31p 285,099

Withdrawn: 9.4.85

264 Little Chapel

265 Fort Grey

266 St. Apolline Chapel

267 Petit Port

268 Little Russel

269 The Harbour, Herm

270 Saints

271 St. Saviour

272 New Jetty (inscr 'Cambridge Berth')

273 Belvoir, Herm

GUERNSEY 11ᵖ
274 La Seigneurie, Sark

GUERNSEY 13ᵖ
276 St. Saviour's Reservoir

GUERNSEY 12ᵖ
275 Petit Bot

GUERNSEY 14ᵖ
277 St. Peter Port

GUERNSEY 15ᵖ
278 Havelet

GUERNSEY 16ᵖ
279 Hostel of St. John

GUERNSEY 18ᵖ
280 Le Variouf

GUERNSEY 20ᵖ
281 La Coupee, Sark

GUERNSEY 21ᵖ
282 King's Mills

GUERNSEY 26ᵖ
283 Town Church

GUERNSEY 30ᵖ
284 Grandes Rocques

GUERNSEY 40ᵖ
285 Torteval Church

GUERNSEY £1
287 Albecq

GUERNSEY 50ᵖ
286 Bordeaux

GUERNSEY £2
288 L'Ancresse

Views

(Des C. Abbott. Litho Questa)

1984 (18 SEPT)–**91**. Perf 14½ (C)

296	**264**	1p multicoloured (c)	10	10
297	**265**	2p multicoloured (c)	10	10
		a. Booklet pane. Nos. 297×2, 299×4, 300×2 and 305×2 (d)	1·60	
298	**266**	3p multicoloured (a)	10	10
		a. Booklet pane. Nos. 298, 299×2, 306×4 and 309×3 (f)	2·50	
299	**267**	4p multicoloured (a)	10	10
		a. Booklet pane. Nos. 299×2, 304×3 and 307×5	2·50	
		b. Booklet pane. Nos. 299, 304 and 307, each ×5	3·00	
		c. Booklet pane. Nos. 299×4, 306b×3 and 309c×3 (g) . . .	2·75	
		d. Booklet pane. Nos. 299,301, 306b×3 and 309d×3 (h) . . .	3·25	
		e. Black ptg double		
300	**268**	5p multicoloured (c)	15	10
		a. Booklet pane. Nos. 300×2, 301×2, 309×3 and 310b×3 (j)	3·75	
301	**269**	6p multicoloured (c)	15	15
		a. Booklet pane. Nos. 301×4, 308×4 and 310×2 (l)	3·25	
		b. Uncoated paper		
		c. Black ptg double		
302	**270**	7p multicoloured (c)	15	15
303	**271**	8p multicoloured (c)	20	15
304	**272**	9p multicoloured (a)	20	10
		a. Booklet pane. Nos. 304×4 and 308×6 (b)	2·50	
		b. Booklet pane. Nos. 304×2 and 308×8 (b)	2·50	
		c. Black ptg double		
305	**273**	10p multicoloured (a)	25	15
		a. Booklet pane. Nos. 305 and 308, each ×5 (e)	3·00	

306	**274**	11p multicoloured (c)	25	15
		a. Booklet pane. Nos. 306 and 309, each ×5 (f)	3·25	
306b	**275**	12p multicoloured (g)	35	15
		ba. Booklet pane. Nos. 306b and 309c, each ×5	3·00	
		bb. Booklet pane. Nos. 306b and 309d, each ×4 (h)	3·50	
		bc. Black ptg double		
307	**276**	13p multicoloured (a)	25	25
308	**277**	14p multicoloured (a)	25	20
		a. Booklet pane. Nos. 308 and 310, each ×5 (i)	3·75	
		b. Uncoated paper		
309	**278**	15p multicoloured (c)	30	30
		a. Booklet pane. Nos. 309 and 310b, each ×5 (j)	5·50	
		b. Imperf at sides and foot (horiz pair)		
309c	**279**	16p multicoloured (g)	30	20
		ca. Black and red ptgs double . .		
309d	**280**	18p multicoloured (h)	30	20
		da. Black ptg double		
310	**281**	20p multicoloured (a)	45	25
		a. Uncoated paper		
310b	**282**	21p multicoloured (i)	45	30
310c	**283**	26p multicoloured (j)	70	50
		ca. Imperf at sides and foot (horiz pair)	£900	
311	**284**	30p multicoloured (c)	65	60
312	**285**	40p multicoloured (a)	70	70
313	**286**	50p multicoloured (a)	80	75
314	**287**	£1 multicoloured (a)	1·90	1·40
315	**288**	£2 multicoloured (c)	3·75	2·75
296/315		Set of 25	12·00	9·00
		First Day Covers (5)		15·00
		Presentation Packs (3) . . . . . 15·00		
		Stamp-cards (set of 25) . . . . 7·00		22·00
		Set of 25 Gutter Pairs . . . . 24·00		

For 11p, 12p, 15p and 16p stamps in a smaller size see Nos. 398/9a.

Booklet panes Nos. 297a, 298a, 299a/c, 304a/b, 305a, 306a and 306ba have margins all round and were issued, folded and loose, within the booklet covers.

Booklet panes Nos. 299d, 300a, 306bb, 308a and 309a have the outer edges imperforate on three sides and were also issued loose within the booklet covers.

Nos. 299e, 301c, 306bc and 309da come from an example of booklet pane No. 299d.

Nos. 31b, 308b and 310a come from examples of booklet panes Nos. 301a and 308a.

Printings: (a) 18.9.84; (b) 19.3.85; (c) 23.7.85; (d) 2.12.85; (e) 1.4.86; (f) 30.3.87; (g) 28.3.88; (h) 28.2.89; (i) 27.12.89; (j) 2.4.91

Plate Nos.:All values 1A, 1B, 1C, 1D (each ×5)

Sheets: 1p, 3p, 8p, 12p, 14p, 15p, 18p, 26p, 40p, 100 (2 panes 10×5); others 100 (2 panes 5×10)

Imprint: Bottom, right-hand margin of each pane

Quantities sold: 1p 1,397,906; 2p 1,240,037; 3p 460,949; 4p 478,679; 5p 690,128; 6p 560,950; 7p 302,367; 8p 425,421; 9p 1,959,119; 10p 1,692,125; 11p 1,510,077; 12p 2,837,219; 13p 730,405; 14p 3,925,313; 15p 2,631,599; 16p 1,322,353; 18p 1,398,065; 20p 2,149,053; 21p 1,675,329; 26p 210,575; 30p 790,261; 40p 604,514; 50p 765,831; £1 647,055; £2 666,177

Withdrawn: 21.5.93

289 'A Partridge in a Pear Tree'

290 'Two Turtle Doves'

291 'Three French Hens'

292 'Four Colly Birds'

293 'Five Gold Rings'

294 'Six Geese a-laying'

295 'Seven Swans a-swimming'

296 'Eight Maids a-milking'

297 'Nine Drummers drumming'

298 'Ten Pipers piping'

299 'Eleven Ladies dancing'

300 'Twelve Lords a-leaping'

'The Twelve Days of Christmas'

(Des R. Downer. Litho Questa)

1984 (20 NOV). Perf 14½ (C)

316	**289**	5p multicoloured	15	15
		a. Sheetlet of 12. Nos. 316/27 .	2·00	
317	**290**	5p multicoloured	15	15
318	**291**	5p multicoloured	15	15
319	**292**	5p multicoloured	15	15
320	**293**	5p multicoloured	15	15
321	**294**	5p multicoloured	15	15
322	**295**	5p multicoloured	15	15
323	**296**	5p multicoloured	15	15
324	**297**	5p multicoloured	15	15
325	**298**	5p multicoloured	15	15
326	**299**	5p multicoloured	15	15
327	**300**	5p multicoloured	15	15
316/27		Set of 12	2·00	1·75
		First Day Cover		2·00
		Presentation Pack	2·75	

Sheets: 12 (4×3) containing Nos. 316/27 se-tenant

Imprint: Bottom, left-hand margin

Quantity sold: 271,168 sheetlets

Withdrawn: 19.11.85

301 Sir John Doyle and Coat of Arms

302 Battle of Germantown, 1777

303 Reclaiming Braye du Valle, 1806

304 Mail for Alderney, 1812

150th Death Anniversary of Lieutenant-General Sir John Doyle

(Des E. Stemp. Photo Courvoisier)

1984 (20 NOV). Granite paper. Perf 11½ (C)

328	**301**	13p multicoloured	30	25
329	**302**	29p multicoloured	65	60
330	**303**	31p multicoloured	75	70
331	**304**	34p multicoloured	90	85
328/31		Set of 4	2·40	2·10
		First Day Cover		2·50
		Presentation Pack	3·25	
		Set of 4 Gutter Pairs	4·75	

Cylinder Nos.: All values A1–1–1–1–1, B1–1–1–1–1, C1–1–1–1–1, D1–1–1–1–1

Sheets: 50 (2 panes 5×5)

Quantities sold: 13p 642,178; 29p 460,535; 31p 450,051; 34p 465,982

Withdrawn: 19.11.85

Yearbook 1984

1984 (1 DEC). Comprises Nos. 287/95, 298/9, 304/5, 307/8, 310, 312/14, 316/31 and A13/17

Yearbook	31·00

Withdrawn: 29.3.86

305 Cuckoo Wrasse

306 Red Gurnard

307 Red Mullet

308 Mackerel

309 Oceanic Sunfish

Fishes

(Des P. Barrett. Photo Courvoisier)

1985 (22 JAN). Granite paper. Perf 11½ (C)

332	**305**	9p multicoloured	30	25
333	**306**	13p multicoloured	40	25
334	**307**	29p multicoloured	1·00	90
335	**308**	31p multicoloured	1·00	90
336	**309**	34p multicoloured	1·10	90
332/6		Set of 5	3·50	3·00
		First Day Cover		3·25
		Presentation Pack	5·00	
		Set of 5 Gutter Pairs	7·00	

Cylinder Nos.: 13p, 29p A1–1–1–1–1, B1–1–1–1–1, C1–1–1–1–1, D1–1–1–1–1; others A1–1

1–1, B1–1–1–1, C1–1–1–1, D1–1–1–1

Sheets: 50 (2 panes 5 × 5)

Quantities sold: 9p 465,322; 13p 724,941; 29p 221,392; 31p 174,948; 34p 157,422

Withdrawn: 21.1.86

310 Dove

40th Anniversary of Peace in Europe

(Des C. Abbott. Litho Questa)

1985 (9 MAY). Perf 14×14½ (C)
337	**310**	22p multicoloured	60	50
		First Day Cover		90
		Presentation Pack	1·25	
		Gutter Pair	1·25	

Plate Nos.: 1A, 1B, 1C, 1D (each ×4)

Sheets: 50 (2 panes 5×5)

Imprint: Bottom, right-hand margin of each pane

Quantity sold: 246,024

Withdrawn: 8.5.86

311 I.Y.Y. Emblem and Young People of Different Races

312 Girl Guides cooking over Fire

International Youth Year

(Des Suzanne Brehaut (9p), Mary Harrison (31p). Litho Questa)

1985 (14 MAY). Perf 14 (C)
338	**311**	9p multicoloured	25	15
339	**312**	31p multicoloured	75	70
338/9		Set of 2	1·00	85
		First Day Cover		1·25
		Presentation Pack (with No. 342)	2·40	

Plate Nos.: Both values 1A, 1B, 1C, 1D, 1E, 1F (each ×6)

Sheets: 20 (5×4)

Imprint: Bottom, right-hand margin

Quantities sold: 9p 1,246,421; 31p 264,938

Withdrawn: 13.5.86

313 Stave of Music enclosing Flags

314 Stave of Music and Musical Instruments

Europa. European Music Year

(Des Fiona Sloan (14p), Katie Lillington (22p). Litho Questa)

1985 (14 MAY). Perf 14×14½ (C)
340	**313**	14p multicoloured	30	25
341	**314**	22p multicoloured	60	55
340/1		Set of 2	90	80
		First Day Cover		1·40
		Presentation Pack	2·50	

Plate Nos.: Both values 1A, 1B, 1C, 1D, 1E, 1F (each ×6)

Sheets: 20 (4×5)

Imprint: Bottom, right-hand margin

Quantities sold: 14p 1,742,651; 22p 879,421

Withdrawn: 13.5.86

315 Guide Leader, Girl Guide and Brownie

75th Anniversary of Girl Guide Movement

(Des Karon Mahy. Litho Questa)

1985 (14 MAY). Perf 14 (C)
342	**315**	34p multicoloured	1·00	90
		First Day Cover		1·25

Plate Nos.: 1A, 1B, 1C, 1D (each ×6)

Sheets: 20 (5×4)

Imprint: Bottom, right-hand margin

Quantity sold: 182,426

Withdrawn: 13.5.86

316 Santa Claus

317 Lussibruden (Sweden)

318 King Balthazar

319 Saint Nicholas
(Netherlands)

320 La Befana
(Italy)

321 Julenisse
(Denmark)

322 Christkind
(Germany)

323 King Wenceslas
(Czechoslovakia)

324 Shepherd
of Les
Baux
(France)

325 King Caspar

326 Baboushka
(Russia)

327 King
Melchior

Christmas. Gift-bearers

(Des C. Abbott. Photo Courvoisier)

1985 (19 NOV). *Granite paper.* Perf 12½ (C)

343	**316**	5p multicoloured	25	15
		a. *Sheetlet* of 12. *Nos.* 343/54 .	3·50	
344	**317**	5p multicoloured	25	15
345	**318**	5p multicoloured	25	15
346	**319**	5p multicoloured	25	15
347	**320**	5p multicoloured	25	15
348	**321**	5p multicoloured	25	15
349	**322**	5p multicoloured	25	15
350	**323**	5p multicoloured	25	15
351	**324**	5p multicoloured	25	15
352	**325**	5p multicoloured	25	15
353	**326**	5p multicoloured	25	15
354	**327**	5p multicoloured	25	15
343/54		*Set of* 12	3·50	1·75
		First Day Cover		3·75
		Presentation Pack	5·00	

Sheets: 12 (4×3) containing Nos. 343/54 *se-tenant*

Imprint: Central, bottom margin

Quantity sold: 236,937 sheetlets

Withdrawn: 18.11.86

328 'Vraicing'

329 'Castle Cornet'

330 'Rocquaine
Bay'

331 'Little Russel'

332 'Seaweed-
gatherers'

Paintings by Paul Jacob Naftel

(Des and photo Harrison)

1985 (19 NOV). Perf 15×14 (C)

355	**328**	9p multicoloured	20	20
356	**329**	14p multicoloured	25	25
357	**330**	22p multicoloured	65	65
358	**331**	31p multicoloured	1·00	1·00
359	**332**	34p multicoloured	1·25	1·25
355/9		*Set of* 5	3·00	3·00
		First Day Cover		3·25
		Presentation Pack	4·00	
		Set of 5 *Gutter Pairs*	6·00	

Cylinder Nos.: All values 1A, 1B (each ×5)

Sheets: 50 (2 panes 5×5)

Imprint: Left-hand margin of each pane

Quantities sold: 9p 398,472; 14p 452,728; 22p 164,922; 31p 197,422;
34p 173,428

Withdrawn: 18.11.86

Yearbook 1985

1985 (DEC). *Comprises Nos.* 296/7, 300/3, 306, 309, 311, 315, 332/59 *and* A18/27

                    Yearbook . . . . 52·00

Withdrawn: 31.12.86

333 Squadron off Nargue Island, 1809

334 Battle of the Nile, 1798

335 Battle of St. Vincent, 1797

336 H.M.S. *Crescent* off Cherbourg, 1793

337 Battle of the Saints, 1782

150th Death Anniversary of Admiral Lord De Saumarez

(Des T. Thompson. Photo Courvoisier)

1986 (4 FEB). *Granite paper.* Perf 11½ (C)

360	**333**	9p multicoloured	30	25
361	**334**	14p multicoloured	40	30
362	**335**	29p multicoloured	75	70
363	**336**	31p multicoloured	1·00	95
364	**337**	34p multicoloured	1·00	1·00
360/4		*Set of* 5	3·25	3·00
		First Day Cover		3·25
		Presentation Pack	4·00	
		Set of 5 *Gutter Pairs*	6·50	

Cylinder Nos.: All values A1–1–1–1–1, B1–1–1–1–1

Sheets: 40 (2 panes 5×4)

Quantities sold: 9p 456,518; 14p 706,727; 29p 157,693; 31p 163,612; 34p 160,724

Withdrawn: 3.2.87

338 Profile of Queen Elizabeth II (after R. Maklouf)

60th Birthday of Queen Elizabeth II

(Des C. Abbott. Litho Questa)

1986 (21 APR). Perf 14 (C)

365	**338**	60p multicoloured	1·50	1·25
		First Day Cover		2·00
		Presentation Pack	2·50	
		Gutter Pair	3·00	

Plate Nos.: 1A, 1B, 1C, 1D (each ×4)

Sheets: 40 (2 panes 5×4)

Imprint: Bottom, right-hand margin of each pane

Quantity sold: 169,661

Withdrawn: 20.4.87

339 Northern Gannet and Nylon Net ('Operation Gannet')

340 Loose-flowered Orchid

341 Guernsey Elm

Europa. Nature and Environmental Protection

(Des P. Newcombe. Photo Courvoisier)

1986 (22 MAY). *Granite paper.* Perf 11½ (C)

366	**339**	10p multicoloured	30	30
367	**340**	14p multicoloured	40	40
368	**341**	22p multicoloured	70	70
366/8		*Set of* 3	1·25	1·25
		First Day Cover		1·90
		Presentation Pack	1·90	

Cylinder Nos.: All values A1–1–1–1–1, B1–1–1–1–1, C1–1–1–1–1, D1–1–1–1–1

Sheets: 20 (4 × 5)

Quantities sold: 10p 977,212; 14p 995,123; 22p 662,565

Withdrawn: 21.5.87

342   Prince Andrew and Miss Sarah Ferguson   **343**

Royal Wedding

(Des C. Abbott. Litho Questa)

1986 (23 JULY). Perf 14 (14p) or 13½×14 (34p), both comb

369	**342**	14p multicoloured	60	50
370	**343**	34p multicoloured	1·00	90
369/70		*Set of 2*	1·60	1·40
		First Day Cover		2·00
		Presentation Pack	2·40	
		Set of 2 Gutter Pairs	3·25	

Plate Nos.: Both values 1A, 1B, 1C, 1D, 1E, 1F (each ×5)

Sheets: 50 (2 panes 5×5)

Imprint: Bottom, right-hand margin of each pane

Quantities sold: 14p 292,018; 34p 199,297

Withdrawn: 22.7.87

344 Bowls   **345** Cricket

346 Squash   **347** Hockey

348 Swimming   **349** Shooting

Sport in Guernsey

(Des R. Goldsmith. Litho Questa)

1986 (24 JULY). Perf 14½ (C)

371	**344**	10p multicoloured	25	20
372	**345**	14p multicoloured	35	20
		a. *Black (face value, inscr etc.) printed treble*		
373	**346**	22p multicoloured	50	45
		a. *Black (face value, inscr etc.) printed treble*		
374	**347**	29p multicoloured	90	80
375	**348**	31p multicoloured	90	80
376	**349**	34p multicoloured	1·00	90
371/6		*Set of 6*	3·50	3·00
		First Day Cover		3·25
		Presentation Pack	4·25	
		Set of 4 Gutter Pairs	7·00	

Plate Nos.: All values 1A, 1B, 1C, 1D (each ×4)

Sheets: 50 (2 panes 5×5)

Imprint: Bottom, right-hand margin of each pane

Quantities sold: 10p 399,897; 14p 985,699; 22p 212,203; 29p 141,882; 31p 157,751; 34p 156,164

Withdrawn: 23.7.87

350 Guernsey Museum and Art Gallery, Candie Gardens   **351** Fort Grey Maritime Museum

352 Castle Cornet   **353** National Trust of Guernsey Folk Museum

Centenary of Guernsey Museums

(Des Sir Hugh Casson. Litho Questa)

1986 (18 NOV). Perf 14 (C)

377	**350**	14p multicoloured	. . . .	30	15
378	**351**	29p multicoloured	. . . .	85	80
379	**352**	31p multicoloured	. . . .	85	80
380	**353**	34p multicoloured	. . . .	1·00	90
377/80		*Set of 4*	. . . .	2·75	2·40
		First Day Cover	. . . .		3·00
		Presentation Pack	. . . .	3·25	
		Set of 4 Gutter Pairs	. . . . . .	5·50	

Plate Nos.: All values 1A, 1B, 1C, 1D (each ×5)

Sheets: 50 (2 panes 5×5)

Imprint: Bottom, right-hand margin of each pane

Quantities sold: 14p 796,879; 29p 141,974; 31p 159,326; 34p 144,074

Withdrawn: 17.11.87

354 'While Shepherds Watched their Flocks by Night'

355 'In the Bleak Mid-Winter'

356 'O Little Town of Bethlehem'

357 'The Holly and the Ivy'

358 'O Little Christmas Tree'

359 'Away in a Manger'

360 'Good King Wenceslas'

361 'We Three Kings of Orient Are'

362 'Hark the Herald Angels Sing'

363 'I saw Three Ships'

364 'Little Donkey'

365 'Jingle Bells'

Christmas. Carols

(Des Wendy Bramall. Photo Courvoisier)

1986 (18 NOV). *Granite paper.* Perf 12½ (C)

381	**354**	6p multicoloured	. . . .	20	20
		a. Sheetlet of 12. Nos. 381/92 .		2·50	
382	**355**	6p multicoloured	. . . .	20	20
383	**356**	6p multicoloured	. . . .	20	20
384	**357**	6p multicoloured	. . . .	20	20
385	**358**	6p multicoloured	. . . .	20	20
386	**359**	6p multicoloured	. . . .	20	20
387	**360**	6p multicoloured	. . . .	20	20
388	**361**	6p multicoloured	. . . .	20	20
389	**362**	6p multicoloured	. . . .	20	20
390	**363**	6p multicoloured	. . . .	20	20
391	**364**	6p multicoloured	. . . .	20	20
392	**365**	6p multicoloured	. . . .	20	20
381/392		*Set of 12*	. . . .	2·50	2·10
		First Day Cover	. . . .		2·75
		Presentation Pack	. . . .	3·25	

Sheets: 12 (4×3) containing Nos. 381/92 *se-tenant*

Imprint: Central, bottom margin

Quantity sold: 226,119 sheetlets

Withdrawn: 17.11.87

Yearbook 1986

1986 (DEC). *Comprises Nos.* 360/92 *and* A28/31

Yearbook . . . . 34·00

Withdrawn: 31.12.87

366a Duke of Richmond and Map of 1787
(*illustration reduced to half size*)

Bicentenary of Duke of Richmond's Survey of Guernsey

(Des J. Cooter. Litho Questa)

1987 (10 FEB). Perf 14½×14 (C)
MS393 134×103 mm **366a** 14p, 29p, 31p,

34p multicoloured	2·50	2·75
First Day Cover		4·50
Presentation Pack	3·75	

Quantity sold: 176,655

Withdrawn: 9.2.88

367 Post Office Headquarters

368 Architect's Elevation of Post Office Headquarters

369 Guernsey Grammar School

370 Architect's Elevation of Grammar School

Europa. Modern Architecture

(Des R. Reed. Litho Cartor)

1987 (5 MAY). Perf 13×13½ (C)

394	**367**	15p multicoloured	25	20
		a. Horiz pair. Nos. 394/5	75	76
395	**368**	15p multicoloured	25	20
396	**369**	22p multicoloured	30	35
		a. Horiz pair. Nos. 396/7	1·25	1·25
397	**370**	22p multicoloured	30	35
394/7		Set of 4	1·75	1·00
		First Day Cover		2·25
		Presentation Pack	2·50	

Plate Nos.: Both values 1A, 1B, 1C, 1D (each ×4)

Sheets: 20 (4×5), the two designs for each value printed together, *se-tenant*, in horizontal pairs throughout the sheets

Quantities sold: 15p 595,661 pairs; 22p 434,886 pairs

Withdrawn: 4.5.88

Coil Stamps

(Photo Harrison)

1987 (15 MAY)–**88**. As Nos. 306, 306*b*, 309 and 309*c*, but smaller. 22×18 mm (11*p*, 16*p*) or 18×22 mm (12*p*, 15*p*). Perf 14×14½ (11p, 16p) or 14½×14 (12p, 15p), all comb

398	**274**	11p multicoloured (*a*)	50	50
398*a*	**275**	12p multicoloured (*b*)	40	40
399	**278**	15p multicoloured (*a*)	60	60
399*a*	**279**	16p multicoloured (*b*)	50	50
398/9*a*		Set of 4	1·75	1·75
		First Day Covers (2)		14·00

Printings: (*a*) 15.5.87; (*b*) 28.3.88

Coils: Rolls of 1000 (*a*) or 500 (*b*)

Withdrawn: 26.12.89 11p, 15p; 22.5.92 12p, 16p

371 Sir Edmund Andros and La Plaiderie, Guernsey

372 Governor's Palace, Virginia

373 Governor Andros in Boston

374 Map of New Amsterdam (New York), 1661

350th Birth Anniversary of Sir Edmund Andros (colonial administrator)

(Des B. Sanders. Photo Courvoisier)

1987 (7 JULY). *Granite paper.* Perf 12 (C)

400	**371**	15p multicoloured	30	15
401	**372**	29p multicoloured	80	60
402	**373**	31p multicoloured	85	75
403	**374**	34p multicoloured	1·10	1·00
400/3		*Set of 4*	2·75	2·25
		First Day Cover		2·75
		Presentation Pack	3·25	
		Set of 4 Gutter Pairs	5·50	

Cylinder Nos.: All values A1–1–1–1–1, B1–1–1–1–1

Sheets: 40 (2 panes 5×4)

Quantites sold: 15p 707,843; 29p 129,462; 31p 136,308; 34p 129,527

Withdrawn: 6.7.88

375 The Jester's Warning to Young William

376 Hastings Battlefield

377 Norman Soldier with Pennant

378 William the Conqueror

379 Queen Matilda and Abbaye aux Dames, Caen

380 William's Coronation Regalia and Halley's Comet

900th Death Anniversary of William the Conqueror

(Des P. le Vasseur. Litho Cartor)

1987 (9 SEPT). Perf 13½×14 (C)

404	**375**	11p multicoloured	20	15
405	**376**	15p multicoloured	30	25
		a. Horiz pair. Nos. 405/6	60	60
406	**377**	15p multicoloured	30	25
407	**378**	22p multicoloured	60	60
		a. Horiz pair. Nos. 407/8	1·25	1·25

408	**379**	22p multicoloured	60	60
409	**380**	34p multicoloured	1·00	1·10
404/9		*Set of 6*	2·75	2·75
		First Day Cover		3·00
		Presentation Pack	3·75	
		Set of 4 Gutter Pairs	5·50	

Plate Nos.: All values 1A, 1B, 1C, 1D (each ×4)

Sheets: 40 (2 panes 4×5), the two designs for the 15p and 22p values were printed together, *se-tenant*, in horizontal pairs throughout the sheets

Imprint: Bottom, left-hand margin

Quantities sold: 11p 639,904; 15p 241,572 pairs; 22p 142,718 pairs; 34p 131,655

Withdrawn: 8.9.88

381 John Wesley preaching on the Quay, Alderney

382 Preaching at Mon Plaisir, St. Peter Port

383 Preaching at Assembly Rooms

384 Wesley and La Ville Baudu (early Methodist meeting place)

385 Wesley and first Methodist Chapel, St. Peter Port

Bicentenary of John Wesley's Visit to Guernsey

(Des R. Geary. Litho Questa)

1987 (17 NOV). Perf 14½ (C)

410	**381**	7p multicoloured	20	15
411	**382**	15p multicoloured	25	25
412	**383**	29p multicoloured	80	75
413	**384**	31p multicoloured	90	85
414	**385**	34p multicoloured	90	85
410/14		*Set of 5*	2·75	2·50
		First Day Cover		3·00
		Presentation Pack	3·75	
		Set of 5 Gutter Pairs	5·50	

Plate Nos.: All values 1A, 1B, 1C, 1D (each ×4)

Sheets: 50 (2 panes 5×5)

Imprint: Bottom, right-hand margin of each pane

Quantities sold: 7p 762,772; 15p 887,797; 29p 122,322; 31p 126,591; 34p 125,863

Withdrawn: 16.11.88

Yearbook 1987

1987 (DEC). *Comprises Nos.* **MS**393/7, 400/14 *and* A32/6

Yearbook . . . . 37·00

Withdrawn: 31.12.88

386 *Golden Spur* off St. Sampson's Harbour

387 Entering Hong Kong Harbour

388 Anchored off Macao

389 In China Tea Race

390 *Golden Spur* and Map showing Voyage of 1872–74

Guernsey Shipping (2nd series). Golden Spur *(full-rigged ship)*

(Des R. Granger Barrett. Litho B.D.T.)

1988 (9 FEB). Perf 13½ (C)

415	**386**	11p multicoloured	. . . .	25	25
416	**387**	15p multicoloured	. . . .	35	35
417	**388**	29p multicoloured	. . . .	1·00	85
418	**389**	31p multicoloured	. . . .	1·00	85
419	**390**	34p multicoloured	. . . .	1·20	95
415/19		*Set of 5*	. . . .	3·50	3·00
		First Day Cover			3·50
		Presentation Pack	. . . .	4·00	
		Set of 5 Gutter Pairs	. . . . . .	6·50	

Plate Nos.: All values 1A, 1B, 1C, 1D (each ×4)

Sheets: 50 (2 panes 5×5)

Imprint: Central, side margins of each pane

Quantities sold: 11p 213,291; 15p 214,048; 29p 136,246; 31p 143,815; 34p 141,177

Withdrawn: 8.2.89

391 Rowing Boat and Bedford 'Rascal' Mail Van

392 Rowing Boat and Vickers Viscount 800 Mail Plane

393 Postman on Bicycle and Horse-drawn Carriages, Sark

394 Postmen on Bicycles and Carriage

Europa. Transport and Communications

(Des C. Abbott. Litho Questa)

1988 (10 MAY). Perf 14½ (C)

420	**391**	16p multicoloured	. . . .	35	35
		a. Horiz pair. Nos. 420/1	. . . . .	80	70
421	**392**	16p multicoloured	. . . .	35	35
422	**393**	22p multicoloured	. . . .	70	70
		a. Horiz pair. Nos. 422/3	. . . . .	1·40	1·40
423	**394**	22p multicoloured	. . . .	70	70
420/3		*Set of 4*	. . . .	2·00	1·90
		First Day Cover			2·25
		Presentation Pack	. . . .	2·50	

Plate Nos.: Both values 1A, 1B, 1C, 1D (each ×5)

Sheets: 20 (4×5), the two designs for each value printed together, *se-tenant*, in horizontal pairs throughout the sheets

Imprint: Top, right-hand margin

Quantities sold: 16p 387,699 pairs: 22p 359,634 pairs

Withdrawn: 9.5.89

395 Frederick Corbin Lukis and Lukis House, St. Peter Port

396 Natural History Books and Reconstructed Pot

397 Lukis directing Excavation of Le Creux ès Faies and Prehistoric Beaker

398 Lukis House Observatory and Garden

399 Prehistoric Artifacts

Birth Centenary of Frederick Corbin Lukis (archaeologist)

(Des Wendy Bramall, Photo Courvoisier)

1988 (12 JULY). *Granite paper*. Perf 12½ (C)

424	**395**	12p multicoloured	25	25
425	**396**	16p multicoloured	30	25
426	**397**	29p multicoloured	90	85
427	**398**	31p multicoloured	90	85
428	**399**	34p multicoloured	90	90
424/8		*Set of 5*	3·00	2·75
		First Day Cover		3·00
		Presentation Pack	3·75	
		Set of 5 Gutter Pairs	6·00	

Cylinder Nos.: 29p, 34p A1–1–1–1, B1–1–1–1, C1–1–1–1, D1–1–1–1; others A1–1–1–1–1, B1–1–1–1–1, C1–1–1–1–1, D1–1–1–1–1

Sheets: 40 (2 panes 5×4)

Quantities sold: 12p 634,056; 16p 510,713; 29p 120,538; 31p 114,192; 34p 134,358

Withdrawn: 11.7.89

400 *Cougar, Rocky* and *Annabella* (powerboats) and Westland Wessex Rescue Helicopter off Jethou

401 *Paul Picot* and other Powerboats in Gouliot Passage

402 Start of Race at St. Peter Port

403 Admiralty Chart showing Course

World Offshore Powerboat Championships

(Des and photo Courvoisier)

1988 (6 SEPT). *Granite paper*. Perf 12 (C)

429	**400**	16p multicoloured	35	25
430	**401**	30p multicoloured	85	85
431	**402**	32p multicoloured	1·00	90
432	**403**	35p multicoloured	1·10	1·00
429/32		*Set of 4*	3·00	2·75
		First Day Cover		3·00
		Presentation Pack	3·75	
		Set of 4 Gutter Pairs	6·00	

Cylinder Nos.: 16p, 32p A1–1–1–1, B1–1–1–1; 30p, 35p C1–1–1–1, D1–1–1–1

Sheets: 40 (2 panes 5×4) 16p, 30p or (2 panes 4×5) others

Quantities sold: 16p 582,190; 30p 127,183; 32p 166,804; 35p 128,552

Withdrawn: 5.9.89

404 Joshua Gosselin and Herbarium

405 Hares-tail Grass

406 Dried Hares-tail Grass

407 Variegated Catchfly

408 Dried Variegated Catchfly

409 Rock Sea Lavender

Bicentenary of Josha Gosselin's *Flora Sarniensis*

(Des M. Oxenham. Litho Cartor)

1988 (15 NOV). Perf 13½×14 (C)

433	**404**	12p multicoloured	25	25
434	**405**	16p multicoloured	40	35
		a. Horiz pair. Nos. 434/5	80	70
435	**406**	16p multicoloured	40	35
436	**407**	23p multicoloured	55	50
		a. Horiz pair. Nos. 436/7	1·10	1·00
437	**408**	23p multicoloured	55	50
438	**409**	35p multicoloured	1·00	1·00
433/8		Set of 6	2·75	2·50
		First Day Cover		3·25
		Presentation Pack	3·50	
		Set of 4 Gutter Pairs	5·50	

Plate Nos.: All values 1A, 1B, 1C, 1D (each ×4)

Sheets: 40 (2 panes 4×5), the two designs for the 16p and 23p values printed together, *se-tenant*, in horizontal pairs throughout the sheets

Imprint: Bottom, left-hand margin

Quantities sold: 12p 562,702; 16p 378,679 pairs; 23p 141,152 pairs; 35p 133,205

Withdrawn: 14.11.89

410 Coutances Cathedral, France

411 Interior of Notre Dame du Rosaire Church, Guernsey

412 Stained Glass, St. Sampson's Church, Guernsey

413 Dol-de-Bretagne Cathedral, France

414 Bishop's Throne, Town Church, Guernsey

415 Winchester Cathedral

416 St. John's Cathedral, Portsmouth

417 High Altar, St. Joseph's Church, Guernsey

418 Mont Saint-Michel, France

419 Chancel, Vale Church, Guernsey

420 Lychgate, Forest Church, Guernsey

421 Marmoutier Abbey, France

Christmas. Ecclesiastical Links

(Des R. Downer. Litho Questa)

1988 (15 NOV). Perf 14½ (C)

439	**410**	8p multicoloured	20	20
		a. Sheetlet of 12. Nos. 439/50	2·25	
440	**411**	8p multicoloured	20	20
441	**412**	8p multicoloured	20	20
442	**413**	8p multicoloured	20	20
443	**414**	8p multicoloured	20	20
444	**415**	8p multicoloured	20	20
445	**416**	8p multicoloured	20	20
446	**417**	8p multicoloured	20	20
447	**418**	8p multicoloured	20	20
448	**419**	8p multicoloured	20	20
449	**420**	8p multicoloured	20	20
450	**421**	8p multicoloured	20	20
439/50		Set of 12	2·25	2·25
		First Day Cover		2·75
		Presentation Pack	3·25	

Sheets: 12 (4×3) containing Nos. 439/50 *se-tenant*

Imprint: Bottom, left-hand margin

Quantity sold: 185,939 sheetlets

Withdrawn: 14.11.89

Yearbook 1988

1988 (DEC). *Comprises Nos. 306b, 309c and 415/50*
Yearbook . . . . 35·00

Withdrawn: 31.12.89

422 Lé Cat (Tip Cat)

423 Girl with Cobo Alice Doll

424 Lé Colimachaön (hopscotch)

Europa. Children's Toys and Games

(Des P. le Vasseur. Litho Cartor)

1989 (28 FEB). Perf 13½ (C)

451	**422**	12p multicoloured	25	20
452	**423**	16p multicoloured	40	40
453	**424**	23p multicoloured	80	85
451/3		*Set of 3*	1·25	1·25
		First Day Cover		1·60
		Presentation Pack	1·90	

Plate Nos.: All values 1A, 1B, 1C (each ×4)

Sheets: 20 (4 × 5)

Imprint: Top, right-hand margin

Quantities sold: 12p 839,111; 16p 829,156; 23p 448,761

Withdrawn: 27.2.90

425 Outline Map of Guernsey

Coil Stamps

(Photo Harrison)

1989 (3 APR–27 DEC). *No value expressed.* Perf 14½×14 (C)

454	**425**	(–) ultramarine (b)	60	60
455		(–) emerald (a)	65	70
454/5		*Set of 2*	1·25	1·25
		First Day Covers (2)		10·00

No. 454 is inscribed 'MINIMUM BAILIWICK POSTAGE PAID' and No. 455 'MINIMUM FIRST CLASS POSTAGE TO UK PAID'. They were originally sold at 14p and 18p, but this was changed in line with postage rate rises.

Printings: (a) 3.4.89; (b) 27.12.89

Coils: Rolls of 500, numbered on the reverse of every fifth stamp

Withdrawn: 30.6.96

426 Guernsey Airways De Havilland D.H.86 Dragon Express and Mail Van

427 Supermarine Southampton II Flying Boat at Mooring

428 B.E.A. De Havilland D.H.89 Dragon Rapide

429 Short S.25 Sunderland MK V Flying Boat taking off

430 Air U.K. British Aerospace BAe 146

431 Avro Shackleton M.R.3

50th Anniversaries of Guernsey Airport (Nos. 456, 458 and 460) and 201 Squadron's Affiliation with Guernsey (Nos. 457, 459 and 461)

(Des N. Foggo. Litho B.D.T.)

1989 (5 MAY). Perf 13½ (C)

456	**426**	12p multicoloured	35	30
		a. Booklet pane. No. 456×6 . .	2·00	
457	**427**	12p multicoloured	35	30
458	**428**	18p multicoloured	50	50
		a. Booklet pane. No. 458×6 . .	3·00	
459	**429**	18p multicoloured	50	50

460	**430**	35p multicoloured	1·00	90
		a. Booklet pane. No. 460×6 . .	6·00	
461	**431**	35p multicoloured	1·00	1 00
456/61		Set of 6	3·25	3·25
		First Day Cover		4·75
		Presentation Pack	4·50	
		Set of 4 Gutter Pairs	6·50	

Each booklet pane has margins all round with text printed at the foot.

Plate Nos.: All values 1A, 1B (each ×4)

Sheets: 50 (2 panes 5×5)

Imprint: Central, side margins of each pane

Quantities sold: No. 456, 461,080; No. 457, 362,154; No. 458, 436,134; No. 459, 388,274; No. 460, 172,574; No. 461, 149,134

Withdrawn: 4.5.90

432 'Queen Elizabeth II' (June Mendoza)

Royal Visit

(Des A. Theobald. Lithi B.D.T.)

1989 (23 MAY). Perf 15×14

462	**432**	30p multicoloured	75	80
		First Day Cover		1·75
		Presentation Pack	2·00	

Plate Nos.: 1A (×5)

Sheets: 20 (5×4)

Imprint: Top, right-hand margin

Quantity sold: 180,900

Withdrawn: 22.5.90

433 Ibex at G.W.R. Terminal, St. Peter Port

434 Great Western (paddle-steamer) in Little Russel

435 St. Julien passing Casquets Light

436 Roebuck off Portland

437 Antelope and Boat Train on Weymouth Quay

Centenary of Great Western Railway Steamer Service to Channel Islands

(Des C. Jaques. Litho B.D.T.)

1989 (5 SEPT). Perf 13½ (C)

463	**433**	12p multicoloured	20	20
464	**434**	18p multicoloured	45	45
465	**435**	29p multicoloured	70	75
466	**436**	34p multicoloured	1·00	95
467	**437**	37p multicoloured	1·20	1·10
463/7		Set of 5	3·25	3·00
		First Day Cover		3·50
		Presentation Pack	6·00	
		Set of 5 Gutter Pairs	6·00	
MS468		115×117 mm. Nos. 463/7	3·00	3·25
		First Day Cover		7·00

Plate Nos.: All values 1A, 1B (each ×4)

Sheets: 50 (2 panes 5×5)

Imprint: Central, side margins of each pane

Quantities sold: 12p 741,870; 18p 666,520; 29p 223,570; 34p 202,570; 37p 209,020; miniature sheet 74,127

Withdrawn 4.9.90

438 Two-toed Sloth

439 Capuchin Monkey

440 White-lipped Tamarin

441 Common Squirrel-Monkey

442 Common Gibbon

10th Anniversary of Guernsey Zoological Trust. Animals of the Rainforest

(Des Anne Farncombe. Litho Cartor)

1989 (17 NOV). Perf 13½×14) (C)

469	**438**	18p multicoloured	. . . .	70	70
		a. Strip of 5. Nos. 469/73	. . . .	3·50	3·50
470	**439**	29p multicoloured	. . . .	70	70
471	**440**	32p multicoloured	. . . .	70	70
472	**441**	34p multicoloured	. . . .	70	70
473	**442**	37p multicoloured	. . . .	70	70
469/73		Set of 5	. . . .	3·50	3·50
		First Day Cover	. . . .		3·75
		Presentation Pack	. . . .	4·25	
		Stamp-cards (set of 5)	. . . . .	2·00	6·00

Plate Nos.: 1B (×4)

Sheets: 20 (5×4). Nos. 469/73 were printed in *se-tenant* strips of 5 across the sheet

Imprint: Top, right-hand margin

Quantities sold: 148,505 of each value

Withdrawn: 16.11.90

Christmas. Christmas Tree Decorations

(Des Wendy Bramall. Litho B.D.T.)

1989 (17 NOV). Perf 13 (C)

474	**443**	10p multicoloured	. . . .	25	20
		a. Sheetlet of 12. Nos. 474/85	.	2·50	
475	**444**	10p multicoloured	. . . .	25	20
476	**445**	10p multicoloured	. . . .	25	20
477	**446**	10p multicoloured	. . . .	25	20
478	**447**	10p multicoloured	. . . .	25	20
479	**448**	10p multicoloured	. . . .	25	20
480	**449**	10p multicoloured	. . . .	25	20
481	**450**	10p multicoloured	. . . .	25	20
482	**451**	10p multicoloured	. . . .	25	20
483	**452**	10p multicoloured	. . . .	25	20
484	**453**	10p multicoloured	. . . .	25	20
485	**454**	10p multicoloured	. . . .	25	20
474/85		Set of 12	. . . .	2·50	2·25
		First Day Cover	. . . .		3·00
		Presentation Pack	. . . .	3·50	

Sheets: 12 (3×4) containing Nos. 474/85 *se-tenant*

Imprint: Central, left-hand margin

Quantity sold: 229,000 sheetlets

Withdrawn: 16.11.90

Yearbook 1989

1989 (17 NOV). *Comprises Nos. 309d, 451/3, 456/62,* **MS**468/85 *and* A37/41

Yearbook . . . . 31·00

Withdrawn: 31.12.90

443 Star

444 Fairy

445 Candles

446 Bird

447 Present

448 Carol-singer

449 Christmas Cracker

450 Bauble

451 Christmas Stocking

452 Bell

453 Fawn

454 Church

455 Sark Post Office, c 1890

456 Sark Post Office, 1990

457 Arcade Post Office Counter, St. Peter Port, c 1840

458 Arcade Post Office Counter, St. Peter Port, 1990

GUERNSEY 1990-ARCADE POST OFFICE **24**P

Europa. Post Office Buildings

(Des C. Abbott. Litho Enschedé)

1990 (27 FEB). Perf 13½ × 14 (C)

486	**455**	20p blackish brown, sepia and pale cinnamon	....	45	45
487	**456**	20p multicoloured	....	45	45
488	**457**	24p blackish brown, sepia and pale cinnamon	....	60	65
489	**458**	24p multicoloured	....	60	65
486/9		Set of 4	....	1·90	2·00
		First Day Cover	....		2·40
		Presentation Pack	....	2·40	

Plate Nos.: Nos. 486 and 488 1A, 1B (each ×3); Nos. 487 and 489 1A, 1B (each ×4)

Sheets: 20 (4×5)

Imprint: Central, side margins

Quantities sold: No. 486, 498,819; No. 487, 398,759; 488, 495,039; No. 489, 397,759

Withdrawn: 26.2.91

459 Penny Black and Mail Steamer off St. Peter Port, 1840

460 Penny Red, 1841, and Pillar Box of 1853

461 Bisected 2d., 1940, and German Army Band

462 Regional 3d., 1958, and Guernsey Emblems

463 Independent Postal Administration 1½d., 1969, and Queue at Main Post Office

150th Anniversary of the Penny Black

(Des Jennifer Toombs. Litho Questa)

1990 (3 MAY). Perf 14 (C)

490	**459**	14p multicoloured	....	35	35
491	**460**	20p multicoloured	....	45	45
492	**461**	32p multicoloured	....	80	80
493	**462**	34p multicoloured	....	1·00	1·00
494	**463**	37p multicoloured	....	1·00	1·00
490/4		Set of 5	....	3·25	3·25
		First Day Cover	....		3·75
		Presentation Pack	....	5·50	
		Set of 5 Gutter Pairs	......	6·50	
MS495		151×116 mm. Nos. 490/4	......	3·25	3·50
		First Day Cover	....		9·50

No. **MS**495 also commemorates 'Stamp World London 90' International Stamp Exhibition. It was reissued on 24 August 1990 overprinted for 'NEW ZEALAND 1990' and sold at this international stamp exhibition in Auckland.

Plate Nos.: 14p, 32p 1A, 1B (each ×4); 20p, 34p 1C, 1D (each ×4); 37p 1A, 1B, 1C, 1D (each ×4)

Sheets: 50 (2 panes 5×5)

Imprint: Bottom corner, right-hand margin of each pane

Quantities sold: 14p 687,850; 20p 662,800; 32p 155,960; 34p 143,850; 37p 174,830; miniature sheet 92,701

Withdrawn: 2.5.91

464 Lt. Philip Saumarez writing Log Book

465 Anson's Squadron leaving Portsmouth, 1740

466 Ships at St. Catherine's Island, Brazil

467 H.M.S. *Tryal* (sloop) dismasted, Cape Horn, 1741

468 Crew of H.M.S. *Centurion* on Juan Fernandez

250th Anniversary of Anson's Circumnavigation

(Des R. Granger Barrett. Litho Enschedé)

1990 (26 JULY). Perf 13½×14 (C)

496	**464**	14p multicoloured	30	30
497	**465**	20p multicoloured	40	40
498	**466**	29p multicoloured	80	80
499	**467**	34p multicoloured	1·00	90
500	**468**	37p multicoloured	1·10	95
496/500		Set of 5	3·25	3·00
		First Day Cover		3·75
		Presentation Pack	3·75	
		Stamp-cards (set of 5)	2·00	6·00
		Set of 5 Gutter Pairs	6·50	

Plate Nos.: 14p, 20p, 29p 1A, 1B, 1C, 1D (each ×4); 34p, 37p 1A, 1B (each ×4)

Sheets: 50 (2 panes 5×5)

Imprint: Central, side margins of each pane

Quantities sold: 14p 985,850; 20p 481,400; 29p 162,800; 34p 143,500; 37p 138,450

Withdrawn: 25.7.91

469 Grey Seal and Pup

470 Bottle-nosed Dolphin

471 Basking Shark

472 Common Porpoise

Marine Life

(Des Jennifer Toombs. Litho Questa)

1990 (16 OCT). Perf 14½ (C)

501	**469**	20p multicoloured	45	45
502	**470**	26p multicoloured	95	95
503	**471**	31p multicoloured	1·00	1·00
504	**472**	37p multicoloured	1·25	1·25
501/4		Set of 4	3·25	3·25
		First Day Cover		4·25
		Presentation Pack	4·00	
		Set of 4 Gutter Pairs	6·50	

Plate Nos.: 20p, 31p 1A, 1B (each ×4); 26p, 37p 1C, 1D (each ×4)

Sheets: 50 (2 panes 5×5)

Imprint: Top, right-hand margin of each pane

Quantities sold: 20p 973,900; 26p 478,200; 31p 328,650; 37p 303,600

Withdrawn: 15.10.91

473 Blue Tit and Great Tit

474 Snow Bunting

475 Common Kestrel

476 Common Starling

477 Western Greenfinch

478 European Robin

479 Winter Wren

480 Barn Owl

481 Mistle Thrush

482 Grey Heron

483 Chaffinch

484 Common Kingfisher

Christmas. Winter Birds

(Des Wendy Bramall. Litho B.D.T.)

1990 (16 OCT). Perf 13 (C)

505	**473**	10p multicoloured	35	30
		a. Sheetlet of 12. Nos. 505/16 .	3·25	
506	**474**	10p multicoloured	35	30
507	**475**	10p multicoloured	35	30
508	**476**	10p multicoloured	35	30
509	**477**	10p multicoloured	35	30
510	**478**	10p multicoloured	35	30
511	**479**	10p multicoloured	35	30
512	**480**	10p multicoloured	35	30
513	**481**	10p multicoloured	35	30
514	**482**	10p multicoloured	35	30
515	**483**	10p multicoloured	35	30
516	**484**	10p multicoloured	35	30
505/16		Set of 12	3·25	3·25
		First Day Cover		3·50
		Presentation Pack	4·25	

Sheets: 12 (3×4) containing Nos. 505/16 se-tenant

Imprint: Central, left-hand margin

Quantity sold: 237,602 sheetlets

Withdrawn: 15.10.91

Yearbook 1990

1990 (1 NOV). Comprises Nos. 486/9, **MS**495, 496/516, A12a and A42/6

Yearbook .... 32·00

Withdrawn: 31.12.91

485 Air Raid and 1941 ½d. Stamp

486 1941 1d. Stamp

487 1944 2½d. Stamp

50th Anniversary of First Guernsey Stamps

(Des C. Abbott. Litho B.D.T.)

1991 (18 FEB). Perf 10½ (C)

517	**485**	3½p multicoloured	1·00	1·10
		a. Booklet pane. Nos. 517/19 .	4·00	
518	**486**	53p multicoloured	1·30	1·50
519	**487**	57p multicoloured	1·30	1·50
517/19		Set of 3	3·25	3·75
		First Day Cover		4·00
		Presentation Pack	4·25	
		Set of 3 Gutter Pairs	7·50	

Booklet pane No. 517a exists in three versions, which differ in the order of the stamps from left to right and in the information printed on the pane margins.

Plate Nos.: 37p, 53p 1A, 1B (each ×4); 57p 1A, 1B, 1C, 1D (each ×4)

Sheets: 40 (2 panes 5×4)

Imprint: Central, side margins

Quantities sold: 37p 260,015; 53p 250,536; 57p 250,219

Withdrawn: 17.2.92

488 Visit of Queen Victoria to Guernsey, and Discovery of Neptune, 1846

489 Visit of Queen Elizabeth II and Prince Philip to Sark, and Flight of 'Sputnik' (1st artificial satellite, 1957)

490 Maiden Voyage of Sarnia (ferry), and 'Vostok 1' (first manned space flight), 1961

491 Cancelling Guernsey Stamps, and First Manned Landing on Moon, 1969

Europa. Europe in Space

(Des Jennifer Toombs. Litho Enschedé)

1991 (30 APR). Perf 13½×14 (C)

520	488	21p multicoloured	....	55	50
521	489	21p multicoloured	....	55	50
522	490	26p multicoloured	....	65	60
523	491	26p multicoloured	....	65	60
520/3		*Set of 4*	....	1·90	1·90
		First Day Cover	....		2·25
		Presentation Pack	....	2·75	

Plate Nos.: Both values 1A, 1B (each ×5)

Sheets: 20 (4×5)

Imprint: Central, side margins

Quantities sold: No. 520, 390,924; No. 521, 390,834; No. 522, 369,404; No. 523, 370,244

Withdrawn: 29.4.92

492 Children in Guernsey Sailing Trust 'GP14' Dinghy

493 Guernsey Regatta

494 Lombard Channel Islands' Challenge Race

495 Rolex Swan Regatta

496 Old Gaffers' Association Gaff-rigged Yacht

Centenary of Guernsey Yacht Club

(Des C. Abbott. Litho B.D.T.)

1991 (2 JULY). Perf 14 (C)

524	492	15p multicoloured	....	45	15
525	493	21p multicoloured	....	70	25
526	494	26p multicoloured	....	80	80
527	495	31p multicoloured	....	90	1·10
528	496	37p multicoloured	....	1·00	1·40
524/8		*Set of 5*	....	3·50	3·25
		First Day Cover	....		3·75
		Presentation Pack	....	4·25	
		Set of 5 Gutter Pairs	......	7·00	
MS529		163×75 mm. Nos. 524/8	....	3·50	4·00
		First Day Cover	....		7·00

Stamps from No. **MS**529 show 'GUERNSEY' and the face value in yellow.

Plate Nos.: 37p 1C, 1D (each ×5); others 1A, 1B (each ×5)

Sheets: 50 (2 panes 5×5)

Imprint: Top corner, right-hand margin of each pane

Quantities sold: 15p 711,043; 21p 708,743; 26p 188,894; 31p 158,938; 37p 138.543; miniature sheet 81,012

Withdrawn: 1.7.92

497 Pair of Oystercatchers

498 Three Ruddy Turnstones

499 Dunlins and Ruddy Turnstones

500 Curlew and Ruddy Turnstones

501 Ringed Plover with Chicks

502 Black-headed Gull, Sea Campion and Sea Radish

503 Yellow Horned Poppy

504 Pair of Common Stonechats, Hare's Foot Clover and Fennel

505 Hare's Foot Clover, Fennel and Slender Oat

506 Ruddy Turnstone and Sea Kale on Shore

Nature Conservation. L'Eree Bank Reserve

(Des Wendy Bramall. Litho Questa)

1991 (15 OCT). Perf 14½ (C)

530	**497**	15p multicoloured	40	45
		a. Horiz strip of 5. Nos. 530/4 .	2·50	2·50
531	**498**	15p multicoloured	40	45
532	**499**	15p multicoloured	40	45
533	**500**	15p multicoloured	40	45
534	**501**	15p multicoloured	40	45
535	**502**	21p multicoloured	50	50
		a. Horiz strip of 5. Nos. 535/9 .	2·50	2·50
536	**503**	21p multicoloured	50	50
537	**504**	21p multicoloured	50	50
538	**505**	21p multicoloured	50	50
539	**506**	21p multicoloured	50	50
530/9		Set of 10	3·75	4·00
		First Day Cover		4·50
		Presentation Pack	4·50	
		Stamp-cards (set of 10)	4·00	8·50

Plate Nos.: Both values 1A, 1B, 1C, 1D (each ×4)

Sheets: 20 (5×4), the five designs for each value printed together, se-tenant, in horizontal strips throughout the sheets.

Imprint: Bottom, left-hand margin

Quantities sold: 15p 270,830 strips; 21p 272,198 strips

Withdrawn: 14.10.92

507 'Rudolph the Red-nosed Reindeer' (Melanie Sharpe)

508 'Christmas Pudding' (James Quinn)

509 'Snowman' (Lisa Guille)

510 'Snowman in Top Hat' (Jessica Ede-Golightly)

511 'Robins and Christmas Tree' (Sharon Le Page)

512 'Shepherds and Angels' (Anna Coquelin)

513 'Nativity' (Claudine Lithou)

514 'Three Wise Men' (Jonathan Le Noury)

515 'Star of Bethlehem and Angels' (Marcia Mahy)

516 'Christmas Tree' (Laurel Garfield)

517 'Santa Claus' (Rebecca Driscoll)

518 'Snowman and Star' (Ian Lowe)

Christmas. Children's Paintings

(Litho B.D.T.)

1991 (15 OCT). Perf 13½×13 (C)

540	**507**	12p multicoloured	30	30
		a. Sheetlet of 12. Nos. 540/51 .	3·25	
541	**508**	12p multicoloured	30	30
542	**509**	12p multicoloured	30	30
543	**510**	12p multicoloured	30	30
544	**511**	12p multicoloured	30	30
545	**512**	12p multicoloured	30	30
546	**513**	12p multicoloured	30	30
547	**514**	12p multicoloured	30	30
548	**515**	12p multicoloured	30	30
549	**516**	12p multicoloured	30	30
550	**517**	12p multicoloured	30	30
551	**518**	12p multicoloured	30	30
540/51		Set of 12	3·25	3·25
		First Day Cover		3·50
		Presentation Pack	3·75	

Sheets: 12 (3×4) containing Nos. 540/51 se-tenant

Imprint: Central, left-hand margin

Quantity sold: 192,203 sheetlets

Withdrawn: 14.10.92

Yearbook 1991

1991 (1 NOV). *Comprises Nos. 310b/c, 517/51, A12b and A47/51*

Yearbook . . . . 30·00

Withdrawn: 31.12.92

519 Queen Elizabeth 'll in 1952

520 In 1977

521 In 1986

522 In 1991

40th Anniversary of Accession

(Des C. Abbott. Litho Questa)

1992 (6 FEB). Perf 14 (C)

552	**519**	23p multicoloured	. . . .	50	50
553	**520**	28p multicoloured	. . . .	65	65
554	**521**	33p multicoloured	. . . .	90	90
555	**522**	39p multicoloured	. . . .	1·10	1·10
552/5		Set of 4	. . . .	2·75	2·75
		First Day Cover	. . . .		3·25
		Presentation Pack	. . . .	3·25	
		Set of 4 Gutter Pairs	. . . . . .	5·50	

Plate Nos.: All values 1A, 1B (each ×6)

Sheets: 50 (2 panes 5×5)

Quantities sold: 23p 773,200; 28p 479,095; 33p 212,446; 39p 219,900

Withdrawn: 5.2.93

523 Christopher Columbus

524 Examples of Columbus's Signature

525 *Santa Maria*

526 Map of First Voyage

Europa. 500th Anniversary of Discovery of America by Columbus

(Des R. Ollington. Litho Walsall)

1992 (6 FEB). Perf 13½×14 (C)

556	**523**	23p multicoloured	. . . .	65	60
557	**524**	23p multicoloured	. . . .	65	60
558	**525**	28p multicoloured	. . . .	1·25	1·25
559	**526**	28p multicoloured	. . . .	1·25	1·25
556/9		Set of 4	. . . .	3·25	3·25
		First Day Cover	. . . .		3·75
		Presentation Pack	. . . .	3·75	
MS560		157×77 mm. Nos. 556/9	. . . .	4·50	5·00
		First Day Cover	. . . .		6·00

No. **MS**560 was reissued on 22 May 1992 overprinted for 'WORLD COLUMBIAN STAMP EXPO 92' and sold at this international stamp exhibition in Chicago. (*Price* 5·00 *unused*, 6·00 *used*, 9·00 *on first day cover*).

Plate Nos.: All values 1A, 1B, 1C (each ×4)

Sheets: 20 (4×5)

Imprint: Bottom, right-hand margin

Quantities sold: No. 556, 543,672; No. 557, 575,663; No. 558, 363,124; No. 559, 364,684; miniature sheet 157,166

Withdrawn: 5.2.93

527a Guernsey Calves

150th Anniversary of Royal Guernsey Agricultural and Horticultural Society

(Des R. Goldsmith, Litho Questa)

1992 (22 MAY). *Sheet* 93×71 *mm. Perf* 14 (C)

MS561 **527a** 75p multicoloured . . . . 2·10   2·00
First Day Cover . . . .   3·25
Presentation Pack . . . . 2·75

Quantity sold: 142,549

Withdrawn: 21.5.93

528 Stephanotis floribunda *1p*

529 Potted Hydrangea *2p*

530 Stock *3p*

531 Anemones *4p*

532 Gladiolus *5p*

533 *Asparagus plumosus, Gypsophila paniculata* *6p*

534 Guernsey Lily *7p*

535 Enchantment Lily *8p*

536 Clematis 'Freckles' *9p*

537 Alstroemeria *10p*

538 Standard Carnation *16p*

539 Standard Rose *18p*

540 Spray Rose *20p*

541 Mixed Freesia *23p*

542 Standard Rose *24p*

543 Iris 'Ideal' *25p*

544 Freesia 'Pink Glow' *26p*

545 Lisianthus *28p*

546 Spray Chrysanthemum *30p*

547 Spray Carnation *40p*

548 Single Freesia *50p*

549 Floral Arrangement *£1*

550 Chelsea Flower Show Exhibit *£2*

551 'Floral Fantasia' (exhibit) *£3*

54

Horticultural Exports

(Des R. Gorringe. Litho Walsall (Nos. 572a, 572ba, 574a, 575a, 576b and 577a), Questa (No. 576a), Cartor (No. 582a) or B.D.T. (others))

1992 (22 MAY)–**97**. Perf 14 (£1, £2) or 13 (others), all comb

562	**528**	1p multicoloured (b)	10	10
563	**529**	2p multicoloured (b)	10	10
564	**530**	3p multicoloured (a)	10	10
565	**531**	4p multicoloured (a)	15	15
566	**532**	5p multicoloured (a)	15	15
567	**533**	6p multicoloured (b)	15	15
568	**534**	7p multicoloured (b)	20	20
569	**535**	8p multicoloured (b)	20	20
570	**536**	9p multicoloured (b)	20	25
571	**537**	10p multicoloured (a)	25	25
572	**538**	16p multicoloured (a)	50	35
		a. Perf 14 (ab)	60	50
		ab. Lavender ptg double		
		ac. Booklet pane. Nos. 572a×5		
		and 574a×3 (a)	4·00	
		ad. Booklet pane of 8 (b)	3·25	
572b	**539**	18p multicoloured (e)	55	45
		ba. Perf 14	55	45
		bb. Booklet pane of 8	4·00	
573	**540**	20p multicoloured (a)	60	50
574	**541**	23p multicoloured (a)	60	55
		a. Perf 14	80	60
		ab. Brownish grey ptg double . .		
		ac. Booklet pane of 8	6·00	
575	**542**	24p multicoloured (b)	70	60
		a. Perf 14	80	60
		ab. Booklet pane of 8	6·00	
576	**543**	25p multicoloured (c)	70	60
		a. Perf 14½×15	80	60
		ab. Booklet pane of 4	3·00	
576b	**544**	26p multicoloured (e)	70	60
		ba. Perf 14	80	60
		bb. Booklet pane of 4	3·00	
577	**545**	28p multicoloured (b)	80	65
		a. Perf 14	1·10	65
		ab. Booklet pane of 4	3·50	
578	**546**	30p multicoloured (b)	80	70
579	**547**	40p multicoloured (a)	1·00	75
580	**548**	50p multicoloured (a)	1·20	90
581	**549**	£1 multicoloured (a)	2·00	1·50
582	**550**	£2 multicoloured (b)	4·00	3·00
582a	**551**	£3 multicoloured (d)	6·00	5·00
562/82a		Set of 24	18·00	16·00
		First Day Covers (5)		25·00
		Presentation Packs (3) . . . . . 25·00		
		Stamp-cards (set of 24)	5·00	27·00
		Set of 24 Gutter Pairs . . . . . 40·00		

Nos. 572a, 572ba, 574a, 575a, 576a, 576ba and 577a were only issued in booklets with the upper and lower edges of the panes imperforate.

For No. 581 in miniature sheets see Nos. **MS**644 (with imprint date '1994') and **MS**681 (with imprint date '1995').

Printings: (a) 22.5.92; (b) 2.3.93; (c) 18.2.94; (d) 24.1.96; (e) 2.1.97, each with appropriate imprint date

Plate Nos.: £1 1A, 1B (each ×8); £3 1A, 1B, 1C, 1D (each ×5); others 1A, 1B, 1C, 1D (each ×6)

Sheets: 1p, 2p, 3p, 4p, 5p, 6p, 7p, 8p, 9p, 10p, 18p, 20p, 40p 100 (2 panes 10×5); 16p, 23p, 24p, 25p, 26p, 28p, 30p, 50p (2 panes 5×10); £1, £2, £3 50 (2 panes 5×5)

Imprints: 1p, 2p, 3p, 4p, 5p, 6p, 7p, 8p, 9p, 10p, 18p, 20p, 40p, £1, £2 left-hand corner, top and bottom margin; £3 central, side margins; others top of side margin

Withdrawn: 31.8.99 1p to £2; 31.8.2003 £3

552 Building the Ship

553 Loading the Cargo

554 Ship at Sea

555 Ship under Attack

556 Crew swimming Ashore

'Operation Asterix' (excavation of Roman ship)

(Des Studio Legrain. Litho Cartor)

1992 (18 SEPT). Perf 13 (C)

583	**552**	16p multicoloured	45	35
		a. Booklet pane. Nos. 583/7		
		plus label	3·50	
584	**553**	23p multicoloured	60	45
585	**554**	28p multicoloured	80	70
586	**555**	33p multicoloured	95	90
587	**556**	39p multicoloured	1·10	1·00
583/7		Set of 5	3·50	3·00
		First Day Cover		4·25
		Presentation Pack . . . . 4·25		
		Set of 5 Gutter Pairs . . . . . . 7·00		

Booklet pane No. 583a has margins all round and exists with marginal inscriptions in either English, French, Italian or German.

Plate Nos.: All values 1A, 1B, 1C, 1D (each ×4)

Sheets: 50 (2 panes 5×5)

Imprint: Central, side margins

Quantities sold: 16p 904,428; 23p 743,228; 28p 308,091; 33p 281,941; 39p 291,841

Withdrawn: 17.9.93

557 Tram No. 10 decorated for Battle of Flowers

558 Tram No. 10 passing Hougue a la Perre

559 Tram No. 1 at St. Sampsons

560 First Steam Tram at St. Peter Port, 1879

561 Last Electric Tram, 1934

Guernsey Trams

(Des A. Peck. Litho Enschedé)

1992 (17 NOV). Perf 13½ (C)

588	**557**	16p multicoloured	....	45	30
589	**558**	23p multicoloured	....	60	35
590	**559**	28p multicoloured	....	75	80
591	**560**	33p multicoloured	....	80	1·00
592	**561**	39p multicoloured	....	1·00	1·10
588/92		*Set of 5*	....	3·25	3·25
		First Day Cover	....		4·25
		Presentation Pack	....	4·75	
		Set of 5 Gutter Pairs	......	7·50	

Plate Nos.: 39p, 1A, 1B, 1C, 1D (each ×6); others 1A, 1B (each ×6)

Sheets: 50 (2 panes 5×5)

Imprint: Central, side margins of each pane

Quantities sold: 16p 366,400; 23p 282,520; 28p 181,670; 33p 130,920; 39p 156,170

Withdrawn: 16.11.93

562 Man in Party Hat

563 Girl and Christmas Tree

564 Woman and Balloons

565 Mince Pies and Champagne

566 Roast Turkey

567 Christmas Pudding

568 Christmas Cake

569 Fancy Cakes

570 Cheese

571 Nuts

572 Ham

573 Chocolate Log

Christmas. Seasonal Fayre

(Des Wendy Bramall. Litho B.D.T.)

1992 (17 NOV). Perf 13 (C)

593	**562**	13p multicoloured	....	30	30
		a. Sheetlet of 12. Nos. 593/604	3·50		
		ab. Gold ptg double	....		
594	**563**	13p multicoloured	....	30	30
595	**564**	13p multicoloured	....	30	30
596	**565**	13p multicoloured	....	30	30
597	**566**	13p multicoloured	....	30	30
598	**567**	13p multicoloured	....	30	30
599	**568**	13p multicoloured	....	30	30
600	**569**	13p multicoloured	....	30	30
601	**570**	13p multicoloured	....	30	30
602	**571**	13p multicoloured	....	30	30
603	**572**	13p multicoloured	....	30	30
604	**573**	13p multicoloured	....	30	30
593/604		*Set of 12*	....	3·50	3·25
		First Day Cover	....		4·00
		Presentation Pack	....	4·50	

Sheets: 12 (3×4) containing Nos. 593/604 *se-tenant*, forming a composite design showing family during Christmas meal

Imprint: Central, left-hand margin

Quantity sold: 183,550 sheetlets

Withdrawn: 16.11.93

Yearbook 1992

1992 (18 NOV). *Comprises Nos.* 552/61, 564/6, 571/4, 579/81, 583/604, A12c *and* A52/5

	Yearbook	30·00

Withdrawn: 31.12.93

24 GUERNSEY **574** Rupert Bear, Bingo and Dog

574a Rupert and Friends
(*illustration reduced. Actual size 116×97 mm*)

Rupert Bear and Friends (cartoon characters created by Mary and Herbert Tourtel)

(Des J. Harold. Litho Walsall)

1993 (2 FEB). Perf 13½×13 (C)

605	**574**	24p multicoloured	. . . .	50	50
		First Day Cover	. . . .		2·00
		Gutter Pair	. . . .	1·50	

MS606 116×97 mm. **574a** 16p Airplane and castle; 16p Professor's servant and Autumn Elf; 16p Algy Pug; 16p Baby Badger on sledge; 24p Bill Badger, Willie Mouse, Reggie Rabbit and Podgy playing in snow; 24p Type **574**; 24p The Balloonist avoiding Gregory on toboggan; 24p Tiger Lily and Edward Trunk . . . . 4·50 4·00
    a. Black ptg double . . . .
    First Day Cover . . . . 4·50
    Presentation Pack (Nos. 605/6) . . . . 6·00

The 24p values in No. **MS**606 are as Type **574**; the 16p designs are smaller, each 25½×26 mm.

Plate Nos.: 24p 1A, 1B (each ×4)

Sheets: 50 (2 panes 5×5)

Imprint: Top left-hand margin of each pane

Quantities sold: 24p 523,690; miniature sheet 107,258

Withdrawn: 1.2.94

24 GUERNSEY **575** Tapestry by Kelly Fletcher

24 GUERNSEY **576** 'Le Marchi a Paisson' (etching and aquatint, Sally Reed)

28 GUERNSEY **577** 'Red Abstract' (painting, Molly Harris)

28 GUERNSEY **578** 'Dress Shop, King's Road' (painting, Damon Bell)

Europa. Contemporary Art

(Des B. Bell. Litho Enschedé)

1993 (7 MAY). Perf 13½×14 (C)

607	**575**	24p multicoloured	. . . .	70	70
608	**576**	24p multicoloured	. . . .	70	70
609	**577**	28p multicoloured	. . . .	80	80
610	**578**	28p multicoloured	. . . .	80	80
607/10		Set of 4	. . . .	2·75	2·75
		First Day Cover	. . . .		3·00
		Presentation Pack	. . . .	3·00	

Plate Nos.: 24p (No. 607) 1A, 1B, 1C, 1D (each ×5); others 1A, 1B (each ×5)

Sheets: 20 (4×5)

Imprint: Central, side margins

Quantities sold: No. 607, 289,838; No. 608, 292,450; No. 609, 283,627; No. 610, 280,150

Withdrawn: 6.5.94

579 Arrest of Guernsey Parliamentarians, Fermain Bay

580 Parliamentary Ships attacking Castle Cornet

581 Parliamentary Captives escaping

582 Castle Cannon firing at St. Peter Port

583 Surrender of Castle Cornet, 19 December 1651

350th Anniversary of Siege of Castle Cornet

(Des C. Abbott. Litho Questa)

1993 (7 MAY). Perf 14½×14 (C)

611	**579**	16p multicoloured	35	35
612	**580**	24p multicoloured	60	60
613	**581**	28p multicoloured	75	75
614	**582**	33p multicoloured	85	85
615	**583**	39p multicoloured	90	90
611/15		Set of 5	2·75	3·00
		First Day Cover		3·75
		Presentation Pack	3·75	
		Set of 5 Gutter Pairs	6·00	
MS616		203×75 mm. Nos. 611/15	3·25	4·00
		First Day Cover		4·25

Plate Nos.: All values 1A, 1B (each ×5)

Sheets: 40 (2 panes 4×5)

Imprint: Central, right-hand margin

Quantities sold: 16p 253,310; 24p 289,408; 28p 125,877; 33p 124,981; 39p 125,761; miniature sheet 184,308

Withdrawn: 6.5.94

584 Playing Cards **585** Fountain Pens **586** Envelope-folding Machine

587 Great Britain 1855 4d Stamp **588** Thomas de la Rue and Mauritius £1 Banknote

Birth Bicentenary of Thomas de la Rue (printer)

(Des J. Stephenson. Litho (16, 24, 28p) or recess (33, 39p) Enschedé)

1993 (27 JULY). Perf 13½ (C)

617	**584**	16p multicoloured	40	40
		a. Booklet pane of 4 with margins all round	1·50	
618	**585**	24p multicoloured	65	65
		a. Booklet pane of 4 with margins all round	2·25	
619	**586**	28p multicoloured	80	80
		a. Booklet pane of 4 with margins all round	3·00	
620	**587**	33p carmine-lake	95	95
		a. Booklet pane of 4 with margins all round	3·25	
621	**588**	39p blackish green	1·10	1·10
		a. Booklet pane of 4 with margins all round	3·75	
617/21		Set of 5	3·50	3·50
		First Day Cover		3·75
		Presentation Pack	4·00	
		Set of 5 Gutter Pairs	7·25	

Plate Nos.: 16p, 24p 1A×4; 28p 1A, 1B (each ×4); 33p, 39p 1A

Sheets: 50 (2 panes 5×5)

Imprint: Central, side margins of each pane

Quantities sold: 16p 465,736; 24p 452,982; 28p 111,030; 33p 113,299; 39p 119,548

Withdrawn: 26.7.94

589 'The Twelve Pearls'

590 'Healing Rays'

591 'Hand of God over the Holy City'

592 'Wing and Seabirds' (facing left)

593 'Christ the Healer'

594 'Wing and Seabirds' (facing right)

595 'The Young Jesus in the Temple'

596 'The Raising of Jarius' Daughter'

597 'Suffer Little Children to come unto Me'

598 'Pilgrim's Progress'

599 'The Light of the World'

600 'Raphael, Archangel of Healing, with Tobias'

Christmas. Stained Glass Windows by Mary-Eily de Putron from Chapel of Christ the Healer

(Des Jennifer Toombs. Litho B.D.T.)

1993 (2 NOV.) Perf 13 (C)

622	**589**	13p multicoloured	. . . .	30	30
		a. Sheetlet. Nos. 622/33	. . . . .	3·50	
623	**590**	13p multicoloured	. . . .	30	30
624	**591**	13p multicoloured	. . . .	30	30
625	**592**	13p multicoloured	. . . .	30	30
626	**593**	13p multicoloured	. . . .	30	30
627	**594**	13p multicoloured	. . . .	30	30
628	**595**	13p multicoloured	. . . .	30	30
629	**596**	13p multicoloured	. . . .	30	30
630	**597**	13p multicoloured	. . . .	30	30
631	**598**	13p multicoloured	. . . .	30	30
632	**599**	13p multicoloured	. . . .	30	30
633	**600**	13p multicoloured	. . . .	30	30
622/33		Set of 12	. . . .	3·50	3·25
		First Day Cover	. . . .		4·00
		Presentation Pack	. . . .	4·00	

Sheets: 12 (3×4) containing Nos. 622/33 *se-tenant*

Imprint: Central, left-hand margin

Quantity sold: 150,594 sheetlets

Withdrawn: 1.11.94

Yearbook 1993

1993 (2 NOV). *Comprises Nos. 562/3, 567/70, 575, 577/8, 582, 605/33, A12d/e and A56/9*

Yearbook . . . . 32·00

Withdrawn: 30.12.94

601 Les Fouaillages (ancient burial ground)

602 Mounted Celtic Warrior

603 Jars, Arrow Heads and Stone Axe from Les Fouaillages

604 Sword, Spear Head and Torque from King's Road Burial

Europa. Archaeological Discoveries

(Des Miranda Schofield. Litho Cartor)

1994 (18 FEB). Perf 13½ (C)

634	**601**	24p multicoloured	....	55	55
635	**602**	24p multicoloured	....	55	55
636	**603**	30p multicoloured	....	80	75
637	**604**	30p multicoloured	....	80	75
634/7		Set of 4	....	2·40	2·25
		First Day Cover	....		2·75
		Presentation Pack	....	2·75	

Some sheets of No. 635 were overprinted with the 'Hong Kong '94' emblem on the left margin for sale at this philatelic exhibition.

Plate Nos.: All values 1A

Sheets: 10 (2×5) with large inscribed margin at left

Quantities sold: No. 634, 241,910; No. 635, 241,943; No. 636, 237,126; No. 637, 232,797; 'Hong Kong '94' margin opt 31,124 sheets.

Withdrawn: 17.2.95

605a Canadian Supermarine Spitfires MK V over Normandy Beaches

50th Anniversary of D-Day

(Des N. Trudgian. Litho B.D.T.)

1994 (6 JUNE). Sheet 93×71 mm. Perf 14 (C)

MS638	**605a**	£2 multicoloured	....	4·00	4·25
		First Day Cover	....		6·50
		Presentation Pack	....	5·00	

Quantity sold: 156,793

Withdrawn: 5.6.95

Guernsey 16

606 Peugeot 'Type 3', 1894

Guernsey 24

607 Mercedes 'Simplex', 1903

Guernsey 35

608 Humber Tourer, 1906

Guernsey 41

609 Bentley Sports Tourer, 1936

Guernsey 60

610 MG TC Midget, 1948

Centenary of First Car in Guernsey

(Des R. Ollington. Litho B.D.T.)

1994 (19 JULY). Perf 14½×14 (C)

639	**606**	16p multicoloured	....	40	40
		a. Booklet pane of 4 with margins all round	....	1·75	
640	**607**	24p multicoloured	....	60	45
		a. Booklet pane of 4 with margins all round	....	2·75	
641	**608**	35p multicoloured	....	90	1·00
		a. Booklet pane of 4 with margins all round	....	4·00	
642	**609**	41p multicoloured	....	1·00	1·00
		a. Booklet pane of 4 with margins all round	....	4·25	
643	**610**	60p multicoloured	....	1·50	1·40
		a. Booklet pane of 4 with margins all round	....	6·50	
639/43		Set of 5	....	4·00	3·75
		First Day Cover	....		4·25
		Presentation Pack	....	4·75	
		Set of 5 Gutter Pairs	......	9·00	

Plate Nos.: 60p 1A, 1B, 1C, 1D (each ×5); others 1A, 1B (each ×5)

Sheets: 50 (2 panes 5×5)

Imprint: Central, side margins of each pane

Quantities sold: 16p 279,325; 24p 238,478; 35p 114,668; 41p 116,567; 60p 117,435

Withdrawn: 18.7.95

610a Floral Arrangement
(*illustration reduced. Actual size* 110×90 *mm*)

'Philakorea '94' International Stamp Exhibition, Seoul

(Des R. Gorringe and M. Whyte. Litho Cartor)

1994 (16 AUG). *Sheet* 110×90 *mm containing stamp as No.* 581 *with changed imprint date.* Perf 13 (C)
MS644 **610a** £1 multicoloured . . . . 2·20 3·00
First Day Cover . . . . 5·50
Presentation Pack . . . . 4·50

Quantity sold: 78,679
Withdrawn: 15.8.95

611 *Trident* (Herm Ferry)

612 Handley Page HPR-7 Super Dart Herald of Channel Express

613 Britten Norman Trislander G-JOEY of Aurigny Air Services

614 *Bon Marin de Serk* (Sark Ferry)

615 Map of Bailiwick

25th Anniversary of Guernsey Postal Administration

(Des A. Copp. Litho Questa)

1994 (1 OCT). Perf 14 (C)

645	**611**	16p multicoloured	35	30
646	**612**	24p multicoloured	55	50
647	**613**	35p multicoloured	75	75
648	**614**	41p multicoloured	85	85
649	**615**	60p multicoloured	1·40	1·25
645/9		Set of 5	3·50	3·25
		First Day Cover		3·75
		Presentation Pack	4·50	
		Stamp-cards (set of 5)	1·60	5·50
MS650		150×100 mm. Nos. 645/9	4·00	4·25
		First Day Cover		5·50

Plate Nos.: All values 1A (×5)

Sheets: 20 (5×4)

Imprint: Central, left-hand margin

Quantities sold: 16p 218,779; 24p 188,946; 35p 129,318; 41p 139,622; 60p 140,855; miniature sheet 63,283

Withdrawn: 30.9.95

616 Dolls' House

617 Doll

618 Teddy in Bassinette

619 Sweets in Pillar Box and Playing Cards

620 Spinning Top

621 Building Blocks

622 Rocking Horse

623 Teddy Bear

624 Tricycle

625 Wooden
Duck

626 Hornby Toy
Locomotive

627 Ludo Game

Christmas. Bygone Toys

(Des A. Peck. Litho B.D.T.)

1994 (1 OCT). Perf 13 (C)

651	**616**	13p multicoloured	. . . .	40	20
		a. Sheetlet. Nos. 651/6	. . . . . .	2·00	
652	**617**	13p multicoloured	. . . .	40	20
653	**618**	13p multicoloured	. . . .	40	20
654	**619**	13p multicoloured	. . . .	40	20
655	**620**	13p multicoloured	. . . .	40	20
656	**621**	13p multicoloured	. . . .	40	20
657	**622**	24p multicoloured	. . . .	75	60
		a. Sheetlet. Nos. 657/62	. . . . .	3·50	
658	**623**	24p multicoloured	. . . .	75	60
659	**624**	24p multicoloured	. . . .	75	60
660	**625**	24p multicoloured	. . . .	75	60
661	**626**	24p multicoloured	. . . .	75	60
662	**627**	24p multicoloured	. . . .	75	60
651/62		Set of 12	. . . .	5·00	4·25
		First Day Covers (2)	. . . .		6·50
		Presentation Pack	. . . .	5·75	

Sheets: 6 (3×2) containing Nos. 650/5 or 656/61 se-tenant

Imprint: Bottom, left-hand margin

Quantities sold: 13p 192,937 sheetlets; 24p 133,416 sheetlets

Withdrawn: 30.9.95

Yearbook 1994

1994 (1 OCT). Comprises Nos. 576, 634/62 and A60/76
Yearbook (softback) . . . . 40·00
Yearbook (hardback) . . . . . . 65·00

Withdrawn: 29.12.95

628 Seafood 'Face'

629 Buckets and
Spade 'Face'

630 Flowers 'Face'

631 Fruit and
Vegetables 'Face'

632 Sea Shells and
Seaweed 'Face'

633 Anchor and Life
Belts 'Face'

634 Glasses, Cork and
Cutlery 'Face'

635 Butterflies and
Caterpillars 'Face'

Greetings Stamps. 'The Welcoming Face of Guernsey'

(Des R. Ollington. Litho Questa)

1995 (28 FEB). Perf 14 (C)

663	**628**	24p multicoloured	. . . .	60	55
664	**629**	24p multicoloured	. . . .	60	55
665	**630**	24p multicoloured	. . . .	60	55
666	**631**	24p multicoloured	. . . .	60	55
667	**632**	24p multicoloured	. . . .	60	55
668	**633**	24p multicoloured	. . . .	60	55
669	**634**	24p multicoloured	. . . .	60	55
670	**635**	24p multicoloured	. . . .	60	55
663/70		Set of 8	. . . .	4·25	4·00
		First Day Cover	. . . .		5·00
		Presentation Pack	. . . .	5·00	
		Stamp-cards (set of 8)	. . . . .	1·75	6·00
		Set of 8 Gutter Pairs	. . . . . .	8·50	
MS671		137×109 mm. Nos. 663/70	. . . . . .	4·25	4·25
		First Day Cover	. . . .		6·00

Plate Nos.: All values 1A, 1B (each x5)

Sheets: 50 (2 panes 5×5)

Imprint: Central, left-hand margin

Quantities sold: No. 663, 138,328; No. 664, 113,568; No. 665, 138,555; No. 666, 138,474; No. 667, 113,520; No. 668, 113,568; No. 669, 113,573; No. 670, 113,580; miniature sheet 128,702

Withdrawn: 27.2.96

636 Winston Churchill and Wireless

637 Union Jack and Royal Navy Ships off St. Peter Port

638 Royal Arms and Military Band

639 *Vega* (Red Cross supply ship)

640 Rejoicing Crowd

50th Anniversary of Liberation

(Des M. Whyte. Litho Enschedé)

1995 (9 MAY). Perf 13½×14 (C)

672	**636**	16p multicoloured	45	30
673	**637**	24p multicoloured	60	50
674	**638**	35p multicoloured	90	90
675	**639**	41p multicoloured	90	90
676	**640**	60p multicoloured	1·50	1·25
672/6		Set of 5	4·00	3·50
		First Day Cover		4·50
		Presentation Pack	5·50	
		Set of 5 Gutter Pairs	8·00	
MS677		189×75 mm. Nos. 672/6	4·25	4·50
		First Day Cover		6·00

Plate Nos.: 60p 1A, 1B, 1C, 1D (each ×4); others 1A, 1B (each ×4)

Sheets: 50 (2 panes 5×5)

Imprint: Central, side margins

Quantities sold: 16p 558,373; 24p 410,244; 35p 130,472; 41p 158,351; 60p 159,394; miniature sheet 86,502

Withdrawn: 8.5.96

641 Silhouette of Doves on Ground

642 Silhouette of Doves in Flight

Europa. Peace and Freedom

(Des K. Bassford. Litho Walsall)

1995 (9 MAY). Perf 14 (C)

678	**641**	25p multicoloured	50	65
679	**642**	30p multicoloured	65	85
678/9		Set of 2	1·10	1·50
		First Day Cover		2·00
		Presentation Pack	2·10	

The designs of Nos. 678/9 each provide a stereogram or hidden three-dimensional image of a single dove designed by D. Burder.

Plate Nos.: Both values 1A, 1B, 1C (each ×4)

Sheets: 10 (2×5)

Imprint: Central, bottom margin

Quantities sold: 25p 219,750; 30p 171,902

Withdrawn: 8.5.96

643 Prince Charles, Castle Cornet and Bailiwick Arms

Royal Visit

(Des C. Abbott. Litho Questa)

1995 (9 MAY). Perf 14 (C)

680	**643**	£1.50 multicoloured	2·90	3·25
		First Day Cover		4·00
		Presentation Pack	4·00	
		Gutter Pair	7·00	

Plate Nos.: 1A, 1B, 1C, 1D (each ×5)

Sheets: 40 (2 panes 5×4)

Imprint: Central, left-hand margin

Quantity sold: 140,954

Withdrawn: 8.5.96

643a (*illustration reduced. Actual size* 110×90 *mm*)

'Singapore '95' International Stamp Exhibition

(Des R. Gorringe and M. Whyte. Litho Cartor)

1995 (1 SEPT). *Sheet* 110×90 *mm containing stamp as No.
581 with changed imprint date.* Perf 13 (C)

MS681	**643a**	£1 multicoloured	2·75	2·75
		First Day Cover		4·50
		Presentation Pack	3·75	

Quantity sold: 64,768

Withdrawn: 31.8.96

644

645

646

647

50th Anniversary of United Nations

(Des K. Basstord. Litho and embossed Enschedé)

1995 (24 OCT). Pert 14×13½ (C)

682	**644**	50p pale new blue and gold	1·10	1·10
		a. *Block of* 4. *Nos.* 682/5	4·25	4·25
683	**645**	50p pale new blue and gold	1·10	1·10
684	**646**	50p pale new blue and gold	1·10	1·10
685	**647**	50p pale new blue and gold	1·10	1·10
682/5		*Set of* 4	4·00	4·25
		First Day Cover		5·00
		Presentation Pack	5·00	

Plate Nos.: 1A–1A

Sheets: 36 (6×6). Nos. 682/5 were printed together, *se-tenant*,
throughout the sheet with each block of 4 showing the complete
United Nations emblem

Imprint: Central, side margins

Quantity sold: 448,348

Withdrawn: 23.10.96

648   'Christmas Trees for Sale in Bern'   **649**
(Cornelia Nussbrum-Weibel)

650   'Evening Snowfall'   **651**
(Katerina Mertikas)

652   'It came upon a Midnight Clear'   **653**
(Georgia Guback)

654   'Children of the World'   **655**

Christmas. 50th Anniversary of U.N.I.C.E.F.

(Adapted M. Whyte from U.N.I.C.E.F. Christmas Cards. Litho B.D.T.)

1995 (16 NOV). Perf 13 (C)

686	**648**	13p multicoloured	40	35
		a. Horiz pair. Nos. 686/7	80	70
687	**649**	13p multicoloured	40	35
688	**650**	13p + 1p multicoloured	40	45
		a. Horiz pair. Nos. 688/9	80	90
689	**651**	13p + 1p multicoloured	40	45
690	**652**	24p multicoloured	70	70
		a. Horiz pair. Nos. 690/1	1·40	1·40
691	**653**	24p multicoloured	70	70
692	**654**	24p + 2p multicoloured	70	70
		a. Horiz pair. Nos. 692/3	1·40	1·40
693	**655**	24p + 2p multicoloured	70	70
686/93		Set of 8	4·00	4·00
		First Day Cover		5·00
		Presentation Pack	5·00	

Sheets: 12 (4×3), the two designs for each value printed together, *se-tenant*, in horizontal pairs throughout the sheets, each pair forming a composite design

Quantities sold: Nos. 686/7, 540,858; Nos. 688/9, 352,684; Nos. 690/1, 365,098; Nos. 692/3, 365,740

Withdrawn: 15.11.96

Yearbook 1995

1995 (1 DEC). *Comprises Nos. 663/93 and A77/84*

Yearbook .... 42·00

Withdrawn: 31.12.97

656 Princess Anne (President, Save the Children Fund) and Children

657 Queen Elizabeth II and people of the Commonwealth

Europa. Famous Women

(Des D. Miller. Litho B.D.T.)

1996 (21 APR). Perf 14 (C)

694	**656**	25p multicoloured	55	50
695	**657**	30p multicoloured	70	75
694/5		Set of 2	1·25	1·25
		First Day Cover		2·00
		Presentation Pack	2·00	

The background designs of Nos. 694/5 continue on to the vertical sheet margins.

Plate Nos.: Both values 1A, 1B (each ×4)

Sheets: 10 (2×5)

Quantities sold: 25p 224,821; 30p 268,410

Withdrawn: 20.4.97

658   England v U.S.S.R., 1968   **659**

660   Italy v Belgium, 1972   **661**

662   Ireland v Netherlands, 1988   **663**

664   Denmark v Germany, 1992 Final   **665**

European Football Championship

(Des M. Whyte. Litho Questa)

1996 (25 APR). Perf 14½×14 (C)

696	**658**	16p multicoloured	55	55
		a. Horiz pair. Nos. 696/7	1·20	1·10
697	**659**	16p multicoloured	55	55
698	**660**	24p multicoloured	75	75
		a. Horiz pair. Nos. 698/9	1·50	1·50
699	**661**	24p multicoloured	75	75
700	**662**	35p multicoloured	80	80
		a. Horiz pair. Nos. 700/1	1·60	1·60
701	**663**	35p multicoloured	80	80
702	**664**	41p multicoloured	95	95
		a. Horiz pair. Nos. 702/3	2·00	1·90
703	**665**	41p multicoloured	95	95
696/703		Set of 8	6·00	5·50
		First Day Cover		6·00
		Presentation Pack	6·00	
		Souvenir Folder (complete sheets)	24·00	

Plate Nos.: All values 1A (×4)

Sheets: 8 (2×4) the two designs for each value printed together, se-tenant, in horizontal pairs throughout sheets with illustrated margins, each pair forming a composite design

Quantities sold: 16p 386,746; 24p 369,805; 35p 360,860; 41p 364,757

Withdrawn: 24.4.97

666a Maj-Gen. Brock meeting Tecumseh (Indian Chief) (24p); Maj-Gen. Isaac Brock on Horseback, 1812 (£1) (*illustration reduced. Actual size* 110×90 *mm*)

'CAPEX '96' International Stamp Exhibition, Toronto

(Des A. Peck. Litho Enschedé)

1996 (8 JUNE). *Sheet* 110×90 *mm.* Perf 13½ (C)
MS704 666a 24p, £1 multicoloured . . . . . 2·50 2·75
First Day Cover . . . . 4·00
Presentation Pack . . . . 3·75

Quantity sold: 93,054

Withdrawn: 7.6.97

667 Runner   **668** Throwing   **669** Throwing
the Javelin   the Discus

670 Wrestling   **671** Jumping

Centenary of Modern Olympic Games Ancient Greek Athletes

(Des K. Bassford. Litho Questa)

1996 (19 JULY). Perf 14 (C)

705	**667**	16p black, orange-yellow & orge	50	40
706	**668**	24p black, orange-yellow & orge	95	90
707	**669**	41p black, orange-yellow & orge	1·10	1·25
708	**670**	55p black, orange-yellow & orge	1·40	1·50
709	**671**	60p black, orange-yellow & orge	1·60	1·75
705/9		Set of 5	5·00	5·25
		First Day Cover		5·50
		Presentation Pack	6·00	
		Set of 5 Gutter Pairs	10·00	
MS710		192×75 mm. Nos. 705/9	5·25	5·25
		First Day Cover		5·75

No. 708 also includes the 'OLYMPHILEX '96' International Stamp Exhibition, Atlanta, logo.

Plate Nos.: All values 1A, 1B (each ×3)

Sheets: 55p 50 (2 panes 5×5); others 100 (2 panes 10×5)

Imprint: Central, right-hand margin of top pane

Quantities sold: 16p 337,288; 24p 305,309; 41p 132,730; 55p 122,263; 60p 141,372; miniature sheet 87,045

Withdrawn: 18.7.97

672 Humphrey Bogart as   **673** Peter Sellers as
Philip Marlowe   Inspector Clouseau

674 Basil Rathbone as   **675** Margaret Rutherford as
Sherlock Holmes   Miss Marple

676 Warner Oland as Charlie Chan

Centenary of Cinema. Screen Detectives

(Des R. Ollington. Litho Enschedé)

1996 (6 NOV). Perf 15×14 (C)

711	**672**	16p multicoloured	40	40
		a. Booklet pane. No. 711×3 with margins all round	1·10	
		b. Booklet pane. Nos. 711/15 with margins all round	4·00	
712	**673**	24p multicoloured	60	60
		a. Booklet pane. No. 712×3 with margins all round	1·90	
713	**674**	35p multicoloured	85	85
		a. Booklet pane. No. 713×3 with margins all round	2·50	
714	**675**	41p multicoloured	90	90
		a. Booklet pane. No. 714×3 with margins all round	2·75	
715	**676**	60p multicoloured	1·40	1·40
		a. Booklet pane. No. 715×3 with margins all round	4·25	
711/15		Set of 5	3·75	3·75
		First Day Cover		4·75
		Presentation Pack	4·75	
		Set of 5 Gutter Pairs	7·50	

Plate Nos.: All values 1A, 1B (each ×4)

Sheets: 50 (2 panes 5×5)

Imprint: Central, side margins

Quantities sold: 16p 140,740; 24p 141,567; 35p 141,953; 41p 139,648; 60p 138,363

Withdrawn: 5.11.97

677 The Annunciation

678 Journey to Bethlehem

679 Arrival at the Inn

680 Angel and Shepherds

681 Mary, Joseph and Jesus in Stable

682 Shepherds worshipping Jesus

683 Three Kings following Star

684 Three Kings with Gifts

685 The Presentation in the Temple

686 Mary and Jesus

687 Joseph warned by Angel

688 The Flight into Egypt

689 Mary cradling Jesus

690 The Nativity

Christmas

(Des P. le Vasseur. Litho B.D.T.)

1996 (6 NOV). Perf 13 (C)

716	**677**	13p multicoloured	30	25
		a. Sheetlet. Nos. 716/27	3·50	
717	**678**	13p multicoloured	30	25
718	**679**	13p multicoloured	30	25
719	**680**	13p multicoloured	30	25
720	**681**	13p multicoloured	30	25
721	**682**	13p multicoloured	30	25
722	**683**	13p multicoloured	30	25
723	**684**	13p multicoloured	30	25
724	**685**	13p multicoloured	30	25
725	**686**	13p multicoloured	30	25
726	**687**	13p multicoloured	30	25
727	**688**	13p multicoloured	30	25
728	**689**	24p multicoloured	60	40
729	**690**	25p multicoloured	60	60
716/29		Set of 14	4·25	3·50
		First Day Cover		5·00
		Presentation Pack	5·00	
		Set of 2 Gutter Pairs (24, 25p)		2·40

Plate Nos.: 24p, 25p 1A, 1B (each ×4)

Sheets: 13p 12 (4×3) containing Nos. 716/27 se-tenant; 24p, 25p 100 (2 panes 5×10)

Imprint: 13p bottom, left-hand margin; 24p, 25p central, side margins

Quantities sold: 13p 1,212,144 sheetlets; 24p 416,811; 25p 121,820

Withdrawn: 5.11.97

Yearbook 1996

1996 (1 DEC). *Comprises Nos. 582a, 694/729 and A85/95*
Yearbook . . . . 50·00

Sold out: 6.99

691 Holly Blue (*Celastrina argiolus*)

692 Hummingbird Hawk-moth (*Macroglossum stellatarum*)

693 Emperor Moth (*Saturnia pavonia*)

694 Brimstone (*Gonepteryx rhamni*)

695a Painted Lady (*Cynthia cardui*)

Endangered Species. Butterflies and Moths

(Des A. Peck. Litho B.D.T.)

1997 (12 FEB). Perf 14 (C)

730	**691**	18p multicoloured	. . . .	55	50
731	**692**	25p multicoloured	. . . .	65	60

732	**693**	26p multicoloured	. .	05	85
733	**694**	37p multicoloured	. . . .	1·10	1·10
730/3		*Set of 4*		2·75	2·75
		First Day Cover			3·25
		Presentation Pack	3·25		
		Souvenir Folder (complete sheets)		25·00	

MS734 92×68 mm. **695a** £1 multicoloured.

Perf 13½ (C)	. . . .	2·50	2·50
	First Day Cover			3·75
	Presentation Pack	3·50	

No. **MS**734 includes the 'HONG KONG '97' International Stamp Exhibition logo on the sheet margin.

Plate Nos.: All values 1A, 1B (each ×4)

Sheets: 10 (2×5) with designs extending into side margins

Quantities sold: 18p 244,917; 25p 244,899; 26p 168,917; 37p 169,909; miniature sheet 147,990

Withdrawn: 11.2.98

26 **696** Gilliatt fighting Octopus

31 **697** Gilliatt grieving on Rock

Europa. Tales and Legends. Scenes from Les Travailleurs de la Mer by Victor Hugo

(Des M. Wilkinson. Litho Cartor)

1997 (24 APR.) Perf 13½ (C)

735	**696**	26p multicoloured	. . . .	55	60
736	**697**	31p multicoloured	. . . .	75	65
735/6		*Set of 2*		1·25	1·25
		First Day Cover			2·10
		Presentation Pack	2·10	

Plate Nos.: Both values 1A, 1B (each ×4)

Sheets: 10 (2×5) with enlarged inscribed margins at left

Quantities sold: 26p 246,098; 31p 246,080

Withdrawn: 23.4.98

698 Shell Beach, Herm

699 La Seigneurie, Sark

700 Castle Cornet, Guernsey

Guernsey Scenes (1st series)

(Litho B.D.T.)

1997 (24 APR). *Self-adhesive.* Perf 9½ (diecut)

737	**698**	18p multicoloured	....	60	30
		a. Booklet pane of 8	....	4·75	
738	**699**	25p multicoloured	....	70	60
		a. Booklet pane of 8	....	5·50	
739	**700**	26p multicoloured	....	80	75
		a. Booklet pane of 4	....	3·25	
737/9		*Set of 3*	....	1·90	1·50
		First Day Cover	....		3·00
		Presentation Pack	....	3·00	

Nos. 737/9 were issued in stamp booklets or as rolls of 100 (18p and 25p).
See also Nos. 770/3.

Quantities sold: 18p 2,789,925; 25p 2,788,039; 26p 415,882

Withdrawn: 31.3.98

701a 19th-century Shipyard, St. Peter Port (30p);
Costa Rica Packet (barque) (£1)
(illustration reduced. Actual size 110×90 *mm)*

'PACIFIC '97' World Philatelic Exhibition, San Francisco

(Des C. Abbott. Litho Questa)

1997 (29 MAY). *Sheet* 110×90 *mm.* Perf 14 (C)

MS740	**701a**	30p brn-olive & gold; £1 mult	3·00	3·00
		First Day Cover		4·00
		Presentation Pack	3·75	

Quantity sold: 86,711

Withdrawn: 28.5.98

702 Transistor Radio, Microphone and Radio Logos

703 Television, Video Camera and Satellite Dish

704 Fax Machine, Telephones and Mobile Phone

705 Printing Press, Newspaper and Type

706 Stamp, Coding Machine and Postbox

707 C.D., Computer and Disk

Methods of Communication

(Des Miranda Schofield. Litho Cartor)

1997 (21 AUG). Perf 13½×13 (C)

741	**702**	18p multicoloured	....	40	40
742	**703**	25p multicoloured	....	60	60
743	**704**	26p multicoloured	....	60	60
744	**705**	37p multicoloured	....	90	85
745	**706**	43p multicoloured	.......●..	1·20	1·00
746	**707**	63p multicoloured	....	1·50	1·50
741/6		*Set of 6*	....	5·00	4·50
		First Day Cover	....		5·50
		Presentation Pack	....	5·25	
		Set of 6 Gutter Pairs	......	9·00	

Plate Nos.: All values 1A, 1B (each ×4)

Sheets: 50 (2 panes 5×5)

Imprint: Central, side margins

Quantities sold: 18p 193,539; 25p 144,558; 26p 143,542; 37p 140,565; 43p 143,565; 63p 193,524

Withdrawn: 20.8.98

708 Teddy Bear making Cake

709 Teddy Bears decorating Christmas Tree

710 Two Teddy Bears in Armchair

711 Teddy Bear as Father Christmas

712 Teddy Bears unwrapping Presents

713 Teddy Bears eating Christmas Dinner

Christmas. Teddy Bears

(Des Sally Diamond. Litho Walsall)

1997 (6 NOV). Perf 14½×14 (C)

747	**708**	15p multicoloured		45	45
748	**709**	25p multicoloured		70	70
749	**710**	26p multicoloured		70	70
750	**711**	37p multicoloured		1.00	1.00
751	**712**	43p multicoloured		1.10	1.10
752	**713**	63p multicoloured		1.60	1.60
747/52		Set of 6		5.00	5.00
		First Day Cover			5.50
		Presentation Pack		5.25	
		Set of 6 Gutter Pairs		10.00	
MS753		123×107 mm. Nos. 747/52		4.50	4.50
		First Day Cover			5.75

Plate Nos.: All values 1A, 1B (each ×4)

Sheets: 50 (2 panes 5×5)

Imprint: Central, right-hand margin

Quantities sold: 15p 1,793,893; 25p 443,027; 26p 143,322; 37p 118,980; 43p 119,090; 63p 118,894; miniature sheet 86,125

Withdrawn: 5.11.98

714 Visiting Guernsey, 1957

715 Coronation Day, 1953 (inscr '1947')

716 Royal Family, 1957

717 On Royal Yacht, 1972

718 Queen Elizabeth and Prince Philip at Trooping the Colour, 1987

719 Queen Elizabeth and Prince Philip, 1997

Golden Wedding of Queen Elizabeth and Prince Philip

(Des M. Whyte. Litho Questa)

1997 (20 NOV). Perf 14½ (C)

754	**714**	18p multicoloured	40	40
		a. Booklet pane. Nos. 754/5,		
		each ×3	3·25	
		b. Booklet pane. Nos. 754/9 . .	5·50	
755	**715**	25p multicoloured	60	60
756	**716**	26p multicoloured	60	60
		a. Booklet pane. Nos. 756/7,		
		each ×3	5·00	
757	**717**	37p multicoloured	90	90
758	**718**	43p multicoloured	1·00	1·00
		a. Booklet pane. Nos. 758/9,		
		each ×3	8·75	
759	**719**	63p multicoloured	1·40	1·40
754/9		Set of 6	4·50	4·50
		First Day Cover		5·50
		Presentation Pack	5·25	
		Set of 6 Gutter Pairs	9·00	

Plate Nos.: All values 1A, 1B (each ×6)

Sheets: 50 (2 panes 5×5)

Imprint: Central, right-hand margin

Quantities sold: 18p 220,866; 25p 218,707; 26p 218,240; 37p 216,772; 43p 217,837; 63p 216,874

Withdrawn: 19.11.98

Yearbook 1997

1997 (1 DEC). Comprises Nos. 572b, 576b, 730/59, A70b, A72b/c and A96/101

Yearbook . . . . 50·00

Sold out: 9.99

720 11th-century
(St. Martin)

721 12th-century
(St. Saviour)

722 13th-century
(Vale)

723 14th-century
(St. Sampson)

724 15th-century
(Torteval)

725 16th-century
(Castel)

726 17th-century
(St. Andrew)

727 18th-century
(Forest)

728 19th-century (St.
Pierre du Bois)

729 20th-century
(St. Peter Port)

The Millennium Tapestries Project

(Des Sally Diamond. Litho Questa)

1998 (10 FEB). Perf 15×14½ (C)

760	**720**	25p multicoloured	60	60
		a. Horiz strip of 10 or two strips		
		of 5. Nos. 760/9	5·50	5·50
		b. Booklet pane. Nos. 760/1,		
		each ×2, and 762/3 with		
		margins all round	3·50	
		c. Booklet pane. Nos. 760/1		
		and 768/9, each ×2 with		
		margins all round	3·50	
761	**721**	25p multicoloured	60	60
762	**722**	25p multicoloured	60	60
		a. Booklet pane. Nos. 762/3,		
		each ×2, and 764/5 with		
		margins all round	3·50	

763	**723**	25p multicoloured	. . . .	60	60
764	**724**	25p multicoloured	. . . .	60	60
		a. Booklet pane. Nos. 764/5, each ×2, and 768/7 with margins all round		3·50	
765	**725**	25p multicoloured	. . . .	60	60
766	**726**	25p multicoloured	. . . .	60	60
		a. Booklet pane. Nos. 766/7, each ×2, and 768/9 with margins all round		3·50	
767	**727**	25p multicoloured	. . . .	60	60
768	**728**	25p multicoloured	. . . .	60	60
769	**729**	25p multicoloured	. . . .	60	60
760/9		Set of 10		5·50	5·50
		First Day Cover			6·25
		Presentation Pack		6·00	

Plate Nos.: 1A, 1B (each ×4)

Sheets: 50 (10×5); the ten designs printed together, *se-tenant*, in horizontal strips throughout the sheet

Imprint: Central, side margins

Withdrawn: 9.2.99

730 Fort Grey

731 Grand Havre

732 Little Chapel

733 Guernsey Cow

Guernsey Scenes (2nd series)

(Des Joanna Brehaut. Litho B.D.T.)

1998 (25 MAR). *Self-adhesive. Perf 9½ (diecut)*

770	**730**	(20p) multicoloured	. . . .	45	55
		a. Horiz pair. Nos. 770/1		90	1·10
		b. Booklet pane. Nos. 770/1, each ×4 with margins all round		3·75	
771	**731**	(20p) multicoloured	. . . .	45	55
772	**732**	(25p) multicoloured	. . . .	55	65
		a. Horiz pair. Nos. 772/3		1·10	1·25
		b. Booklet pane. Nos. 772/3, each ×4 with margins all round		4·75	
773	**733**	(25p) multicoloured	. . . .	55	65
770/3		Set of 4		1·75	2·10
		First Day Cover			3·00
		Presentation Pack		3·00	

Nos. 770/1 are inscribed 'Bailiwick Minimum Postage Paid' and were initially sold at 20p. Nos. 772/3 are inscribed 'UK Minimum Postage Paid' and were initially sold at 25p.

Nos. 770/3 were issued in stamp booklets or as rolls of 100, each roll containing two designs.

Sold out: 6.2001

734 Fairey IIIC, Balloon, Sopwith Camel and Avro 504

735 Fairey Swordfish, Tiger Moth, Supermarine Walrus and Gloster Gladiator

736 Hawker Hurricane, Supermarine Spitfire, Vickers Wellington, Short Sunderland (flying boat), Westland Lysander and Bristol Blenheim

737 De Havilland Mosquito, Avro Lancaster, Auster III, Gloster Meteor and Horsa Glider

738 Canberra, Hawker Sea Fury, Bristol Sycamore, Hawker Hunter, Handley Page Victor and BAe Lightning

739 Panavia Tornado GR1, BAe Hawk, BAe Sea Harrier, Westland Lynx (helicopter) and Hawker Siddeley Nimrod

80th Anniversary of the Royal Air Force

(Des C. Abbott. Litho Cartor)

1998 (7 MAY). Perf 13½×13 (C)

774	**734**	20p multicoloured	50	50
775	**735**	25p multicoloured	60	60
776	**736**	30p multicoloured	70	70
777	**737**	37p multicoloured	90	85
778	**738**	43p multicoloured	1·00	95
779	**739**	63p multicoloured	1·40	1·40
774/9		Set of 6	5·00	4·50
		First Day Cover		5·75
		Presentation Pack	5·25	

Plate Nos.: All values 1A (×5)

Sheets: 50 (5×10)

Imprint: Central, side margins

Withdrawn: 6.5.99

740a Jules Rimet (first President of FIFA) (30p); Bobby Moore and Queen Elizabeth II, 1966 (£1.75) (*illustration reduced. Actual size* 110×90 mm)

150th Anniversary of the Cambridge Rules for Football

(Des A. Peck. Litho Enschedé)

1998 (7 MAY). *Sheet* 110×90 mm. Perf 13½×14 (C)

MS780	**740a**	30p, £1.75 multicoloured ...	3·50	4·00
		First Day Cover		5·50
		Presentation Pack	5·25	

Withdrawn: 6.5.99

741 Girls in Traditional Costume watching Sheep Display, West Show

742 Marching Band and 'Battle of Flowers' Exhibit, North Show

743 Prince Charles, Monument and Tank, Liberation Day

744 Goat, Dahlias and Show-jumping, South Show

Europa. National Festivals

(Des Sally Diamond. Litho Enschedé)

1998 (11 AUG). Perf 13½ (C)

781	**741**	20p multicoloured	45	45
782	**742**	25p multicoloured	55	55
783	**743**	30p multicoloured	65	65
784	**744**	37p multicoloured	85	85
781/4		Set of 4	2·25	2·25
		First Day Cover		3·75
		Presentation Pack	3·50	

Plate Nos.: All values 1A, 1B, 1C (each ×4)

Sheets: 10 (2×5) with enlarged inscribed margin at left

Imprint: Central, right-hand margin

Withdrawn: 10.8.99

745 Outboard Motorboat

746 St. John Ambulance Inshore Rescue Dinghy

747 Pilot Boat, St. Peter Port

748 *Flying Christine III* (St. John Ambulance launch)

749 Crab-fishing Boat

750 Herm Island Ferry

762 Royal Yacht *Britannia*

751 *Sarnia* (St. Peter Port Harbour Authority launch)

752 *Leopardess* (States' fisheries protection launch)

753 Trawler

754 Powerboat

755 Dart 18 Racing Catamaran

756 30ft Bermuda-rigged Sloop

757 Motor Cruiser

758 Ocean-going Sailing Yacht

759 Motor Yacht, Beaucette Marina

Maritime Heritage

(Des M. Wilkinson. Litho Walsall (1p to 75p), litho and embossed Walsall (£1, £3) or Questa (£5))

1998 (11 AUG)–**2000**. Perf 14 (1p to 9p), 14½×14 (10p to 75p), 14×14½ (£1, £3) or 15×14½ (£5), all comb

785	**745**	1p multicoloured (*b*)	10	10
786	**746**	2p multicoloured (*b*)	10	10
787	**747**	3p multicoloured (*b*)	10	10
788	**748**	4p multicoloured (*b*)	10	10
789	**749**	5p multicoloured (*b*)	10	10
790	**750**	6p multicoloured (*b*)	10	10
791	**751**	7p multicoloured (*b*)	15	20
792	**752**	8p multicoloured (*b*)	15	20
793	**753**	9p multicoloured (*b*)	20	25
794	**754**	10p multicoloured (*b*)	20	25
795	**755**	20p multicoloured (*c*)	40	45
796	**756**	30p multicoloured (*c*)	60	65
797	**757**	40p multicoloured (*b*)	80	85
798	**758**	50p multicoloured (*b*)	1·00	1·10
799	**759**	75p multicoloured (*b*)	1·50	1·30
800	**760**	£1 multicoloured (*b*)	2·00	1·80
801	**761**	£3 multicoloured (*c*)	6·00	5·50
802	**762**	£5 multicoloured (*a*)	13·00	10·00
785/802		Set of 18	24·00	19·00
		First Day Covers (3)		27·00
		Presentation Packs (3)	26·00	
		Set of 17 *Gutter Pairs* (1p to £3)	25·00	

Printings: (*a*) 11.8.98; (*b*) 27.7.99; (*c*) 4.8.2000

Plate Nos.: £5 1A, 1B, 1C, 1D (each ×5); others 1A, 1B (each ×4)

Sheets: 1p to £3 50 (2 panes 5×5); £5 10 (5×2)

Imprint: Side margins (£5) or centre, left-hand margin (others)

Sold out: 11.2002 (£5)

760 *Queen Elizabeth 2* (liner)

761 *Oriana* (liner)

769 Modern Tree, Teletubby Po and Playstation

770 1960s Tinsel Tree, Toy Bus and Doll

771 1930s Gold Foil Tree, Panda and Toy Tank

772 1920s Tree, Model of *Bluebird* and Doll

773 1900 Tree, Teddy Bear and Toy Train

774 1850s Tree, Wooden Doll and Spinning Top

150th Anniversary of the Introduction of the Christmas Tree

(Des R. Ollington. Litho B.D.T.)

1998 (10 NOV). Perf 13½ (C)

810	**769**	17p multicoloured	40	40
811	**770**	25p multicoloured	60	60
812	**771**	30p multicoloured	70	70
813	**772**	37p multicoloured	90	90
814	**773**	43p multicoloured	1·00	1·00
815	**774**	63p multicoloured	1·50	1·50
810/15		Set of 6	4·50	4·50
		First Day Cover		5·50
		Presentation Pack	5·50	
MS816		160×94 mm. Nos. 810/15	5·00	7·00
		First Day Cover		6·00

Plate Nos.: 17p, 25p 1A, 1B (each ×4); others 1A (×4)

Sheets: 50 (5×10)

Imprint: Central, side margins

Withdrawn: 9.11.99

Yearbook 1998

1998 (1 DEC). *Comprises Nos. 760/816 and A110/23*
Yearbook . . . . 54·00

Sold out: 4.2001

775 Elizabeth Bowes-Lyon, 1907

776 On Wedding Day, 1923

777 Holding Princess Elizabeth, 1926

778 At Coronation, 1937

779 Visiting Bombed Areas of London, 1940

780 Fishing near Auckland, New Zealand, 1966

781 At Guernsey Function, 1963

782 Receiving Flowers on Birthday, 1992

783 Presenting Trophy, Sandown Park Races, 1989

784 Opening Royal Norfolk Regimental Museum, Norwich, 1990

Life and Times of Queen Elizabeth the Queen Mother

(Des R. Ollington. Litho Cartor)

1999 (4 FEB). Perf 13 (C)

817	**775**	25p multicoloured	70	65
		a. Horiz strip of 10 or two strips of 5. Nos. 817/26	6·50	6·50
		b. Booklet pane. Nos. 817/18, each ×2, and 819/20, with margins all round	4·00	
		c. Booklet pane. Nos. 817/18 and 825/6, each ×2, with margins all round	4·00	
818	**776**	25p multicoloured	70	65
819	**777**	25p multicoloured	70	65
		b. Booklet pane. Nos. 819/20, each x2, and 821/2, with margins all round	4·00	
820	**778**	25p multicoloured	70	65
821	**779**	25p multicoloured	70	65
		b. Booklet pane. Nos. 821/2, each x2, and 823/4, with margins all round	4·00	
822	**780**	25p multicoloured	70	65
823	**781**	25p multicoloured	70	65
		b. Booklet pane. Nos. 823/4, each x2, and 825/6, with margins all round	4·00	
824	**782**	25p multicoloured	70	65
825	**783**	25p multicoloured	70	65
826	**784**	25p multicoloured	70	65
817/26		Set of 10	6·50	6·00
		First Day Cover		6·75
		Presentation Pack	6·75	

Plate Nos.: 1A, 1B (each ×5)

Sheets: 50 (10×5), the ten designs printed together, se-tenant, as horizontal strips throughout the sheets

Imprint: Central, side margins

Withdrawn: 3.2.2000

785 *Spirit of Guernsey*, 1995

786 *Sir William Arnold*, 1973

787 *Euphrosyne Kendal*, 1954

788 *Queen Victoria*, 1929

789 *Arthur Lionel*, 1912

790 *Vincent Kirk Ella*, 1888

175th Anniversary of Royal National Lifeboat Institution

(Des K. Wisdom. Litho Cartor)

1999 (27 APR). Perf 13½×13 (C)

827	**785**	20p multicoloured	50	50
828	**786**	25p multicoloured	60	60
829	**787**	30p multicoloured	70	70
830	**788**	38p multicoloured	90	90
831	**789**	44p multicoloured	1·10	1·10
832	**790**	64p multicoloured	1·50	1·50
827/32		Set of 6	5·00	4·75
		First Day Cover		6·00
		Presentation Pack	5·75	

Plate Nos.: All values 1A (×5)

Sheets: 50 (5×10)

Imprint: Central, side margins

Withdrawn: 26.4.2000

791 Burnet Rose and Local Carriage Label

792 Atlantic Puffin

793 Small Heath Butterfly

794 Shells on Shell Beach

Europa. Parks and Gardens. Herm Island

(Des Colleen Corlett. Litho Walsall)

1999 (27 APR). Perf 13½×13 (C)

833	**791**	20p multicoloured	50	45
834	**792**	25p multicoloured	60	55

835	**793**	30p multicoloured	....	70	65
836	**794**	38p multicoloured	....	90	80
833/6		*Set of 4*	....	2·50	2·40
		First Day Cover	....		3·75
		Presentation Pack	....	3·50	

Plate Nos.: All values 1A, 1B (each ×4)

Sheets: 10 (2×5) with enlarged illustrated margin at left (20, 30p) or right (25, 38p)

Imprint: Central right (20, 30p) or left (25, 38p) margin

Withdrawn: 26.4.2000

795 Prince Edward and Miss Sophie Rhys-Jones (*illustration reduced. Actual size 93×70 mm*)

Royal Wedding

(Des Sally Diamond. Litho B.D.T.)

1999 (19 JUNE). *Sheet 93×70 mm.* Perf 13 (C)

MS837	**795**	£1 multicoloured	....	2·50	2·25
		First Day Cover	....		3·75
		Presentation Pack	....	3·50	

Withdrawn: 18.6.2000

796 Major-General Le Marchant (founder) and Cadet at Sword Drill

797 Duke of York (official sponsor) and Cadet on Horseback

798 Field-Marshal Earl Haig and Cadets on Parade

799 Field-Marshal Viscount Montgomery and Bridging Exerxcise

800 David Niven (actor) and Rifle Practice

801 Sir Winston Churchill and Tank

Bicentenary of The Royal Military Academy, Sandhurst

(Des R. Ollington. Litho B.D.T.)

1999 (27 JULY). Perf 14 (C)

838	**796**	20p multicoloured	....	50	45
839	**797**	25p multicoloured	....	60	55
840	**798**	30p multicoloured	....	75	70
841	**799**	38p multicoloured	....	90	85
842	**800**	44p multicoloured	....	1·10	1·00
843	**801**	64p multicoloured	....	1·50	1·50
838/43		*Set of 6*	....	4·75	4·50
		First Day Cover	....		5·50
		Presentation Pack	....	6·00	

Plate Nos.: All values 1A (×4)

Sheets: 50 (5×10)

Imprint: Lower side margins

Withdrawn: 26.7.2000

802 The Nativity

803 Virgin Mary and Child

804 Holy Family

805 Cattle around Manger

806 Adoration of the Shepherds

807 Adoration of the Magi

Christmas. Wood Carvings by Denis Brehaut from Notre Dame Church

(Des Sally Diamond. Litho Questa)

1999 (19 OCT). Perf 14×14½ (C)

844	**802**	17p multicoloured	45	40
845	**803**	25p multicoloured	60	55
846	**804**	30p multicoloured	75	70
847	**805**	38p multicoloured	90	85
848	**806**	44p multicoloured	1·10	1·00
849	**807**	64p multicoloured	1·50	1·50
844/9		Set of 6	4·75	4·75
		First Day Cover		5·50
		Presentation Pack	5·75	
MS850	159×86 mm. Nos. 844/9		5·50	5·50
		First Day Cover		6·00

Plate Nos.: All values 1A, 1B, 1C (each ×4)

Sheets: 50 (5×10)

Imprint: Bottom, right-hand margin

Withdrawn: 18.10.2000

Yearbook 1999

1999 (1 DEC). Comprises Nos. 817/49 and A125/39

Yearbook . . . . 55·00

808 'Space Bus' (Fallon Ephgrave)

809 'Children holding Hands' (Abigail Downing)

810 'No Captivity' (Laura Martin)

811 'Post Office of the Future' (Sarah Haddow)

812 'Solar-powered Car' (Sophie Medland)

813 'Woman flying' (Danielle McIver)

New Millennium. 'Stampin' the Future' (children's stamp design competition)

(Litho Questa)

2000 (1 JAN). Perf 14×14½ (C)

851	**808**	20p multicoloured	60	45
852	**809**	25p multicoloured	60	55
853	**810**	30p multicoloured	70	65
854	**811**	38p multicoloured	90	80
855	**812**	44p multicoloured	1·00	95
856	**813**	64p multicoloured	1·40	1·40
851/6		Set of 6	4·75	4·75
		First Day Cover		5·50
		Presentation Pack	5·50	

Plate Nos.: All values 1A, 1B (each ×5)

Sheets: 50 (5×10)

Imprint: Lower right-hand margin

Withdrawn: 31.12.2000

814 Bristol Blenheim

815 Hawker Hurricane

816 Boulton Paul Defiant II

817 Gloster Gladiator

818 Bristol Beaufighter IF   **819** Supermarine Spitfire IIc

60th Anniversary of Battle of Britain. R.A.F. Aircraft

(Des R. Ollington. Litho Cartor)

2000 (28 APR). Perf 13½×13 (C)

857	**814**	21p multicoloured	50	50
		a. Booklet pane. Nos. 857 and 859/61	3·50	
		b. Booklet pane. Nos. 857/8, 860 and 862	3·50	
		c. Booklet pane. Nos. 857/9 and 861	3·00	
858	**815**	26p multicoloured	60	55
		a. Booklet pane. Nos. 858/61 .	3·50	
859	**816**	36p multicoloured	95	85
860	**817**	40p multicoloured	1·00	95
861	**818**	45p multicoloured	1·10	1·10
862	**819**	65p multicoloured	1·50	1·50
		a. Booklet pane. No. 862×2 ..	3·00	
857/62		Set of 6	5·50	5·00
		First Day Cover		5·50
		Presentation Pack	5·75	

Plate Nos.: All values 1A (×5)

Sheets: 50 (5×10)

Imprint: Central, side margins

Withdrawn: 27.4.2001

820 Guernsey Flag on Kite and '2000'

821 Stylized Sails bearing National Flowers

822 'Building Europe'

823 Rainbow and Three Doves

Europa

(Des J.-P. Cousin (36p), KWL (others). Litho B.D.T.)

2000 (9 MAY). Perf 13 (C)

863	**820**	21p multicoloured	50	45
864	**821**	26p multicoloured	60	55
865	**822**	36p multicoloured	1·00	90
866	**823**	65p multicoloured	1·60	1·60
863/6		Set of 4	3·40	3·40
		First Day Cover		4·00
		Presentation Pack	4·00	

Plate Nos.: All values 1A (×4)

Sheets: 10 (2×5) with enlarged inscribed margin at left

Imprint: Centre, right-hand margin

Withdrawn: 8.5.2001

824 Iris Stylosa

825 Watsonia

826 Richardia maculata

827 Narcissus bulbocodium

828 Triteleia laxa

829 Tigridia pavonia

GUERNSEY 26

830 *Agapanthus umbellatus*

GUERNSEY 26

831 *Sparaxis*

GUERNSEY 26

832 *Pancratium maritimum*

GUERNSEY 26

833 *Nerine sarniensis*

834 Town Church, St. Peter Port

835 Children leaving St. Sampson's Church

836 Flying Kite by Vale Church

837 Carol singing outside St. Pierre du Bois Church

838 Building Snowman near St. Martin's Church

839 Street Scene including St. John's Church, St. Peter Port

'A Botanist's Sketchbook'. Restoration of Candie Gardens, St. Peter Port

(Des Petula Stone. Litho Enschedé)

2000 (4 AUG). Perf 13½×13 (C)

867	**824**	26p multicoloured	55	55
		a. Horiz strip of 10 or two strips		
		of 5. Nos. 867/76	5·50	5·50
868	**825**	26p multicoloured	55	55
869	**826**	26p multicoloured	55	55
870	**827**	26p multicoloured	55	55
871	**828**	26p multicoloured	55	55
872	**829**	26p multicoloured	55	55
873	**830**	26p multicoloured	55	55
874	**831**	26p multicoloured	55	55
875	**832**	26p multicoloured	55	55
876	**833**	26p multicoloured	55	55
867/76		Set of 10	5·50	5·50
		First Day Cover		6·25
		Presentation Pack	6·50	

Plate Nos.: All values 1A, 1B (each ×5)

Sheets: 50 (10×5). Nos. 867/76 were printed together, *se-tenant*, in horizontal strips of 10 throughout the sheet

Imprint: Upper side margins

Withdrawn: 3.8.2001

Christmas. Guernsey Churches

(Des Gill Brown. Litho Questa)

2000 (19 OCT). Perf 14½×14 (C)

877	**834**	18p multicoloured	40	40
878	**835**	26p multicoloured	60	55
879	**836**	36p multicoloured	90	85
880	**837**	40p multicoloured	95	95
881	**838**	45p multicoloured	1·10	1·10
882	**839**	65p multicoloured	1·50	1·50
877/82		Set of 6	5·00	4·75
		First Day Cover		7·00
		Presentation Pack	6·00	
MS883		160×86 mm. Nos. 877/82	5·50	6·00
		First Day Cover		8·00

Plate Nos.: All values 1A (×5)

Sheets: 50 (5×10)

Imprint: Bottom, right-hand margin

Withdrawn: 18.10.2001

Yearbook 2000

2000 (1 DEC). *Comprises Nos. 795/6, 801, 851/83 and A140/61*

		Yearbook	65·00

840 Queen Victoria and Diamond Jubilee Statue

841 Letter of Thanks to Guernsey, 1846

842 Statues of Queen Victoria and Prince Albert

843 Stone commemorating 1846 Visit

844 Statue of Prince Albert

845 Victoria Tower, 1848

Death Centenary of Queen Victoria

(Des A. Fothergill. Litho Questa)

2001 (22 JAN). Perf 15×14½ (C)

884	**840**	21p multicoloured	50	50
885	**841**	26p multicoloured	60	55
886	**842**	36p multicoloured	90	85
887	**843**	40p multicoloured	95	95
888	**844**	45p multicoloured	1·10	1·10
889	**845**	65p multicoloured	1·50	1·50
884/9		Set of 6	5·00	5·00
		First Day Cover		6·00
		Presentation Pack	5·75	
MS890	165×80 mm. Nos. 884/9. Perf 14½ (C)		6·00	7·00
		First Day Cover		7·50

No. **MS**890 includes the logo of the 'Hong Kong 2001' Stamp Exhibition on the sheet margin.

Plate Nos.: All values 1A (×4)

Sheets: 50 (10×5)

Imprint: Central, left-hand margin

Withdrawn: 21.1.2002

846 River Kingfisher

847 Garganey

848 Little Egret

849 Little Ringed Plover

Europa. Water Birds

(Des Wendy Bramall. Litho B.D.T.)

2001 (1 FEB). Perf 14×15 (C)

891	**846**	21p multicoloured	60	40
892	**847**	26p multicoloured	90	75
893	**848**	36p multicoloured	1·20	1·00
894	**849**	65p multicoloured	1·70	1·90
891/4		Set of 4	4·00	3·50
		First Day Cover		4·50
		Presentation Pack	4·50	

Plate Nos.: All values 1A (×4)

Sheets: 10 (2×5) with enlarged inscribed margins at left

Imprint: Central, right-hand margin

Withdrawn: 31.1.2002

850 Cavalier King
Charles Spaniel

851 Miniature Schnauzer

852 German
Shepherd Dog

853 Cocker Spaniel

854 West Highland
White Terrier

855 Dachshund

Centenary of Guernsey Dog Club

(Des A. Peck. Litho B.D.T.)

2001 (26 APR). Perf 13 (C)

895	**850**	22p multicoloured	55	50
896	**851**	27p multicoloured	65	60
897	**852**	36p multicoloured	90	85
898	**853**	40p multicoloured	95	95
899	**854**	45p multicoloured	1·10	1·10
900	**855**	65p multicoloured	1·50	1·50
895/900		Set of 6	5·00	5·00
		First Day Cover		5·75
		Presentation Pack	6·00	

Plate Nos.: All values 1A (×4)

Sheets: 50 (10×5)

Imprint: Upper right-hand margin

Withdrawn: 25.4.2002

856 La Corbière
Sunset

857 Rue des
Hougues

858 St. Saviour's
Reservoir

859 Shell Beach,
Herm

860 Telegraph Bay,
Alderney

861 Alderney Railway

862 Vazon Bay

863 La Coupée,
Sark

864 Les Hanois
Lighthouse

865 Albecq Beach

Island Scenes

(Des Sally Diamond)

2001 (26 APR). *Self-adhesive.* Perf 14 (die-cut). (*a*) *Litho Enschedé* (*from sheetlets of 10 and booklets*)

901	**856**	(22p) multicoloured	45	50
		a. Sheetlet of 10. Nos. 901/10	5·00	
		b. Booklet pane. Nos. 901/5,		
		each ×2	4·50	
902	**857**	(22p) multicoloured	45	50

903	**858**	(22p) multicoloured	45	50
904	**859**	(22p) multicoloured	45	50
905	**860**	(22p) multicoloured	45	50
906	**861**	(27p) multicoloured	55	60
		b. Booklet pane. Nos. 906/10,		
		each ×2	5·50	
907	**862**	(27p) multicoloured	55	60
908	**863**	(27p) multicoloured	55	60
909	**864**	(27p) multicoloured	55	60
910	**865**	(27p) multicoloured	55	60
901/10		*Set of 10*	5·00	5·50
		First Day Cover		6·00
		Presentation Pack	6·00	

(b) Photo Enschedé (from rolls of 100)

911	**856**	(22p) multicoloured	45	50
		a. Strip of 5. Nos. 911/15 ...	2·25	
912	**857**	(22p) multicoloured	45	50
913	**858**	(22p) multicoloured	45	50
914	**859**	(22p) multicoloured	45	50
915	**860**	(22p) multicoloured	45	50
916	**861**	(27p) multicoloured	55	60
		a. Strip of 5. Nos. 916/20 ...	2·75	
917	**862**	(27p) multicoloured	55	60
918	**863**	(27p) multicoloured	55	60
919	**864**	(27p) multicoloured	55	60
920	**865**	(27p) multicoloured	55	60
911/20		*Set of 10*	5·00	5·50

Nos. 901/5 and 911/15 were intended for postage within the Bailiwick and are inscribed 'GY'. They were each initially sold at 22p. Nos. 906/10 and 916/20 were intended for postage to Great Britain and are inscribed 'UK'. They were each initially sold at 27p.

Sheets: Nos. 901/10 were printed in sheetlets of 10 (2×5) or in booklets with the surplus self-adhesive paper around each stamp retained. Nos. 911/20 were printed in rolls of 100, one for each rate, and have the surplus self-adhesive paper removed. The photogravure printing can be identified by the lack of outlines around the inscriptions.

Sold out: By 7.2004 booklets and rolls of 100

866 Droplets of Water on Leaf ('Vision')

867 Ruby-throated Hummingbird ('Understanding')

868 Butterfly's Wing ('Individuality')

869 Sea Shell ('Strength')

870 Honeycomb ('Community')

871 Dandelion ('Maturity')

Incorporation of Guernsey Post Ltd

(Des Charlotte Barnes. Litho Walsall)

2001 (1 AUG). (*a*) Perf 13½×13 (C)

921	**866**	22p multicoloured	45	50
		a. Booklet pane of 3	1·25	
922	**867**	27p multicoloured	55	60
		a. Booklet pane of 3	1·60	
923	**868**	36p multicoloured	70	75
		a. Booklet pane of 3	2·10	
924	**869**	40p multicoloured	80	85
		a. Booklet pane of 3	2·40	
925	**870**	45p multicoloured	90	95
		a. Booklet pane of 3	2·50	
926	**871**	65p multicoloured	1·25	1·40
		a. Booklet pane of 3	3·75	
921/6		*Set of 6*	4·50	5·00
		First Day Cover		5·75
		Presentation Pack	5·75	

(*b*) *Design as No. 28 (1969 £1), but redrawn and printed in litho. Perf 14×14½ (C)*

927	**18**	£1 multicoloured	5·00	5·50
		a. Booklet pane of 1	5·00	

No. 927 was only sold as part of a £8.05 stamp booklet but loose panes were provided free to regular Guernsey Philatelic Bureau customers. In addition to the change of printing process, No. 927 differs from the original 1969 stamp by showing the Queen's portrait without a tiara and by having 'GUERNSEY BAILIWICK' in white instead of grey.

Plate Nos.: All values 1A (×4)

Sheets: 50 (5×10)

Imprint: Upper right-hand margin

Withdrawn: 31.7.2002

872 'Tree of Joy', St. Peter Port

873 Cross, Les Cotils Christian Centre

874 Les Ruettes Cottage, St. Saviour's

875 Farmhouse, Le Preel, Castel

876 Sark Post Office

877 High Street, St. Peter Port

Christmas. Festive Lights

(Des Sally Diamond. Litho Questa)

2001 (16 OCT). Perf 14×14½ (C)

928	**872**	19p multicoloured	40	45
929	**873**	27p multicoloured	55	60
930	**874**	36p multicoloured	70	75
931	**875**	40p multicoloured	1·00	1·10
932	**876**	45p multicoloured	1·10	1·20
933	**877**	65p multicoloured	1·50	1·60
928/33		Set of 6	5·00	5·50
		First Day Cover		5·75
		Presentation Pack	5·75	
MS934		150×100 mm. Nos. 928/33	6·00	6·50
		First Day Cover		5·75

No. **MS**934 includes the 'Hafnia 01' International Stamp Exhibition logo on the sheet margin.

Plate Nos.: 19p, 27p 1A, 1B, 1C, 1D (each ×4); others 1A (×4)

Sheets: 50 (5×10)

Imprint: Upper right-hand margin

Withdrawn: 15.10.2002

Yearbook 2001

2001 (1 DEC). *Comprises Nos.* 884/910, 921/6, 928/34 *and* A162/83

Yearbook . . . . 65·00

878 Victor Hugo and St. Peter Port

879 Cosette

880 Valjean

881 Inspector Javert

882 Cosette and Marius

883 Novel and score for *Les Misérables* (musical by Alain Boublil and Claude-Michel Schönberg)

Birth Bicentenary of Victor Hugo (French author). Les Misérables (novel)

(Des R. Ollington. Litho Cartor)

2002 (6 FEB). Perf 13½×13 (C)

935	**878**	22p multicoloured	45	50
936	**879**	27p multicoloured	55	60
937	**880**	36p multicoloured	75	80
938	**881**	40p multicoloured	90	95
939	**882**	45p multicoloured	1·00	1·10
940	**883**	65p multicoloured	1·50	1·60
935/40		Set of 6	5·00	5·25
		First Day Cover		5·75
		Presentation Pack	5·75	
MS941		150×100 mm. Nos. 935/40	5·25	6·00
		First Day Cover		7·00

The 27p value reproduces the main image from promotional material for Cameron Mackintosh's musical production.

Plate Nos.: All values 1A (×4)

Sheets: 50 (5×10)

Imprint: Central, side margins

Withdrawn: 5.2.2003

884 Juggling

885 Clowns

886 Trapeze Artists

887 Knife Thrower

888 Acrobat

889 High-wire Cyclist

890 Queen Elizabeth and Crowd

891 Queen Elizabeth at St. Peter Port

892 Queen Elizabeth and Prince Philip at St. Anne's School, Alderney

893 Queen Elizabeth and La Seigneurie, Sark

894 At Millennium Stone, L'Ancresse

895 In Evening Dress, and Floodlit Castle Cornet

Europa. The Circus

(Des R. Carter. Litho Questa)

2002 (6 FEB). Perf 14½ (C)

942	**884**	22p multicoloured	45	50
943	**885**	27p multicoloured	55	60
944	**886**	36p multicoloured	70	75
945	**887**	40p multicoloured	80	85
946	**888**	45p multicoloured	90	95
947	**889**	65p multicoloured	1·25	1·40
942/7		Set of 6	4·50	5·00
		First Day Cover		6·50
		Presentation Pack	5·75	

Plate Nos.: All values 1A (×4)

Sheets: 10 (2×5) with enlarged illustrated margins at right

Imprint: Central, left-hand margin

Withdrawn 5.2.2003

Golden Jubilee

(Des Sarah Thomas. Litho B.D.T.)

2002 (30 APR). Perf 13½ (C)

948	**890**	22p multicoloured	45	50
		a. Booklet pane. Nos. 948 and 951/3 with margins all round	3·50	
		b. Booklet pane. Nos. 948/50 and 953 with margins all round	3·00	
		c. Booklet pane. Nos. 948/53 with margins all round	4·50	
949	**891**	27p multicoloured	55	60
		a. Booklet pane. Nos. 949/52 with margins all round	3·00	
950	**892**	36p multicoloured	70	75
951	**893**	40p multicoloured	80	85
952	**894**	45p multicoloured	90	95
953	**895**	65p multicoloured	1·25	1·40
948/53		Set of 6	4·50	5·00
		First Day Cover		5·75
		Presentation Pack	5·75	

Plate Nos.: All values 1A (×4)

Sheets: 50 (10×5)

Imprint: Upper right-hand margin

Withdrawn: 29.4.2003

896a Original Pillar Box, Union Street

150th Anniversary of First Pillar Box

(Des Sally Diamond. Litho Questa)

2002 (30 APR). Sheet 55×90 mm. Perf 14½×14 (C)

MS954	**896a**	£1.75, multicoloured	4·00	4·50
		First Day Cover		6·00
		Presentation Pack	4·50	

Withdrawn: 29.4.2003

897 Family and Ferry, La Maseline

898 Passenger Tractors

899 Campsite

900 Cyclists at La Coupée

901 Swimming in Venus Pool

902 La Seigneurie Gardens

903 Posting Cards

904 Carriage Ride

905 Tea at a Café

906 On the Beach at Creux Harbour

Holidays on Sark

(Des M. Remphry. Litho B.D.T.)

2002 (30 JULY). Perf 13 (C)

955	**897**	27p multicoloured	55	60
		a. Block of 10 of two horiz strips of 5. Nos. 955/64 . . .	5·50	6·00
956	**898**	27p multicoloured	55	60
957	**899**	27p multicoloured	55	60
958	**900**	27p multicoloured	55	60
959	**901**	27p multicoloured	55	60
960	**902**	27p multicoloured	55	60
961	**903**	27p multicoloured	55	60
962	**904**	27p multicoloured	55	60
963	**905**	27p multicoloured	55	60
964	**906**	27p multicoloured	55	60
955/64		Set of 10	5·50	6·00
		First Day Cover		6·50
		Presentation Pack	6·50	

Plate Nos.: 1A (×4)

Sheets: 50 (5×10). Nos. 955/64 were printed together, se-tenant, in blocks of 10 throughout the sheet

Imprint: Upper side margins

Withdrawn: 29.7.2003

907 Elizabeth College and Cadet Corps Parade, 1934

908 Captain Le Patourel in Action, Tunisia, 1942, and V.C.

909 Captain Le Patourel and Nurse, 1943

910 Award Ceremony, Cairo, 1943

911 Major Le Patourel welcomed Home to Guernsey, 1948

912 Herbert Le Patourel carrying the King's Colour, 1968

60th Anniversary of Herbert Le Patourel's Victoria Cross

(Des A. Theobald. Litho Cartor)

2002 (30 JULY). Perf 13½×13 (C)

965	**907**	22p multicoloured	45	50
966	**908**	27p multicoloured	55	60
967	**909**	36p multicoloured	70	75
968	**910**	40p multicoloured	80	85
969	**911**	45p multicoloured	90	95
970	**912**	65p multicoloured	1·25	1·40
965/70		*Set of 6*	4·50	5·00
		First Day Cover		5·75
		Presentation Pack	5·75	

Plate Nos.: All values 1A (×4)

Sheets: 50 (5×10)

Imprint: Central, side margins

Withdrawn: 29.7.2003

913a Queen Elizabeth the Queen Mother and Bouquet
(illustration reduced. Actual size 140×98 mm)

Queen Elizabeth the Queen Mother Commemoration

(Des M. Whyte. Litho and die-stamped Enschedé)

2002 (4 AUG). *Sheet* 140×98 *mm*. Perf 13½ (C)

MS971	**913a**	£2 multicoloured	4·00	4·25
		First Day Cover		5·00
		Presentation Pack	5·00	

Withdrawn: 3.8.2003

914 Mary and Jesus

915 Mary, Joseph and Jesus in the Stable

916 Angel appearing to Shepherds

917 Shepherds with Mary and Jesus

918 Three Wise Men

919 Stable with Star Overhead

Christmas

(Des Petula Stone. Litho Cartor)

2002 (17 OCT). Perf 13 (C)

972	**914**	22p multicoloured	45	50
973	**915**	27p multicoloured	55	60
974	**916**	36p multicoloured	70	75
975	**917**	40p multicoloured	80	85
976	**918**	45p multicoloured	90	95
977	**919**	65p multicoloured	1·25	1·40
972/7		*Set of 6*	4·50	5·00
		First Day Cover		5·75
		Presentation Pack	5·75	
MS978		130×102 mm. Nos. 972/7	4·50	5·00
		First Day Cover		5·75

Plate Nos.: All values 1A (×5)

Sheets: 50 (5×10)

Imprint: Central, side margins

Withdrawn: 16.10.2003

Yearbook 2002

2002 (1 DEC). Comprises Nos. 935/78 and **MS**A184/202
Yearbook 05 00

920 Lancaster Bomber
and Crew

921 Flight of Lancaster
bombers crossing
English coast

922 Lancaster
bombers in
enemy
searchlights

923 Dropping
bouncing
bombs

924 H.M.S. *Charybdis*
(cruiser) and H.M.S.
Limbourne (destroyer)

**Memories of the Second World War (1st issue). 60th
Anniversary of Operation Tunnel (£1.50) and
Dambusters Raid (others).**

(Des N. Watton. Litho Questa)

2003 (30 JAN). Perf 14½ (£1.50) or 14 (others) (both comb)

979	**920**	22p multicoloured	45	50
980	**921**	27p multicoloured	55	60
981	**922**	36p multicoloured	70	75
982	**923**	40p multicoloured	80	85
983	**924**	£1.50 multicoloured	3·00	3·25
979/83		Set of 5	5·50	5·75
		First Day Cover		6·50
		Presentation Pack	6·50	

See also Nos. 1027/31.

Plate Nos.: All values 1A (×5)

Sheets: 50 (5×10)

Imprint: Upper right-hand margin

Withdrawn: 29.1.2004

925 Hurdling

926 Cycling

927 Gymnastics

928 Sailing

929 Golf

930 Running

Island Games, Guernsey

(Des Charlotte Barnes. Litho Cartor)

2003 (30 JAN). Perf 12½ (C)

984	**925**	22p multicoloured	45	50
985	**926**	27p multicoloured	55	60
986	**927**	36p multicoloured	70	75
987	**928**	40p multicoloured	80	85
988	**929**	45p multicoloured	90	95
989	**930**	65p multicoloured	1·25	1·40
984/9		Set of 6	4·50	5·00
		First Day Cover		5·75
		Presentation Pack	5·75	
MS990		140×75 mm. Nos. 984/9	4·50	5·00
		First Day Cover		5·75

Plate Nos.: All values 1A (×4)

Sheets: 50 (5×10)

Imprint: Central, side margins

Withdrawn: 29.1.2004

931 St. Peter Port
Harbour
('Naturally
Guernsey',
2003)

932 Motor-cruiser
off Guernsey
('The islands
of Guernsey',
1995)

933 'Children on
the Seashore'
(Renoir)
('Holiday
Guernsey',
1988)

934 St. Peter Port
Harbour
('Bailiwick of
Guernsey',
1978)

935 St. Peter Port
and Cliffs
('Guernsey –
The Charming
Channel
Island', 1968)

936 Secluded
Bay
('Guernsey',
1956)

Europa. Poster Art

(Des M. Quéru. Litho De La Rue)

2003 (10 APR). Perf 14½ (C)

991	**931**	22p multicoloured	....	45	50
992	**932**	27p multicoloured	....	55	60
993	**933**	36p multicoloured	....	70	75
994	**934**	40p multicoloured	....	80	85
995	**935**	45p multicoloured	....	90	95
996	**936**	65p multicoloured	....	1·25	1·50

991/6		Set of 6	4·50	5·00
		First Day Cover		5·75
		Presentation Pack	5·75	

Sheets: 10 (2×5) with enlarged illustrated margin at right
Imprint: Central, left-hand margin
Withdrawn: 9.4.2004

937a H.M.S. *Guernsey*
(*illustration reduced. Actual size* 117×84 *mm*)

Decommissioning of H.M.S. Guernsey *(fishery protection patrol vessel)*

(Des K. Taylor. Litho De La Rue)

2003 (10 APR). *Sheet* 117×84 *mm. Perf* 13½×14 (C)

MS997	**937a**	£1.50 multicoloured	......	3·00	3·25
		First Day Cover			4·00
		Presentation Pack	4·00		

Withdrawn: 9.4.2004

938 Princess Diana
and Baby Prince
William

939 Prince William,
aged 3, with
Prince Charles
and Prince Harry
at Kensington
Palace

940 Aged 4, in
Parachute
Regiment
Uniform

941 Aged 7, with
Prince Harry on
his First Day at
Wetherby School

942 Aged 8, with
Prince Charles
at Guards Polo

943 Aged 9, on Ski
Slopes with
Princess Diana

944 On First Day
at Eton, 1995

945 With Prince
Charles and
Prince Harry at
Balmoral, 1997

946 Wearing Hard Hat
during Community
Project in Chile,
2000

947 Playing Polo,
2002

21st Birthday of Prince William of Wales

(Des Sally Diamond. Litho Enschedé)

2003 (21 JUNE). Perf 13½×13 (C)

998	**938**	27p multicoloured	55	60
		a. Horiz strip of 10. Nos. 998/1007	5·50	6·00
		b. Perf 13½×14	55	60
		ba. Booklet pane. Nos. 998b, 1000b, 1003b/4b and 1006b/7b with margins all round	3·25	
		bb. Booklet pane. Nos. 998b, 1001b, 1003b/5b and 1007b with margins all round	3·25	
		bc. Booklet pane. Nos. 998b/1000b, 1002b, 1005b and 1007b with margins all round	3·25	
999	**939**	27p multicoloured	55	60
		b. Perf 13½×14	55	60
		ba. Booklet pane. Nos. 999b/1002b and 1005b/6b with margins all round	3·25	
		bb. Booklet pane. Nos. 999b, 1001b/1004b and 1006b with margins all round	3·25	
1000	**940**	27p multicoloured	55	60
		b. Perf 13½×14	55	60
1001	**941**	27p multicoloured	55	60
		b. Perf 13½×14	55	60
1002	**942**	27p multicoloured	55	60
		b. Perf 13½×14	55	60
1003	**943**	27p multicoloured	55	60
		b. Perf 13½×14	55	60
1004	**944**	27p multicoloured	55	60
		b. Perf 13½×14	55	60
1005	**945**	27p multicoloured	55	60
		b. Perf 13½×14	55	60
1006	**946**	27p multicoloured	55	60
		b. Perf 13½×14	55	60
1007	**947**	27p multicoloured	55	60
		b. Perf 13½×14	55	60
998/1007		Set of 10	5·50	6·00
		First Day Cover		6·50
		Presentation Pack	6·50	

Nos. 998b/1007b were only issued in £8.10 booklets, No. SB72.

Plate Nos.: Both values 1A (×4)

Sheets: 50 (10×5). Nos. 998/1007 were printed together, *se-tenant*, in horizontal strips of ten throughout the sheet

Imprint: Upper side margins

Withdrawn: 20.6.2004

GUERNSEY £5   **948** Letters of Alphabet

(Des A. Fothergill. Litho and die-stamped Enschedé)

2003 (3 JULY). Perf 13½ (C)

1008	**948**	£5 pale orange, royal blue and silver	10·00	10·50
		First Day Cover		11·00
		Presentation Pack		11·00

The alphabet letters are printed in thermochromic ink which fades from pale orange to white when exposed to heat.

Sheets: 4 (4×1)

949 Sleeping Boy and Christmas Tree

950 Boy opening Shutter to see Santa's Sleigh

951 Santa on Roof with Reindeer

952 Santa with Presents

953 Santa leaving Presents under Christmas Tree

954 Santa in Sleigh

Christmas. Scenes from Poem 'Twas the Night before Christmas' by Clement Clarke Moore

(Des Petula Stone. Litho DLR)

2003 (16 OCT). Perf 14×14½ (C)

1009	**949**	10p multicoloured	20	25
1010	**950**	27p multicoloured	55	60
1011	**951**	36p multicoloured	70	75
1012	**952**	40p multicoloured	80	85
1013	**953**	45p multicoloured	90	95
1014	**954**	65p multicoloured	1·25	1·50
1009/14		Set of 6	4·25	4·75
		First Day Cover		5·75
		Presentation Pack	5·75	
MS1015	130×104 mm. Nos. 1009/14	. . . .	4·25	4·75
		First Day Cover		5·75

Plate Nos.: All values 1A (×4)

Sheets: 50 (5×10)

Imprint: Upper right-hand margin

Withdrawn: 15.10.2004

Yearbook 2003

2003 (1 DEC). *Comprises Nos. 979/***MS**1015 *and* **MS**A203/22
Yearbook . . . . 70·00

955a Golden Snub-nosed Monkey
(*illustration reduced. Actual size* 120×85 *mm*)

Endangered Species (1st series). Golden Snub-nosed Monkey

(Des J. Kirk. Litho De La Rue)

2004 (29 JAN). *Sheet* 120×85 *mm.* Perf 14 (C)

MS1016	**955a**	£2 multicoloured	6·50	6·50
		First Day Cover		8·50
		Presentation Pack	8·50	

Withdrawn: 28.1.2005

956 'Rosemoor'

957 'Arctic Queen'

958 'Harlow Carr'

959 'Guernsey Cream'

960 'Josephine'

961 'Blue Moon'

962 'Wisley'

963 'Liberation'

964 'Royal Velvet'

965 'Hyde Hall'

Raymond Evison's Guernsey Clematis
(Des R. Evison. Litho Cartor)

2004 (29 JAN). *Self-adhesive.* Perf 12½ (die-cut)

1017	**956**	(22p) multicoloured	75	75
		a. *Sheetlet. Nos.* 1017/26 . . .	8·00	
		b. *Booklet pane. Nos.*1017/21, each ×2	7·00	
		c. *Booklet pane. Nos.*1017/21, each ×2	7·00	
1018	**957**	(22p) multicoloured	75	75
1019	**958**	(22p) multicoloured	75	75
1020	**959**	(22p) multicoloured	75	75
1021	**960**	(22p) multicoloured	75	75
1022	**961**	(27p) multicoloured	85	85
		a. *Booklet pane. Nos.* 1022/6, each ×2	8·75	
		b. *Booklet pane. Nos.* 1022/6, each ×2	8·75	
1023	**962**	(27p) multicoloured	85	85
1024	**963**	(27p) multicoloured	85	85
1025	**964**	(27p) multicoloured	85	85
1026	**965**	(27p) multicoloured	85	85
1017/26		Set of 10	8·00	8·00
		First Day Cover		9·00
		Presentation Pack	9·00	

Nos. 1017/21 were intended for postage within the Bailiwick and are inscribed "GY". They were each initially sold at 22p. Nos. 1022/6 were intended for postage to Great Britain and are inscribed "UK". They were each initially sold at 27p.

Sheets: 10 (5×2). Nos. 1017/26 were printed in sheetlets of 10 containing Nos. 1017/26 or in booklets containing either Nos. 1017/21×2 or Nos. 1022/6×2, both with the surplus self-adhesive paper around each stamp retained. Stamps from booklet panes Nos. 1017b and 1022a were peeled directly from the cover in two blocks 3×3 and 2×2, the blocks separated by a gutter containing text. Stamps from booklet panes Nos. 1017c and 1022b were issued in booklets of ten panes, the panes separated from the booklet by a line of rouletting.

966 Supermarine Spitfire

967 Landing Craft and Ship

968 Troops going Ashore at Gold Beach

969 Troops in Water

970 *Vega* (Red Cross supply ship)

Memories of the Second World War (2nd issue). 60th Anniv of D-Day Landings

(Des N. Watton. Litho BDT)

2004 (12 MAY). Perf 15×14 (£1.50) or 14 (others) (both comb)

1027	**966**	26p multicoloured	85	85
1028	**967**	32p multicoloured	1·00	1·00
1029	**968**	36p multicoloured	1·20	1·20
1030	**969**	40p multicoloured	1·30	1·30
1031	**970**	£1.50 multicoloured	5·00	5·00
1027/31		Set of 5	9·25	9·25
		First Day Cover		11·50
		Presentation Pack . . . . . . 11·50		

Plate Nos.: All values 1A (×4)

Sheets: 50 (5×10)

Imprint: Upper side margins

Withdrawn: 11.5.2005

971 Sandcastle, Rider, Bucket and Spade, Deckchair and Canoeist

972 Pathway Sign, Walking Trails, Bench and Guernsey Landscapes

973 Lighthouse and Yachts in Marina, St. Peter Port

974 Glasses of Red Wine and Meals on Table

975 Statue-menhir at Castel and Loop Holed Tower, Le Gran'mere Statue-menhir, Little Chapel and Victor Hugo Statue

976 Guernsey Lily, Wildflowers and Robin

Europa. Holidays

(Des P. Furness. Litho BDT)

2004 (12 MAY). Perf 13½.

1032	**971**	26p multicoloured	85	85
1033	**972**	32p multicoloured	1·10	1·10
1034	**973**	36p multicoloured	1·20	1·20
1035	**974**	40p multicoloured	1·30	1·30
1036	**975**	45p multicoloured	1·50	1·50
1037	**976**	65p multicoloured	2·10	2·10
1032/7		Set of 6	8·00	8·00
		First Day Cover		10·00
		Presentation Pack . . . . 10·00		

Sheets: 10 (2×5) with enlarged illustrated margins at right

Imprint: Central, left-hand margin

Withdrawn: 11.5.2005

977 Three Crowns (Loyalty)

978 Three Ships (Trade)

979 Knotted Rope (Unity)

980 Three Castle Turrets (Protection)

981 Three Scrolls (Justice)

982 Three Leaping Fish (Industry)

800th Anniv of Allegiance to England

(Des Charlotte Barnes. Litho Enschedé)

2004 (24 JUNE). Perf 13½×14 (C)

1038	**977**	26p multicoloured	85	85
1039	**978**	32p multicoloured	1·10	1·10
1040	**979**	36p multicoloured	1·20	1·20
1041	**980**	40p multicoloured	1·30	1·30
1042	**981**	45p multicoloured	1·50	1·50
1043	**982**	65p multicoloured	2·10	2·10
1038/43		Set of 6	8·00	8·00
		First Day Cover		10·00
		Presentation Pack	10·00	

MS1044   140×80 mm. Nos. 1038/43.
P 14×13½ . . . .   8·00   8·00
              First Day Cover . . . .   10·00

Plate Nos.: All values 1A (×5)

Sheets: 50 (10×5)

Imprint: Upper side margins

Withdrawn: 23.6.2005

983 Discus Thrower

984 Javelin Thrower

985 Runners

986 Wrestlers

987a Olympic Sports
(*illustration reduced. Actual size* 152×85 *mm*)

Olympic Games, Athens, Greece

(Des A. Fothergill. Litho BDT)

2004 (29 JULY). Perf 13½ (C)

1045	**983**	32p multicoloured	1·00	1·00
		a. Booklet pane. No. 1045×2 and Nos. 1046/7 with margins all round	4·75	
		b. Booklet pane. No. 1045, No. 1047×2 and No. 1048 with margins all round	6·00	
		c. Booklet pane. Nos. 1045/6 and 1048×2 with margins all round	6·50	
		d. Booklet pane. Nos. 1045/8 with margins all round	5·75	
1046	**984**	36p multicoloured	1·20	1·20
		a. Booklet pane. No. 1046×2 and Nos. 1047/8 with margins all round	6·00	
1047	**985**	45p multicoloured	1·50	1·50
1048	**986**	65p multicoloured	2·10	2·10
1045/8		Set of 4	5·75	5·75
		First Day Cover		7·75
		Presentation Pack	7·75	

MS1049   152×98 mm. **987a** £1 multicoloured. Perf 15×14 (C) . . . .   3·25   3·25
              a. Booklet pane. No. **MS**1049   3·25
              First Day Cover . . . .   5·25
              Presentation Pack . . . .   5·25

Plate Nos.: All values 1A (×4)

Sheets: 50 (10×5)

Imprint: Upper side margins

Withdrawn: 28.7.2005

988 'Little Donkey'

989 'While Shepherds Watched'

990 'Away in a Manger'

991 'Unto Us a Child is Born'

992 'We Three Kings'

993 Angels Wings

994 Bauble

995 Holly

996 Detail of Snowman

997 Star atop Tree

Plate Nos.: All values 1A (×4)

Sheets: 50 (5×10) The 20p values were printed together, *se-tenant*, in horizontal strips of 5 with the backgrounds forming a composite design

Imprint: Upper and lower side margins

Yearbook 2004
2004 (1 DEC). *Comprises Nos.* **MS**1016/59 *and* A223/47
Yearbook . . . . 65·00

'The Innocence of Christmas'
(Des J. Almer. Litho Cartor)

2004 (28 OCT). Perf 13 (C)

1050	**988**	20p multicoloured	65	65
		a. Horiz strip of 5. *Nos.* 1050/4	3·25	
1051	**989**	20p multicoloured	65	65
1052	**990**	20p multicoloured	65	65
1053	**991**	20p multicoloured	65	65
1054	**992**	20p multicoloured	65	65
1055	**993**	32p multicoloured	1·10	1·10
1056	**994**	36p multicoloured	1·20	1·20
1057	**995**	40p multicoloured	1·30	1·30
1058	**996**	45p multicoloured	1·50	1·50
1059	**997**	65p multicoloured	2·20	2·20
1050/9		*Set of* 10	10·50	10·50
		First Day Covers (2)		14·50
		Presentation Pack	13·50	

POSTAGE DUE STAMPS

D **1** Castle Cornet

D **2** Castle Cornet

(Des R. Barrett. Photo Delrieu)

1969 (1 OCT). *Face value in black; background colour given.*
No wmk. Perf 12½×12 (C)

D1	D **1**	1d plum	2·00	1·25
D2		2d bright green	2·00	1·25
D3		3d vermilion	3·00	4·00
D4		4d ultramarine	4·00	5·00
D5		5d yellow-ochre	6·00	4·00
D6		6d turquoise-blue	6·00	4·50
D7		1s lake-brown	10·00	8·00
D1/7		*Set of 7*	30·00	25·00

Sheets: 60 (10×6)

Quantities sold: 1d 82,802; 2d 75,340; 3d 74,532; 4d 74,659; 5d
71,129; 6d 72,912; 1s 71,659

Withdrawn and Invalidated: 14.2.72

Decimal Currency

(Des R. Granger Barrett. Photo Delrieu)

1971 (15 FEB)–**76**. *No wmk.* Perf 12½×12 (C)

D8	D **2**	½p plum (*a*)	10	10
D9		1p bright green (*a*)	10	10
D10		2p vermilion (*a*)	10	10
D11		3p ultramarine (*a*)	10	10
D12		4p yellow-ochre (*a*)	10	10
D13		5p turquoise-blue (*a*)	10	10
D14		6p violet (*c*)	10	10
D15		8p yellow-orange (*b*)	20	25
D16		10p lake-brown (*a*)	20	15
D17		15p grey (*c*)	30	40
D8/17		*Set of 10*	1·25	1·25
D1/13, 16		*Presentation Pack* (*a*)	75·00	
D8/17		*Presentation Pack* (*c*)	2·00	

Printings: (*a*) 15.2.71; (*b*) 7.10.75; (*c*) 10.2.76

Sheets: 60 (10×6)

Withdrawn: 14.2.72 Presentation Pack (Nos. D1/13 and D16); 1.8.78
½p to 15p (½p and 1p sold out by 6.78)

D **3** St. Peter Port

(Photo Delrieu)

1977 (2 AUG)–**80**. *Face value in black; background colour
given.* Perf 13 (C)

D10	D **3**	½p lake-brown (*a*)	10	10
D19		1p bright purple (*a*)	10	10
D20		2p bright orange (*a*)	10	10
D21		3p vermilion (*a*)	10	10
D22		4p turquoise-blue (*a*)	10	10
D23		5p yellow-green (*a*)	10	10
D24		6p turquoise-green (*a*)	10	10
D25		8p brown-ochre (*a*)	10	10
D26		10p ultramarine (*a*)	10	10
D27		14p green (*b*)	15	15
D28		15p bright violet (*a*)	15	15
D29		16p rose-red (*b*)	20	20
D18/29		*Set of 12*	1·25	1·25
D18/26, 28		*Presentation Pack*	2·00	

Printings: (*a*) 2.8.77; (*b*) 5.2.80

Sheets: 50 (5×10)

Withdrawn: 12.7.83 (Presentation Pack sold out earlier)

D **4** Milking Cow

D **5** Vale Mill

D **6** Sark Cottage

D **7** Quay-side, St.
Peter Port

D **8** Well, Water Lane,
Moulin Huet

D **9** Seaweed
Gathering

D **10** Upper Walk, White
Rock

D **11** Cobo Bay

D **12** Saint's Bay

D**13** La Coupée, Sark

D **14** Old Harbour, St.
Peter Port

D **15** Greenhouse,
Doyle Road, St.
Peter Port

Guernsey Scenes, c. 1900

(Des C. Abbott. Litho Questa)

1982 (13 JULY). Perf 14½ (C)

D30	D **4**	1p indigo, blue-black & brt grn .	10	10
D31	D **5**	2p yellow-brown, sepia & azure	10	10
D32	D **6**	3p blackish green, black & lilac .	10	10
D33	D **7**	4p bottle green, blk & dull orge	10	10
D34	D **8**	5p deep violet-blue, blue-black and turquoise-green	10	10
D35	D **9**	16p dp grey-blue, dp bl & cobalt .	30	35
D36	D **10**	18p steel bl, indigo & apple grn .	35	40
D37	D **11**	20p brown-olive, agate & pale bl	40	45
D38	D **12**	25p Prussian blue, blue-black and rose-pink	50	55
D39	D **13**	30p deep bluish green, blackish olive and bistre-yellow	60	65
D40	D **14**	50p olive-brown, sepia and dull violet-blue	1·00	1·10
D41	D **15**	£1 lt brown, brown & pale brn .	2·00	2·10
D30/41		*Set of 12*	5·25	5·75
		Presentation Pack	5·75	

Sheets: 50 (5×10)

Imprint: Bottom corner, right-hand margin

Withdrawn: 30.9.2001

STAMP BOOKLETS

Prices given are for complete booklets. Booklets Nos. SB1/12 are stitched.

B **1** Military Uniforms

1969 (12 DEC). *White covers as Type B **1**, printed in black*

SB1 2s. booklet containing 3×4d (No. 18*a*), 2×5d (No. 19*a*) and 2×1d (No. 14*c*) (*cover showing Trooper, Royal Guernsey Cavalry (Light Dragoons), 1814*) 50

SB2 4s booklet containing 6×4d (No. 18*a*), 4×5d (No. 19*a*) and 4×1d (No. 14*c*) (*cover showing Officer, St. Martin's Company (La Milice Bleue), Guernsey, 1720*) . . . . 1·50

SB3 6s booklet containing 9×4d (No. 18*a*), 6×5d (No. 19*a*) and 6×1d (No. 14*c*) (*cover showing Colour Sergeant of Grenadiers and Rifleman, East (Town) Regiment, Guernsey, 1833*) . . . . 1·50

Withdrawn: 14.2.72

1970 (29 JUNE). *White covers as Type B **1**. Printed in black (SB4), green (SB5) or red (SB6). Same composition as Nos. SB1/3*

SB4 2s booklet (*cover showing Officer, Royal Guernsey Horse Artillery, 1793*) . . . . 2·00

SB5 4s booklet (*cover showing Gunner, Royal Guernsey Artillery, 1743*) . . . . 9·00

SB6 5s booklet (*cover showing Sergeant, Royal Guernsey Light Infantry, 1832*) . . . . 9·00

Quantities sold: 2s (SB1, SB4), 81,928; 4s (SB2, SB5), 23,817; 6s (SB3, SB6), 25,123

Withdrawn: 14.2.72

Decimal Currency

1971 (15 FEB). *White covers as Type B **1**. Printed in black (SB7), green (SB8) or red (SB9)*

SB7 10p booklet containing 2×½p (No. 44*a*), 2×2p (No. 47*a*) and 2×2½p (No. 48*b*) (*cover showing Officer, Royal Guernsey Horse Artillery, 1850*) 85

SB8 20p booklet containing 4×½p (No. 44*a*), 4×2p (No. 47*a*) and 4×2½p (No. 48*b*) (*cover showing Sergeant, Guernsey Light Infantry (Grenadiers), 1826*) 70

SB9 30p booklet containing 6×½p (No. 44*a*), 6×2p (No. 47*a*) and 6×2½p (No 48*b*) (*cover showing Sergeant and Bandsman, Royal Guernsey Light Infantry (North Regiment), 1866*) . . . . . 1·00

Withdrawn: 27.6.73 (SB7); 12.3.75 (SB8); 15.1.75 (SB9)

1973 (? APR). *White covers as Type B* **1**. *Printed in black* (SB10), *green (SB11) or red (SB12)*

SB10 10p booklet containing 9 × ½p (No. 44ab), 2 × 2p (No. 47ab) and 2 × 2½p (No. 48ba) (*cover showing Officer, Guernsey Horse Artillery, 1828*) 40

SB11 20p booklet containing 4 × ½p (No. 44ab), 4 × 2p (No. 47ab) and 4 × 2½p (No. 48ba) (*cover showing Grenadier, Guernsey Light Infantry, 1792*) 45

SB12 30p booklet containing 6 × ½p (No. 44ab), 6 × 2p (No. 47ab) and 6 × 2½p (No. 48ba) (*cover showing Insignia, Royal Guernsey Light Infantry*) 70

Nos. SB10/12 are inscribed 'January 1973' on back cover.

Withdrawn: 1.4.75

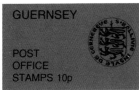

B **2** Arms of Guernsey

1974 (2 APR). *Silver (SB13) or gold cover (SB140 as Type B* **2**

SB13 10p booklet containing five ½p stamps and three 2½p in *se-tenant* strip (No. 98a) 35

SB14 35p booklet containing four ½p stamps, six 2½p and six 3p in *se-tenant* pane (No. 98b) 75

The strips and panes have the left-hand selvedge stuck into booklet covers and then folded and supplied in plastic wallets.

Withdrawn: 6.2.79

1977 (8 FEB). *Green cover as Type B* **2**

SB15 20p booklet containing No. 99a 55

The note beneath No. SB14 also applies here.

Withdrawn: 12.2.80

BOOKLET PANES from Nos. SB16/18 are loose within card covers supplied in plastic sachets.

1978 (7 FEB). *Blue cover as Type B* **2**

SB16 10p booklet containing No. 99b 35

Withdrawn: 12.2.80

1979 (13 FEB). *Covers as Type B* **2**

SB17 10p booklet containing No. 178a (*black and green cover*) 40

SB18 30p booklet containing No. 179a (*black and red cover*) 90

Withdrawn: 23.2.82

B **3** Castle Cornet

1980 (6 MAY). *Horiz covers as Type B* **3**. *Folded*

SB19 30p booklet containing No. 177a (*blue printed cover, Type C*) 60

SB20 50p booklet containing No. 177b (*brown printed cover showing view from the sea*) . . 90

Withdrawn: 4.5.83

1981 (24 FEB). *Covers similar to Type B* **3**, *but vert. Folded*

SB21 60p booklet containing No. 180a (*red printed cover showing Fort Grey*) 90

SB22 £1.20 booklet containing No. 180b (*green printed cover showing Rokaine Castle*) . . . . . 1·90

Withdrawn 23.2.84

1982 (2 FEB). *Covers similar to Type B* **3** *showing Fort George. Folded*

SB23 70p booklet containing No. 181b (*orange printed cover showing main entrance*) . . . . . 1·50

SB24 £1.30 booklet containing No. 181c (*magenta printed cover showing aerial view of Citadel*) 1·90

Withdrawn: 22.7.85

1983 (14 MAR). *Covers similar to Type B* **3**. *Folded*

SB25 £1 booklet containing No. 180c (*new blue printed cover showing States Office, St. Peter Port*) . . . . 1·90

SB26 £1.30 booklet containing No. 180d (*sepia printed cover showing Constable's Office, St. Peter Port*) . . . . 2·25

Withdrawn: 22.7.85

BOOKLET PANES from Nos. SB27/38 are loose within card covers.

B **4** View of Post Office Headquarters, St. Peter Port

1984 (18 SEPT). *Multicoloured covers as Type B* **4**
SB27 £1 booklet containing No. 299*a* . . . . 2·50
SB28 £1.30 booklet containing No. 299*b* (*cover
showing Head Post Office, St. Peter Port*) . . 3·00

Quantities sold: SB27 50,393; SB28 25,372
Withdrawn: 1.87

1985 (19 MAR). *Multicoloured covers as Type B* **4**
SB29 £1.20 booklet containing No. 304*a* (*cover
showing French Halles, St. Peter Port*) . . . . . 2·50
SB30 £1.30 booklet containing No. 304*b* (*cover
showing Market Halls, St. Peter Port*) . . . . . . 2·50

Quantities sold: SB29 49,248; SB30 45,463
Withdrawn: 8.87

1985 (2 DEC). *Multicoloured cover as Type B* **4**, *but vert*
SB31 50p booklet containing No. 297*a* (*cover
showing Victoria Tower, St. Peter Port*) . . . . . 1·60

Quantity sold: 55,768
Withdrawn: 8.87

1986 (1 APR). *Multicoloured cover as Type B* **4**, *but vert*
SB32 £1.20 booklet containing No. 305*a* (*cover
showing St. James-the-Less, St. Peter Port*) . 3·00

Quantity sold: 32,627
Withdrawn: 2.89

1987 (30 MAR). *Multicoloured covers as Type B* **4**, *but vert*
SB33 £1 booklet containing No. 298*a* (*cover
showing Lukis Observatory, St. Peter Port*) . . 2·50
SB34 £1.30 booklet containing No. 306*a* (*cover
showing Weighbridge, St. Peter Port*) . . . . . . 3·25

Quantities sold: SB33 42,478; SB34 36,369
Withdrawn: 2.89

1988 (28 MAR). *Multicoloured covers as Type B* **4**, *but vert*
SB35 £1 booklet containing No. 299*c* (*cover
showing North Pier Light, St. Peter Port*) . . . 2·75
SB36 £1·40 booklet containing No. 306*ba* (*cover
showing Castle Light, St. Peter Port*) . . . . . . 3·00

Quantities sold: SB35 41,092; SB36 39,478
Withdrawn: 2.90

1989 (28 Feb). *Multicoloured covers as Type B* **4**, *but vert*
SB37 £1 booklet containing No. 299*d* (*cover
showing Town Church, St. Peter Port*) . . . . 3·25
SB38 £1·20 booklet containing No. 306*bb* (*cover
showing St. Barnabas Church, St. Peter Port*) 3·50

Quantities sold: SB37 47,175; SB38 41,235
Withdrawn: 12.90

B **5** Opening Ceremony, 1939
(*illustration reduced. Actual size* 163×97 *mm*)

50th Anniversary of Guernsey Airport
1989 (5 MAY). *Multicoloured cover, Type B* **5**. *Booklet
contains text and illustrations on panes and interleaving
pages. Stitched*
SB39 £3.90 booklet containing Nos. 456*a*, 458*a* and
460*a* . . . . 11·00

Quantity sold: 38,025
Sold out: By 11.89

1989 (27 DEC). *Multicoloured covers as Type B* **4**, *but vert*
SB40 £1.20 booklet containing No. 301*a* (*cover
showing Fish Market, St. Peter Port*) . . . . . . 3·25
SB41 £1.70 booklet containing No. 308*a* (*cover
showing Lloyds Bank, St. Peter Port*) . . . . . . 3·75

Quantities sold: SB40 31,736; SB41 31,743
Withdrawn: 21.5.92

B**6** Crown Hotel
(*illustration reduced. Actual size* 163×97 *mm*)

50th Anniversary of First Guernsey Stamps
1991 (18 FEB). *Multicoloured cover, Type B* **6**. *Booklet
contains text on panes and text and illustrations on
interleaving pages. Stitched*
SB42 £4.41 booklet containing No. 517*a*×3 . . . . . . 12·00

Quantity sold: 31,955
Withdrawn: 17.2.92

1991 (2 APR). *Multicoloured covers as Type B* **4**, *but vert*
SB43 £1.30 booklet containing No. 300a (cover
  showing Golden Lion Inn, St Peter Port) .. 3.75
SB44 £1.80 booklet containing No. 309a (cover
  showing National Trust Building, St. Peter Port 5.50

Quantities sold: SB43 36,066; SB44 26,029

Withdrawn: 21.5.92

B **7** Carnations

1992 (22 MAY). *Multicoloured covers as Type B* **7**. *Without barcode on the reverse*. *Panes attached by selvedge*
SB45 £1.45 booklet containing pane No. 572ac
  (cover Type B **7**) 4.00
SB46 £1.80 booklet containing pane No. 574ac
  (cover showing mixed freesias) 6.00

Withdrawn: 31.8.99

B **8** Bow of Ship and Relics
(*illustration reduced. Actual size* 163×97 mm)

'Operation Asterix'

1992 (18 SEPT). *Multicoloured cover, Type B* **8**. *Booklet contains text and illustrations on interleaving pages. Stitched*
SB47 £5.60 booklet containing No. 583a×4 ...... 13.00

Quantity sold: 24,211

Withdrawn: 17.9.93

1993 (2 MAR)–**95**. *Multicoloured covers as Type B* **7**, *but different Guernsey Post Office logo. Without barcode on the reverse. Panes attached by selvedge*
SB48 £1.12 booklet containing pane No. 577ab
  (cover showing Lisianthus) 4.00

SB49 £1.28 booklet containing pane No. 572ad
  (cover Type B **7**) 3.25
  a. With barcode sticker on reverse (6.95) ... 7.00
  b. Barcode printed on reverse (10.95) 4.00
SB50 £1.92 booklet containing pane No. 575ab
  (cover showing standard roses) 6.00
  a. With barcode sticker on reverse (3.95) ... 9.00
  b. Barcode printed on reverse (6.95) 5.25

Withdrawn: 31.8.99

B **9** Thomas de la Rue
(*illustration reduced. Actual size* 163×97 mm)

Birth Bicentenary of Thomas de la Rue (printer)

1993 (27 JULY). *Multicoloured cover as Type B* **9**. *Booklet contains text and illustrations on interleaving pages. Stapled*
SB51 £5.60 booklet containing panes Nos.
  617a/21a 12.00

Withdrawn: 26.7.94

1994 (18 FEB). *Multicoloured cover as Type B* **7**, *but different Guernsey Post Office logo. With barcode on reverse. Pane attached by selvedge*
SB52 £1 booklet containing pane No. 576ab (cover
  showing Iris 'Ideal') 3.00

Withdrawn: 31.8.99

B **10** Guernsey View and 1936 Bentley
(*illustration reduced. Actual size* 162×97 mm)

Centenary of First Car in Guernsey

1994 (19 JULY). *Black and grey cover as Type B* **10**. *Booklet contains text and illustrations on labels attached to panes and on interleaving pages. Stitched*
SB53 £7 booklet containing panes Nos. 639a/43a . 18.00

Withdrawn 18.7.95

B **11** Coins, Postbox and Stamps 'Face'

Greetings Stamps. 'The Welcoming Face of Guernsey'

1995 (28 FEB). *Multicoloured cover as Type B* **11**. *Miniature sheet folded and attached by selvedge*
SB54   £1.92 booklet containing No. **MS**671 ...... 4·50
Withdrawn: 27.2.96

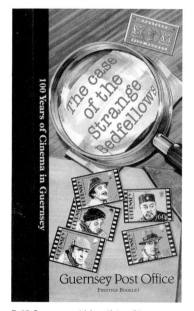

B **12** Stamps and Magnifying Glass

Centenary of Cinema. Screen Detectives

1996 (6 NOV). *Multicoloured cover as Type B* **12**. *Booklet contains text and illustrations on margins of panes and interleaving pages. Stitched*
SB55   £7.04 booklet containing panes Nos.
       711*a*/15*a* .... 16·00
Quantity sold: 18,370
Withdrawn: 5.11.97

B **13** Freesia 'Pink Glow'

1997 (2 JAN). *Multicoloured covers as Type B* **13**. *With barcode on reverse. Panes attached by selvedge*
SB56   £1.04 booklet containing pane No. 576*bb*
       (*cover Type B* **13**) .... 3·00
SB57   £1.44 booklet containing pane No. 572*bb*
       (*cover showing Standard Rose*) .... 4·00
SB58   £2 booklet containing No. 576*ab*×2 (*cover showing Iris 'Ideal'*) .... 6·00

Withdrawn: 31.8.99

B **14** Castle Cornet, Guernsey

Guernsey Scenes (1st series)

1997 (24 APR). *Multicoloured covers as Type B* **14**. *Self-adhesive*
SB59   £1.04 booklet containing pane No. 739*a*
       (*cover as Type B* **14**) .... 3·25
SB60   £1.44 booklet containing pane No. 737*a*
       (*cover showing Shell Beach, Herm*) ...... 4·75
SB61   £2 booklet containing pane No. 738*a* (*cover showing La Seigneurie, Sark*) .... 5·50

Withdrawn: 31.3.98

B **15** Queen Elizabeth and Prince Philip
(*illustration reduced. Actual size* 162×95 *mm*)

Golden Wedding

1997 (20 NOV). *Multicoloured cover as Type* B **15**. *Booklet contains text and illustrations on panes and interleaving pages. Stitched*
SB62   £8.48 booklet containing Nos. 754*a/b*, 756*a*
and 758*a* . . . .   22·00

Withdrawn: 19.11.98

B **16** Millennium Tapestry
(*illustration reduced. Actual size* 162×97 *mm*)

The Millennium Tapestries Project

1998 (10 FEB). *Multicoloured cover as Type* B **16**. *Booklet contains text and illustrations on pane margins and interleaving pages. Stitched*
SB63   £7.50 booklet containing Nos. 760*b/c*, 762*a*,
764*a* and 766*a* . . . .   17·00

Withdrawn: 9.2.99

B **17** Fort Grey

Guernsey Scenes (2nd series)

1998 (25 MAR). *Multicoloured covers as Type* B **17**. *Self-adhesive*
SB64   £1.60 booklet containing pane No. 770*b*
(*cover as Type* B **17**) . . . .   3·75
SB65   £2 booklet containing pane No. 772*b* (*cover showing Guernsey cow*) . . . .   4·75

Sold out: 6.2001

B **18** Queen Elizabeth the Queen Mother
(*illustration reduced. Actual size* 160×100 *mm*)

Life and Times of Queen Elizabeth the Queen Mother

1999 (4 FEB). *Multicoloured cover as Type* B **18**. *Booklet contains text and illustrations on pane margins and interleaving pages. Stitched*
SB66   £7.50 booklet containing panes Nos. 817*b/c*,
819*b*, 821*b* and 923*b* . . . .   20·00

. Withdrawn: 3.2.2000

B **19** Supermarine Spitfire over St. Peter Port
(*illustration reduced. Actual size* 163×97 *mm*)

60th Anniversary of Battle of Britain

2000 (28 APR). *Multicoloured cover as Type B* **19**. *Booklet contains text and illustrations on interleaving pages. Stitched*
SB67 £6.99 booklet containing pages Nos. 857a/c,
858a and 862a . . . . 17·00

Withdrawn: 27.4.2001

B **20** Albecq Beach
(*illustration reduced. Actual size* 100×60 *mm*)

Island Scenes

2001 (26 APR). *Multicoloured covers as Type B* **20**. *Self-adhesive.*
SB68 (£2.20) booklet containing pane No. 901b
(*cover as Type B* **20**) . . . . 4·50
SB69 (£2.70) booklet containing pane No. 906b
(*cover showing Telegraph Bay, Alderney*) . . . 5·50

Sold out: By 7.2004

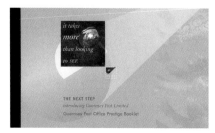

B **21** Droplet of Water on Leaf
(*illustration reduced. Actual size* 160×95 *mm*)

Incorporation of Guernsey Post Ltd

2001 (1 AUG). *Multicoloured cover as Type B* **21**. *Booklet contains text on panes and transparent interleaves. Stitched*
SB70 £8.05 booklet containing panes Nos. 921a/7a 16·00

Withdrawn: 31.7.02

B **22** Queen Elizabeth carrying Bouquet
(*illustration reduced. Actual size* 165×98 *mm*)

Golden Jubilee

2002 (30 APR). *Multicoloured cover as Type B* **22**. *Booklet contains text and photographs on interleaving panes. Stitched*
SB71 £9.05 booklet containing panes Nos. 948a/c
and 949a with Alderney No. **MS**A184 . . . . . . 18·00

Withdrawn: 29.4.2003

B **23** Prince William and His Coat of Arms
(*illustration reduced. Actual size* 162×98 *mm*)

21st Birthday of Prince William of Wales

2003 (21 JUNE). *Multicoloured cover as Type B* **23**. *Booklet contains text and photographs on panes and interleaving pages. Stitched.*
SB72 £8.10 booklet containing panes Nos. 998ba/bc
and 999ba/bb . . . . 16·00

Withdrawn: 20.6.2004

B **24** Clematis 'Pistachio'
(*illustration reduced. Actual size* 100×60 *mm*)

Raymond Evison's Guernsey Clematis
2004 (29 JAN). *Multicoloured covers as Type B* **24**. *Self-adhesive* (*Nos.* SB73/4) *or stitched* (*Nos.* SB75/6).

SB73	(£2.20) booklet containing pane No. 1017*b* (*cover Type B* **24**)	7·00
SB74	(£2.70) booklet containing pane No. 1022*a* (*cover showing Clematis 'Anna Louise'*)	8·75
SB75	(£22) booklet containing ten panes of No. 1017*c* (*cover as Type B* **24**, *but* 181×59 *mm*)	44·00
SB76	(£27) booklet containing ten panes of No. 1022*b*) (*cover showing Clematis 'Anna Louise'*, 181×59 *mm*)	50·00

B **25** Ruins of Ancient Greece
(*illustration reduced. Actual size* 163×98 *mm*)

Olympic Games, Athens, Greece
2004 (29 JULY). *Multicoloured cover as Type B* **25**. *Booklet contains text and illustrations on panes and interleaving pages. Stitched.*

SB77	£9.90 booklet containing panes Nos. 1045*a/d*, 1046*a* and **MS**1049*a*	32·00

ALDERNEY

The following issues are provided by the Guernsey Post Office for use on Alderney. They are also valid for postal purposes throughout the rest of the Bailiwick of Guernsey.

A **1** Island Map

A **2** Hanging Rock

A **3** States' Building, St. Anne

A **4** St. Anne's Church

A **5** Yachts in Braye Bay

A **6** Victoria St, St. Anne

A **7** Map of Channel

A **8** Fort Clonque

A **9** Corblets Bay and Fort

A **10** Old Tower, St. Anne

A **11** Golf Course and Essex Castle

A **12** Old Harbour

A **12a** Quesnard Lighthouse

A **12b** Braye Harbour

A **12c** Island Hall

A **12d** *J. T. Daly* (steam locomotive)

A**12e** *Louis Marchesi of Round Table* (lifeboat)

Island Scenes

(Des G. Drummond. Litho B.D.T. (20p to 28p) or photo Courvoisier (others))

1983 (14 JUNE)–**93**. *Granite paper* (1p to 18p). Perf 15×14 (20p to 28p) or 11½ (others), both comb

A1	A **1**	1p multicoloured (a)	10	10
A2	A **2**	4p multicoloured (a)	10	10
A3	A **3**	9p multicoloured (a)	15	15
A4	A **4**	10p multicoloured (a)	20	15
A5	A **5**	11p multicoloured (a)	20	20
A6	A **6**	12p multicoloured (a)	25	20
A7	A **7**	13p multicoloured (a)	25	20
A8	A **8**	14p multicoloured (a)	30	20
A9	A **9**	15p multicoloured (a)	35	20
A10	A **10**	16p multicoloured (a)	35	25
A11	A **11**	17p multicoloured (a)	40	30
A12	A **12**	18p multicoloured (a)	40	30

A12*a*	A **12a**	20p multicoloured (*b*)	1·00	90
A12*b*	A **12b**	21p multicoloured (*c*)	1·00	90
A12*c*	A **12c**	23p multicoloured (*d*) ..	95	95
A12*d*	A **12d**	24p multicoloured (*e*)	1·75	1·75
A12*e*	A **12e**	28p multicoloured (*e*)	2·25	2·25
A1/12*e*		Set of 17	9·00	8·00
		First Day Covers (6)		25·00
		Presentation Pack (2)	12·00	
		Set of 17 Gutter Pairs	20·00	

Printings: (*a*) 14.6.83; (*b*) 27.12.89; (*c*) 2.4.91; (*d*) 6.2.92; (*e*) 2.3.93

Plate and Cylinder Nos.: 1p, 12p, 13p, 17p, 20p to 28p 1A, 1B, 1C, 1D (each ×4); others 1A, 1B, 1C, 1D (each ×5)

Sheets: 40 (2 panes 5×4)

Imprint: Central, bottom margin

Quantities sold: 1p 1,337,865; 4p 465,887; 9p 680,896; 10p 709,197; 11p 778,483; 12p 573,124; 13p 671,772; 14p 1,027,248; 15p 740,915; 16p 542,970; 17p 404,323; 18p 491,877; 20p 248,694; 21p 233,975; 23p 237,345; 24p 311,144; 28p 134,765

Withdrawn: 4.6.94

A **13** Oystercatcher

A **15** Ringed Plover   A **16** Dunlin

A **14** Ruddy Turnstone

A **17** Curlew

Birds

(Des and photo Harrison)

1984 (12 JUNE). Perf 14½ (C)

A13	A **13**	9p multicoloured	1·10	60
A14	A **14**	13p multicoloured	1·10	75
A15	A **15**	26p multicoloured	2·50	2·75
A16	A **16**	28p multicoloured	2·50	2·75
A17	A **17**	31p multicoloured	2·50	1·70
A13/17		Set of 5	8·75	7·75
		First Day Cover		10·00
		Presentation Pack	12·00	
		Set of 5 Gutter Pairs	20·00	

Cylinder Nos.: All values 1A, 1B (each ×5)

Sheets: 50 (2 panes 5×5)

Imprint: Bottom margin, right hand corner

Quantities sold: 9p 285,931; 13p 360,619; 20p 246,016; 28p 261,370; 31p 334,484

Withdrawn: 11.6.85

A **18** Westland Wessex Hu MK 5 Helicopter of the Queen's Flight   A **19** Britten Norman 'long-nose' Trislander

A **20** De Havilland D.H.114 Heron 1B   A **21** De Havilland D.H.89A Dragon Rapide *Sir Henry Lawrence*

A **22** Saro A.21 Windhover Flying Boat *City of Portsmouth*

50th Anniversary of Alderney Airport

(Des A. Theobald. Photo Courvoisier)

1985 (19 MAR). *Granite paper.* Perf 11½ (C)

A18	A **18**	9p multicoloured	1·40	70
A19	A **19**	13p multicoloured	1·75	1·00
A20	A **20**	29p multicoloured	3·00	2·50
A21	A **21**	31p multicoloured	3·50	2·75
A22	A **22**	34p multicoloured	3·50	2·75
A18/22		Set of 5	12·00	9·00
		First Day Cover		14·00
		Presentation Pack	15·00	

Cylinder Nos.: All values A1–1–1–1–1–1, B1–1–1–1–1–1

Sheets: 25 (5×5)

Quantities sold: 9p 294,437; 13p 321,276; 29p 231,422; 31p 171,528; 34p 162,429

Withdrawn: 18.3.86

A **23** Royal Engineers, 1890

A **24** Duke of Albany's Own Highlanders (72nd Highland Regt), 1856

A **25** Royal Artillery, 1855

A **26** South Hampshire Regiment, 1810

A **27** Royal Irish Regiment, 1782

Regiments of the Alderney Garrison

(Des E. Stemp. Litho Harrison)

1985 (24 SEPT). Perf 14½ (C)

A23	A **23**	9p multicoloured	25	20
A24	A **24**	14p multicoloured	80	40
A25	A **25**	29p multicoloured	80	70
A26	A **26**	31p multicoloured	1·10	1·10
A27	A **27**	34p multicoloured	1·40	1·40
A23/7		Set of 5	4·00	3·50
		First Day Cover		6·00
		Presentation Pack	6·25	
		Set of 5 Gutter Pairs	8·00	

No. A24 shows the tartan and insignia of the 78th Highland Regiment in error.

Plate Nos.: All values 1A, 1B, 1C, 1D (each ×5)
Sheets: 50 (2 panes 5×5)
Imprint: Central, left-hand margin of each pane
Quantities sold: 9p 286,572; 14p 283,493; 29p 224,196; 31p 151,948; 34p 145,422
Withdrawn: 23.9.86

A **28** Fort Groznez

A **29** Fort Tourgis

A **30** Fort Clonque

A **31** Fort Albert

Alderney Forts

(Des R. Reed. Litho Cartor)

1986 (23 SEPT). Perf 13×13½ (C)

A28	A **28**	10p multicoloured	80	20
A29	A **29**	14p multicoloured	90	80
A30	A **30**	31p multicoloured	2·50	3·00
A31	A **31**	34p multicoloured	2·50	3·00
A28/31		Set of 4	6·00	6·25
		First Day Cover		9·00
		Presentation Pack	8·50	
		Set of 4 Gutter Pairs	12·00	

Plate Nos.: All values 1A, 1B, 1C, 1D (each ×5)
Sheets: 50 (2 panes 5×5)
Imprint: Left-hand margin of left-hand pane
Quantities sold: 10p 325,706; 14p 231,891; 31p 143,423; 34p 138,556
Withdrawn: 22.9.87

A **32** Liverpool (full-rigged ship), 1902

A **33** Petit Raymond (schooner), 1906

A **34** *Maina* (yacht), 1910

A **35** *Burton* (steamer), 1911

A **36** *Point Law* (oil tanker), 1975

Alderney Shipwrecks

(Des C. Jacques. Litho Questa)

1987 (5 MAY). Perf 14×14½ (C)

A32	A **32**	11p multicoloured	1·60	50
A33	A **33**	15p multicoloured	1·75	55
A34	A **34**	29p multicoloured	3·75	3·50
A35	A **35**	31p multicoloured	4·00	3·50
A36	A **36**	34p multicoloured	4·00	4·25
A32/6		Set of 5	14·00	11·00
		First Day Cover		13·00
		Presentation Pack	17·00	
		Set of 5 Gutter Pairs	28·00	

Plate Nos.: All values 1A, 1B, 1C, 1D (each ×4)

Sheets: 50 (2 panes 5×5)

Imprint: Bottom, right-hand margin of each pane

Quantities sold: 11p 228,998; 15p 233,861; 29p 139,453; 31p 148,572; 34p 145,641

Withdrawn: 4.5.88

A **37** Moll's Map of 1724

A **38** Bastide's Survey of 1739

A **39** Goodwin's Map of 1831

A **40** General Staff Map of 1943

A **41** Ordnance Survey Map of 1988

250th Anniversary of Bastide's Survey of Alderney

(Des J. Cooter. Litho Enschedé)

1989 (7 JULY). Perf 13½×14 (C)

A37	A **37**	12p multicoloured	25	25
A38	A **38**	18p blk, greenish blue & orge-brn	45	30
A39	A **39**	27p black, greenish blue and dull yellow-green	95	1·10
A40	A **40**	32p black, greenish blue & brt rose-red	1·10	1·10
A41	A **41**	35p multicoloured	1·50	1·40
A37/41		Set of 5	3·75	3·75
		First Day Cover		4·75
		Presentation Pack	5·00	
		Set of 5 Gutter Pairs	7·50	

Plate Nos.: 12p 1–1–1–1; 18p, 27p, 32p 1–1–1; 35p 1–1–1–1–1

Sheets: 50 (2 panes 5×5)

Imprint: Central, both margins of each pane

Quantities sold: 12p 169,993; 18p 194,667; 27p 148,621; 32p 158,600; 35p 153,544

Withdrawn: 6.7.90

A **42** H.M.S. *Alderney* (bomb ketch), 1738

A **43** H.M.S. *Alderney* (frigate), 1742

A **44** H.M.S. *Alderney* (sloop), 1755

A **45** H.M.S. *Alderney* (submarine), 1945

A **46** H.M.S. *Alderney* (patrol vessel), 1979

Royal Navy Ships named after Alderney

(Des A. Theobald. Litho B.D.T.)

1990 (3 MAY). Perf 13½ (C)

A42	A **42**	14p black and olive-bistre	. . . .	25	20
A43	A **43**	20p black and orange-brown	. . .	45	35
A44	A **44**	29p black and cinnamon	. . . . . .	1·00	1·00
A45	A **45**	34p black & pale turquoise-blue	.	1·10	1·50
A46	A **46**	37p black and cobalt	. . . .	1·40	1·50
A42/6		Set of 5	. . . .	3·75	4·00
		First Day Cover	. . . .		5·50
		Presentation Pack	. . . .	4·50	
		Set of 5 Gutter Pairs	. . . . . .	7·50	

Plate Nos.: 14p, 20p, 29p, 34p 1A–1A, 1B–1B; 37p 1A–1A, 1B–1B, 1C–1C, 1D–1D

Sheets: 50 (2 panes 5×5)

Imprint: Central, side margins of each pane

Quantities sold: 14p 290,801; 20p 291,996; 29p 142,011; 34p 146,711; 37p 151,711

Withdrawn: 4.5.91

A **47** Wreck of H.M.S. *Victory*, 1744

A **48** Lighthouse Keeper's Daughter rowing back to the Casquets

A **49** MBB-Bolkow Bo 150D Helicopter leaving pad on St. Thomas Tower

A **50** Migrating Birds over Lighthouse

A **51** Trinity House Vessel *Patricia* and Arms

Automation of the Casquets Lighthouse

(Des A. Theobald. Litho Cartor)

1991 (30 APR). Perf 14×13½ (C)

A47	A **47**	21p multicoloured	. . . .	80	50
A48	A **48**	26p multicoloured	. . . .	1·90	1·70
A49	A **49**	31p multicoloured	. . . .	2·00	2·25
A50	A **50**	37p multicoloured	. . . .	2·75	3·25
A51	A **51**	50p multicoloured	. . . .	3·75	3·50
A47/51		Set of 5	. . . .	10·00	9·50
		First Day Cover	. . . .		11·00
		Presentation Pack	. . . .	12·50	
		Set of 5 Gutter Pairs	. . . . . .	20·00	

Plate Nos.: All values 1A, 1B, 1C, 1D (each ×4)

Sheets: 50 (2 panes 5×5)

Imprint: Central, side margins

Quantities sold: 21p 280,555; 26p 164,155; 31p 158,465; 37p 158,375; 50p 238,825

Withdrawn: 29.4.92

A **52** Two French Warships on Fire

A **53** Crews leaving burning Ships

A **54** French Warship sinking

A **55** 'The Battle of La Hogue'

300th Anniversary of Battle of La Hogue

(Des C Abbott. Litho B.D.T.)

1992 (18 SEPT). Perf 14×15 (50p) or 13½ (others), both comb)

A52	A **52**	23p multicoloured	1·10	1·00
A53	A **53**	28p multicoloured	2·40	2·50
A54	A **54**	33p multicoloured	3·00	3·00
A55	A **55**	50p multicoloured	3·50	3·50
A52/5		Set of 4	9·00	9·00
		First Day Cover		10·00
		Presentation Pack	11·00	
		Set of 4 Gutter Pairs	18·00	

Nos. A52/4 show details of the painting on the 50p value.

Plate Nos.: All values 1A, 1B (each ×5)

Sheets: 50 (2 panes 5×5)

Imprint: Central, right-hand margin (50p) or central, side margins (others)

Quantities sold: 23p 238,820; 28p 188,685; 33p 172,565; 50p 186,096

Withdrawn: 17.9.93

A **56** Spiny Lobster

A **57** Plumrose Anemone

A **58** Starfish

A **59** Sea Urchin

Endangered Species. Marine Life

(Des A. Peck. Litho Questa)

1993 (2 NOV). Perf 14½ (C)

A56	A **56**	24p multicoloured	1·25	1·40
		a. Horiz strip of 4. Nos. A56/9 .	4·50	5·00
A57	A **57**	28p multicoloured	1·25	1·40
A58	A **58**	33p multicoloured	1·25	1·40
A59	A **59**	39p multicoloured	1·25	1·40
A56/9		Set of 4	4·50	5·00
		First Day Cover		5·50
		Presentation Pack	5·50	

Plate Nos.: All values 1A, 1B (each ×5)

Sheets: 16 (4×4), Nos. A56/9 were printed together, se-tenant, in horizontal strips of 4 throughout the sheet

Imprint: Central, right-hand margin

Quantity sold: 216.788 strips

Withdrawn: 1.11.94

A **60** Blue-tailed Damselfly, Dark Hair Water Crowfoot and Branched Bur-reed

A **61** White-toothed Shrew and Flax-leaved St. John's Wort

A **62** Fulmar and Kaffir Fig

A**63** Clouded Yellow (butterfly) and Red Clover

A **64** Bumble Bee, Prostrate Broom and Giant Broomrape

A **65** Dartford Warbler and Lesser Dodder

A **66** Peacock (butterfly) and Stemless Thistle

A **67** Mole and Bluebell

A **68** Great Green
Grasshopper and
Common Gorse

A **69** Six-spot Burnet
(moth) and
Viper's Bugloss

A **73** Atlantic Puffin
and English
Stonecrop

A **74** Emperor (moth)
and Bramble

A **70** Common Blue
(butterfly) and
Pyramidal Orchid

A **70a** Small Tortoiseshell
(butterfly) and
Buddleia

A **75** Pale-spined
Hedgehog and
Pink Oxalis

A **76** Common Tern and
Bermuda Grass

A **71** Common Rabbit
and Creeping
Buttercup

A **72** Greater Black-
backed Gull and
Sand Crocus

A **77** Northern Gannet and
Fucus vesiculosus
(seaweed)

Flora and Fauna

(Des Wendy Bramall. Litho B.D.T. (No. A71a) or Questa
(others))

1994 (5 MAY)–**98**. Perf 14½ (C)

A60	A **60**	1p multicoloured (a)	. . . .	10	10
A61	A **61**	2p multicoloured (a)	. . . .	10	10
A62	A **62**	3p multicoloured (a)	. . . .	10	10
A63	A **63**	4p multicoloured (a)	. . . .	10	10
A64	A **64**	5p multicoloured (a)	. . . .	10	10
A65	A **65**	6p multicoloured (a)	. . . .	15	20
A66	A **66**	7p multicoloured (a)	. . . .	15	20
A67	A **67**	8p multicoloured (a)	. . . .	15	20
A68	A **68**	9p multicoloured (a)	. . . .	20	25
A69	A **69**	10p multicoloured (a)	. . . .	20	25
A70	A **70**	16p multicoloured (a)	. . . .	55	40
		a. Perf 14×15	. . . .	55	50
		ab. Booklet pane of 8	. . . .	4·00	
A70b	A **70a**	18p multicoloured (c)	. . . .	35	40
		ba. Perf 14×15	. . . .	35	40
		bb. Booklet pane of 8	. . . .	3·00	
A71	A **71**	20p multicoloured (a)	. . . .	40	45
		a. Perf 14×15 (d)	. . . .	40	45
		ab. Booklet pane of 8	. . . .	3·25	

A **72a** Rock Pipit and
Sea Stock

A **72b** Sand Digger Wasp
and Sea Bindweed

A72	A **72**	24p multicoloured (a)	50	55
		a. Perf 14×15	50	55
		ab. Booklet pane of 8	3·75	
A72b	A **72a**	25p multicoloured (c)	50	55
		ba. Perf 14×15	50	55
		bb. Booklet pane of 8	4·00	
A72c	A **72b**	26p multicoloured (c)	50	55
A73	A **73**	30p multicoloured (a)	60	65
A74	A **74**	40p multicoloured (a)	80	85
A75	A **75**	50p multicoloured (a)	1·00	1·25
A76	A **76**	£1 multicoloured (a)	2·00	2·25
A77	A **77**	£2 multicoloured (b)	4·00	4·50
A60/77		Set of 21	11·50	13·00
		First Day Covers (5)		17·00
		Presentation Packs (3)	14·00	
		Stamp-cards (set of 21)	4·50	18·00
		Set of 21 Gutter Pairs	23·00	

Nos. A70a, A70ba, A71a, A72a and A72ba were only issued in booklets with the upper and lower edges of the panes imperforate.

Printings: (a) 5.5.94; (b) 28.2.95; (c) 2.1.97; (d) 25.3.98

Plate Nos.: 1p, 3p, 5p, 7p, 9p, 16p, 18p, 20p, 25p, 26p, 40p 1A, 1B (each ×4); 2p, 4p, 6p, 8p, 10p, 24p, 30p, 50p 1C, 1D (each ×4); £1, £2 1A, 1B, 1C, 1D (each ×4)

Sheets: 50 (2 panes 5 × 5)

Imprint: £1, £2 Central left margin of each pane; others central left or right margin of each pane

Sold out: 4.2001 (16p)

A **78** Royal Aircraft Factory SE5A

A**79** Miles Master II and other Miles Aircraft

A **80** Miles Aerovan and Miles Monitor

A **81** Miles Falcon Six winning King's Cup Air Race, 1935

A **82** Miles Hawk Speed Six winning Manx Air Derby, 1947

A**83** Miles Falcon Six breaking U.K.–Cape Record, 1936

Birth Centenary of Tommy Rose (aviator)

(Des C. Abbott. Litho B.D.T.)

1995 (1 SEPT). Perf 14×15 (C)

A78	A **78**	35p multicoloured	95	95
		a. Horiz strip of 3. Nos. A78/80	2·75	2·75
A79	A **79**	35p multicoloured	95	95
A80	A **80**	35p multicoloured	95	95
A81	A **81**	41p multicoloured	1·10	1·10
		a. Horiz strip of 3. Nos. A81/3 .	3·25	3·25
A82	A **82**	41p multicoloured	1·10	1·10
A83	A **83**	41p multicoloured	1·10	1·10
A78/83		Set of 6	6·00	6·00
		First Day Cover		6·75
		Presentation Pack	6·50	
		Gutter strips of 6 (2)	12·00	

Plate Nos.: Both values 1A, 1B, 1C (each ×5)

Sheets: 12 (2 panes 3×2). Nos. A78/80 and A81/3 were printed together, se-tenant, as horizontal strips of 3 throughout the sheet

Imprint: Central, bottom margin

Quantities sold: 35p 361,895 strips; 41p 362,801 strips

Withdrawn: 31.8.96

RETURN OF THE ISLANDERS 15 DECEMBER 1945

A **84a** Returning Islanders
(*illustration reduced. Actual size* 93×70 *mm*)

50th Anniversary of Return of Islanders to Alderney

(Des C. Abbott. Litho B.D.T.)

1995 (16 NOV). *Sheet* 93×70 *mm. Perf* 13½ (C)
MSA84 A **84a**   £1.65 multicoloured . . . . . . 5·00   4·00
First Day Cover . . . .   4·50
Presentation Pack . . . . 5·50

Quantity sold: 139,665
Withdrawn: 15.11.96

A **85** Signallers training on Alderney

A **86** Communications Station, Falkland Islands

A **87** Dish Aerial and Land Rover, Gulf War

A **88** Service with United Nations

25th Anniversary of Adoption of 30th Signal Regiment by Alderney

(Des A. Theobald. Litho Walsall)

1996 (24 JAN). Perf 14 (C)
A85 A **85** 24p multicoloured . . . . 1·10   1·10
        a. Horiz strip of 4. Nos. A85/8 . 4·25   4·25
A86 A **86** 41p multicoloured . . . . 1·10   1·10
A87 A **87** 60p multicoloured . . . . 1·10   1·10

A88 A **88** 75p multicoloured . . . . 1·10   1·10
A85/8   *Set of* 4 . . . . 4·25   4·25
        First Day Cover . . . .   6·00
        Presentation Pack . . . . 6·75
        Gutter Strip of 8 . . . . 8·50

Plate Nos.: All values 1A, 1B, 1C, 1D, 1E, 1F (each x4)

Sheets: 16 (2 panes 4×2). Nos. A85/8 were printed in *se-tenant* strips of 4 across the sheet, each strip forming a composite design

Imprint: Central, bottom margin

Quantities sold: 24p 141,697; 41p 141,631; 60p 141,679; 75p 141,680

Withdrawn: 28.1.97

A **89** Cat with Butterfly

A **90** Blue and White on Table

A **91** Tabby Kitten grooming Blue and White Persian Kitten

A **92** Red Persian under Table

A **93** White Cat with Tortoiseshell in Toy Cart

A **94** Siamese playing with Wool

Cats

(Des P. le Vasseur. Litho B.D.T.)

1996 (19 JULY). Perf 13½ (C)
A89 A **89** 16p multicoloured 45   35
A90 A **90** 24p multicoloured 65   40
A91 A **91** 25p multicoloured 65   65
A92 A **92** 35p multicoloured 95   90

A93　A **93**　41p multicoloured . . . . 1·10　1·00
A94　A **94**　60p multicoloured . . . . 1·75　1·40
A89/94　　　Set of 6 . . . . 5·00　4·25
　　　　　First Day Cover . . . . 　　5·25
　　　　　Presentation Pack . . . . 6·00
　　　　　Set of 6 Gutter Pairs . . . . . . 10·00
MSA95　144×97 mm. Nos. A89/94 . . . . 6·00　6·00
　　　First Day Cover . . . . 　　6·75

Plate Nos.: All values 1A, 1B (each ×4)

Sheets: 50 (2 panes 5×5)

Imprint: Central, right-hand margin of top pane

Quantities sold: 16p 243,841; 24p 243,457; 25p 193,625; 35p 193,393; 41p 192,612; 60p 191,587; miniature sheet 83,144

Withdrawn: 18.7.97

A **95** Harold Larwood

A **96** John Arlott

A **97** Pelham J. Warner

A **98** W. G. Grace

A **99** John Wisden

150th Anniversary of Cricket on Alderney

(Des R. Ollington. Litho Walsall)

1997 (21 AUG). Perf 13½ (C)
A96　A **95**　18p multicoloured . . . . 50　30
A97　A **96**　25p multicoloured . . . . 65　35
A98　A **97**　37p multicoloured . . . . 1·00　1·25
A99　A **98**　43p multicoloured . . . . 1·25　1·50
A100　A **99**　63p multicoloured . . . . 1·60　1·75
A96/100　　Set of 5 . . . . 4·50　4·50
　　　　First Day Cover . . . . 　　5·00
　　　　Presentation Pack . . . . 5·50
　　　　Set of 5 Gutter Pairs . . . . . . 9·00
MSA101　190×75 mm. Nos. A96/100 and label . . . . 7·00　7·50
　　　　First Day Cover . . . . 　　7·75

Plate Nos.: All values 1A, 1B (each ×5)

Sheets: 50 (2 panes 5×5)

Imprint: Central, top and bottom margins

Quantities sold: 18p 240,010; 25p 246,765; 37p 146,969; 43p 146,886; 63p 148,816; miniature sheet 87,220

Withdrawn: 20.8.98

A **100** Railway under Construction

A**101** Ariadne (paddle steamer) at Anchor

A **102** Quarrying Stone

A **103** Quarry Railway

A **104** Queen Victoria and Prince Albert on Alderney

A **105** Royal Yacht Victoria and Albert and Guard of Honour

A **106** Railway Workers greet Queen Victoria

A **107** Royal Party in Railway Wagons

114

Garrison Island (1st series). 150th Anniversary of Harbour

(Des R. Carter. Litho Questa)

1997 (20 NOV)–**98**. Perf 14½×14 (C)

A102	A **100**	18p multicoloured		45	45
		a. Horiz pair. Nos. A102/3 . .		90	90
		b. Booklet pane. Nos. A102/5 with margins all round (10.11.98)		2·25	
		c. Booklet pane. Nos. A102/3 and A106/7 with margin round (10.11.98) .		2·25	
A103	A **101**	18p multicoloured		45	45
A104	A **102**	25p multicoloured		65	65
		a. Horiz pair. Nos. A104/5 . .		1·25	1·25
		b. Booklet pane. Nos. A104/5 and A108/9 with margins all round (10.11.98)		2·75	
A105	A **103**	25p multicoloured		65	65
A106	A **104**	26p multicoloured		70	70
		a. Horiz pair. Nos. A106/7 . .		1·40	1·40
		b. Booklet pane. Nos. A106/9 with margins all round (10.11.98)		3·00	
A107	A **105**	26p multicoloured		70	70
A108	A **106**	31p multicoloured		80	80
		a. Horiz pair. Nos. A108/9 . .		1·60	1·60
A109	A **107**	31p multicoloured		80	80
A102/9		Set of 8		4·75	4·75
		First Day Cover			5·50
		Presentation Pack		5·50	

See also Nos. A116/23, A132/9, A154/61 and A176/83.

Plate Nos.: All values 1A, 1B (each ×4)

Sheets: 20 (4×5), the two designs for each value printed together, se-tenant, in horizontal pairs throughout the sheets, each pair forming a composite design

Imprint: Central, side margins

Quantities sold: 18p 145,264; 25p 145,364; 26p 145,464; 31p 115,164

Withdrawn: 19.11.98

A **108** Modern Superlite Helmet and Wreck of *Point Law* (oil tanker)

A **109** Cousteau-Gagnan Demand Valve and Wreck of *Stella* (steamer)

A **110** Heinke Closed Helmet and *Liverpool* (full-rigged ship)

A **111** Siebe Closed Hemet

A **112** Deane Open Helmet

21st Anniversary of Alderney Diving Club

(Des Victoria Kinnersly. Litho B.D.T.)

1998 (10 FEB). Perf 13 (C)

A110	A **108**	20p multicoloured	60	40
A111	A **109**	30p multicoloured	85	85
A112	A **110**	37p multicoloured	1·00	1·10
A113	A **111**	43p multicoloured	1·30	1·30
A114	A **112**	63p multicoloured	1·90	1·90
A110/14		Set of 5	5·50	5·00
		First Day Cover		5·50
		Presentation Pack	6·00	
		Set of 5 Gutter Pairs	9·50	
MSA115		190×75 mm. Nos. A110/14 and label	5·25	5·25
		First Day Cover		6·00

Plate Nos.: All values 1A, 1B (each ×5)

Sheets: 50 (2 panes 5×5)

Imprint: Central, side margins

Withdrawn: 9.2.99

A **113** Alderney Post Office

A **114** Traders in Victoria Street

A **115** Court House

A**116** Police Station and Fire Engine

A **117** St. Anne's Church

A **118** Wedding Party at Albert Gate

A **119** *Courier* (ferry) at Braye Bay

A **120** Fishermen at Quay

Garrison Island (2nd series)

(Des R. Carter. Litho Questa)

1998 (10 NOV). Perf 14½×14 (C)

A116	A **113**	20p multicoloured	50	50
		a. Horiz pair. Nos. A116/17 .	1·00	1·00
		b. Booklet pane. Nos. A116/19 with margins all round	2·00	
		c. Booklet pane. Nos. A116/17 and A120/1 with margins all round	2·25	
A117	A **114**	20p multicoloured	50	50
A118	A **115**	25p multicoloured	60	60
		a. Horiz pair. Nos. A118/19 .	1·25	1·25
		b. Booklet pane. Nos. A118/19 and A122/3 with margins all round	3·00	
A119	A **116**	25p multicoloured	60	60
A120	A **117**	30p multicoloured	70	70
		a. Horiz pair. Nos. A120/1 .	1·40	1·40
		b. Booklet pane. Nos. A120/3 with margins all round . . .	3·00	
A121	A **118**	30p multicoloured	70	70

A122	A **119**	37p multicoloured	85	85
		a. Horiz pair. Nos. A122/3 . .	1·75	1·75
A123	A **120**	37p multicoloured	85	85
A116/23		Set of 8	4·75	4·75
		First Day Cover		5 60
		Presentation Pack	6·00	

Plate Nos.: 20p, 30p 1A (×4); 25p, 37p 1B (×4)

Sheets: 20 (4×5), the two designs for each value were printed together, *se-tenant*, in horizontal pairs throughout the sheets, each pair forming a composite design

Imprint: Central, side margins

Withdrawn: 9.11.99

A **121a** Stained Glass Window commemorating Mary Rogers (Chief Stewardess) (25p); *Stella* leaving Southampton (£1.75) (*illustration reduced. Actual size* 110×90 *mm*)

Centenary of the Wreck of Stella (mail steamer)

(Des Joanna Brehaut. Litho B.D.T.)

1999 (5 FEB). *Sheet* 110×90 *mm*. Perf 14 (C)

MSA124	A **121a**	25p, £1.75, multicoloured	5·00	6·00
		First Day Cover		6·50
		Presentation Pack	6·00	

Withdrawn: 3.2.2000

A **122** Solar Eclipse at 10.15 am

A **123** At 10.51 am

A **124** At 11.14 am

A **125** At 11.16 am

A **126** At 11.17 am

A **127** At 11.36 am

Total Eclipse of the Sun on 11 August

(Des Victoria Kinnersly. Litho Enschedé)

1999 (27 APR). Perf 13½×13 (C)

A125	A **122**	20p multicoloured	. . . .	50	50
A126	A **123**	25p multicoloured	. . . .	60	60
A127	A **124**	30p multicoloured	. . . .	70	70
A128	A **125**	38p multicoloured	. . . .	90	90
A129	A **126**	44p multicoloured	. . . .	1·00	1·40
A130	A **127**	64p multicoloured	. . . .	1·50	1·90
A125/30		Set of 6	. . . .	4·75	5·50
		First Day Cover	. . . .	6·25	
		Presentation Pack	. . . . . .	5·50	
		Set of 6 Gutter Pairs	. . . .	9·75	

MSA131 191×80 mm. Nos. A125/30 and
label . . . . 4·75 5·50
First Day Cover . . . . 7·00
Postcard . . . . 1·00

No. **MS**A131 also includes the 'PHILEXFRANCE '99', Paris, and the 'iBRA '99', Nuremberg, emblems on the sheet margin.

Plate Nos.: All values 1A, 1B (each ×4)
Sheets: 50 (2 panes 5×5)
Imprint: Central, side margins
Withdrawn: 26.4.2000

A **128** Field Gun and Crew, Fort Grosnez, c 1855

A **129** Parade of 9th Bn, Royal Garrison Artillery

A **130** The Arsenal, Fort Albert, c 1862

A **131** Royal Engineers loading Wagons

A **132** 2nd Bn, Royal Scots on Parade

A **133** Garrison at Work, Fort Tourgis, c 1865

A **134** Gun Emplacement, Fort Houmet Herbé, c 1870

A **135** Royal Alderney Artillery Militia loading Cannon

Garrison Island (3rd series). Forts

(Des R. Carter. Litho Questa)

1999 (19 OCT). Perf 14½×14 (C)

A132	A **128**	20p multicoloured		45	45
		a. Horiz pair. Nos. A132/3 . .		90	90
		b. Booklet pane. Nos. A132/5, with margins all round		1·75	
		c. Booklet pane. Nos. A13 and A138/9, with margins all round		2·25	
		d. Booklet pane. Nos. A13 and A136/7, with margins all round		2·00	
A133	A **129**	20p multicoloured		45	45
A134	A **130**	25p multicoloured		55	55
		a. Horiz pair. Nos. A134/5 . .		1·00	1·10
		b. Booklet pane. Nos. A134/7, with margins all round		2·25	
		c. Booklet pane. Nos. A13 and A138/9, with margins all round		2·50	
A135	A **131**	25p multicoloured		55	55
A136	A **132**	30p multicoloured		65	65
		a. Horiz pair. Nos. A136/7 . .		1·25	1·25
		b. Booklet pane. Nos. A136/9, with margins all round		2·75	
A137	A **133**	30p multicoloured		65	65
A138	A **134**	38p multicoloured		80	80
		a. Horiz pair. Nos. A138/9 . .		1·60	1·60
A139	A **135**	38p multicoloured		80	80
A132/9		Set of 8		4·50	4·50
		First Day Cover			5·50
		Presentation Pack		5·50	

Plate Nos.: All values 1A, 1B (each ×4)

Sheets: 20 (4×5), the two designs for each value were printed together, se-tenant, in horizontal pairs throughout the sheets, each pair forming a composite design

Imprint: Central, right-hand margin

Withdrawn: 18.10.2000

Nos. A142/5 include the W.W.F. emblem.

Booklet panes Nos. A140a and A141a show the upper and lower edges of the panes imperforate and have margins at left and right

Plate Nos.: All values 1A (×6)

Sheets: 10 (2×5) with enlarged illustrated margin at left

Imprint: Central, right-hand margin

Withdrawn: 3.2.2001

A **136** Peregrine Falcon attacking Ruddy Turnstone

A **137** Two Falcons and Prey

A **142** Wombles around Map of Alderney

A **143** Alderney and Shansi on Beach

A **138** Falcon guarding Eggs

A **139** Falcon feeding Young

A **144** Wellington by Lighthouse

A **145** Madame Cholet and Bungo having Picnic

A **140** Falcon and Prey

A **141** Two Young Falcons

A **146** Tomsk playing Golf

A **147** Orinoco at Airport

Endangered Species. Peregrine Falcon

(Des R. Gorringe. Litho Questa)

2000 (4 FEB). Perf 14½×14 (C)

A140	A **136**	21p multicoloured	50	45
		a. Booklet pane of 10	5·00	
A141	A **137**	26p multicoloured	55	55
		a. Booklet pane of 10	5·75	
A142	A **138**	34p multicoloured	80	75
A143	A **139**	38p multicoloured	85	80
A144	A **140**	44p multicoloured	1·20	1·00
A145	A **141**	64p multicoloured	1·50	1·50
A140/5		Set of 6	5·00	4·50
		First Day Cover		5·50
		Presentation Pack	5·50	

'A Wombling Holiday' (characters from children's television programme)

(Des Sally Diamond. Litho Questa)

2000 (28 APR). Perf 14½×14 (C)

A146	A **142**	21p multicoloured	45	45
A147	A **143**	26p multicoloured	55	55
A148	A **144**	36p multicoloured	75	75
A149	A **145**	40p multicoloured	90	85
A150	A **146**	45p multicoloured	1·10	95
A151	A **147**	65p multicoloured	1·50	1·40
A146/51		Set of 6	4·75	4·50
		First Day Cover		5·50
		Presentation Pack	5·50	
		Set of 6 Gutter Pairs	9·50	
MSA152	160×86 mm. Nos. A146/51		4·70	5·00
		First Day Cover		5·50

No. **MS**A152 also includes the logo for 'The Stamp Show 2000', International Stamp Exhibition, London, on the sheet margin.

Plate Nos.: All values 1A (×4)
Sheets: 50 (2 panes 5×5)
Imprint: Lower right-hand margin
Withdrawn: 27.4.2001

A **148a** Queen Elizabeth the Queen Mother on Alderney, 1984
(illustration reduced. Actual size 93×70 mm)

Queen Elizabeth the Queen Mother's 100th Birthday

(Des M. Whyte. Litho Walsall)

2000 (4 AUG). *Sheet 93×70 mm. Perf 13½ (C)*
MSA153   A **148a**   £1.50, multicoloured   4·00   3·75
                                 First Day Cover . . . .   4·50
                                 Presentation Pack . . . . .   4·50

Withdrawn: 3.8.2001

A **149** Regimental Boxing Tournament

A **150** Sports Day, Alderney Gala Week, 1924

A **151** Regimental Orchestra playing at Ball

A **152** Garrison Ball in Fort Albert Mess, 1873

A **153** Royal Engineers' Colour Party, 1859

A **154** Royal Artillery on Parade, Queen's 40th Birthday, 1859

A **155** Royal Artillery Guard of Honour

A**156** Arrival of Maj.-Gen. Marcus Slade, 1863

Garrison Island (4th series). Events

(Des R. Carter. Litho Cartor)

2000 (19 OCT). Perf 13 (C)

A154	A **149**	21p multicoloured		
		a. Horiz pair. Nos. A154/5. . .	45	45
		b. Booklet pane. Nos. A154/7	90	85
		with margins all round . . .		
		c. Booklet pane. Nos. A154/5	1·75	
		and A160/1 with margins		
		all round		
A155	A **150**	21p multicoloured	2·40	
A156	A **151**	26p multicoloured	45	45
		a. Horiz pair. Nos. A156/7 . .	55	55
		b. Booklet pane. Nos. A156/9	1·10	1·10
		with margins all round . . .	2·40	
A157	A **152**	26p multicoloured	55	55
A158	A **153**	36p multicoloured	75	75
		a. Horiz pair. Nos. 158/9 . . .	1·75	1·50
		b. Booklet pane. Nos.		
		A158/61 *with margins all*		
		round	3·00	
A159	A **154**	36p multicoloured	75	75
A160	A **155**	40p multicoloured	90	85
		a. Horiz pair. Nos. A160/1 . .	2·00	1·75
A161	A **156**	40p multicoloured	90	85
A154/61		*Set of 8*	5·00	4·75
		First Day Cover		6·25
		Presentation Pack	6·25	

Plate Nos.: All values 1A (×4)

Sheets: 20 (4×5), the two designs for each value were printed together, *se-tenant*, in horizontal pairs throughout the sheets, each pair forming a composite design

Imprint: Central, right-hand margin

Withdrawn: 18.10.2001

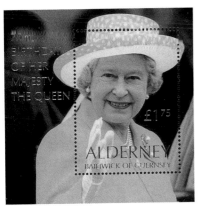

A **157a** Queen Elizabeth II

75th Birthday of Queen Elizabeth II

(Des C. Abbott. Litho and die-stamped. B.D.T.)

2001 (1 FEB). *Sheet 70×70 mm. Perf 14 (C)*
MSA162   A **157a**   £1.75, multicoloured ..   4·00   3·75
                                 First Day Cover . . . .   4·50
                                 Presentation Pack . . . . .   4·50

Withdrawn: 31.1.2002

A **158** Nurse with
Clipboard and
Patient in X-Ray

A **159** Nurse with Tray
and Mignot
Memorial
Hospital

A **160** Doctor and
Princess Anne
visiting Hospital,
1972

A **161** Nurse from
1960s and
Maternity Unit

A **162** Nurse from 1957
and Queen
Elizabeth II laying
Hospital
Foundation
Stone

A **163** Nurse of 1926
with Baby and
opening of
Original Hospital

Community Services (1st series). Healthcare

(Des Sally Diamond. Litho Walsall)

2001 (26 APR)–**02**. Perf 14×14½ (C)
A163   A **158**   22p multicoloured (a)   45   50
                       a. Perf 13½×13 (b)   60   80
                       ab. Booklet pane. Nos.
                       A163a/6a with margins all
                       round . . . .   3·00
                       ac. Booklet pane. Nos.
                       A163a/4a and A167a/8a
                       with margins all round . . .   3·90
A164   A **159**   27p multicoloured (a)   55   60
                       a. Perf 13½×13 (b)   55   60
A165   A **160**   36p multicoloured (a)   70   75
                       a. Perf 13½×13 (b)   70   75
                       ab. Booklet pane. Nos.
                       A165a/8a with margins all
                       round . . . .   3·90
A166   A **161**   40p multicoloured (a)   80   85
                       a. Perf 13½×13 (b) . . . .   1·00   1·20
A167   A **162**   45p multicoloured (a)   90   95
                       a. Perf 13½×13 (b) . . . .   1·30   1·50
A168   A **163**   65p multicoloured (a) . . . .   1·25   1·40
                       a. Perf 13½×13 (b) . . . .   1·50   2·00
A163/8   *Set of 6* . . . .   4·50   5·00
                   First Day Cover . . . .   5·75
                   Presentation Pack . . . . . .   5·75

Nos. A63a/8a were only issued in £9.40 stamp booklets.
See also Nos. A197/202.

Printings: (a) 26.4.01; (b) 17.10.02

Plate Nos.: All values 1A (×4)

Sheets: 10 (2×5) with enlarged illustrated margin at left (22, 27, 36p)
or right (40, 45, 65p)

Imprint: Central, right-hand margin (22, 27, 36p) or central, left-hand
margin (40, 45, 65p)

Withdrawn: 25.4.2002 (sheets)

A **164** 'Feathery'
Golf Ball,
1901

A **165** Golfing
Fashions of
the 1920s

A **166** Alderney
Golf Course
in 1970s

A **167** Modern
Putter

A **168** Modern
Golf Gloves
and Shoes

A **169** Modern
'lofted
wood'

30th Anniversary of Alderney Golf Club

(Des Colleen Corlett. Litho Questa)

2001 (1 AUG). Perf 14½ (C)

A169	A **164**	22p multicoloured	. . . .	45	50
A170	A **165**	27p multicoloured	. . . .	55	60
A171	A **166**	36p multicoloured	. . . .	80	75
A172	A **167**	40p multicoloured	. . . .	90	85
A173	A **168**	45p multicoloured	. . . .	1·00	95
A174	A **169**	65p multicoloured	. . . .	1·40	1·40
A169/74			Set of 6	5·00	5·00
			First Day Cover		5·75
			Presentation Pack	5·75	
			Set of 6 Gutter Pairs	9·00	
MSA175		190×75 mm. Nos. A169/74		5·00	5·50
			First Day Cover		6·50

No. **MS**A175 shows the 'Philanippon '01' logo on the margin.

Plate Nos.: All values 1A (×5)

Sheets: 50 (2 panes 5×5)

Imprint: Upper right-hand margin

Withdrawn: 31.7.2002

A **170** Construction of
New Breakwater,
1853

A **171** Official Party
inspecting Harbour,
1853

A **172** H.M.S. *Emerald*
(steam frigate)
aground, 1860

A **173** Disembarking
Troops from
H.M.S. *Emerald*,
1860

A **174** Moored Torpedo
Boats, 1890

A **175** Quick-firing Gun
on Railway
Wagon, 1890

A **176** H.M.S. *Majestic*
(battleship) at
Anchor, 1901

A **177** Torpedo Boats
outside Harbour,
1901

121

Garrison Island (5th series). The Royal Navy

(Des R. Carter. Litho Cartor)

2001 (16 OCT). Perf 13 (C)

A176	A **170**	22p multicoloured	45	50
		a. Horiz pair. Nos. A176/7	90	
		b. Booklet pane. Nos. A176/9 with margins all round	2·00	
		c. Booklet pane. Nos. A176/7 and A182/3 with margins all round	2·50	
A177	A **171**	22p multicoloured	45	50
A178	A **172**	27p multicoloured	55	60
		a. Horiz pair. Nos. A178/9	1·10	
		b. Booklet pane. Nos. A178/81 with margins all round	2·50	
		c. Booklet pane. Nos. A178/9 and A182/3 with margins all round	2·75	
A179	A **173**	27p multicoloured	55	60
A180	A **174**	36p multicoloured	70	75
		a. Horiz pair. Nos. A180/1	1·40	
		b. Booklet pane. Nos. A180/3 with margins all round	3·00	
A181	A **175**	36p multicoloured	70	75
A182	A **176**	40p multicoloured	80	85
		a. Horiz pair. Nos. A182/3	1·60	
A183	A **177**	40p multicoloured	80	85
A176/83		Set of 8	5·00	5·25
		First Day Cover		6·00
		Presentation Pack	6·00	

Plate Nos: All values 1A (×4)

Sheets: 20 (4 × 5), the two designs for each value were printed together, *se-tenant*, in horizontal pairs throughout the sheets, each pair forming a composite design

Imprint: Central, right-hand margin

Withdrawn: 15.10.2002.

A **178a** Queen Elizabeth and Prince Philip arriving at London Airport, Feb 1952
(*illustration reduced. Actual size* 159×98 *mm*)

Golden Jubilee

(Des A. Fothergill. Litho B.D.T.)

2002 (6 FEB). Sheet 159×98 mm. Perf 13½ (C)

MSA184	A **178a**	£2 blackish purple and gold	4·00	4·25
		First Day Cover		5·00
		Presentation Pack	5·00	

Withdrawn: 5.2.2003

A **179** Northern Hobby

A **180** Black Kite

A **181** Merlin

A **182** Honey Buzzard

A **183** Osprey

A **184** Marsh Harrier

Migrating Birds (1st series). Raptors

(Des G. Austin. Litho Questa)

2002 (30 APR). Perf 14 (C)

A185	A **179**	22p multicoloured	45	50
A186	A **180**	27p multicoloured	55	60
A187	A **181**	36p multicoloured	70	75
A188	A **182**	40p multicoloured	85	85
A189	A **183**	45p multicoloured	1·00	95
A190	A **184**	65p multicoloured	1·50	1·40
A185/90		Set of 6	5·00	5·00
		First Day Cover		5·75
		Presentation Pack	5·75	
MSA191		170×80 mm. Nos. A185/90	5·00	5·00
		First Day Cover		5·75

Plate Nos.: All values 1A (×4)

Sheets: 10 (2×5)

Imprint: Central, left-hand margin

Withdrawn: 29.4.2003

A **185** Coal Fire Beacon, 1725

A **186** Oil Lantern, 1779

A **187** Argand Lamp, 1790

A **188** Revolving Light, 1818

A 189 Electric Light, 1952

A **190** Ambulance Technician, and Ambulance Station

A **191** Ambulance Technician using Radio, and Ambulance

A **192** Doctor, and loading Patient onto Aircraft

A **193** Pilot, and Trislander over Alderney

A **194** Emergency Operator, and Patient on Stretcher

A **195** Lifeboatman, and *Roy Barker One* (lifeboat)

50th Anniversary of Electrification of Les Casquets Lighthouse

(Des N. Watton. Litho Enschedé)

2002 (30 JULY). Perf 13×13½ (C)

A192	A **185**	22p multicoloured	....	45	50
A193	A **186**	27p multicoloured	....	55	60
A194	A **187**	36p multicoloured	....	70	75
A195	A **188**	45p multicoloured	....	90	95
A196	A **189**	65p multicoloured	....	1·25	1·40
A192/6		*Set of 5*	....	3·75	4·00
		First Day Cover	....		5·00
		Presentation Pack	......	5·00	
		Set of 5 Gutter Pairs	....	7·75	

No. A196 is inscribed 'Elictrification' in error.

Plate Nos.: All values 1A (×4)

Sheets: 50 (2 panes 5×5)

Imprint: Lower left-hand margin

Withdrawn: 29.7.2003

Community Services (2nd series). Emergency Medical Aid

(Des Sally Diamond. Litho Walsall)

2002 (17 OCT). Perf 14×14½ (C)

A197	A **190**	22p multicoloured	....	45	50
		a. Perf 13½×13	....	45	50
		ab. Booklet pane. Nos. A197a/200a, with margins all round	....	2·50	
		ac. Booklet pane. Nos. A197a/8a and A200a/2a, with margins all round	...	3·75	
A198	A **191**	27p multicoloured	....	55	60
		a. Perf 13½×13	....	55	60
A199	A **192**	36p multicoloured	....	70	75
		a. Perf 13½×13	....	70	75
		ab. Booklet pane. Nos. A199a/202a, with margins all round	....	3·50	
A200	A **193**	40p multicoloured	....	80	85
		a. Perf 13½×13	....	80	85

A201	A **194**	45p multicoloured	. . . .	90	95
		a. Perf 13½×13	. . . .	90	95
A202	A **195**	65p multicoloured	. . . .	1·25	1·40
		a. Perf 13½×13	. . . .	1·25	1·40
A197/202		Set of 6	. . . .	4·50	5·00
		First Day Cover	. . . .		5·75
		Presentation Pack	. . . . . .	5·75	

Nos. A197a/202a were only issued in £9.40 stamp booklets.

Plate Nos.: All values 1A (×4)

Sheets: 10 (2×5) with enlarged illustrated margin at left

Imprint: Central, right-hand margin

Withdrawn: 16.10.2003

A **196** St. Edward's Crown
(illustration reduced. Actual size 128×90 mm)

50th Anniversary of Coronation

(Des A. Fothergill. Litho and embossed Enschedé)

2003 (30 JAN). Sheet 128×90 mm. Perf 13½ (C)

MSA203	A **196**	£2 multicoloured	. . . . . .	4·00	4·25
		First Day Cover	. . . .		6·50
		Presentation Pack	. . . . . .	6·50	

Withdrawn: 29.1.2004

A **197** Wright Brothers' Flyer
I, 1903

A **198** Alcock and Brown's
Vickers FB-27 Vimy,
1919

A **199** Douglas DC-3, 1936

A **200** De Havilland DH106
Comet 1, 1946

A **201** British Aerospace/
Aerospatiale
Concorde, 1969

A **202** Projected Airbus
Industrie A380

Centenary of Powered Flight

(Des M.Wilkinson. Litho B.D.T.)

2003 (10 APR). Perf 13½ (C)

A204	A **197**	22p multicoloured	. . . .	45	50
A205	A **198**	27p multicoloured	. . . .	55	60
A206	A **199**	36p multicoloured	. . . .	70	75
A207	A **200**	40p multicoloured	. . . .	80	85
A208	A **201**	45p multicoloured	. . . .	90	95
A209	A **202**	65p multicoloured	. . . .	1·25	1·40
A204/9		Set of 6	. . . .	4·50	5·00
		First Day Cover	. . . .		5·75
		Presentation Pack	. . . . . .	5·75	
		Set of 6 Gutter Pairs	. . . .	9·50	

Plate Nos.: All values 1A (×4)

Sheets: 50 (2 panes 5×5)

Imprint: Central, left-hand margin

Withdrawn: 9.4.2004

A **203** Arctic Tern

A **204** Great Skua

A **205** Sandwich Tern

A **206** Sooty
Shearwater

A **207** Arctic Skua

A **208** Manx
Shearwater

A **209** Policeman with
Clipboard and
Constables on Beat

A **210** Policeman and
Land Rover

A **211** Forensic Team

A **212** Police Constable
and Policeman
with Child Cyclist

A **213** Policeman directing
Traffic and Police at
Scene of Accident

A **214** Policewoman and
Policeman with
Customs Officer

Migrating Birds (2nd series). Seabirds.

(Des G. Austin. Litho Questa)

2003 (3 JULY). Perf 14 (C)

A210	A **203**	22p multicoloured	....	45	50
A211	A **204**	27p multicoloured	....	55	60
A212	A **205**	36p multicoloured	....	75	75
A213	A **206**	40p multicoloured	....	85	85
A214	A **207**	45p multicoloured	....	95	95
A215	A **208**	65p multicoloured	....	1·40	1·40
A210/15		*Set of 6*	....	5·00	5·00
		First Day Cover	....		5·75
		Presentation Pack	......	5·75	
MSA216		80×170 mm. Nos. A210/15	....	5·00	5·00
		First Day Cover	....		5·75

Plate Nos.: All values 1A (×4)

Sheets: 10 (2×5) with enlarged illustrated margin at right

Imprint: Central, left-hand margin

Withdrawn: 2.7.2004

Community Services (3rd series). Alderney Police

(Des Sally Diamond. Litho Walsall)

2003 (16 OCT). Perf 13½×13 (C)

A217	A **209**	22p multicoloured	....	45	50
		a. Booklet pane. Nos.			
		A217/20	....	2·50	
		b. Booklet pane. Nos.			
		A217/18 and A221/2	...	3·25	
		c. Booklet pane. Nos.			
		A217/19 and A221	.....	2·75	
		d. Booklet pane. Nos.			
		A217/18, A220 and A222			
				3·00	
A218	A **210**	27p multicoloured	....	55	60
A219	A **211**	36p multicoloured	....	70	75
		a. Booklet pane. Nos.			
		A219/22	....		
A220	A **212**	40p multicoloured	....	80	85
A221	A **213**	45p multicoloured	....	90	95
A222	A **214**	65p multicoloured	....	1·25	1·40
A217/22		*Set of 6*	....	4·50	5·00
		First Day Cover	....		6·00
		Presentation Pack	......	6·00	

Plate Nos.: All values 1A (×4)

Sheets: 10 (2×5) with enlarged illustrated margin at left

Imprint: Central, right-hand margin

Withdrawn: 15.10.2004

A **215** *Hypholoma fasciculare*

A **216** *Aleuria aurantia*

A **217** *Coprinus micaceus*

A **218** *Langermannia gigantea*

A **219** *Macrolepiota procera*

A **220** *Xylaria hypoxylon*

A **221** Boys playing Football, Tourgis Close

A **222** Three Children playing Football, Braye Beach

A **223** Two Boys playing Football in Playground

A **224** Teenagers playing Football, Arch Bay

A **225** Football Match

A **226** Father and Two Children playing Football, Arch Bay

Fungi

(Des Petula Stone. Litho Enschedé)

2004 (29 JAN). Perf 13½ (C)

A223	A **215**	22p multicoloured	70	70
A224	A **216**	27p multicoloured	85	85
A225	A **217**	36p multicoloured	1·20	1·20
A226	A **218**	40p multicoloured	1·30	1·30
A227	A **219**	45p multicoloured	1·40	1·40
A228	A **220**	65p multicoloured	2·10	2·10
A223/8		*Set of* 6	7·50	7·50
		First Day Cover		9·75
		Presentation Pack	9·75	
		Set of 6 *Gutter Pairs*	12·00	

Plate Nos.: All values 1A (×4)

Sheets: 50 (2 panes 5×5)

Imprint: Upper side margins

Withdrawn: 28.1.2005

Centenary of FIFA (Fédération Internationale de Football Association)

(Des A. Robinson. Litho Cartor)

2004 (12 MAY). Perf 13½ (C)

A229	A **221**	26p multicoloured	85	85
A230	A **222**	32p multicoloured	1·10	1·10
A231	A **223**	36p multicoloured	1·20	1·20
A232	A **224**	40p multicoloured	1·30	1·30
A233	A **225**	45p multicoloured	1·50	1·50
A234	A **226**	65p multicoloured	2·10	2·10
A229/34		*Set of* 6	8·00	8·00
		First Day Cover		10·00
		Presentation Pack	10·00	

Nos. A229/34 were each perforated in a circle contained within an outer perforated square which continued the design.

Plate Nos.: All values 1A (×4)

Sheets: 50 (5×10)

Imprint: Upper and lower side margins

Withdrawn: 11.5.2005

A **227** Northern
Wheatear

A **228** Common
Redstart

A **233** Fire Engine

A **234** Fireman up
Ladder and Fire
Engine at Fort
Tourgis

A **229** Yellow Wagtail

A **230** Hoopoe

A **235** Airport Service
Fire Truck

A **236** Alderney Fire
Station

A **231** Ring Ousel
('Ouzel')

A **232** Sand Martin

A **237** Airport Training
Ground

A **238** Road Accident
Training Exercise

Migrating Birds (3rd series). Passerines

(Des A. Robinson. Litho Enschedé)

2004 (29 JULY). Perf 13½ (C)

A235	A **227**	26p multicoloured	85	85
A236	A **228**	32p multicoloured	1·10	1·10
A237	A **229**	36p multicoloured	1·20	1·20
A238	A **230**	40p multicoloured	1·30	1·30
A239	A **231**	45p multicoloured	1·50	1·50
A240	A **232**	65p multicoloured	2·10	2·10
A235/40		Set of 6	8·00	8·00
		First Day Cover		10·00
		Presentation Pack	10·00	
MSA241	170×80 mm. Nos. A235/40		8·00	8·00
		First Day Cover		10·00

Plate Nos.: All values 1A, 1B, 1C, 1D (each ×4)

Sheets: 10 (2×5) with enlarged illustrated right-hand margin

Imprint: Central, left-hand margin

Withdrawn: 28.7.2005

Community Services (4th series). Fire Service

(Des M. Legg. Litho Walsall)

2004 (28 OCT). Perf 13½ ×13 (C)

A242	A **233**	26p multicoloured	85	85
		a. Booklet pane. Nos. A242/5 with margins all round	4·50	
		b. Booklet pane. Nos. A242/3 and A246/7 with margins all round	5·50	
		c. Booklet pane. Nos. A242/4 and A246 with margins all round	4·50	
		d. Booklet pane. Nos. A242/3, A245 and A247 with margins all round	5·50	
A243	A **234**	32p multicoloured	1·10	1·10
A244	A **235**	36p multicoloured	1·20	1·20
		a. Booklet pane. Nos. A244/7 with margins all round	6·00	

A245	A **236**	40p multicoloured	....	1·30	1·30
A246	A **237**	45p multicoloured	....	1·50	1·50
A247	A **238**	65p multicoloured	....	2·10	2·10
A242/7		Set of 6	....	0·00	8·00
		First Day Cover	....		10·00
		Presentation Pack	...... 10·00		

Plate Nos.: All values 1A×4

Sheets: 10 (2×5) with enlarged illustrated left-hand margin

Imprint: Central, right-hand margin

STAMP BOOKLETS

PRICES given are for complete booklets.

AB **1** Common Blue and Pyramidal Orchid
(*illustration reduced. Actual size* 99×60 *mm*)

1994 (5 MAY)–**95**. *Multicoloured covers as Type* AB **1**. *Without barcode on the reverse. Panes attached by selvedge*
ASB1 £1.28 booklet containing pane No. A70*ab*
(*cover Type* AB **1**) .... 4·00
    a. With barcode sticker on reverse (1995) ... 7·00
ASB2 £1.92 booklet containing pane No. A72*ab*
(*cover showing Great Black-backed Gull and Sand Crocus*) .... 3·75

1997 (2 JAN). *Multicoloured covers as Type* AB **1**. *Without barcode on the reverse. Panes attached by selvedge*
ASB3 £1.44 booklet containing pane No. A70*bb*
(*cover showing Small Tortoiseshell* (*butterfly*) *and Buddleia*) .... 3·00
ASB4 £2 booklet containing pane No. A72*bb* (*cover showing Rock Pipit and Sea Stock*) .... 4·00
Sold out: 9.99 (No. ASB3)

1998 (25 MAR). *Multicoloured cover as Type* AB **1**. *With barcode on the reverse. Pane attached by selvedge*
ASB5 £1.60 booklet containing pane No. A71*ab*
(*cover showing Common Rabbit and Creeping Buttercup*) .... 3·25

AB **2** Map of Alderney
(*illustration reduced. Actual size* 164×98 *mm*)

Garrison Island (1st and 2nd series)

1998 (10 NOV). *Multicoloured cover as Type AB* **2** *containing text and illustrations on panes and interleaving pages. Stitched*
ASB6 £8.48 booklet containing panes Nos. A102*b/c*, A104*b*, A106*b*, A116*b/c*, A118*b* and 120*b* .. 20·00
Withdrawn: 9.11.99

Garrison Island (3rd series). Forts

1999 (19 OCT). *Multicoloured cover as Type AB* **2** *containing text and illustrations on panes and interleaving pages. Stitched*
ASB7 £6.78 booklet containing panes Nos. A132*b/d*, A134*b/c*. and A136*b* (*cover showing view of fortified coastline*) . . . . 13·00
Withdrawn: 18.10.2000

AB **3** Peregrine Falcon
(*illustration reduced*). *Actual size 105×60 mm*)

Endangered Species. Peregrine Falcon

2000 (4 FEB). *Multicoloured covers as Type AB* **3**. *Panes attached by selvedge*
ASB8 £2.10 booklet containing pane No. A140*a* (*cover Type AB* **3**) . . . . 5·00
ASB9 £2.60 booklet containing pane No. A141*a* (*cover showing falcon with prey*) . . . . 5·75
Withdrawn: 3.2.2001

Garrison Island (4th series). Events

2000 (19 OCT). *Multicoloured cover as Type AB* **2** *containing text and illustrations on panes and interleaving pages. Stitched.*
ASB10 £7.38 booklet containing panes Nos. A154*b*, A154*c*×2, A156*b*×2 and A158*b* (*cover showing Braye Road with Fort Albert in the distance*) . . . . 14·50
Withdrawn: 18.10.2001

Garrison Island (5th series). The Royal Navy

2001 (16 OCT). *Multicoloured cover as Type AB* **2** *containing text and illustrations on panes and interleaving pages. Stitched.*
ASB11 £7.50 booklet containing panes Nos. A176*b*, A176*c*×2, A178*b/c*, and A180*b* (cover showing Alderney Harbour) . . . . 15·00
Withdrawn: 15.10.2002

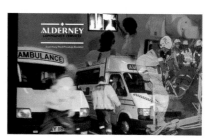

AB **4** Medical and Rescue Services
(*illustration reduced*. *Actual size 162×98 mm*)

Community Services (1st and 2nd series)

2002 (17 OCT). *Multicoloured cover as Type AB* **4** *containing text and illustrations on panes and interleaving pages. Stitched.*
ASB12 £9.40 booklet containing panes Nos. A163*ab/ac*, A165*ab*, A197*ab/ac* and A199*ab* . 19·00
Withdrawn: 16.10.2003

Community Services (3rd series)

(Des M. Legg)

2003 (16 OCT). *Multicoloured cover as Type AB* **4** *containing text and illustrations on panes and interleaving pages. Stitched.*
ASB13 £9.40 booklet containing panes Nos. A217*a/d* and A219*a* . . . . 19·00
Withdrawn: 15.10.2004

Community Services (4th series)

(Des M. Legg)

2004 (28 OCT). *Multicoloured cover as Type AB* **4** *containing text and illustrations on panes and interleaving pages. Stitched.*
ASB14 £9.76 booklet containing panes Nos. A242*a/d* and A244*a*×2 . . . . 32·00

Isle of Man

REGIONAL ISSUES

Although specifically issued for regional use, these issues were initially valid for use throughout the U.K. Regional issues ceased to be valid in the Isle of Man from 5 July 1973 when the island established its own independent postal administration and introduced its own stamps.

DATES OF ISSUE. Conflicting dates of issue have been announced for some of the regional issues, partly explained by the stamps being released on different dates by the Philatelic Bureau in Edinburgh or the Philatelic Counter in London and in the regions. We have adopted the practice of giving the earliest known dates, since once released the stamps could have been used anywhere in the U.K.

INVALIDATION. Nos. 1/7 were invalidated as from 1 March 1972 in common with other British 'fsd' stamps. Nos. 8/11 were invalidated for use in the Isle of Man on 5 July 1973, but, together with other British stamps, were accepted for the prepayment of postage on letters from the island until 5 August 1973. The Manx Regionals remained valid for use in the rest of the United Kingdom and were withdrawn from sale at the British Post Office Philatelic Sales counters on 4 July 1974.

1 Multiple Crowns

2

3

(Des J. Nicholson. Portrait by Dorothy Wilding Ltd. Photo Harrison)

1958–68. Wmk Type **1**. Perf 15×14 (C)

1	**2**	2½d carmine-red (8.6.64)		40	1·25
2	**3**	3d deep lilac (18.8.58)		20	20
		a. Chalk-surfaced paper (17.5.63)		10·00	10·00
		p. One centre phosphor band (27.6.68)		20	50
3		4d ultramarine (7.2.66)		1·40	1·40
		p. Two phosphor bands (5.7.67) .		20	30
1/3p		Set of 3		70	1·60
1		First Day Cover			45·00
2		First Day Cover			32·00
3		First Day Cover			10·00

Cylinder Nos.: 2½d 1; 3d (ord and phos) 1; 4d (ord and phos) 1

Sheets; 240 (12×20)

Quantities sold (ordinary only): 2½d 4,298,160; 3d 35,959,420 (up to 31.3.68 and including 1,080,000 on chalky paper); 4d 1,363,840

Withdrawn: 31.8.66 2½d

Sold out: 11.67 4d ordinary; 12.68 3d ordinary, 4d phosphor; 4.69 3d phosphor

1968–69. No wmk. Chalk-surfaced paper. One centre phosphor band (Nos. 5/6) or two phosphor bands (others). Perf 15×14 (C)

4	**3**	4d blue (24.6.68)		25	30
5		4d olive-sepia (4.9.68)		25	40
6		4d bright vermilion (26.2.69)		45	75
7		5d royal blue (4.9.68)		45	75
4/7		Set of 4		1·25	2·00
5, 7		First Day Cover			4·00

Cylinder Nos.: 4d (blue) 1; 4d (olive-sepia) 1; 4d (bright vermilion) 1; 5d 1

Sheets: 240 (12×20)

Sold out: 16.7.69 4d blue

Withdrawn: 14.3.71 (locally), 25.11.71 (British Philatelic Counters) 4d

4

Decimal Currency

(Des J. Matthews. Portrait after plaster cast by Arnold Machin. Photo Harrison)

1971 (7 JULY). Chalk-surfaced paper. One centre phosphor band (2½p) or two phosphor bands (others). Perf 15×14 (C)

8	**4**	2½p bright magenta		20	15
9		3p ultramarine		20	15
10		5p reddish violet		40	60
11		7½p chestnut		40	75
8/11		Set of 4		1·10	1·50
		First Day Cover			3·00
		Presentation Pack		2·75	

All values were originally issued on ordinary cream paper, but the 2½p and 3p later appeared on white fluorescent paper.

Cylinder Nos.: (dot and no dot): 2½p 3, phos 5; 3p 1, phos 4; 5p 4, phos 12; 7½p 4, phos 10

Sheets: 200 (10×20)

Withdrawn: 4.7.73 (locally), 4.7.74 (British Philatelic Counters)

INDEPENDENT POSTAL ADMINISTRATION

The Isle of Man established an independent postal administration on 5 July 1973 and introduced its own stamps.

NO WATERMARK. All the following issues are on unwatermarked paper *unless otherwise stated*.

5 Castletown

6 Port Erin

7 Snaefell

8 Laxey

9 Tynwald Hill

10 Douglas Promenade

11 Port St. Mary

12 Fairy Bridge

13 Peel

14 Cregneish

15 Ramsey Bay

16 Douglas Bay

17 Manx Cat

18 Monk's Bridge, Ballasalla

19 Derbyhaven

20 Manx Loaghtyn Ram

21 Manx Shearwater

22 Viking Longship

(Des J. Nicholson. Photo Courvoisier)

1973 (5 JULY)**–75**. *Granite paper.* Perf 11½ (C)

12	**5**	½p multicoloured (*ab*)	10	10
13	**6**	1p multicoloured (*ae*)	10	10
14	**7**	1½p multicoloured (*ak*)	10	10
15	**8**	2p multicoloured (*aj*)	10	10
16	**9**	2½p multicoloured (*a*)	10	10
17	**10**	3p mult (*sage-green border*) (*ac*) .	10	10
		a. Error. Olive-bistre border † . . .	£150	£100
18	**11**	3½p mult (*olive-brown border*) (*ad*) .	10	10
		a. Error. Grey-brown border † . . .	£150	£100
19	**12**	4p multicoloured (*a*)	10	10
20	**9**	4½p multicoloured (*f*)	20	15
21	**13**	5p multicoloured (*ah*)	15	10
22	**10**	5½p multicoloured (*g*)	20	15
23	**14**	6p multicoloured (*al*)	20	15
24	**8**	7p multicoloured (*g*)	20	15
25	**15**	7½p multicoloured (*a*)	20	20
26		8p multicoloured (*f*)	25	25

27	**16**	9p multicoloured (an)	20	20
20	**17**	10p multicoloured (an)	35	20
29	**18**	11p multicoloured (i)	35	30
30	**19**	13p multicoloured (i)	40	35
31	**20**	20p multicoloured (an)	50	50
32	**21**	50p multicoloured (an)	1·00	1·10
33	**22**	£1 multicoloured (am)	2·00	2·00
12/33		*Set of 22*	6·00	6·00
		First Day Cover (7)		7·75
		Presentation Pack (6)	9·00	

†These errors occur on printings (c) and (d). That on the 3p resembles the border colour of the ½p and that on the 3½p the 2p. Intermediate shades also exist, but are not covered by the listing.

Printings: (a) 5.7.73; (b) 1.11.73; (c) 16.4.74; (d) 29.7.74; (e) 2.9.74; (f) 8.1.75; (g) 28.5.75; (h) 16.6.75; (i) 29.10.75; (j) 1.12.75; (k) 2.2.76; (l) 20.9.76; (m) 16.2.77; (n) 7.7.77

Printings (a) and (i) have thick shiny gum, but all the other printings have matt, almost invisible gum. Printings (f), (g) and (i) are inscribed '1975'. The remainder are inscribed '1973'.

Sheets: 50 (5×10) ½p to 9p, 11p, 13p; (10×5) 10p, 20p to £1

Withdrawn: 31.12.78 (except ½p, 3p and 3½p values in booklets withdrawn 15.5.79. In addition 2p and 3½p values were kept available for use on postal orders after 31.12.78 until finally withdrawn on 30.6.83 (2p) or 31.12.85 (3½p))

23 Landing of the Vikings on Man, A.D. 938

Inauguration of Postal Independence

(Des J. Nicholson. Photo Harrison)

1973 (5 JULY). Perf 14 (C)

34	**23**	15p multicoloured	35	30
		First Day Cover		1·10
		Presentation Pack	1·40	

For 15p inscr 'POST OFFICE DECENNIUM 1983' see No. 256.

Cylinder Nos.: 1A (×4)

Sheets: 50 (10×5)

Quantity sold: 350,000

Sold out: Soon after issue

24 No. 1 *Sutherland*, 1873　　**25** No. 4 *Caledonia*, 1885

26 No. 13 *Kissack*, 1910

27 No. 3 *Pender*, 1873

Steam Railway Centenary

(Des J. Nicholson. Photo Harrison)

1973 (4 AUG). Perf 15×14 (C)

35	**24**	2½p multicoloured	15	10
36	**25**	3p multicoloured	15	15
37	**26**	7½p multicoloured	25	25
38	**27**	9p multicoloured	25	25
35/8		*Set of 4*	70	70
		First Day Cover		1·90
		Presentation Pack	1·50	

Cylinder Nos.: All values 1A (×5)

Sheets: 50 (5×10)

Quantities sold: 2½p 617,122; 3p 808,173; 7½p 331,695; 9p 324,414

Withdrawn: 3.8.74

28 Leonard Randles, First Winner, 1923

29 Alan Holmes, Double Winner, 1957

Golden Jubilee of Manx Grand Prix

(Des J. Nicholson. Litho John Waddington)

1973 (4 SEPT). Perf 14 (C)

39	**28**	3p multicoloured	10	10
40	**29**	3½p multicoloured	15	15
39/40		*Set of 2*	25	25
		First Day Cover		90
		Presentation Pack	70	
		Set of 2 Gutter Pairs	60	

Plate Nos.: Both values 1A, 1B, 1C, 1D (each ×4)

Sheets: 50 (2 panes 5×5)

Imprint: Central, bottom margin

Quantities sold: 3p 550,347; 3½p 653,355

Withdrawn: 3.9.74

30 Princess Anne and Capt. Mark Philips

35 Stanley Woods, 1935

Royal Wedding

(Des A. Larkins and litho De La Rue)

1973 (14 NOV). Perf 13½ (C)

41	**30**	25p multicoloured	45	50
		First Day Cover		85
		Presentation Pack	90	
		Gutter Pair	90	

Plate Nos.: 1A, 1B (each ×4)

Sheets: 50 (5 panes 5×5)

Imprint: Right-hand corner, bottom margin

Quantity sold: 400,813

Withdrawn: 13.11.74

36 Freddy Frith, 1937

31 Badge, Citation and Sir William Hillary (founder)

32 Wreck of *St. George*, 1830

37 Max Deubel and Emil Horner, 1961

33 *Manchester & Salford*, 1868–87

34 *Osman Gabriel*

38 Mike Hailwood, 1961

150th Anniversary of Royal National Institution

(Des J. Nicholson. Photo Courvoisier)

1974 (4 MAR). *Granite paper.* Perf 11½ (C)

42	**31**	3p multicoloured	10	10
43	**32**	3½p multicoloured	15	10
44	**33**	8p multicoloured	25	25
45	**34**	10p multicoloured	30	25
42/5		Set of 4	70	60
		First Day Cover		1·00
		Presentation Pack	1·00	

Sheets: 100 (10×10)

Quantities sold: 3p 674,984; 3½p 849,990; 8p 374,941; 10p 375,043

Withdrawn: 3.3.75

Tourist Trophy Motor Cycle Races (1st issue)

(Des J. Nicholson. Litho De La Rue)

1974 (29 MAY). Perf 13×13½ (C)

46	**35**	3p multicoloured	10	10
47	**36**	3½p multicoloured	10	10
48	**37**	8p multicoloured	25	20
49	**38**	10p multicoloured	25	20
46/9		Set of 4	60	55
		First Day Cover		1·00
		Presentation Pack	1·00	
		Set of 4 Gutter Pairs	1·25	

See also Nos. 63/6.

Plate Nos.: All values 1A, 1B, 1C, 1D (each ×6); 3p also 1A (×4)–2A–2A, 1B (×4)–2B–2B, 1C (×4)–2C–2C, 1D (×4)–2D–2D; 8p also 1A–1A–2A–1A (×3), 1B–1B–2B–1B (×3), 1C–1C–2C–1C (×3), 1D–1D–2D–1D (×3)

Sheets: 50 (2 panes 5×5)

Imprint: Right-hand corner, bottom margin

Quantities sold: 3p 578,045; 3½p 816,235; 8p 334,760; 10p 403,177

Withdrawn: 28.5.75

39 Rushen Abbey and Arms

40 Magnus Haraldson rows King Edgar on the Dee

41 King Magnus and Norse Fleet

42 Bridge at Avignon and Bishop's Mitre

Historical Anniversaries. Events described on stamps

(Des J. Nicholson, from ideas by G. Kneale. Litho Questa (3½p, 10p) or John Waddington (others))

1974 (18 SEPT). Perf 14 (C)

50	**39**	3½p multicoloured	10	10
51	**40**	4½p multicoloured	10	10
52	**41**	8p multicoloured	15	15
53	**42**	10p multicoloured	20	20
50/3		*Set of 4*	50	50
		First Day Cover		85
		Presentation Pack	85	
		Set of 4 Gutter Pairs	1·00	

Plate Nos.: All values 1A, 1B, 1C, 1D (each ×4)

Sheets: 50 (2 panes 5×5)

Imprint: Right-hand corner, bottom margin and left-hand corner, top margin

Quantities sold: 3½p 931,610; 4½p 1,025,044; 8p 450,418; 10p 425,305

Withdrawn: 17.9.75

43 Churchill and Bugler Dunne at Colenso, 1899

44 Churchill and Government Buildings, Douglas

45 Churchill and Manx A.A Gun Crew

46 Churchill as Freeman of Douglas

Birth Centenary of Sir Winston Churchill

(Des G. Kneale. Photo Courvoisier)

1974 (22 NOV). *Granite paper*. Perf 11½ (C)

54	**43**	3½p multicoloured	10	10
55	**44**	4½p multicoloured	10	10
56	**45**	8p multicoloured	15	15
57	**46**	20p multicoloured	30	25
54/7		*Set of 4*	60	55
		First Day Cover		85
		Presentation Pack	1·40	
MS58		121×91 mm. Nos. 54/7	75	75
		First Day Cover		1·25

No. **MS**58 is inscribed '30th NOV. 1974.

Sheets: 25 (5×5)

Quantities sold: 3½p 916,748; 4½p 853,537; 8p 424,691; 20p 429,586; miniature sheet 362,089

Withdrawn: 21.11.75

47 Cabin School and Names of Pioneers

48 Terminal Tower Building, John Gill and Robert Carran

49 Robert and Margaret Clague, and Clague House Museum

50 *William T. Graves* and Thomas Quayle

Manx Pioneers in Cleveland, Ohio

(Des J. Nicholson. Photo Courvoisier)

1975 (14 MAR). *Granite paper*. Perf 11½ (C)

59	**47**	4½p multicoloured		10	10
60	**48**	5½p multicoloured		10	10
61	**49**	8p multicoloured		15	15
62	**50**	10p multicoloured		25	25
59/62		Set of 4		55	55
		First Day Cover			75
		Presentation Pack		80	

Sheets: 50 (5×10)

Quantities sold: 4½p 473,352; 5½p 999,802; 8p 433,352; 10p 447,945

Withdrawn: 13.3.76 (5½p sold out 12.75)

51 Tom Sheard, 1923

52 Walter Handley, 1925

53 Geoff Duke, 1955

54 Peter Williams, 1973

Tourist Trophy Motor Cycle Races (2nd issue)

(Des J. Nicholson. Litho John Waddington)

1975 (28 MAY). Perf 13½ (C)

63	**51**	5½p multicoloured		10	10
64	**52**	7p multicoloured		15	15
65	**53**	10p multicoloured		15	15
66	**54**	12p multicoloured		25	20
63/6		Set of 4		60	55
		First Day Cover			2·40
		Presentation Pack		1·00	
		Set of 4 Gutter Pairs		1·25	

Plate Nos.: 5½p, 7p 1B, 1D (each ×5); 10p 1A, 1B, 1C (each ×5); 12p 1A, 1C (each ×5)

Sheets: 50 (2 panes 5×5)

Imprint: Right-hand corner, bottom margin

Quantities sold: 5½p 633,250; 7p 520,285; 10p 399,710; 12p 440,208

Withdrawn: 27.5.76

55 Goldie and the Nunnery, Douglas

56 Goldie and Map of Africa

57 Goldie and Royal Geographical Society Emblem

58 River Scene on the Niger

50th Death Anniversary of Sir George Goldie

(Des G. Kneale. Photo Courvoisier)

1975 (9 SEPT). *Granite paper*. Perf 11½ (C)

67	**55**	5½p multicoloured		10	10
68	**56**	7p multicoloured		15	15
69	**57**	10p multicoloured		15	15
70	**58**	12p multicoloured		25	25
67/70		Set of 4		65	65
		First Day Cover			90
		Presentation Pack		1·00	

Sheets: 50 (10×5) 7p, 10p; (5×10) others

Quantities sold: 5½p 488,317; 7p 426,849; 10p 373,771; 12p 439,843

Withdrawn: 8.9.76

59 Title Page of Manx Bible

60 Rev. Philip Moore and Ballaugh Old Church

61 Bishop Hildesley and Bishops Court

62 John Kelly saving Bible Manuscript

Christmas and Bicentenary of Manx Bible

(Des J. Nicholson. Litho Quocta)

1975 (29 OCT). Perf 14 (C)

71	**59**	5½p multicoloured	10	10
72	**60**	7p multicoloured	15	15
73	**61**	11p multicoloured	20	20
74	**62**	13p multicoloured	25	25
71/4		Set of 4	60	60
		First Day Cover		85
		Presentation Pack	1·00	
		Set of 4 Gutter Pairs	1·25	

Plate Nos. 13p 1C, 1D (each ×4); others 1A, 1B (each ×4)

Sheets: 50 (2 panes 5×5)

Quantities sold: 5½p 738,774; 7p 607,377; 11p 405,126; 13p 402,463

77	**65**	13p multicoloured	30	30
		a. Black (face value and inscr) printed double		
78	**66**	20p multicoloured . . . .,	35	35
75/8		Set of 4	60	80
		First Day Cover		90
		Presentation Pack	1·00	
		Set of 4 Gutter Pairs	1·20	
MS79		150×90 mm. Nos. 75/8. Perf 14 (C) .	80	1·00
		First Day Cover		3·75
		Presentation Pack	1·90	

Plate Nos.: 5½p, 20p 1A, 1C (each x4); others 1B, 1D (each ×4)

Sheets: 50 (2 panes 5×5)

Quantities sold: 5½p 487,310; 7p 524,144; 13p 558,348; 20p 424,728; miniature sheet 209,367

Withdrawn: 11.3.77

63 William Christian listening to Patrick Henry

64 Conveying the Fincastle Resolutions

65 Patrick Henry and William Christian

66 Christian as an Indian Fighter

67 First Horse Tram, 1876

68 'Toast-rack' Tram, 1890

69 Horse-bus, 1895

70 Royal Tram, 1972

Bicentenary of American Revolution and Col. William Christian Commemoration

(Des and litho John Waddington)

1976 (12 MAR). Perf 13½ (C)

75	**63**	5½p multicoloured	10	10
76	**64**	7p multicoloured	15	15

Douglas Horse Trams Centenary

(Des J. Nicholson. Photo Courvoisier)

1976 (26 MAY). Granite paper. Perf 11½ (C)

80	**67**	5½p multicoloured	10	10
81	**68**	7p multicoloured	15	15

82	**69**	11p multicoloured	20	20
83	**70**	13p multicoloured	25	25
80/3		*Set of* 4	65	65
		First Day Cover		1·00
		Presentation Pack	1·00	

Sheets 25 (5×5)

Quantities sold: 5½p 627,083; 7p 480,417; 11p 391,871; 13p 389,604

Withdrawn: 25.5.77

71 Barroose Beaker **72** Souvenir Teapot **73** Laxey Jug

74 Cronk Aust Food Vessel **75** Sansbury Bowl

76 Knox Urn

Europa. Ceramic Art

(Des J. Nicholson. Photo Courvoisier)

1976 (28 JULY). *Granite paper*. Perf 11½ (C)

84	**71**	5p multicoloured	20	20
		a. *Strip of 3. Nos.* 84/6	60	60
85	**72**	5p multicoloured	20	20
86	**73**	5p multicoloured	20	20
87	**74**	10p multicoloured	20	20
		a. *Strip of 3 Nos.* 87/9	60	60
88	**75**	10p multicoloured	20	20
89	**76**	10p multicoloured	20	20
84/9		*Set of 6*	1·10	1·10
		First Day Cover		2·10
		Presentation Pack	1·50	

Sheets: 9 (3×3) containing the three designs of each value horizontally and vertically *se-tenant*

Quantities sold: 5p 256,400 of each design; 10p 262,900 of each design

Sold out: 20.11.76 (5p); 12.76 (10p)

77 Diocesan Banner **78** Onchan Banner

79 Castletown Banner **80** Ramsey Banner

Christmas and Centenary of Mothers' Union

(Des G. Kneale. Litho Questa)

1976 (14 OCT). Perf 14½ (C)

90	**77**	6p multicoloured	10	10
91	**78**	7p multicoloured	15	15
92	**79**	11p multicoloured	20	20
93	**80**	13p multicoloured	25	25
90/3		*Set of 4*	65	65
		First Day Cover		80
		Presentation Pack	1·00	

Plate Nos.: 6p 1B (×5); 11p 1A (×5); others 1C (×5)

Sheets: 50 (10×5)

Imprint: Right-hand corner, bottom margin and left-hand corner, top margin

Quantities sold: 6p 905,752; 7p 890,762; 11p 397,807; 13p 390,057

Withdrawn: 13.10.77

81 Queen Elizabeth II **82** Queen Elizabeth and Prince Philip

83 Queen Elizabeth II

Silver Jubilee

(Des A. Larkins. Litho and recess De La Rue)

1977 (1 MAR). Perf 14×13 (7p) or 13×14 (others), both comb

94	**81**	6p multicoloured	10	10
95	**82**	7p multicoloured	20	20
96	**83**	25p multicoloured	50	50
94/6		*Set of 3*	70	70
		First Day Cover		85
		Presentation pack	1·00	
		Set of 3 Gutter Pairs	1·40	

Plate Nos.: 6p, 7p 1A (×5)–2A, 1B (×5)–2B, 1C (×5)–2C, 1D (×5)–2D; 25p 1B, 1D (each ×6)

Sheets: 50 (2 panes 5×5)

Imprint: Right-hand corner, bottom margin

Quantities sold: 6p 942,356; 7p 911,191; 25p 651,101

Withdrawn: 28.2.78

84 Carrick Bay from 'Tom-the-Dipper'

85 View from Ramsey

Europa. Landscapes

(Des J. Nicholson. Litho Questa)

1977 (26 MAY). Perf 13½×14 (C)

97	**84**	6p multicoloured	15	15
98	**85**	10p multicoloured	25	25
97/8		*Set of 2*	40	40
		First Day Cover		55
		Presentation Pack	75	
		Set of 2 Gutter Pairs	80	

Plate Nos.: 6p 1A, 1B, 1C, 1D, 2A, 2B, 2C, 2D (each ×4); 10p 1A, 1B, 1C, 1D (each ×5), 2A–1A–1A–2A–1A, 2B–1B–1B–2B–1B, 2C–1C–1C–2C–1C, 2D–1D–1D–2D–1D

Sheets: 40 (2 panes 4×5)

Imprint: Right-hand corner, bottom margin and left-hand corner, top margin

Quantities sold: 6p 778,685; 10p 843,525

Withdrawn: 25.5.78

86 F. A. Applebee, 1912

87 St. John Ambulance Brigade at Governor's Bridge, c. 1938

88 Scouts working Scoreboard

89 John Williams, 1976

Linked Anniversaries

(Des J. Nicholson. Litho John Waddington)

1977 (26 MAY). Perf 13½ (C)

99	**86**	6p multicoloured	15	10
100	**87**	7p multicoloured	15	15
101	**88**	11p multicoloured	25	25
102	**89**	13p multicoloured	25	30
99/102		*Set of 4*	70	65
		First Day Cover		85
		Presentation Pack	1·00	
		Set of 4 Gutter Pairs	1·40	

The events commemorated are: 70th anniversary of Manx TT; 70th anniversary of Boy Scouts; centenary of St. John Ambulance Brigade.

Plate Nos.: 11p 1A, 1C (each ×4); others 1B, 1D (each ×4)

Sheets: 50 (2 panes 5×5)

Imprint: Right-hand corner, bottom margin

Quantities sold: 6p 525,703; 7p 875,303; 11p 431,053; 13p 440,403

Withdrawn: 25.5.78

90 Old Summer House, Mount Morrison, Peel

91 Wesley preaching in Castletown Square

92 Wesley preaching outside Bradden Church

93 New Methodist Church, Douglas

Bicentenary of the First Visit of John Wesley

(Des and photo Courvoisier)

1977 (19 OCT). *Granite paper.* Perf 11½ (C)

103	**90**	6p multicoloured	15	10
104	**91**	7p multicoloured	15	15
105	**92**	11p multicoloured	25	25
106	**93**	13p multicoloured	25	25
103/6		*Set of 4*	70	65
		First Day Cover		85
		Presentation Pack	1·00	

Sheets: 50 (5×10)

Quantities sold: 6p 661,755; 7p 976,155; 11p 373,805; 13p 366,905

Withdrawn: 18.10.78

94 H.M.S. *Ben-My-Chree* and Short Type 184 Seaplane, 1915

95 H.M.S. *Vindex* and Bristol Scout C, 1915

96 Boulton Paul Defiant over Douglas Bay, 1941

97 Sepecat Jaguar over Ramsey, 1977

R.A.F. Diamond Jubilee

(Des A. Theobald. Litho John Waddington)

1978 (28 Feb). Perf 13½×14

107	**94**	6p multicoloured	15	10
108	**95**	7p multicoloured	15	15
109	**96**	11p multicoloured	25	25
110	**97**	13p multicoloured	25	25
107/10		*Set of 4*	70	65
		First Day Cover		95
		Presentation Pack	1·00	
		Set of 4 Gutter Pairs	1·40	

Plate Nos.: All values 1A, 1C (each ×4)

Sheets: 50 (2 panes 5×5)

Quantities sold: 6p 690,536; 7p 875,811; 11p 416,082; 13p 422,797

Withdrawn: 27.2.79

98 Watch Tower, Langness

99 Jurby Church

100 Government Buildings

101 Tynwald Hill

102 Milner's Tower

103 Laxey Wheel

104 Castle Rushen

105 St. Ninian's Church

106 Tower of Refuge

107 St. German's Cathedral

108 Point of Ayre Lighthouse

109 Corrin's Tower

110 Douglas Head Lighthouse

111 Fuchsia

112 Manx Cat

113 Red-billed Chough

114 Viking Warrior

114a Queen Elizabeth II

(Des G. Kneale (£2), J. Nicholson (others). Litho Questa (½p to 16p), photo Courvoisier (20p to £2))

1978 (28 FEB)–**81**. (a) Perf 14 (C)

111	**98**	½p multicoloured (a)	. . . .	10	10
		a. Perf 14½	. . . .	20	10
112	**99**	1p multicoloured (a)	. . . .	10	10
		a. Perf 14½	. . . .	20	10
113	**100**	6p multicoloured (a)	. . . .	30	30
114	**101**	7p multicoloured (a)	. . . .	35	35
		a. Perf 14½	. . . .	8·50	6·50
115	**102**	8p multicoloured (a)	. . . .	25	25
		a. Perf 14½	. . . .	35	35
116	**103**	9p multicoloured (a)	. . . .	35	35
		a. Perf 14½	. . . .	35	35
117	**104**	10p multicoloured (a)	. . . .	40	40
		a. Perf 14½	. . . .	35	35
118	**105**	11p multicoloured (a)	. . . .	40	40
		a. Perf 14½	. . . .	40	40
119	**106**	12p multicoloured (a)	. . . .	40	25
		a. Perf 14½	. . . .	50	40
120	**107**	13p multicoloured (a)	. . . .	60	60
		a. Perf 14½	. . . .	30	25
121	**108**	14p multicoloured (a)	. . . .	60	60
		a. Perf 14½	. . . .	30	25
122	**109**	15p multicoloured (a)	. . . .	75	75
		a. Perf 14½	. . . .	30	25
123	**110**	16p multicoloured (a)	. . . .	55	30
		a. Perf 14½	. . . .	26·00	21·00

(b) *Granite paper.* Perf 11½ (C)

124	**111**	20p multicoloured (b)	. . . .	50	35
125	**112**	25p multicoloured (b)	. . . .	65	45
126	**113**	50p multicoloured (b)	. . . .	90	75
127	**114**	£1 multicoloured (b)	. . . .	1·90	2·00
128	**114a**	£2 multicoloured (c)	. . . .	3·50	3·50
111/28		Set of 18 (cheapest)	. . . . . .	8·00	10·00
		First Day Covers* (5)	. . . . . .		12·00
		Presentation Packs (4)	. . . . . 14·00		

*The most common versions of the three low and medium value first day covers prepared by the Philatelic Bureau were franked with Nos. 111a, 112/15, 116a, 117/18, 119a, 120, 121a, 122 and 123a. Some examples can be found with the ½p as No. 111, the 11p as No. 118a or the 13p as No. 120a. First day covers prepared by dealers or collectors on the island were franked with Nos. 111/18, 119a/20a, 121, 122a and 123.

Printings: (a) 28.2.78; (b) 18.10.78; (c) 29.9.81

Although both perforations of Nos. 111/23 were printed at the same time, some did not appear in use until some time after 28 February 1978. Earliest dates for these are as follows: 1p (112a) 8.79, 7p (114a) 8.78, 8p (115a) 6.80, 10p (117a) 8.79, 12p (119) 9.80.

Plate Nos.: ½, 6, 8, 9, 10, 11, 12, 13, 14, 15, 16p 1A, 1B, 1C, 1D (each ×4); 1p 1A, 1B, 1C, 1D (each ×4) (No. 112); 1A–1A–2A–1A, 1B–1B–2B–1B, 1C–1C–2C–1C, 1D–1D–2D–1D; 7p 1A, 1B, 1C, 1D (each ×4) (No. 114); 2A, 2B, 2C, 2D (each ×4) (No. 114a); £2 A1–1–1–1, B1–1–1–1, others none

Sheets: 25 (5×5) (£2); 50 (1, 7, 10, 12, 13, 14, 15, 16p 5×10; others 10×5)

Imprint: ½p to 16p left-hand corner, top margin and right-hand corner, bottom margin; 20p to £1 none; £2 central bottom margin

Withdrawn: 30.6.83 1p to 16p; 31.12.83 20p to £1; 31.12.85 ½p; 30.6.90 £2

115 Queen Elizabeth in Coronation Regalia

25th Anniversary of Coronation

(Des G. Kneale. Litho Questa)

1978 (24 MAY). Perf 14½×14 (C)

132	**115**	25p multicoloured	50	45
		First Day Cover		65
		Presentation Pack	85	
		Gutter Pair	1·00	

Plate Nos.: 1A, 1B (each ×6)

Sheets: 50 (2 panes 5×5)

Imprint: Left-hand corner, top margin and right-hand corner, bottom margin

Quantity sold: 575,996

Withdrawn: 23.5.79

116 Wheel-headed Cross-slab

117 Celtic Wheelcross

118 Keeil Chiggyrt Stone

119 Olaf Liotulfson Cross

120 Odd's and Thorleif's Crosses

121 Thor Cross

Europa. Sculpture

(Des J. Nicholson. Photo Courvoisier)

1978 (24 MAY). Granite paper. Perf 11½ (C)

133	**116**	6p multicoloured	10	10
		a. Strip of 3. Nos. 133/5	25	25
134	**117**	6p multicoloured	10	10
135	**118**	6p multicoloured	10	10
136	**119**	11p multicoloured	20	20
		a. Strip of 3. Nos. 136/8	60	60
137	**120**	11p multicoloured	20	20
138	**121**	11p multicoloured	20	20
133/8		Set of 6	85	80
		First Day Cover		1·10
		Presentation Pack	1·25	

Sheets: 9 (3×3) The three designs of each value were printed together, se-tenant, in horizontal and vertical strips throughout

Quantities sold: 6p 3,821,152; 11p 3,788,667

Withdrawn: 23.5.79

122 J. K. Ward and Ward Library, Peel

123 Swimmer, Cyclist and Walker

124 American Bald Eagle, Manx Arms and Maple Leaf

125 Lumber Camp at Three Rivers, Quebec

141

Anniversaries and Events. Events described on stamps

(Des John Waddington (7p), G. Knoale (11p), J. Nicholson
(others). Litho John Waddington)

1978 (10 JUNE). *Invisible gum.* Perf 13½ (C)

139	**122**	6p multicoloured	10	10
140	**123**	7p multicoloured	20	15
141	**124**	11p multicoloured	25	25
142	**125**	13p multicoloured	25	25
139/42		Set of 4	70	65
		First Day Covers (3)		1·00
		Presentation Packs (2)	1·00	
		Set of 4 Gutter Pairs	1·40	

Plate Nos.: 6p 1A, 1B, 1C, 1D (each ×4); others 1B, 1D (each ×4)

Sheets: 50 (2 panes 5×5)

Imprint: Central, bottom margin

Quantities sold: 6p 629,041; 7p 873,067; 11p 393,907; 13p 383,048

Withdrawn: 9.6.79

126 Hunt the Wren

Christmas

(Des J. Nicholson. Litho John Waddington)

1978 (18 OCT). Perf 13 (C)

143	**126**	5p multicoloured	20	20
		First Day Cover		40
		Presentation Pack	45	
		Gutter Pair	40	

Plate Nos.: 1B, 1D (each ×4)

Sheets: 50 (2 panes 5×5)

Imprint: Central, bottom margin

Quantity sold: 1,000,000

Sold out: 4.79 (stamp) or 8.79 (presentation pack)

127 P. M. C. Kermode
(founder) and *Nassa
kermodei*

128 Peregrine Falcon

129 Fulmar

130 *Epitriptus cowini* (fly)

Centenary of Natural History and Antiquarian Society

(Des J. Nicholson. Litho Questa)

1070 (27 FEB). Perf 14 (C)

144	**127**	6p multicoloured	10	10
145	**128**	7p multicoloured	20	15
146	**129**	11p multicoloured	25	25
147	**130**	13p multicoloured	25	25
144/7		Set of 4	70	65
		First Day Cover		90
		Presentation Pack	1·00	
		Set of 4 Gutter Pairs	1·40	

Plate Nos.: 6p 1A, 1B, 1C, 1D (each ×4); 13p 1A, 1B (each ×4);
others 1C, 1D (each ×4)

Sheets: 50 (2 panes 5×5)

Imprint: Left-hand corner, top margin and right-hand corner, bottom
margin

Quantities sold: 6p 642,126; 7p 790,515; 11p 411,863; 13p 390,454

Withdrawn: 26.2.80

131 Postman, 1859

132 Postman, 1979

Europa. Communications

(Des A. Theobald. Litho Questa)

1979 (16 MAY). Perf 14½ (C)

148	**131**	6p multicoloured	15	10
149	**132**	11p multicoloured	25	25
148/9		Set of 2	40	35
		First Day Cover		50
		Presentation Pack	85	

Plate Nos.: 6p 1A, 1B (each ×6); 11p 1A, 1B (each ×5)

Sheets: 20 (4×5)

Imprint: Right-hand corner, bottom margin

Quantities sold: 6p 1,301,039; 11p 1,290,318

Sold out: By 10.79 (stamps)

Withdrawn: 15.5.80 (presentation pack)

133 Viking Longship
Emblem

134 'Three Legs of
Man' Emblem

135 Viking Raid at
Garwick

136 10th-century Meeting
of Tynwald

137 Tynwald Hill and
St. John's Church

138 Procession to
Tynwald Hill

Two types of 3p:

Type I. Wrongly inscribed 'INSULAREM'.
'1979' imprint date.

Type II. Inscription corrected to 'INSULARUM'.
'1980' imprint date.

Millennium of Tynwald

(Des J. Nicholson. Litho Harrison (3, 4p), John Waddington
(others))

1979 (16 MAY)–**80**. (a) Perf 14½×14 (C)

150	**133**	3p multicoloured (*Type* I) (a)	10	10
		a. Booklet pane. Nos. 150×4, 151×2 (*4p stamps at top*) . . .	60	
		ab. Do. (*4p stamps in centre*) . . .	1·25	
		b. Type II (b)	10	10
		ba. Booklet pane. Nos. 150b×4, 151×2 (4p stamps at bottom)	50	

151	**134**	4p multicoloured (*ab*)	10	10
		(*b*) Perf 13 (C)		
152	**135**	6p multicoloured (*a*)	15	10
153	**136**	7p multicoloured (*a*)	20	20
154	**137**	11p multicoloured (*a*)	25	25
155	**138**	13p multicoloured (*a*)	30	25
150/5		Set of 6	1·00	90
		First Day Cover		95
		Presentation Pack	1·25	
		Set of 6 Gutter Pairs	2·00	

See also Nos. 188/9.

Printings: (*a*) 16.5.79; (*b*) 29.9.80. Inscribed '1980'

Plate Nos.: 3, 4p 1A (×6); 13p 1G (×4); others 1E (×4)

Sheets: 3, 4p 80 (10 panes 2×3, 5 panes 2×2); others 40 (2 panes
4×5). The 3 and 4p values were printed together, *se-tenant*, each
pane of 6 containing four 3p and two 4p, the 4p being in either
positions 1 and 2 or 3 and 4. The panes of 4 contain the 4p value
only. For details of No. 150ba see after No. 189.

Imprint: 3, 4p right-hand corner, bottom margin; others central,
bottom margin

Quantities sold: 6p 381,334; 7p 465,473; 11p 341,204; 13p 241,162

Withdrawn: 15.5.80 6p to 13p; 25.3.87 3p, 4p

139 Queen and Court on
Tynwald Hill

140 Queen and Procession
from St. John's Church
to Tynwald Hill

Royal Visit

(Des G. Kneale. Litho Questa)

1979 (5 JULY). Perf 14½ (C)

156	**139**	7p multicoloured	15	15
157	**140**	13p multicoloured	25	25
156/7		Set of 2	40	40
		First Day Cover		50
		Presentation pack	75	
		Set of 2 Gutter Pairs	80	

Plate Nos.: 7p 1A, 1B (each ×4); 13p 1C, 1D (each ×4)

Sheets: 50 (2 panes 5×5)

Imprint: Right-hand corner, bottom margin

Quantities sold: 7p 641,930; 13p 436,516

Withdrawn: 4.7.80

141 Odin's Raven

Voyage of **Odin's Raven**

(Des J. Nicholson. Litho Questa)

1979 (19 OCT). Perf 14×14½ (C)

158	**141**	15p multicoloured	....	35	30
		First Day Cover	....		50
		Presentation Pack	....	75	
		Gutter Pair	....	70	

See also No. **MS**180.

Plate Nos.: 1A, 1B, 1C, 1D (each ×4)

Sheets: 50 (2 panes 5×5)

Imprint: Right-hand corner, bottom margin

Quantity sold: 412,631

Withdrawn: 18.10.80

142 John Quilliam seized by Press Gang

143 Steering H.M.S. *Victory*, Battle of Trafalgar

144 Captain John Quilliam and H.M.S. *Spencer*

145 Captain John Quilliam (member of the House of Keys)

150th Death Anniversary of Captain John Quilliam

(Des A. Theobald. Litho Questa)

1979 (19 OCT). Perf 14 (C)

159	**142**	6p multicoloured	....	15	15
160	**143**	8p multicoloured	....	20	15
161	**144**	13p multicoloured	....	25	25
162	**145**	15p multicoloured	....	30	25
159/62		*Set of 4*	....	80	70
		First Day Cover	....		85
		Presentation Pack	....	1·00	
		Set of 4 Gutter Pairs	......	1·60	

Plate Nos.: 6p 1C, 1D (each ×4); others 1A, 1B (each ×4)

Sheets: 50 (2 panes 5×5)

Imprint: Right-hand corner, bottom margin

Quantities sold: 6p 608,876; 8p 858,665; 13p 360,821; 15p 360,400

Withdrawn: 18.10.80

146 Young Girl with Teddybear and Cat

147 Father Christmas with Young Children

Christmas and International Year of the Child

(Des Mrs. E. Moore. Litho John Waddington)

1979 (19 OCT). Perf 13 (C)

163	**146**	5p multicoloured	....	10	10
164	**147**	7p multicoloured	....	20	20
163/4		*Set of 2*	....	30	30
		First Day Cover	....		50
		Presentation Pack	....	60	
		Set of 2 Gutter Pairs	....	60	

Plate Nos.: Both values 1A, 1B, 1C, 1D (each ×4)

Sheets: 50 (2 panes 5×5)

Imprint: Central, left-hand margin

Quantities sold: 5p 1,036,495; 7p 1,087,734

Withdrawn: 18.10.80

148 Conglomerate Arch, Langness

149 Braaid Circle

150 Cashtal-yn-Ard

151 Volcanic Rocks at Scarlett

152 Sugar-loaf Rock

150th Anniversary of Royal Geographical Society

(Des J. Nicholson. Litho Questa)

1980 (5 FEB). Perf 14½ (C)

165	**148**	7p multicoloured	15	15
166	**149**	8p multicoloured	20	20
167	**150**	12p multicoloured	25	25
168	**151**	13p multicoloured	25	25
169	**152**	15p multicoloured	30	25
165/9		Set of 5	1·00	1·00
		First Day Cover		1·10
		Presentation Pack	1·40	
		Set of 5 Gutter Pairs	2·00	

Plate Nos.: 12p 1A, 1B, 1C, 1D (each ×4); 15p 1C, 1D (each ×4); others 1A, 1B (each ×4)

Sheets: 50 (2 panes 5×5)

Imprint: Right-hand corner, bottom margin

Quantities sold: 7p 842,859; 8p 837,710; 12p 361,362; 13p 360,261; 15p 360,310

Withdrawn: 4.2.81

153 Mona's Isle I

154 Douglas I

155 H.M.S. Mona's Queen II sinking U-boat

156 H.M.S. King Orry III at Surrender of German Fleet

157 Ben-My-Chree IV

158 Lady of Mann II

150th Anniversary of Isle of Man Steam Packet Company

(Des J. Nicholson. Photo Courvoisier)

1980 (6 MAY). Granite paper. Perf 11½ (C)

170	**153**	7p multicoloured	15	15
171	**154**	8p multicoloured	20	20
172	**155**	11½p multicoloured	20	20
173	**156**	12p multicoloured	25	25
174	**157**	13p multicoloured	25	25
175	**158**	15p multicoloured	30	25
170/5		Set of 6	1·00	1·10
		First Day Cover		1·00
		Presentation Pack	2·40	
		Set of 6 Gutter Pairs	2·00	
MS176	180×125 mm. Nos. 170/5		1·25	1·25
		First Day Cover		3·50

No. **MS**176 was issued to commemorate the 'London 1980' International Stamp Exhibition.

Cylinder Nos.: All values A1–1–1–1, B1–1–1–1, C1–1–1–1, D1–1–1–1

Sheets: 40 (2 panes 5×4)

Imprint: Central, bottom margin

Quantities sold: 7p 512,449; 8p 624,090; 11½p 381,466; 12p 367,943; 13p 368,138; 15p 376,596; miniature sheet 300,678

Withdrawn: 5.5.81

159 Stained Glass Window, T. E. Brown Room, Manx Museum

160 Clifton College, Bristol

Europa. Personalities. Thomas Edward Brown (poet and scholar) Commemoration

(Des G. Kneale. Photo Courvoisier)

1980 (6 MAY). Granite paper. Perf 11½ (C)

177	**159**	7p multicoloured	15	15
178	**160**	13½p multicoloured	25	25
177/8		Set of 2	50	50
		First Day Cover		60
		Presentation Pack	75	
		Set of 2 Gutter Pairs	1·00	

Cylinder Nos.: Both values A1–1–1–1–1, B1–1–1–1–1, C1–1–1–1–1, D1–1–1–1–1

Sheets: 20 (2 panes 2×5)

Imprint: Bottom margin at right-hand corner of left-hand pane

Quantities sold: 7p 1,726,009; 13½p 1,708,590

161 King Olav V and *Norge* (Norwegian royal yacht)

Visit of King Olav V of Norway, August 1979

(Des J. Nicholson. Litho Questa)

1980 (13 JUNE). Perf 14×14½ (C)

179	**161**	12p multicoloured	30	30
		First Day Cover		50
		Presentation Pack	75	
		Gutter Pair	60	
MS180		125×157 mm. Nos. 158 and 179 . .	75	75
		First Day Cover		2·00

No. **MS**180 also commemorates the 'NORWEX 80' stamp exhibition, Oslo.

Plate Nos.: 1C, 1D (each ×4)

Sheets: 40 (2 panes 5×4)

Imprint: Right-hand corner, bottom margin

Quantities sold: 12p 449,267; miniature sheet 401,424

Withdrawn: 12.6.81

162 Winter Wren and View of Calf of Man

163 European Robin and View of Port Erin Marine Biological Station

Christmas and Wildlife Conservation Year

(Des J. Nicholson. Litho John Waddington)

1980 (29 SEPT). Perf 13½×14 (C)

181	**162**	6p multicoloured	15	10
182	**163**	8p multicoloured	30	20
181/2		Set of 2	45	30
		First Day Cover		70
		Presentation Pack	1·00	
		Set of 2 Gutter Pairs	90	

Plate Nos.: 6p 1B, 1D (each ×4); 8p 1A, 1C (each ×4)

Sheets: 40 (2 panes 4×5)

Imprint: Right-hand corner, bottom margin

Quantities sold: 6p 967,976; 8p 942,323

Withdrawn: 28.9.81

164 William Kermode and Brig *Robert Quayle*, 1819

165 'Mona Vale', Van Diemen's Land, 1834

166 Ross Bridge, Tasmania

167 'Mona Vale', Tasmania (completed 1868)

168 Robert Q. Kermode and Parliament Buildings, Tasmania

Kermode Family in Tasmania Commemoration

(Des A. Theobald. Litho Questa)

1980 (29 SEPT). Perf 14½ (C)

183	**164**	7p multicoloured	15	15
184	**165**	9p multicoloured	20	20
185	**166**	13½p multicoloured	25	25
186	**167**	15p multicoloured	30	25
187	**168**	17½p multicoloured	30	30
183/7		Set of 5	1·10	1·00
		First Day Cover		1·00
		Presentation Pack	1·50	
		Set of 5 Gutter Pairs	2·25	

Plate Nos.: All values 1C, 1D (each ×4)

Sheets: 40 (2 panes 5×4)

Imprint: Right-hand corner, bottom margin

Quantities sold: 7p 416,487; 9p 498,880; 13½p 318,353; 15p 314,837; 17½p 315,107

Withdrawn: 28.9.81

169 Peregrine Falcon

170 Loaghtyn Ram

Booklet stamps

(Des J. Nicholson. Litho Harrison)

1980 (29 SEPT). Perf 14½×14 (C)

188	**169**	1p multicoloured	20	20
		a. Booklet pane. Nos. 151, 188 and 189, each ×2	60	
189	**170**	5p multicoloured	30	30
188/9		Set of 2	50	50
		First Day Cover (Nos. 150b ×2, 151×2, 188 and 189) . . .	1·10	
		Presentation Pack (Nos.150b ×2, 151×2, 188 and 189) . . .	1·25	

In addition to Booklets SB11/12 Nos. 188/9 also come from special booklet sheets of 60. These sheets contain No. 150ba×5 and No. 188a×5.

Plate Nos.: 1A (×7)

Withdrawn: 25.3.87

171 Luggers passing Red Pier, Douglas

172 Peel Lugger *Wanderer* rescuing survivors from the *Lusitania*

173 Nickeys leaving Port St. Mary Harbour

174 Nobby entering Ramsey Harbour

175 Nickeys *Sunbeam* and *Zebra* at Port Erin

Centenary of Royal National Mission to Deep Sea Fishermen

(Des J. Nicholson. Litho Questa)

1981 (24 FEB). Perf 14 (C)

190	**171**	8p multicoloured	15	15
191	**172**	9p multicoloured	20	20
192	**173**	18p multicoloured	30	30
193	**174**	20p multicoloured	30	30
194	**175**	22p multicoloured	35	35
190/4		Set of 5	1·25	1·25
		First Day Cover		1·50
		Presentation pack	1·50	
		Set of 5 Gutter Pairs	2·50	

Plate Nos.: 8p 1E, 1F (each ×4); 9p 1G, 1H (each ×4); 22p 1A, 1B (each ×4); others 1C, 1D (each ×4)

Sheets: 40 (2 panes 5×4)

Imprint: Right-hand corner, bottom margin

Quantities sold: 8p 566,522; 9p 583,358; 18p 334,765; 20p 315,511; 22p 324,607

Withdrawn: 23.2.82

176 'Crosh Cuirn' Superstition

177 'Bollan Cross' Superstition

Europa. Folklore

(Des J. Nicholson. Litho Questa)

1981 (22 MAY). Perf 14½ (C)

195	**176**	8p multicoloured	15	10
196	**177**	18p multicoloured	30	30
195/6		Set of 2	45	40
		First Day Cover		65
		Presentation Pack	75	
		Set of 2 Gutter Pairs	90	

Plate Nos.: 1A, 1B (each ×4)

Sheets: 24 (2 panes 3×4)

Imprint: Right-hand corner, bottom margin

Quantities sold: 8p 1,261,267; 18p 1,243,459

Withdrawn: 21.5.82

178 Lt. Mark Wilks (Royal Manx Fencibles) and Peel Castle

179 Ensign Mark Wilks and Fort St. George, Madras

180 Governor Mark Wilks and Napoleon, St. Helena

181 Col. Mark Wilks (speaker of the House of Keys) and Estate, Kirby

150th Death Anniversary of Colonel Mark Wilks

(Des A. Theobald. Litho Questa)

1981 (22 MAY). Perf 14 (C)

197	**178**	8p multicoloured	20	20
198	**179**	20p multicoloured	30	30
199	**180**	22p multicoloured	40	35
200	**181**	25p multicoloured	45	35
197/200		Set of 4	1·25	1·10
		First Day Cover		1·50
		Presentation Pack	1·60	
		Set of 4 Gutter Pairs	2·50	

Plate Nos.: 8, 20p 1A, 1B (each ×5); others 1A, 1B (each ×4)

Sheets: 40 (2 panes 5×4)

Imprint: 22p none; others right-hand corner, bottom margin

Quantities sold: 8p 371,280; 20p 278,840; 22p 294,480; 25p 272,640

Withdrawn: 21.5.82

182 Miss Emmeline Goulden (Mrs. Pankhurst) and Mrs. Sophia Jane Goulden

Centenary of Manx Women's Suffrage

(Des A. Theobald. Litho Questa)

1981 (22 MAY). Perf 14 (C)

201	**182**	9p, olive-grey and stone	20	20
		First Day Cover		40
		Presentation Pack	50	
		Gutter Pair	40	

Plate Nos.: 1C, 1D (each ×3)

Sheets: 40 (2 panes 5×4)

Imprint: Right-hand corner, bottom margin

Quantity sold: 657,760

Withdrawn: 21.5.82

183 Prince Charles and Lady Diana Spencer

Royal Wedding

(Des G. Kneale. Litho Harrison)

1981 (29 JULY). Perf 14 (C)

202	**183**	9p black, bright blue & pale blue	15	20
203		25p black, bright blue and pink	75	80
202/3		Set of 2	90	1·00
		First Day Cover		1·75
		Presentation Pack	1·75	
		Set of 2 Gutter Pairs	2·00	
MS204		130×183 mm. Nos. 202/3×2	2·00	2·00
		First Day Cover		11·00

Plate Nos.: 9p 1C, 1D (each ×3); 25p 1A, 1B (each ×3)

Sheets: 50 (2 panes 5×5)

Imprint: Central, bottom margin

Quantities sold: 9p 668,864; 25p 474,364; miniature sheet 327,094

Withdrawn: 28.7.82

184 Douglas War Memorial, Poppies and Inscription

185 Major Robert Cain (war hero)

148

186 Festival of Remembrance, Royal Albert Hall

187 T.S.S. *Tynwald* at Dunkirk, May, 1940

60th Anniversary of the Royal British Legion

(Des A. Theobald. Photo Courvoisier)

1981 (29 SEPT). *Granite paper.* Perf 11½ (C)

205	**184**	8p multicoloured	....	20	20
206	**185**	10p multicoloured	....	25	25
207	**186**	18p multicoloured	....	30	30
208	**187**	20p multicoloured	....	35	35
205/8		Set of 4	....	1·00	1·00
		First Day Cover	....		1·25
		Presentation Pack	....	1·40	
		Set of 4 Gutter Pairs	......	2·00	

Cylinder Nos.: 8p 1–1–1–1, B1–1–1–1; others A1–1–1–1, B1–1–1–1

Sheets: 40 (2 panes 4×5)

Imprint: Central, bottom margin

Quantities sold: 8p 314,794; 10p 799,326; 18p 284,059; 20p 261,194

Withdrawn: 28.9.82

188 Nativity Scene (stained glass window, St. George's Church)

189 Children from Special School performing Nativity Play

Christmas

(Des John Waddington (7p), G. Kneale (9p). Litho John Waddington)

1981 (29 SEPT). Perf 14 (C)

209	**188**	7p multicoloured	....	15	15
210	**189**	9p multicoloured	....	20	20
209/10		Set of 2	....	35	35
		First Day Cover	....		55
		Presentation pack	....	75	
		Set of 2 Gutter Pairs	....	70	

The 7p value also commemorates the bicentenary of St. George's Church, Douglas and the 9p the International Year for Disabled Persons.

Plate Nos.: 7p 1A, 1B (each ×6); 9p 1A, 1B, 1C, 1D (each ×6)

Sheets: 40 (2 panes 2×10)

Imprint: Right-hand corner, bottom margin

Quantities sold: 7p 855,407; 9p 362,892

Withdrawn: 28.9.82

190 Joseph and William Cunningham (founders of Manx Boy Scout Movement) and Cunningham House Headquarters

191 Baden-Powell visiting Isle of Man, 1911

192 Baden-Powell and Scout-Emblem

193 Scouts and Baden-Powell's Last Message

194 Scout Salute, Handshake, Emblem and Globe

149

75th Anniversary of Boy Scout Movement and 125th Birth Anniversary of Lord Baden-Powell

(Des G. Kneale. Litho Questa)

1982 (23 FEB). Perf 14×14½ (19½p) or 13½×14 (others), all comb

211	**190**	9p multicoloured	20	15
212	**191**	10p multicoloured	25	25
213	**192**	19½p multicoloured	45	40
214	**193**	24p multicoloured	50	45
215	**194**	29p multicoloured	70	60
211/15		*Set of 5*	1·90	1·75
		First Day Cover		2·00
		Presentation Pack	2·40	
		Set of 5 Gutter Pairs	4·00	

Plate Nos.: 9p 1A, 1B (each ×4); 29p 1A, 1B (each ×5); others 1C, 1D (each ×4)

Sheets: 40 (2 panes 5×4)

Imprint: Right-hand corner, bottom margin

Quantities sold: 9p 748,353; 10p 868,401; 19½p 364,487; 24p 368,346; 29p 370,466

Withdrawn: 22.2.83

195 *The Principals and Duties of Christianity (first book printed in Manx, 1707), and Bishop T. Wilson*

196 Landing at Derbyhaven (visit of Thomas, 2nd Earl of Derby, 1507)

Europa. Historic Events

(Des A. Theobald. Photo Courvoisier)

1982 (1 JUNE). *Granite paper.* Perf 12×12½ (C)

216	**195**	9p multicoloured	15	10
217	**196**	19½p multicoloured	40	40
216/17		*Set of 2*	55	50
		First Day Cover		85
		Presentation Pack	85	
		Set of 2 Gutter Pairs	1·10	

Cylinder Nos.: Both values A1–1–1–1–1, B1–1–1–1–1

Sheets: 24 (2 panes 3×4)

Imprint: Right-hand corner, bottom margin

Quantities sold: 9p 1,120,457; 19½p 1,129,315

Withdrawn: 31.5.83

197 Charlie Collier (first TT race (single cylinder) winner) and Tourist Trophy Race, 1907

198 Freddie Dixon (Sidecar and Junior TT winner) and Junior TT race, 1927

199 Jimmie Simpson (TT winner and first to lap at 60, 70 and 80 mph) and Senior TT, 1932

200 Mike Hailwood (winner of fourteen TTs) and Senior TT, 1961

201 Jock Taylor (Sidecar TT winner, 1978, 1980 and 1981) and Sidecar TT (with Benga Johansson), 1980

75th Anniversary of Tourist Trophy Motorcycle Races

(Des J. Nicholson. Litho Questa)

1982 (1 JUNE). Perf 14 (C)

218	**197**	9p multicoloured	15	15
219	**198**	10p multicoloured	15	15
220	**199**	24p multicoloured	60	50
221	**200**	26p multicoloured	60	50
222	**201**	29p multicoloured	60	55
218/22		*Set of 5*	1·90	1·60
		First Day Cover		2·10
		Presentation Pack	3·00	
		Stamp Cards (set of 5)	1·25	4·00
		Set of 5 Gutter Pairs	4·00	

Plate Nos.: All values 1B, 1C, 1D (each ×4)

Sheets: 40 (2 panes 5×4)

Imprint: Right-hand corner, bottom margin

Quantities sold: 9p 837,930; 10p 866,223; 24p 351,406; 26p 361,063; 29p 355,690

Withdrawn: 11.6.83

202 *Mona I*

203 *Manx Maid II*

150th Anniversary of Isle of Man Steam Packet Company Mail Contract

(Des J. Nicholson. Litho Questa)

1982 (5 OCT). Perf 13½ (C)
223	**202**	12p multicoloured	30	25
224	**203**	19½p multicoloured	45	45
223/4		Set of 2	75	70
		First Day Cover		90
		Presentation Pack	1·25	
		Set of 2 Gutter Pairs	1·50	

Plate Nos.: Both values 1A (×4)

Sheets: 40 (2 panes 5×4)

Imprint: Right-hand bottom margin

Quantities sold: 12p 701,044; 19½p 291,100

Withdrawn: 4.10.83

204 The Three Wise Men

205 Snow Scene and European Robin

Christmas

(Des and litho John Waddington)

1982 (5 OCT). Perf 13 (C)
225	**204**	8p multicoloured	15	15
226	**205**	11p multicoloured	30	30
225/6		Set of 2	45	45
		First Day Cover		70
		Presentation Pack	85	
		Set of 2 Gutter Pairs	1·00	

Plate Nos.: 8p: 1A, 1C (each ×4), 11p 1B, 1D (each ×4)

Sheets: 40 (8p 2 panes 5×4), (11p 2 panes 4×5)

Imprint: Right-hand corner, bottom margin (8p); Top right-hand margin (11p)

Quantities sold; 8p 740,651; 11p 787,552

Withdrawn: 4.10.83

206 Princess Diana with Prince William

21st Birthday of the Princess of Wales and Birth of Prince William

(Des G. Kneale. Litho Questa)

1982 (12 OCT). Sheet 100×83 mm. Perf 14½×14 (C)
MS227	**206**	50p multicoloured	1·50	1·50
		First Day Cover		4·50
		Presentation Pack	1·75	

Quantity sold: 218,759

Withdrawn: 11.10.83

207 Opening of Salvation Army Citadel, and T. H. Cannell, J.P.

208 Early Meeting-place and Gen. William Booth

209 Salvation Army Band

210 Treating Lepers, and Lt.-Col. Thomas Bridson

Centenary of Salvation Army in Isle of Man

(Des A. Theobald. Photo Courvoisier)

1983 (15 FEB). *Granite paper.* Perf 11½ (C)

228	**207**	10p multicoloured	20	15
229	**208**	12p multicoloured	30	25
230	**209**	19½p multicoloured	45	45
231	**210**	26p multicoloured	65	60
228/31		*Set of* 4	1·40	1·25
		First Day Cover		1·60
		Presentation Pack	2·10	
		Set of 4 *Gutter Pairs*	2·75	

Cylinder Nos.: All values B1–1–1–1–1

Sheets: 40 (2 panes 4×5)

Imprint: Central, bottom margin

Quantities sold: 10p 467,665; 12p 567,863; 19½p 267,929; 26p 288,069

Withdrawn: 14.2.84

211 Atlantic Puffins

212 Northern Gannets

213 Lesser Black-backed Gulls

214 Great Cormorants

215 Black-legged Kittiwakes

216 Shags

217 Grey Herons

218 Herring Gulls

219 Razorbills

220 Greater Black-backed Gulls

221 Common Shelducks

222 Oystercatchers

223 Arctic Terns

224 Common Guillemots

225 Common Redshanks

226 Mute Swans

227 'Queen Elizabeth II' (Ricardo Macarron)

152

Sea Birds and Queen's Portrait (£5)

(Des Colleen Corlett (£5), J. Nicholson (others). Litho Questa)

1983 (15 FEB)–**85**. Perf 14 (20p to £1), 14×13½ (£5) or 14½ (others), all comb

232	**211**	1p multicoloured (a)	30	30
233	**212**	2p multicoloured (a)	30	30
234	**213**	5p multicoloured (a)	60	40
235	**214**	8p multicoloured (a)	60	40
236	**215**	10p multicoloured (a)	60	35
237	**216**	11p multicoloured (a)	60	35
238	**217**	12p multicoloured (a)	70	40
239	**218**	13p multicoloured (a)	70	40
240	**219**	14p multicoloured (a)	70	40
241	**220**	15p multicoloured (a)	80	50
242	**221**	16p multicoloured (a)	80	50
243	**222**	18p multicoloured (a)	80	50
244	**223**	20p multicoloured (b)	1·00	70
245	**224**	25p multicoloured (b)	1·25	75
246	**225**	50p multicoloured (b)	1·75	1·50
247	**226**	£1 multicoloured (b)	3·00	2·25
248	**227**	£5 multicoloured (c)	9·00	10·00
232/48		Set of 17	21·00	18·00
		First Day Covers (4)		24·00
		Presentation Packs (4) ..... 24·00		

Printings: (a) 15.2.83; (b) 14.9.83; (c) 31.1.85

Plate Nos.: 1p to £1 1A, 1B, 1C, 1D (each ×4); £5 1A, 1B (each ×4)

Sheets: 10 (5×2) £5; 50 (5×10) others

Imprint: £5 Right-hand margin; others right-hand corner, bottom margin

Withdrawn: 30.6.88 1p to 18p; 31.12.88 20p to £1; 4.7.94 £5

228 Design Drawings by Robert Casement for the Great Laxey Wheel

229 Robert Casement and the Great Laxey Wheel

Europa. The Great Laxey Wheel

(Des J. Nicholson. Litho Questa)

1983 (18 MAY). Perf 14 (C)

249	**228**	10p black, azure and buff	25	20
250	**229**	20½p multicoloured	50	55
249/50		Set of 2	75	75
		First Day Cover		1·00
		Presentation Pack .... 1·10		
		Set of 2 Gutter Pairs ..... 1·50		

Plate Nos.: 10p 1A, 1B (each ×3); 20½p 1A, 1B (each ×4)

Sheets: 12 (2 panes 2×3)

Imprint: Right-hand corner, bottom margin

Quantities sold: 10p 653,743; 20½p 686,084

Withdrawn 17.5.84

230 Nick Keig (international yachtsman) and Trimaran *Three Legs of Man III*

231 King William's College, Castletown

232 Sir William Bragg (winner of Nobel Prize for Physics) and Spectrometer

233 General Sir George White V.C. and Action at Charasiah

150th Anniversary of King William's College

(Des J. Nicholson (10p, 31p), Colleen Corlett (12p, 28p). Photo Courvoisier)

1983 (18 MAY). *Granite paper*. Perf 11½ (C)

251	**230**	10p multicoloured	15	15
252	**231**	12p multicoloured	20	20
253	**232**	28p multicoloured	55	55
254	**233**	31p multicoloured	65	65
251/4		Set of 4	1·40	1·40
		First Day Cover		1·50
		Presentation Pack .... 2·00		
		Set of 4 Gutter Pairs ...... 3·00		

Cylinder Nos.: 10p C1–1–1–1–1, D1–1–1–1–1; 12p C1–1–1–1, D1–1–1–1; 28p A1–1–1–1, B1–1–1–1; 31p A1–1–1–1–1, B1–1–1–1–1

Sheets: 40 (2 panes 5×4)

Imprint: Central, bottom margin

Quantities sold: 10p 552,573; 12p 693,004; 28p 263,814; 31p 242,393

Withdrawn: 17.5.04

234 New Post Office Headquarters, Douglas

235 Landing of the Vikings on Man, AD 938

World Communications Year and 10th Anniversary of Isle of Man Post Office Authority

(Des Colleen Corlett (10p), J. Nicholson (15p). Litho Questa)

1983 (5 JULY). Perf 14½ (C)

255	**234**	10p multicoloured	25	25
256	**235**	15p multicoloured	35	40
255/6		Set of 2	60	65
		First Day Cover		90
		Presentation Pack	90	
		Stamp Cards (set of 2)	90	1·40
		Set of 2 Gutter Pairs	1·25	

Plate Nos.: Both values 1A, 1B, 1C, 1D (each ×5)

Sheets: 40 (2 panes 4×5)

Imprint: Central, right-hand margin

Quantities sold: 10p 269,843; 15p 222,013

Withdrawn: 4.7.84

236 Shepherds

237 Three Kings

Christmas

(Des Colleen Corlett. Litho John Waddington)

1983 (14 SEPT). Perf 13 (C)

257	**236**	9p multicoloured	20	20
258	**237**	12p multicoloured	30	30
257/8		Set of 2	50	50
		First Day Cover		85
		Presentation Pack	85	
		Set of 2 Gutter Pairs	1·00	

Plate Nos.: Both values 1A, 1B, 1C, 1D (each ×5)

Sheets: 40 (2 panes 5×4)

Imprint: Right-hand corner, bottom margin

Quantities sold: 9p 642,763; 12p 656,060

Withdrawn: 13.9.84

238 Manx King (full-rigged ship)

239 Hope (barque)

240 Rio Grande (brig)

241 Lady Elizabeth (barque)

242 Sumatra (barque)

243 Wreck of Lady Elizabeth as shown on Falkland Islands Stamp

The Karran Fleet

(Des J. Nicholson (10p to 31p); Colleen Corlett, J. Nicholson and J. Smith (miniature sheet). Litho Questa)

1984 (14 FEB). Perf 14 (C)

259	**238**	10p multicoloured	20	15
260	**239**	13p multicoloured	30	20
261	**240**	20½p multicoloured	45	35
262	**241**	28p multicoloured	65	50
263	**242**	31p multicoloured	75	65
259/63		Set of 5	2·10	1·60
		First Day Cover		2·00
		Presentation Pack	2·75	
		Set of 5 Gutter pairs	4·20	
MS264		103×94 mm. 28p Type **241**; 31p Type **243** (sold at 60p)	2·25	1·50
		First Day Cover		3·00
		Presentation Pack	2·75	

No. **MS**264 was issued to commemorate links between the Isle of Man and the Falkland Islands.

Plate Nos.: All values 1A, 1B (each ×4)

Sheets: 40 (2 panes 5×4)

Imprint: Right-hand corner, bottom margin

Quantities sold: 10p 389,728; 13p 417,637; 20½p 253,949; 28p 238,292; 31p 236,196; miniature sheet 137,031

Withdrawn: 13.2.85

244 C.E.P.T. 25th Anniversary Logo

Europa

(Des J. Larrivière, adapted Colleen Corlett. Photo Courvoisier)

1984 (27 APR). *Granite paper*. Perf 12×11½ (C)

265	**244**	10p dull orange, deep reddish brown and pale orange . . .	30	25
266		20½p lt blue, dp blue & pale blue	50	50
		Set of 2	80	75
		First Day Cover	2·00	
		Presentation Pack	2·50	

Cylinder Nos.: 10p B1–1–1; 20½p A1–1–1

Sheets: 20 (4×5)

Imprint: Central, right-hand margin

Quantities sold: 10p 705,410; 20½p 715,479

Withdrawn: 26.4.85

245 Railway Air Services De Havilland D.H.84 Dragon Mk 2

246 West Coast Air Services De Havilland D.H.86A Dragon Express *Ronaldsway*

247 B.E.A. Douglas DC-3

248 B.E.A. Vickers Viscount 800

249 Telair Britten Norman Islander

50th Anniversary of First Official Airmail to the Isle of Man and 40th Anniversary of International Civil Aviation Organization

(Des A. Theobald. Litho Questa)

1984 (27 APR). Perf 14 (C)

267	**245**	11p multicoloured	. . . .	35	30
268	**246**	13p multicoloured	. . . .	40	30
269	**247**	26p multicoloured	. . . .	70	65
270	**248**	28p multicoloured	. . . .	70	65
271	**249**	31p multicoloured	. . . .	70	65
267/71		*Set of 5*		2·50	2·25
		First Day Cover			2·75
		Presentation Pack		2·75	
		Set of 5 Gutter Pairs		5·00	

Plate Nos.: All values 1C, 1D (each ×4)

Sheets: 40 (2 panes 5×4)

Imprint: Right-hand corner, bottom margin

Quantities sold: 11p 399,155; 13p 440,623; 26p 234,165; 28p 173,841; 31p 171,890

Withdrawn: 26.4.85

Year Pack 1983

1984. *Comprises Nos. 228/47, 249/58*

Year Pack . . . . 15·00

Withdrawn: 31.3.85

250 Window from Glencrutchey House, Douglas

251 Window from Lonan Old Church

Christmas. Stained-glass Windows

(Des D. Swinton. Litho John Waddington)

1984 (21 SEPT). Perf 14 (C)

272	**250**	10p multicoloured	. . . .	20	20
273	**251**	13p multicoloured	. . . .	40	40
272/3		*Set of 2*		60	60
		First Day Cover			90
		Presentation Pack		90	
		Set of 2 Gutter Pairs		1·25	

Plate Nos.: Both values 1A, 1C (each ×6)

Sheets: 40 (2 panes 4×5)

Imprint: Top right-hand margin

Quantities sold: 10p 652,870; 13p 668,084

Withdrawn: 20.9.85

252 William Cain's Birthplace, Ballasalla

253 The *Anna* Leaving Liverpool, 1852

254 Early Australian Railway

255 William Cain as Mayor of Melbourne, and Town Hall

256 Royal Exhibition Buildings, Melbourne

William Cain (civic leader, Victoria) Commemoration

(Des J. Nicholson. Litho Questa)

1984 (21 SEPT). Perf 14½×14 (C)

274	**252**	11p multicoloured	25	20
275	**253**	22p multicoloured	50	50
276	**254**	28p multicoloured	70	65
277	**255**	30p multicoloured	70	65
278	**256**	33p multicoloured	70	65
274/8		Set of 5	2·50	2·40
		First Day Cover		2·75
		Presentation Pack	3·00	
		Set of 5 Gutter Pairs	5·00	

Plate Nos.: All values 1B (×4)

Sheets: 40 (2 panes 5×4)

Imprint: Right-hand corner, bottom margin

Quantities sold: 11p 393,219; 22p 280,598; 28p 223,515; 30p 220,913; 33p 213,933

Withdrawn: 20.9.85

257 Queen Elizabeth II and Commonwealth Parliamentary Association Badge

258 Queen Elizabeth II and Manx Emblem

Links with the Commonwealth. 30th Commonwealth Parliamentary Association Conference

(Des and litho John Waddington)

1984 (21 SEPT). Perf 14 (C)

279	**257**	14p multicoloured	35	25
280	**258**	33p multicoloured	65	65
279/80		Set of 2	1·00	1·00
		First Day Cover		1·50
		Presentation Pack	2·75	
		Set of 2 Gutter Pairs	2·00	

Plate Nos.: Both values 1A, 1C (each ×7)

Sheets: 40 (2 panes 5×4)

Imprint: Right-hand corner, bottom margin

Quantities sold: 14p 373,204; 33p 231,073

Withdrawn: 20.9.85

Year Pack 1984

1985 (1 JAN). *Comprises Nos. 259/80*

	Year Pack	17·00

Withdrawn: 31.12.85

259 Cunningham House Headquarters, and Mrs. Willie Cunningham and Mrs. Joseph Cunningham (former Commissioners)

260 Princess Margaret, Isle of Man Standard and Guides

261 Lady Olave Baden-Powell opening Guide Headquarters, 1955

156

262 Guide Uniforms from 1910 to 1985

263 Guide Handclasp, Salute and Early Badge

75th Anniversary of Girl Guide Movement

(Des Colleen Corlett. Photo Courvoisier)

1985 (31 JAN). *Granite paper.* Perf 11½ (C)

281	**259**	11p multicoloured	. . . .	30	25
282	**260**	14p multicoloured	. . . .	35	30
283	**261**	29p multicoloured	. . . .	70	60
284	**262**	31p multicoloured	. . . .	75	75
285	**263**	34p multicoloured	. . . .	90	85
281/5		Set of 5	. . . .	2·75	2·50
		First Day Cover	. . . .		3·00
		Presentation Pack	. . . .	3·00	
		Set of 5 Gutter Pairs	. . . . . .	5·50	

Cylinder Nos.: 11p, 34p A1–1–1–1–1, B1–1–1–1–1; others A1–1–1–1, B1–1–1–1

Sheets: 40 (2 panes 4×5)

Imprint: Central, bottom margin of each pane

Withdrawn: 30.1.86

264 Score of Manx National Anthem

265 William H. Gill (lyricist)

266 Score of Hymn 'Crofton'

267 Dr. John Clague (composer)

Europa. European Music Year

(Des D. Swinton. Photo Courvoisier)

1985 (24 APR). *Granite paper.* Perf 11½ (C)

286	**264**	12p black, orange-brn & chestnut	30	30
		a. *Horiz pair. Nos. 286/7*	75	75
287	**265**	12p black, orange-brn & chestnut	30	30
288	**266**	22p black, brt blue & new bl . . .	80	70
		a. *Horiz pair. Nos. 288/9*	1·60	1·50
289	**267**	22p black, brt new blue & new bl	80	70
286/9		Set of 4	2·10	1·75
		First Day Cover		2·00
		Presentation Pack	2·50	

Cylinder Nos.: Both values A1–1–1, B1–1–1

Sheets: 20 (4×5). The two designs for each value printed together, *se-tenant*, in horizontal pairs throughout the sheets

Imprint: Central, bottom margin

Withdrawn: 23.4.86

268 Charles Rolls in 20 h.p. Rolls Royce (1906 Tourist Trophy Race)

269 W Bentley in 3 litre Bentley (1922 Tourist Trophy Race)

270 F. Gerard in E.R.A. (1950 British Empire Trophy Race)

271 Brian Lewis in Alfa Romeo (1934 Mannin Moar Race)

272 Jaguar 'XJ-SC' ('Roads Open' Car, 1984 Motor-cycle T.T. Races)

273 Tony Pond and Mike Nicholson in Vauxhall 'Chevette' (1981 Rothmans International Rally)

Century of Motoring

(Des A. Theobald. Litho Questa)

1985 (25 MAY). Perf 14 (C)

290	**268**	12p multicoloured	. . . .	25	25
		a. Horiz pair. Nos. 290/1	. . . . .	60	60
291	**269**	12p multicoloured	. . . .	25	25
292	**270**	14p multicoloured	. . . .	30	25
		a. Horiz pair. Nos. 292/3	. . . . .	60	60
293	**271**	14p multicoloured	. . . .	30	25
294	**272**	31p multicoloured	. . . .	1·00	90
		a. Horiz pair. Nos. 294/5	. . . . .	2·00	2·00
295	**273**	31p multicoloured	. . . .	1·00	90
290/5		Set of 6	. . . .	2·75	2·50
		First Day Cover	. . . .		2·75
		Presentation Pack	. . . .	3·25	
		Stamp Cards (set of 6)	. . . .	3·00	7·25
		Set of 3 Gutter Blocks of 4	.	5·50	

Plate Nos.: All values 1A, 1B (each ×6)

Sheets: 40 (2 panes 4×5). The two designs for each value printed together, se-tenant, in horizontal pairs throughout the sheets

Imprint: Right-hand corner, bottom margin of each pane

Withdrawn: 24.5.86

274 Queen Alexandra and Victorian Sergeant with Wife

275 Queen Mary and Royal Air Force Family

276 Earl Mountbatten and Royal Navy Family

277 Prince Michael of Kent and Royal Marine with Parents, 1982

Centenary of the Soldiers', Sailors' and Airmen's Families Association

(Des Colleen Corlett. Litho Questa)

1985 (4 SEPT). Perf 14 (C)

296	**274**	12p multicoloured	. . . .	25	20
297	**275**	15p multicoloured	. . . .	35	30
298	**276**	29p multicoloured	. . . .	65	55
299	**277**	34p multicoloured	. . . .	90	85
296/9		Set of 4	. . . .	1·90	1·75
		First Day Cover	. . . .		3·00
		Presentation Pack	. . . .	2·50	
		Set of 4 Gutter Pairs	. . . . . .	4·00	

Plate Nos. 12p, 34p 1A, 1B, 1C, 1D, 1E, 1F, 1G, 1H (each ×6); others 1A, 1B, 1C, 1D, 1E, 1F, 1G, 1H (each ×5)

Sheets: 40 (2 panes 5×4)

Imprint: Right-hand corner, bottom margin of each pane

Withdrawn: 3.9.86

278 Kirk Maughold (Birthplace)

279 Lieut. Gen. Sir Mark Cubbon

280 Memorial Statue, Bangalore, India

Birth Bicentenary of Lieut.-Gen. Sir Mark Cubbon (Indian administrator)

(Des A. Theobald. Litho Questa)

1985 (2 OCT). Perf 14 (C)

300	**278**	12p multicoloured	. . . .	30	25
301	**279**	22p multicoloured	. . . .	70	65
302	**280**	45p multicoloured	. . . .	1·00	95
300/2		Set of 3	. . . .	1·75	1·60
		First Day Cover	. . . .		2·00
		Presentation Pack	. . . .	2·50	
		Set of 3 Gutter pairs	. . . . . .	3·50	

Plate Nos.: All values 1A, 1B, 1C, 1D (each ×4)

Sheets: 40 (2 panes 5×4) 12p or (2 panes 4×5) others

Imprint: Right-hand corner, bottom margin of each pane

Withdrawn: 1.10.86

281 St. Peter's Church, Onchan

282 Royal Chapel of St. John, Tynwald

283 Bride Parish Church

Christmas. Manx Churches

(Des A. Theobald. Litho John Waddington)

1985 (2 OCT). Perf 13×13½ (C)

303	**281**	11p multicoloured	30	25
304	**282**	14p multicoloured	40	35
305	**283**	31p multicoloured	1·00	90
303/5		Set of 3	1·50	1·40
		First Day Cover		1·75
		Presentation Pack	2·00	
		Set of 3 Gutter Pairs	3·00	

Plate Nos.: All values 1A, 1B, 1C, 1D (each ×4)

Sheets: 40 (2 panes 5×4)

Imprint: Right-hand corner, bottom margin of each pane

Withdrawn: 1.10.86

Post Office Yearbook

1985 (9 DEC). *Comprises Nos. 248 and 281/305 in slipcase*
Yearbook . . . . 28·00

Withdrawn: 9.92

Year Pack 1985

1986 (1 JAN). *Comprises Nos. 281/305 with or without No. 248*

Year Pack with No. 248 . . . . . 31·00
Year Pack without No. 248 . . 21·00

Withdrawn: 30.12.86

284 Swimming

285 Race Walking

286 Rifle-shooting

287 Cycling

Commonwealth Games, Edinburgh

(Des C. Abbott. Litho Questa)

1986 (5 FEB). Perf 14½ (C)

306	**284**	12p multicoloured	20	15
307	**285**	15p multicoloured	25	30
308	**286**	31p multicoloured	90	95
309	**287**	34p multicoloured	1·00	95
306/9		Set of 4	2·10	2·10
		First Day Cover		2·50
		Presentation Pack	3·00	
		Set of 4 Gutter Pairs	4·25	

No. 309 also commemorates the 50th anniversary of Manx International Cycling Week.

Plate Nos.: All values 1A, 1B, 1C, 1D (each ×5)

Sheets: 40 (2 panes 5×4)

Imprint: Right-hand corner, bottom margin of each pane

Withdrawn: 4.2.87

288 Viking Necklace and Peel Castle

289 Meayll Circle, Rushen

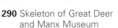

290 Skeleton of Great Deer and Manx Museum

291 Viking Longship Model

292 Open Air Museum, Cregneash

Centenary of Manx Museum

(Des J. Nicholson. Litho Questa)

1986 (5 FEB). Perf 14 (C)

310	**288**	12p multicoloured	20	15
311	**289**	15p multicoloured	25	20
312	**290**	22p multicoloured	65	50
313	**291**	26p multicoloured	80	60
314	**292**	29p multicoloured	90	60
310/14		Set of 5	2·50	1·90
		First Day Cover		2·50
		Presentation Pack	2·75	
		Set of 5 Gutter Pairs	5·00	

Plate Nos.: All values 1A, 1B, 1C, 1D (each ×6)

Sheets: 40 (2 panes 5×4) 12p, 15p, 29p; (2 panes 4×5) others

Imprint: Right-hand corner, bottom margin (12p, 15p, 29p) or bottom left-hand margin (others)

Withdrawn: 4.2.87

293 Viking Longship

294 Celtic Cross Logo

Manx Heritage Year. Booklet stamps

(Des Colleen Corlett. Litho Harrison)

1986 (10 APR). Perf 14½×14 (C)

315	**293**	2p multicoloured	40	40
		a. Booklet pane. Nos. 315×2 and 316×4	2·00	
316	**294**	10p black, apple green and brownish grey	35	35
		a. Booklet pane. No. 316×3 and 3 stamp size labels	1·25	
315/16		Set of 2	90	90
		First Day Cover (Nos. 315×1 and 316×2)		2·00
		Presentation Pack (Nos. 315×1 and 316×2)	1·90	

In addition to Booklets SB14/15 Nos. 315/16 also come from special booklet sheets of 60 containing five each of Nos. 315a and 316a.

Plate Nos.: 1A (×7)

Withdrawn: 25.3.87

295 *Usnea articulata* (lichen) and *Neotinea intacta* (orchid), The Ayres

296 Hen Harrier, Calf of Man

297 Manx Stoat, Eary Chuslin

298 *Stenobothus stigmaticus* (grasshopper), St. Michael's Isle

Europa. Nature and Environment Protection

(Des J. Nicholson and Nancy Corkish. Photo Courvoisier)

1986 (10 APR). Granite paper. Perf 11½ (C)

317	**295**	12p multicoloured	30	30
		a. Horiz pair. Nos. 317/18	60	75
318	**296**	12p multicoloured	30	30
319	**297**	22p multicoloured	60	60
		a. Horiz pair. Nos. 319/20	1·25	1·40
320	**298**	22p multicoloured	60	60
317/20		Set of 4	1·60	1·60
		First Day Cover		2·00
		Presentation Pack	2·10	

Cylinder Nos.: Both values A1–1–1–1–1

Sheets: 20 (4×5). The two designs for each value printed together, *se-tenant*, in horizontal pairs throughout the sheets

Imprint: Central, right-hand margin

Withdrawn: 9.4.87

299 Ellanbane (home of Myles Standish)

300 *Mayflower* crossing the Atlantic, 1620

301 Pilgrim Fathers landing at Plymouth, 1620

302 Captain Myles Standish

**'Ameripex '86' International Stamp Exhibition, Chicago.
Captain Myles Standish of the Mayflower**

(Des C. Abbott. Litho Cartor)

1986 (22 MAY). Perf 13½ (C)

321	**299**	12p multicoloured	20	20
322	**300**	15p multicoloured	25	25
323	**301**	31p multicoloured	90	90
324	**302**	34p multicoloured	95	95
321/4		Set of 4	2·10	2·10
		First Day Cover		2·50
		Presentation Pack	2·40	
MS325		100×75 mm. Nos. 323/4. Perf 12½ .		
		First Day Cover		3·75
		Presentation Pack	2·50	

No. **MS**325 also commemorates the 75th anniversary of
the World Manx Association.

Plate Nos.: All values 1A, 1B, 1C, 1D (each ×5)

Sheets: 20 (5×4)

Imprint: Right-hand corner, bottom margin

Withdrawn: 21.5.87

303 Prince Andrew in   **304** Engagement Photograph
Naval Uniform and
Miss Sarah Ferguson

Royal Wedding

(Des Colleen Corlett. Litho B.D.T.)

1986 (23 JULY). Perf 15×14 (C)

326	**303**	15p multicoloured	25	25
327	**304**	40p multicoloured	1·25	90
326/7		Set of 2	1·50	1·10
		First Day Cover		2·50
		Presentation Pack	2·50	

Plate Nos.: Both values 1A, 1B (each ×5)

Sheets: 20 (4×5)

Imprint: Right-hand corner, bottom margin

Withdrawn: 22.7.87

305 Prince Philip   **306** Queen Elizabeth II

307 Queen Elizabeth II
and Prince Philip

Royal Birthdays

(Des Colleen Corlett. Photo Courvoisier)

1986 (28 AUG). Granite paper. Perf 11½ (C)

328	**305**	15p multicoloured	30	30
		a. Horiz pair. Nos. 328/9	70	70
329	**306**	15p multicoloured	30	30
330	**307**	34p multicoloured	1·10	1·10
328/30		Set of 3	1·60	1·60
		First Day Cover		2·00
		Presentation Pack	2·40	
		Souvenir Folder (complete		
		sheets)	14·00	

Nos. 328/30 also commemorate 'Stockholmia '86' and
350th anniversary of Swedish Post Office.

Cylinder Nos.: 15p A1–1–1–1–1, B1–1–1–1–1, C1–1–1–1–1,
D1–1–1–1–1; 34p A1–1–1–1–1, B1–1–1–1, C1–1–1–1–1,
D1–1–1–1–1

Sheets: 15p 12 (4×3). The two designs printed together, se-tenant,
in horizontal pairs throughout the sheets; 34p 6 (2×3)

Imprint: Central, bottom margin

Withdrawn: 27.8.87

308 European Robins on   **309** Hands releasing Peace
Globe and 'Peace and   Dove
Goodwill' in Braille

310 Clasped Hands and
'Peace' in Sign
Language

161

Christmas and International Peace Year

(Des Colloon Corlett. Litho Questa)

1986 (25 SEPT). Perf 14 (C)

331	**308**	11p multicoloured	30	30
332	**309**	14p multicoloured	30	30
333	**310**	31p multicoloured	80	80
331/3		Set of 3	1·25	1·25
		First Day Cover		1·50
		Presentation Pack	1·75	
		Set of 3 Gutter Pairs	2·75	

No. 331 also commemorates the 50th anniversary of Manx Blind Welfare Society.

Plate Nos.: All values 1A, 1B, 1C, 1D (each ×5)

Sheets: 40 (2 panes 4×5)

Imprint: Right-hand corner, bottom margin of each pane

Withdrawn: 24.9.87

Year Pack 1986

1986 (25 SEPT). *Comprises Nos. 306/33*
Year Pack .... 27·00

Withdrawn: 31.12.87

Post Office Yearbook

1986 (DEC). *Comprises Nos. 306/14, 315a, 316a, 317/27, 328/30 in complete sheets, and 331/3 in slipcase*
Yearbook .... 49·00

Sold out 9.90

311 North Quay

312 Old Fishmarket

313 The Breakwater

314 Jubilee Clock

315 Loch Promenade

316 Beach

Victorian Douglas

(Des A. Theobald. Litho Questa)

1987 (21 JAN–28 MAR). Perf 14×14½ (C)

334	**311**	2p multicoloured (a)	10	10
		a. Booklet pane. Nos. 334×2, 335×2 and 336×4 (2p stamps at top) (b)	1·75	
		ab. Ditto, but 2p stamps at bottom (b)	1·75	
		b. Booklet pane. Nos. 334/7, each ×2 (b)	2·00	
335	**312**	3p multicoloured (a)	10	10
336	**313**	10p multicoloured (a)	25	25
337	**314**	15p multicoloured (a)	30	30
338	**315**	31p multicoloured (a)	90	80
339	**316**	34p multicoloured (a)	1·00	90
334/9		Set of 6	2·40	2·25
		First Day Cover (Nos. 334/9)		2·50
		First Day Covers (2) (se-tenant strips)		5·50
		Presentation Pack (Nos. 334/9)	3·00	
		Set of 6 Gutter Pairs	5·00	

Printings: (a) 21.1.87; (b) 26.3.87

Plate Nos.: All values 1A, 1B, 1C, 1D (each ×4)

Sheets: 40 (2 panes 5×4). In addition to booklets SB16/17 Nos. 334/7 also come from special booklet sheets of 48 containing 6 each of Nos. 334a/b

Imprint: Right-hand corner, bottom margin of each pane

Withdrawn: 20.1.88 sheets; 15.3.88 booklets

317 'The Old Fishmarket and Harbour, Douglas'

318 'Red Sails at Douglas'

319 'The Double Corner, Peel'

320 'Peel Harbour'

Paintings by John Miller Nicholson

(Des A. Theobald. Litho Cartor)

1987 (18 FEB). Perf 13½ (C)

340	**317**	12p multicoloured	20	20
341	**318**	26p multicoloured	70	60

342	**319**	29p multicoloured	. . . .	90	80
343	**320**	34p multicoloured	. . . .	1·00	1·00
340/3		*Set of 4*	. . . .	2·50	2·40
		First Day Cover	. . . .		2·75
		Presentation Pack	. . . .	3·00	
		Set of 4 Gutter Pairs	. . . . . .	5·00	

Plate Nos.: All values 1A, 1B, 1C, 1D (each ×5)

Sheets: 40 (2 panes 5×4)

Imprint: Right-hand corner, bottom margin of each pane

Withdrawn: 17.2.88

321 Sea Terminal, Douglas

322 Tower of Refuge, Douglas

323 Gaiety Theatre, Douglas

324 Villa Marina, Douglas

Europa. Architecture

(Des R. Maddox. Litho B.D.T.)

1987 (29 APR). Perf 13½ (C)

344	**321**	12p multicoloured	. . . .	45	40
		a. Horiz pair. Nos. 344/5	. . . . .	90	1·00
345	**322**	12p multicoloured	. . . .	45	40
346	**323**	22p multicoloured	. . . .	65	50
		a. Horiz pair. Nos. 346/7	. . . . .	1·50	1·75
347	**324**	22p multicoloured	. . . .	65	50
344/7		*Set of 4*	. . . .	2·25	1·60
		First Day Cover	. . . .		2·00
		Presentation Pack	. . . .	2·50	

Plate Nos.: Both values 1A, 1B (each ×5)

Sheets: 10 (2×5). The two designs for each value printed together, *se-tenant*, in horizontal pairs throughout the sheets

Imprint: Central, right-hand margin

Withdrawn: 28.4.88

325 Supercharged BMW 50cc, 1939

326 Manx 'Kneeler' Norton 350cc, 1953

327 MV Agusta 500cc 4, 1956

328 Guzzi 500cc V8, 1957

329 Honda 250cc 6, 1967

80th Anniversary of Tourist Trophy Motor-cycle Races

(Des B. Dix. Litho Cartor)

1987 (27 MAY). Perf 13½×13 (C)

348	**325**	12p multicoloured	. . . .	45	25
349	**326**	15p multicoloured	. . . .	50	35
350	**327**	29p multicoloured	. . . .	90	70
351	**328**	31p multicoloured	. . . .	90	75
352	**329**	34p multicoloured	. . . .	1·00	90
348/52		*Set of 5*	. . . .	3·50	2·75
		First Day Cover	. . . .		4·00
		Presentation Pack	. . . .	4·00	
		Stamp Cards (Set of 5)	. . . .	3·25	4·00
		Set of 5 Gutter Pairs	. . . . . .	7·00	
MS353		150×140 mm. Nos. 348/52. Perf 14×13½ (C)	. . . .	3·50	3·50
		Souvenir Folder	. . . .	6·00	

Nos. 348/53 also commemorate the centenary of the St. John Ambulance Brigade and the miniature sheet also carries the logo of 'Capex '87' International Stamp Exhibition, Toronto on its margin.

Plate Nos.: 12p, 15p, 29p, 31p, 34p 1A, 1B, 1C, 1D (each ×4); miniature sheet 1A (×4)

Sheets: 40 (2 panes 5×4)

Imprint: Right-hand corner, bottom margin of each pane (sheets) or bottom, right-hand margin (miniature sheet)

Withdrawn: 11.6.88

ISLE of MAN 16ᵖ

330 Fuchsia and Wild Roses

ISLE of MAN 29ᵖ

331 Field Scabious and Regwort

ISLE of MAN 31ᵖ

332 Wood Anemone and Celandine

ISLE of MAN 34ᵖ

333 Violets and Primroses

Wild Flowers

(Des Nancy Corkish. Litho Enschedé)

1987 (9 SEPT). Perf 14½×13 (C)

354	**330**	16p multicoloured	. . . .	50	30
355	**331**	29p multicoloured	. . . .	90	80
356	**332**	31p multicoloured	. . . .	90	80
357	**333**	34p multicoloured	. . . .	1·00	80
354/7		Set of 4	. . . .	3·00	2·50
		First Day Cover	. . . .		3·00
		Presentation Pack	. . . .	3·50	

Plate Nos.: All values 1A, 1B (each ×4)

Sheets: 20 (5×4)

Imprint: Right-hand corner, bottom margin

Withdrawn: 8.9.88

334 Stirring the Christmas Pudding

335 Bringing Home the Christmas Tree

336 Decorating the Christmas Tree

Christmas. Victorian Scenes

(Des Colleen Corlett. Litho Questa)

1987 (16 OCT). Perf 14 (C)

358	**334**	12p multicoloured	. . . .	40	35
359	**335**	15p multicoloured	. . . .	50	55
360	**336**	31p multicoloured	. . . .	90	90
358/60		Set of 3	. . . .	1·60	1·60
		First Day Cover	. . . .		2·10
		Presentation Pack	. . . .	2·50	
		Set of 3 Gutter Pairs	. . . . . .	3·25	

Plate Nos.: All values 1A, 1B, 1C, 1D (each ×4)

Sheets: 40 (2 panes 4×5)

Imprint: Right-hand corner, bottom margin of each pane

Withdrawn: 15.10.88

Year Pack 1987

1987 (16 OCT). Comprises Nos. 334/52 and 354/60

Year Pack . . . . 31·00

Withdrawn: 31.12.88

Post Office Yearbook

1987 (DEC). Comprises Nos. 334/43, 344/7 in complete sheets, and **MS**353/60 in slipcase

Yearbook . . . . 40·00

Sold out: 5.91

337 Russell Brookes in Vauxhall Opel (Manx Rally winner, 1985)

338 Ari Vatanen in Ford 'Escort' (Manx Rally winner, 1976)

339 Terry Smith in Ropco 'March 761' (Hill Climb winner, 1980)

340 Nigel Mansell in Williams/ Honda (British Grand Prix winner, 1986 and 1987)

Motor Sport

(Des C. Abbott. Litho Enschedé)

1988 (10 FEB). Perf 13½×14½ (C)

361	**337**	13p multicoloured	75	35
362	**338**	26p multicoloured	1·25	80
363	**339**	31p multicoloured	1·40	90
364	**340**	34p multicoloured	1·60	1·00
361/4		*Set of 4*	4·50	2·75
		First Day Cover		3·50
		Presentation Pack	4·75	

Plate Nos.: All values 1A, 1B (each ×4)

Sheets: 10 (2×5)

Imprint: Central, right-hand margin

Withdrawn: 9.2.89

341 Horse Tram Terminus, Douglas Bay Tramway

342 Snaefell Mountain Railway

343 Marine Drive Tramway

343a Douglas Cable Tramway

344 Douglas Head Incline Railway

345 Douglas and Laxey Coast Electric Tramway Car at Maughold Head

346 Douglas Cable Tramway

347 Manx Northern Railway No. 4, *Caledonia*, at Gob-y-Deigan

348 Laxey Mine Railway Lewin Locomotive *Ant*

349 Port Erin Breakwater Tramway Locomotive *Henry B. Loch*

350 Ramsey Harbour Tramway

351 Locomotive No. 7, *Tynwald*, on Foxdale Line

351a T.P.O. Special leaving Douglas, 3 July 1991

352 Baldwin Reservoir Tramway Steam Locomotive No. 1, *Injebreck*

353 I.M.R. No. 13, *Kissack*, near St. Johns

353a Manx Northern Railway No. 4, *Caledonia*, at Gob-y-Deigan

353b Double-deck Horse Tram, Douglas

354 I.M.R. No. 12, *Hutchinson*, leaving Douglas

355 Groudle Glen Railway Locomotive *Polar Bear*

356 I.M.R. No. 11, *Maitland*, pulling Royal Train, 1963

356a Queen Elizabeth II taking Salute at Trooping the colour

Manx Railways and Tramways, and Queen's Portrait (£2)

(Des Colleen Corlett (£2), A. Theobald (others). Litho B.D.T. (1p to 19p, 21p, 23p), Questa (20p, 25p to £2))

1988 (10 FEB)–**92**. Perf 13 (1p to 19p, 21p, 23p), $14\frac{1}{2} \times 15$ (20p, 25p to £1) or $14\frac{1}{2}$ (£2), all comb

365	**341**	1p multicoloured (a)	10	10
366	**342**	2p multicoloured (a)	10	10
367	**343**	3p multicoloured (a)	10	10
		a. Booklet pane. Nos. 367×2, 370 and 373×2 (b)	3·00	
		b. Booklet pane. Nos. 367×2, 371×2 and 374 (d)	2·50	
367c	**343a**	4p multicoloured (g)	20	10
		ca. Booklet pane. Nos. 367c×3, 374 and 377a	4·00	
		cb. Booklet pane. Nos. 367c×3, 374×4 and 377a . .	4·75	
368	**344**	5p multicoloured (a)	20	20
369	**345**	10p multicoloured (a)	30	30
370	**346**	13p multicoloured (a)	50	50
		a. Booklet pane. Nos. 370×4 and 373×6 (b)	4·00	
371	**347**	14p multicoloured (a)	50	50
		a. Booklet pane. Nos. 371×4 and 374×6 (d)	4·00	
372	**348**	15p multicoloured (af)	50	50
		a. Booklet pane. Nos. 372 and 376×2 (e)	2·75	
		b. Booklet pane. Nos. 372×4 and 376×6 (e)	6·25	
373	**349**	16p multicoloured (a)	50	50
374	**350**	17p multicoloured (ag)	50	50
375	**351**	18p multicoloured (a)	55	55
375a	**351a**	18p multicoloured (h)	70	70
		ab. Booklet pane. Nos. 375a×3 and 377b×2	4·00	
		ac. Booklet pane. Nos. 375a×6 and 377b×4	7·00	
376	**352**	19p multicoloured (af)	60	60
377	**353**	20p multicoloured (c)	60	60
377a	**353a**	21p multicoloured (g)	60	60
377b	**353b**	23p multicoloured (h)	80	80
378	**354**	25p multicoloured (c)	60	60
379	**355**	50p multicoloured (ci)	1·30	1·20
380	**356**	£1 multicoloured (ci)	2·50	2·50
380a	**356a**	£2 multicoloured (e)	5·00	5·00
365/80a		Set of 21	15·00	14·00
		First Day Covers (6)		18·00
		First Day Covers (se-tenant strips) (5)		18·00
		Presentation Packs (4) (ex 4p, 18p (No. 375a), 21p, 23p)	18·00	
		Stamp Cards (1p to £1 ex 4p, 18p (No. 375a), 21p, 23p)	8·00	22·00
		Souvenir Folder (1p to £1 ex 4p, 18p (No. 375a), 21p 23p)	9·00	

Printings: (a) 10.2.88. Inscribed '1988'; (b) 16.3.88. Inscribed '1988'; (c) 21.9.88. Inscribed '1988'; (d) 16.10.89. Inscribed '1989'; (e) 14.2.90. Inscribed '1990'; (f) 1.3.90. Inscribed '1990'; (g) 9.1.91. Inscribed '1991'; (h) 8.1.92. Inscribed '1992'; (i) 16.11.92. Inscribed '1992'

Plate Nos.: 20p, 25p, 50p, £1 1A, 1B (each ×4); £2 1A, 1B (each ×5); others 1A, 1B, 1C, 1D (each ×4)

Sheets: 25 (5×5) (£2) or 50 (5×10) (others). In addition to Booklets Nos. SB18/19 and SB21/4 Nos. 367 and 370/4 also come from special booklet sheets of 50 containing either ten examples of the strips of five or five examples of the strips of ten. No. 372a, a strip of three, was taken from the top or bottom of the strip of ten, No. 372b. The 4p value was only issued in Booklets Nos. SB26/7 and special booklet sheets of 50 containing five vertical strips of No. 367cb, from which No. 367ca could also be obtained, and five extra examples of both Nos. 367c and 377a. In addition to Booklets Nos. SB29/30 No. 375ac was also issued in special booklet sheets of 50 from which No. 375ab could also be obtained.

Imprints: Left-hand margin (£2) or right-hand corner, bottom margin (others).

Withdrawn: 31.12.93 1p to £1; 11.1.94 £2

357 Laying Isle of Man–U.K. Submarine Cable

358 *Flex Service 3* (cable ship)

166

ISLE OF MAN 22P

359 Earth Station, Braddan

22P ISLE OF MAN

360 'INTELSAT 5' Satellite

Europa. Transport and Communications

(Des C. Abbott. Litho Cartor)

1988 (14 APR). Perf 14×13½ (C)

381	**357**	13p multicoloured	50	45
		a. Horiz pair. Nos. 381/2	1·00	90
382	**358**	13p multicoloured	50	45
383	**359**	22p multicoloured	75	75
		a. Horiz pair. Nos. 383/4	1·50	1·50
384	**360**	22p multicoloured	75	75
381/4		Set of 4	2·25	2·20
		First Day Cover		2·50
		Presentation Pack	3·00	

Plate Nos.: Both values 1A, 1B, 1C, 1D (each ×4)

Sheets: 16 (4×4). The two designs of each value printed together, *se-tenant*, in horizontal pairs throughout the sheets

Imprint: Central, right-hand margin

Withdrawn: 13.4.89

361 *Euterpe* (full-rigged ship) off Ramsey, 1863

362 *Vixen* (topsail schooner) leaving Peel for Australia, 1853

363 *Ramsey* (full-rigged ship) off Brisbane, 1870

364 *Star of India* (formerly *Euterpe*) (barque) off San Diego, 1976

Manx Sailing Ships

(Des J. Nicholson. Litho Questa)

1988 (11 MAY). Perf 14 (C)

385	**361**	16p multicoloured	45	30
386	**362**	29p multicoloured	90	90
387	**363**	31p multicoloured	90	90
388	**364**	34p multicoloured	1·10	1·10
385/8		Set of 4	3·00	2·75
		First Day Cover		3·25
		Presentation Pack	3·75	
MS389	110×85 mm. Nos. 385 and 388		1·90	2·00
		First Day Cover		3·00
		Presentation Pack	2·50	

Nos. 386/7 also commemorate the Bicentenary of Australian Settlement.

Plate Nos.: All values 1A, 1B (each ×5)

Sheets: 15 (3×5)

Imprint: Bottom, left-hand margin

Withdrawn: 10.5.89

365 'Magellanica'

366 'Pink Cloud'

367 'Leonora'

368 'Satellite'

369 'Preston Guild'

370 'Thalia'

50th Anniversary of British Fuchsia Society

(Des Colleen Corlett. Litho Enschedé)

1988 (21 SEPT). Perf 13½×14 (C)

390	**365**	13p multicoloured	40	25
391	**366**	16p multicoloured	45	35
392	**367**	22p multicoloured	65	50
393	**368**	29p multicoloured	90	65
394	**369**	31p multicoloured	1·00	70
395	**370**	34p multicoloured	1·10	70
390/5		Set of 6	4·00	3·00
		First Day Cover		3·75
		Presentation Pack	5·00	

Plate Nos.: All values 1A, 1B (each ×5)

Sheets: 20 (4×5)

Imprint: Right-hand margin

Withdrawn: 20.9.89

371 Long-eared Owl

372 European Robin

376 Tortoiseshell and White
Cat

377 Tortoiseshell Cat

373 Grey Partridge

Christmas. Manx Birds

(Des Audrey North. Litho Questa)

1988 (12 OCT). Perf 14 (C)

396	**371**	12p multicoloured	40	30
397	**372**	15p multicoloured	60	65
398	**373**	31p multicoloured	1·25	1·25
396/8		Set of 3	2·00	2·00
		First Day Cover		2·50
		Presentation Pack	2·75	
		Set of 3 Gutter Pairs	4·00	

Plate Nos.: All values 1A, 1B, 1C, 1D (each ×5)

Sheets: 40 (2 panes 5×4)

Imprint: Right-hand corner, bottom margin of each pane

Withdrawn: 11.10.89

Year Pack 1988

1988 (1 NOV). *Comprises Nos. 361/7, 368/75, 376/7, 378/80
and* 381/98

Year Pack	40·00

Withdrawn: 31.12.89

Post Office Yearbook

1988 (1 DEC). *Comprises Nos. 361/7, 368/75, 376/7, 378/80
and* 381/98 *in slipcase*

Yearbook	45·00

Sold out: By 9.93

Manx Cats

(Des P. Layton. Litho Questa)

1989 (8 FEB). Perf 14 (C)

399	**374**	16p multicoloured	50	25
400	**375**	27p multicoloured	90	85
401	**376**	30p multicoloured	1·25	85
402	**377**	40p multicoloured	1·50	1·25
399/402		Set of 4	3·75	2·75
		First Day Cover		3·50
		Presentation Pack	4·50	
		Stamp Cards (set of 4)	3·00	8·00
		Set of 4 Gutter Pairs	7·50	

Plate Nos.: 16p, 27p 1C, 1D, 1G, 1H (each ×4); 30p, 40p 1A, 1B, 1E,
1F (each ×4)

Sheets: 40 (2 panes 5×4)

Imprint: Right-hand corner, bottom margin of each pane

Withdrawn: 7.2.90

378 Tudric Pewter
Clock, *c.* 1903

379 'Celtic Cross'
Watercolour

380 Silver Cup
and Cover,
1902–03

374 Ginger Cat

381 Gold and Silver
Brooches from
Liberty's Cymric
Range

382 Silver Jewel Box,
1900

125th Anniversary of Archibald Knox (artist and designer)

(Des Colleen Corlett. Litho Cartor)

1989 (8 FEB). Perf 13 (C)

403	**378**	13p multicoloured	40	20
404	**379**	16p multicoloured	50	25
405	**380**	23p multicoloured	65	50
406	**381**	32p multicoloured	1·25	1·00
407	**382**	35p multicoloured	1·40	1·00
403/7		Set of 5	3·75	2·75
		First Day Cover		3·00
		Presentation Pack	4·00	
		Set of 5 Gutter Pairs	7·50	

Plate Nos.: All values 1A, 1B, 1C, 1D (each ×5)

Sheets: 40 (2 panes 4×5) 13p, 16p, 23p; (2 panes 5×4) others

Imprint: Bottom, left-hand margin of each pane (13p, 16p, 23p) or right-hand corner, bottom margin of each pane

Withdrawn: 7.2.90

383 William Bligh and Old Church, Onchan

384 Bligh and Loyal Crew cast Adrift

385 Pitcairn Islands 1989 Bicentenary 90c. Stamp

386 Norfolk Island 1989 39c. Bounty Stamp

387 Midshipman Peter Heywood and Tahiti

388 H.M.S. Bounty anchored off Pitcairn

389 Fletcher Christian and Pitcairn Island

Bicentenary of the Mutiny on the Bounty

(Des C. Abbott. Litho B.D.T.)

1989 (28 APR). Perf 14 (C)

408	**383**	13p multicoloured	40	20
		a. Booklet pane. Nos. 408/10 and 412/14	4·25	
		b. Booklet pane. Nos. 408/9 and 411/14	4·00	
409	**384**	16p multicoloured	45	30
410	**385**	23p multicoloured	1·00	1·00
		a. Booklet pane. Nos. 410/11, each ×3	5·50	
411	**386**	27p multicoloured	1·00	1·00
412	**387**	30p multicoloured	70	60
413	**388**	32p multicoloured	70	60
414	**389**	35p multicoloured	70	60
408/14		Set of 7	4·50	4·00
		First Day Cover (ex Nos. 410/11)		4·75
		Presentation Pack (ex Nos. 410/11)	5·50	
MS415	110×85 mm. Nos. 410/11 and 414 .		4·00	4·25
		First Day Cover		4·75

Plate Nos.: 13p, 16p, 30p, 32p, 35p 1A, 1B (each ×4)

Sheets: 20 (4×5) 13p, 16p, 30p, 32p, 35p. The 23p and 27p values were only issued in £5.30 booklets and in the miniature sheet. Booklet panes Nos. 408a/b and 410a each contain two vertical rows of three stamps, separated by a central gutter

Imprint: 13p, 16p, 30p, 32p, 35p Central, left-hand margin

Withdrawn: 27.4.90 13, 16, 30, 32, 35p

390 Skipping and Hopscotch

391 Wheelbarrow, Leapfrog and Piggyback

392 Building Model House and Blowing Bubbles

393 Girl and Doll and Doll's House

Europa. Childrens Games

(Des Colleen Corlett. Litho Enschedé)

1989 (17 MAY). Perf 13½ (C)

416	**390**	13p multicoloured	45	50
		a. Horiz pair. Nos. 416/17	90	1·00
417	**391**	13p multicoloured	45	50

418	**392**	23p multicoloured	70	75
		a. *Horiz pair. Nos.* 418/19	1·40	1·50
419	**393**	23p multicoloured	70	75
416/19		*Set of 4*	2·10	2·25
		First Day Cover		2·75
		Presentation Pack	3·00	

Plate Nos.: Both values 1A, 1B (each ×4)

Sheets: 20 (4×5). The two designs for each value printed together, *se-tenant*, in horizontal pairs throughout the sheets

Imprint: Central, right-hand margin

Withdrawn: 16.5.90

394 Atlantic Puffin

395 Black Guillemot

396 Great Cormorant

397 Black-legged Kittiwake

Sea Birds

(Des W. Oliver. Litho Questa)

1989 (20 SEPT). Perf 14 (C)

420	**394**	13p multicoloured	55	55
		a. *Strip of 4. Nos.* 420/3	2·25	
		ab. *Black ptd double*		
421	**395**	13p multicoloured	55	55
422	**396**	13p multicoloured	55	55
423	**397**	13p multicoloured	55	55
420/3		*Set of 4*	2·25	2·25
		First Day Cover		2·75
		Presentation Pack	3·00	

In addition to a double image of the black printing on the design some examples of No. 420*ab* also show three additional impressions of the imprint at the foot of each stamp.

Examples of Nos. 420/3 sold at 'World Stamp Expo '89', held at Washington D.C. between 17 November and 3 December 1989, carried a commemorative inscription on the bottom sheet margin.

Plate Nos.: 1A, 1B, 1C, 1D (each ×4)

Sheets: 16 (4×4). The four designs were printed together, *se-tenant*, in horizontal and vertical strips throughout the sheet which exists with or without perforations across the side margins

Imprint: Central, right-hand margin

Withdrawn: 19.9.90

398 Red Cross Cadets learning Resuscitation

399 Anniversary Logo

400 Signing Geneva Convention, 1864

401 Red Cross Ambulance

402 Henri Dunant (founder)

125th Anniversary of International Red Cross and Centenary of Noble's Hospital, Isle of Man

(Des A. Theobald. Litho Questa)

1989 (16 OCT). Perf 14 (C)

424	**398**	14p multicoloured	40	30
425	**399**	17p grey and orange-vermilion	60	35
426	**400**	23p multicoloured	75	85
427	**401**	30p multicoloured	1·00	1·10
428	**402**	35p multicoloured	1·25	1·25
424/8		*Set of 5*	3·75	3·50
		First Day Cover		3·75
		Presentation Pack	4·50	
		Set of 5 Gutter Pairs	7·50	

Plate Nos.: 14p, 30p 1A, 1B, 1C, 1D (each ×5); 17p 1A, 1B, 1C, 1D (each ×2); 23p, 35p 1A, 1B, 1C, 1D (each ×4)

Sheets: 40 (2 panes 5×4)

Imprint: Right-hand corner, bottom margin of each pane

Withdrawn: 15.10.90

403 Mother with Baby, Jane Crookall Maternity Home

404 Mother with Child

405 Madonna and Child

406 Baptism, St. Ninian's Church

Christmas. 50th Anniversary of Jane Crookall Maternity Home and 75th Anniversary of St. Ninian's Church, Douglas

(Des Colleen Corlett. Litho Questa)

1989 (16 OCT). Perf 14½ (C)

429	**403**	13p multicoloured	....	50	45
430	**404**	16p multicoloured	....	60	60
431	**405**	34p multicoloured	....	1·10	1·25
432	**406**	37p multicoloured	....	1·25	1·40
429/32		Set of 4	....	3·00	3·25
		First Day Cover	....		3·75
		Presentation Pack	....	3·75	
		Set of 4 Gutter Pairs	......	6·00	

Plate Nos.: 13p, 34p 1A, 1B, 1C, 1D (each ×5); 16p, 37p 1A, 1B, 1C, 1D (each ×4)

Sheets: 40 (2 panes 4×5)

Imprint: Right-hand corner, bottom margin of each pane

Withdrawn: 15.10.90

Year Pack 1989

1989 (16 OCT). *Comprises Nos. 399/409 and 412/32*
Year Pack .... 33·00

Withdrawn: 31.12.90

Post Office Yearbook

1989 (NOV). *Comprises Nos. 399/409, 412/19, 420/3 in complete sheet, and 424/32 in slipcase*
Yearbook .... 41·00

Sold out: By 9.93

407 'The Isle of Man Express going up a Gradient'

408 'A way we have in the Isle of Man'

409 'Douglas – waiting for the Male Boat'

410 'The Last Toast Rack Home, Douglas Parade'

411 'The Last Isle of Man Boat'

Isle of Man Edwardian Postcards

(Des D. Swinton. Litho B.D.T.)

1990 (14 FEB). Perf 14 (C)

433	**407**	15p multicoloured	....	35	35
434	**408**	19p multicoloured	....	60	50
435	**409**	32p multicoloured	....	1·10	80
436	**410**	34p multicoloured	....	1·50	1·10
437	**411**	37p multicoloured	....	1·60	1·50
433/7		Set of 5	....	4·50	3·75
		First Day Cover	....		4·50
		Presentation Pack	....	5·50	
		Stamp Cards (set of 5)	....	3·00	6·50
		Set of 5 Gutter Pairs	......	9·00	

Plate Nos.: All values 1A, 1B, 1C, 1D (each ×4)

Sheets: 40 (2 panes 5×4)

Imprint: Right-hand corner, bottom margin of each pane

Withdrawn: 13.2.91

412 Modern Postman

413 Ramsey Post Office, 1990

414 Postman,
1890

415 Douglas Post Office,
1890

Europa. Post Office Buildings

(Des A. Kellett. Litho Cartor)

1990 (18 APR). Perf 13½ (C)

438	**412**	15p multicoloured	55	55
		a. Horiz pair. Nos. 438/9	1·10	1·10
439	**413**	15p multicoloured	55	55
440	**414**	24p multicoloured	90	80
		a. Horiz pair. Nos. 440/1	1·90	1·75
441	**415**	24p multicoloured	90	80
438/41		Set of 4	2·75	2·40
		First Day Cover		3·00
		Presentation Pack	3·25	

Plate Nos.: Both values 1A, 1B (each ×4)

Sheets: 20 (4×5). The two designs for each value printed together, *se-tenant*, in horizontal pairs throughout the sheets.

Withdrawn 17.4.91

416 Penny Black

417 Wyon Medal, 1837

418 Wyon's Stamp Essay

419 Perkins Bacon Engine-turned Essay, 1839

420 Twopence Blue, 1840

421 Marginal Block of Four Penny Blacks

150th Anniversary of the Penny Black

(Des Colleen Corlett. Eng Inge Madle (No. **MS**447). Recess and litho (No. **MS**447) or litho (others) Enschedé)

1990 (3 MAY). Perf 14×13½ (C)

442	**416**	1p black, buff and gold	15	15
		a. Sheetlet. Horiz strip of 5. Nos. 442/6	4·00	
		b. Sheetlet. No. 442×25	2·25	
		c. Booklet pane. No. 442×8 with margins all round	1·10	
443	**417**	19p gold, black and buff	60	50
		a. Booklet pane. Nos. 443/6×2 with margins all round	7·00	
444	**418**	32p multicoloured	1·25	1·10
445	**419**	34p multicoloured	1·50	1·10
446	**420**	37p multicoloured	1·60	1·10
442/6		Set of 5	4·50	3·75
		First Day Cover		5·50
		Presentation Pack	5·00	
MS447		100×71 mm. **421** £1 black, gold and buff	4·00	3·50
		First Day Cover		4·75
		Presentation Pack	4·75	

Sheetlet No. 442a was reissued on 24 August 1990 overprinted 'From STAMP WORLD LONDON '90 to NEW ZEALAND 1990' for sale at the New Zealand exhibition.

The Penny Black stamps shown on Nos. 442b/c each have different corner letters at foot. The sheetlet of 25 was issued in conjunction with a special postal concession which allowed hand-addresses personal mail for the island to be posted for 1p between 10 am and 12 noon on 6 May 1990.

No. **MS**447 also commemorates 'Stamp World London '90' International Stamp Exhibition, London.

Plate Nos.: No. 442b, 1A, 1B (each ×3)

Sheets: 5 (5×1) containing Nos. 442/6 *se-tenant*, or 25 (5×5) No. 442 only

Imprint: No. 442a. Bottom margin, right-hand corner. No. 442b. Central, bottom margin

Withdrawn: 2.5.91

422 Queen Elizabeth the Queen Mother

90th Birthday of Queen Elizabeth the Queen Mother

(Des Colleen Corlett. Litho B.D.T.)

1990 (4 AUG). Perf 13×13½ (C)

448	**442**	90p multicoloured	3·00	3·00
		First Day Cover		3·75
		Presentation Pack	4·00	

Plate Nos.: 1A, 1B (each ×5)

Sheets: 20 (5×4) containing ten stamps and ten *se-tenant* inscribed labels

Imprint: Central, right-hand margin

Withdrawn: 3.8.91

423 Hawker Hurricane MK 1, Bristol Type 142 Blenheim Mk 1 and Home Defence

424 Supermarine Spitfire, Westland Lysander Mk I and Vickers Walrus with Launch

425 Rearming Hawker Hurricane MK I Fighters

426 Ops Room and Scramble

427 Civil Defence Personnel

428 Anti-aircraft Battery

50th Anniversary of the Battle of Britain

(Des A. Theobald. Litho Questa)

1990 (5 SEPT). Perf 14 (C)

449	**423**	15p multicoloured	35	35
		a. Horiz pair. Nos. 449/50	70	70
450	**424**	15p multicoloured	35	35
451	**425**	24p multicoloured	80	80
		a. Horiz pair. Nos. 451/2	1·60	1·60
452	**426**	24p multicoloured	80	80
453	**427**	29p multicoloured	1·00	1·00
		a. Horiz pair. Nos. 453/4	2·00	2·00
454	**428**	29p multicoloured	1·00	1·00
449/54		Set of 6	4·00	4·00
		First Day Cover		5·00
		Presentation Pack	4·75	
		Souvenir Folder (complete sheets)	18·00	

Plate Nos.: All values 1A, 1B (each ×4)

Sheets: 8 (2×4). The two designs of each value were printed together, *se-tenant*, in horizontal pairs throughout the sheet, each showing composite panel at foot of Dover cliffs (15p), Weald landscape (24p) or London skyline (29p)

Withdrawn: 4.9.91

429 Churchill with Freedom of Douglas Casket

430 Churchill and London Blitz

431 Churchill and Searchlights over Westminster

432 Churchill with Hawker Hurricane MK I Fighters

25th Death Anniversary of Sir Winston Churchill

(Des C. Abbott. Litho Cartor)

1990 (5 SEPT). Perf 13½ (C)

455	**429**	19p multicoloured	45	45
456	**430**	32p multicoloured	1·00	1·00
457	**431**	34p multicoloured	1·25	1·25
458	**432**	37p multicoloured	1·25	1·25
455/8		Set of 4	3·50	3·50
		First Day Cover		4·00
		Presentation Pack	4·00	
		Set of 4 Gutter Pairs	7·00	

Plate Nos.: All values 1A, 1B, 1C, 1D (each ×5)

Sheets: 40 (2 panes 5×4)

Imprint: Right-hand corner, bottom margin of each pane

Withdrawn: 4.9.91

433 Boy on Toboggan and Girl posting Letter

434 Girl on Toboggan and Skaters

435 Boy with Snowman

436 Children throwing Snowballs

Christmas

(Des C. Abbott. Litho B.D.T.)

1990 (10 OCT). Perf 13×13½ (C)

459	**433**	14p multicoloured	40	40
460	**434**	18p multicoloured	50	50
461	**435**	34p multicoloured	1·00	1·00
462	**436**	37p multicoloured	1·25	1·25
459/62		Set of 4	2·75	2·75
		First Day Cover		3·50
		Presentation Pack	3·75	
		Set of 4 Gutter Pairs	5·50	
MS463	123×55 mm. As Nos. 459/62 but face values in black		3·00	3·75
	a. Blue (inscriptions) omitted	£600		
	First Day Cover			4·25
	Presentation Pack	4·00		

Plate Nos.: 18p 1A, 1B, 1C, 1D (each ×5); others 1A, 1B, 1C, 1D (each ×6)

Sheets: 40 (2 panes 4×5)

Imprint: Right-hand corner, bottom margin of each pane

Withdrawn: 9.10.91

Year Pack 1990

1990 (10 OCT). Comprises Nos. 380a and 433/63
Year Pack .... 41·00

Withdrawn: 31.12.91

Post Office Yearbook

1990 (DEC). Comprises Nos. 380a, 433/41, 422a/b, **MS**447 and 448/63 in slipcase
Yearbook .... 50·00

Sold out: By 9.93

437 Henry Bloom Noble and Orphans (Marshall Wane)

438 Douglas (Frederick Frith)

439 Studio Portrait of Three Children (Hilda Newby)

440 Cashtal yn Ard (Christopher Killip)

441 Peel Castle (Colleen Corlett)

Manx Photography

(Des Colleen Corlett. Litho Walsall)

1991 (9 JAN). Perf 14 (C)

464	**437**	17p blackish brn, pale brownish grey and black	35	35
465	**438**	21p deep brown and ochre	50	50
466	**439**	26p blackish brown, stone and brownish black	65	65
467	**440**	31p agate, pale grey-brown & blk	90	90
468	**441**	40p multicoloured	1·10	1·10
464/8		Set of 5	3·25	3·25
		First Day Cover		4·50
		Presentation Pack	4·50	

Plate Nos: 21p 1A–1A, 1B–AB, 40p 1A, 1B (each ×4); others 1A, 1B (each ×3)

Sheets: 20 (4×5)

Imprint: Central, right-hand margin

Withdrawn: 8.1.92

442 Lifeboat, *Sir William Hillary*, Douglas

443 *Osman Gabriel*, Port Erin

444 *Ann and James Ritchie*, Ramsey

445 *The Gough Ritchie*, Port St. Mary

446 *John Batstone*, Peel

447 'Intelsat' Communications Satellite

448 'Ariane' Rocket Launch and Fishing Boats in Douglas Harbour

449 Weather Satellite and Space Station

450 Ronaldsway Airport, Manx Radio Transmitter and Space Shuttle Launch

Europa. Europe in Space

(Des D. Miller. Litho B.D.T.)

1991 (24 APR). Perf 14 (C)

474	**447**	17p multicoloured	....	70	70
		a. Vert pair. Nos. 474/5	......	1·40	1·40
475	**448**	17p multicoloured	....	70	70
476	**449**	26p multicoloured	....	1·00	1·00
		a. Vert pair. Nos. 476/7	......	2·00	2·00
477	**450**	26p multicoloured	....	1·00	1·00
474/7		*Set of 4*	....	3·00	3·00
		First Day Cover	....		3·75
		Presentation Pack	....		3·75

Plate Nos.: Both values 1A, 1B (each ×4)

Sheets: 20 (5×4). The two designs for each value printed together, *se-tenant*, in vertical pairs throughout the sheets, each pair forming a composite design

Imprint: Central, right-hand margin

Withdrawn: 23.4.92

451 Oliver Godfrey with Indian 500cc at Start, 1911

452 Freddie Dixon on Douglas 'Banking' Sidecar, 1923

Manx Lifeboats

(Des A. Peck. Litho Questa)

1991 (13 FEB). Perf 14 (C)

469	**442**	17p multicoloured	....	45	45
470	**443**	21p multicoloured	....	55	55
		a. Black ptg double	....		
471	**444**	26p multicoloured	....	90	90
472	**445**	31p multicoloured	....	1·25	1·25
473	**446**	37p multicoloured	....	1·40	1·40
469/73		*Set of 5*	....	4·00	4·00
		First Day Cover	....		4·50
		Presentation Pack	....	4·50	
		Set of 5 Gutter Pairs	......	8·00	

No. 469 is inscribed 'HILARY' and No. 471 'JAMES & ANN RITCHIE', both in error.

Plate Nos.: All values 1A, 1B, 1C, 1D (each ×4)

Sheets: 40 (2 panes 5×4)

Imprint: Right-hand corner, bottom margin of each pane

Withdrawn: 12.2.92

453 Bill Ivy on Yamaha 125cc, 1968

454 Giacomo Agostini on MV Agusta 500cc, 1972

455 Joey Dunlop on RVF Honda 750cc, 1985

LAXEY HAND-CART

456 Laxey Hand-cart, 1920

DOUGLAS HORSE DRAWN STEAMER

457 Horse-drawn Steamer, Douglas, 1909

MERRYWEATHER HATFIELD PUMP

458 Merryweather 'Hatfield' Pump, 1936

DENNIS F8 PUMPING APPLIANCE

459 Dennis 'F8' Pumping Appliance, Peel, 1953

VOLVO TURNTABLE LADDER

460 Volvo Turntable Ladder, Douglas, 1989

80th Anniversary of Tourist Trophy Mountain Course

(Des A. Theobald. Litho Enschedé)

1991 (30 MAY). Perf 14½×13 (C)

478	**451**	17p multicoloured	50	40
479	**452**	21p multicoloured	65	60
480	**453**	26p multicoloured	80	80
481	**454**	31p multicoloured	1·25	1·10
482	**455**	37p multicoloured	1·50	1·50
478/82		*Set of 5*	4·25	4·00
		First Day Cover		4·50
		Presentation Pack	4·75	
		Stamp Cards (set of 5)	3·00	6·00
		Set of 5 Gutter Pairs	8·50	
MS483		149×144 mm. Nos. 478/82	4·00	4·00
		First Day Cover		5·00
		Souvenir Folder	5·50	

No. **MS**483 was reissued on 16 November 1991 overprinted for the Phila Nippon exhibition, Japan.

Plate Nos.: All values 1A, 1B, 1C, 1D (each ×4)

Sheets: 40 (2 panes 5×4)

Imprint: Right-hand corner, bottom margin of each pane

Withdrawn: 29.5.92

Ninth Conference of Commonwealth Postal Administrations, Douglas

(Des Colleen Corlett. Litho B.D.T.)

1991 (1 JULY). Perf 13 (C)

MS484	119×77 mm. Nos. 367c and 377a,		
	each ×2	1·90	2·00
	First Day Cover		2·50
	Presentation Pack	2·75	

Withdrawn: 30.6.92

Fire Engines

(Des C. Abbott. Litho Questa)

1991 (18 SEPT). Perf 14½ (C)

485	**456**	17p multicoloured	45	40
486	**457**	21p multicoloured	65	65
487	**458**	30p multicoloured	85	90
488	**459**	33p multicoloured	1·25	1·25
489	**460**	37p multicoloured	1·40	1·50
485/9		*Set of 5*	4·25	4·25
		First Day Cover		4·75
		Presentation Pack	4·75	
		Set of 5 Gutter Pairs	8·50	

Plate Nos.: All values 1A, 1B, 1C, 1D (each ×5)

Sheets: 40 (2 panes 4×5)

Imprint: Central, gutter margin

Withdrawn: 17.9.92

461 Mute Swans, Douglas Harbour

462 Black Swans, Curraghs Wildlife Park

463 Whooper Swans, Bishop's Dub, Ballaugh

464 Tundra ('Bewick's') Swans, Eairy Dam, Foxdale

465 Coscoroba Swans, Curraghs Wildlife Park

466 Whooper ('Trumpeter') Swans, Curraghs Wildlife Park

Swans

(Des Colleen Corlett. Litho Cartor)

1991 (18 SEPT). Perf 13 (C)

490	**461**	17p multicoloured	40	40
		a. Horiz pair. Nos. 490/1	80	90
491	**462**	17p multicoloured	40	40
492	**463**	26p multicoloured	1·10	1·00
		a. Horiz pair. Nos. 492/3	2·10	2·00
493	**464**	26p multicoloured	1·10	1·00
494	**465**	37p multicoloured	1·20	1·25
		a. Horiz pair. Nos. 494/5	2·40	2·50
		ab. Black ptg double		
495	**466**	37p multicoloured	1·20	1·25
490/5		Set of 6	5·00	4·75
		First Day Cover		6·00
		Presentation Pack	5·25	

Plate Nos: All values 1A, 1B (each ×4)

Sheets: 20 (4×5). The two designs of each value were printed together, *se-tenant*, in horizontal pairs throughout the sheets, with the backgrounds forming composite designs

Imprint: Central, bottom margin

Withdrawn: 17.9.92

467 The Three Kings

468 Mary with Manger

469 Shepherds with Sheep

470 Choir of Angels

Christmas. Paper Sculptures

(Des D. Swinton. Litho Walsall)

1991 (14 OCT). (a) *Sheet stamps.* Perf 14×14½ (C)

496	**467**	16p multicoloured	45	35
497	**468**	20p multicoloured	65	70
498	**469**	26p multicoloured	85	85
499	**470**	37p multicoloured	1·10	1·10
496/9		Set of 4	2·75	2·50
		First Day Cover		3·25
		Presentation Pack	3·50	

Plate Nos: All values 1A, 1B, 1C, 1D (each ×4)

Sheets: 40 (2 panes 4×5)

Imprint: Central, gutter margin

Withdrawn: 13.10.92

(b) *Booklet stamps. Self-adhesive. Stamps die-cut*

500	**467**	16p multicoloured	60	60
		a. Booklet pane. Nos. 500×8 and 501×4	7·50	
501	**468**	20p multicoloured	1·25	1·25

Year Pack 1991

1991 (14 OCT). *Comprises Nos. 367c, 377a, 464/82 and* **MS**484/99

Year Pack .... 40·00

Withdrawn: 31.12.92

Post Office Yearbook

1991 (14 OCT). *Comprises Nos. 367c, 377a, 464/82 and* **MS**484/99

Yearbook .... 45·00

Withdrawn: 30.11.94

471 North African and Italian Campaigns, 1942–43

472 D-Day, 1944

473 Arnhem, 1944

474 Rhine Crossing, 1945

475 Operations in Near, Middle and Far East, 1945–68

476 Liberation of Falkland Islands, 1982

50th Anniversary of Parachute Regiment

(Des A. Theobald. Litho Questa)

1992 (6 FEB). Perf 14 (C)

502	**471**	23p multicoloured	. . . .	70	70
		a. Horiz pair. Nos. 502/3	. . . . .	1·50	1·50
503	**472**	23p multicoloured	. . . .	70	70
504	**473**	28p multicoloured	. . . .	80	80
		a. Horiz pair. Nos. 504/5	. . . . .	1·60	1·75
505	**474**	28p multicoloured	. . . .	80	80
506	**475**	39p multicoloured	. . . .	1·25	1·25
		a. Horiz pair. Nos. 506/7	. . . . .	2·50	2·75
507	**476**	39p multicoloured	. . . .	1·25	1·25
502/7		Set of 6	. . . .	5·00	5·00
		First Day Cover	. . . .		6·00
		Presentation Pack	. . . .	6·00	
		Souvenir Folder (complete sheets)	. . . .	24·00	

Plate Nos: All values 1A, 1B (each ×5)

Sheets: 8 (2×4). The two designs of each value were printed together, *se-tenant*, in horizontal pairs throughout the sheets

Imprint: Top, left-hand margin

Withdrawn: 5.2.93

477 Queen Elizabeth II at Coronation, 1953

478 Queen visiting Isle of Man, 1979

479 Queen in Evening Dress

480 Queen visiting Isle of Man, 1989

481 Queen arriving for Film Premiere, 1990

40th Anniversary of Accession

(Des D. Miller. Litho B.D.T.)

1992 (6 FEB). Perf 14 (C)

508	**477**	18p multicoloured	. . . .	45	40
509	**478**	23p multicoloured	. . . .	60	60
510	**479**	28p multicoloured	. . . .	70	70
511	**480**	33p multicoloured	. . . .	1·25	1·40
512	**481**	39p multicoloured	. . . .	1·40	1·40
508/12		Set of 5	. . . .	4·00	4·00
		First Day Cover	. . . .		5·00
		Presentation Pack	. . . .	4·50	

Plate Nos: All values 1A, 1B (each ×5)

Sheets: 20 (5×4)

Imprint: Central, bottom margin

Withdrawn: 5.2.93

482 Brittle-stars

483 Phytoplankton

484 Atlantic Herring

485 Great Scallop

486 Dahlia Anemone and Delesseria

Centenary of Port Erin Marine Laboratory

(Des Jennifer Toombs. Litho Questa)

1992 (16 APR). Perf 14×14½ (C)

513	**482**	18p multicoloured	40	35
514	**483**	23p multicoloured	60	55
515	**484**	28p multicoloured	60	55
516	**485**	33p multicoloured	1·25	1·25
517	**486**	39p multicoloured	1·50	1·25
513/17		Set of 5	4·00	3·50
		First Day Cover		4·50
		Presentation Pack	4·75	
		Set of 5 Gutter Pairs	8·00	

Plate Nos.: All values 1A, 1B, 1C, 1D (each ×4)

Sheets: 40 (2 panes 5×4)

Imprint: Top right-hand side, gutter margin

Withdrawn: 15.4.93

487 The Pilgrim Fathers embarking at Delfshaven

488 *Speedwell* leaving Delfshaven

489 '*Mayflower* and *Speedwell* at Dartmouth' **490** (L. Wilcox)

Europa. 500th Anniversary of Discovery of America by Columbus

(Des C. Abbott. Litho Enschedé)

1992 (16 APR). Perf 14×13½ (C)

518	**487**	18p multicoloured	80	80
		a. Horiz pair. Nos. 518/19	1·60	1·60
519	**488**	18p multicoloured	80	80
520	**489**	28p multicoloured	1·75	1·75
		a. Horiz pair. Nos. 520/1	3·50	3·50

521	**490**	28p multicoloured	1·75	1·75
518/21		Set of 4	4·50	4·50
		First Day Cover		5·00
		Presentation Pack	5·25	

Plate Nos.: Both values 1A, 1B (each ×5)

Sheets: 20 (4×5). The two designs of each value were printed together, *se-tenant*, in horizontal pairs throughout the sheets, each pair forming a composite design

Imprint: Central, bottom margin

Withdrawn: 15.4.93

491 Central Pacific Locomotive *Jupiter*, 1869

492 Union Pacific Locomotive No. 119, 1869

493 Union Pacific Locomotive No. 844, 1992

494 Union Pacific Locomotive No. 3985, 1992

495 Golden Spike Ceremony, 10 May 1869
(*illustration reduced. Actual size 105×73 mm*)

Construction of Union Pacific Railroad, 1866–69

(Des A. Peck. Litho Enschedé)

1992 (22 MAY). Perf 13½×14 (C)

522	**491**	33p multicoloured	90	1·00
		a. Horiz pair. Nos. 522/3 plus label	2·50	2·50
		b. Booklet pane. Nos. 522/5×2 and **MS**526	10·00	
523	**492**	33p multicoloured	90	1·00

524	**493**	39p multicoloured	1·25	1·50
		a. *Horiz. pair. Nos.* 524/5 *plus*		
		label . . . . , ,	3·00	3·00
525	**494**	39p multicoloured	1·25	1·50
522/5		Set of 4	4·00	4·50
		First Day Cover		5·00
		Presentation Pack	5·50	
		Souvenir Folder (sheets of		
		10)	22·00	
		Stamp Cards (set of 4)	3·25	6·50
MS526	105×73 mm. **495** £1·50, mult	3·70	4·50
		First Day Cover		7·00
		Presentation Pack	5·50	
		Stamp Card	70	

Booklet pane No. 522*b* contains two blocks of four of Nos. 522/5 with No. **MS**526 between them. Miniature sheets from the booklet show a white margin and line of roulettes at left and right. In the blocks of four each horizontal pair is separated by a half stamp-size label.

Plate Nos.: Both values 1A, 1B (each ×4)

Sheets: 10 (2×5). The two designs for each value were printed together in horizontal pairs separated by a half stamp-size label showing Union Pacific emblem or portraits of Dan and Jack Casement (railroad contractors)

Imprint: Central, right-hand margin

Withdrawn: 21.5.93

496 *King Orry V* in Douglas Harbour

497 Castletown

498 Port St. Mary

499 Ramsey

Manx Harbours

(Des Colleen Corlett. Litho Walsall)

1992 (18 SEPT). Perf 14½×14 (C)

527	**496**	18p multicoloured	45	45
528	**497**	23p multicoloured	55	55
529	**498**	37p multicoloured	1·25	1·25
530	**499**	40p multicoloured	1·25	1·25
527/30		Set of 4	3·25	3·25
		First Day Cover		3·75
		Presentation Pack . . .	4·00	

Plate Nos.: All values 1A, 1B (each ×4)

Sheets: 10 (2×5)

Imprint: Right-hand corner, bottom margin

Withdrawn: 17.9.93

500 *King Orry V* (ex *Saint Eloi*) in 1972 and 1992 (*illustration reduced. Actual size* 111×68 *mm*)

'Genova '92' International Thematic Stamp Exhibition

(Des Colleen Corlett. Litho Walsall)

1992 (18 SEPT). Sheet 111×68 *mm*. Perf 14½×14 (C)

MS531	**500**	18p, £1 multicoloured	3·25	3·50
		First Day Cover		3·75
		Presentation Pack	4·00	

Withdrawn: 17.9.93

501 Window, St. German's Cathedral, Peel

502 Reredos, St. Matthew the Apostle, Douglas

503 Window, St. George's, Douglas

504 Reredos, St. Mary of the Isle Catholic Church, Douglas

505 Window, Trinity Methodist Church, Douglas

Christmas. Manx Churches

(Des Colleen Corlett, Litho Questa)

1992 (13 OCT). Perf 14½ (C)

532	**501**	17p multicoloured	45	40
533	**502**	22p multicoloured	65	65
534	**503**	28p multicoloured	80	80
535	**504**	37p multicoloured	95	95
536	**505**	40p multicoloured	1·00	1·00
		a. Gold ptg double		
532/6		Set of 5	3·50	3·50
		First Day Cover		4·25
		Presentation Pack	4·25	
		Set of 5 Gutter Pairs	7·00	

Plate Nos.: 17p, 22p 1A, 1B, 1C, 1D (each ×5); others 1A, 1B (each ×5)

Sheets: 40 (2 panes 4×5)

Imprint: Right-hand corner, bottom margin of each pane

Withdrawn: 12.10.93

Year Pack 1992

1992 (13 OCT). Comprises Nos. 502/36

Year Pack .... 40·00

Withdrawn: 31.12.93

Post Office Yearbook

1992 (13 OCT). Comprises Nos. 375a, 377b, 502/36 and D25

Yearbook .... 45·00

Withdrawn: 30.11.94

506 Mansell on Lap of Honour, British Grand Prix, 1992

507 Mansell in French Grand Prix, 1992

Nigel Mansell's Victory in Formula 1 World Motor Racing Championship

(Des A. Theobald. Litho Walsall)

1992 (8 NOV). Perf 13½ (C)

537	**506**	20p multicoloured	80	80
538	**507**	24p multicoloured	1·00	1·00
537/8		Set of 2	1·75	1·75
		First Day Cover		2·75
		Presentation Pack	2·75	

Plate Nos.: Both values 1A, 1B (each ×4)

Sheets: 50 (5×10)

Imprint: Bottom margin

Withdrawn: 7.11.93

508 H.M.S. Amazon (frigate)

509 Fingal (lighthouse tender)

510 Sir Winston Churchill (cadet schooner)

511 Dar Mlodziezy (full-rigged cadet ship)

512 Tynwald I (paddle-steamer)

513 Ben Veg (freighter)

514 Waverley (paddle-steamer)

515 Royal Yacht Britannia

516 Francis Drake (ketch)

517 Royal Viking Sky (liner)

518 Lord Nelson (cadet barque)

519 Europa (liner)

520 *Snaefell V* (ferry) leaving Androssan

520a *Seacat* (caramaran ferry)

521 *Lady of Man I* (ferry) off Ramsey

522 *Mona's Queen II* (paddle ferry) leaving Fleetwood

523 *Queen Elizabeth 2* (liner) and *Mona's Queen V* (ferry) off Liverpool

523a Manx Red Ensign

523b Queen Elizabeth II (hologram)

Ships

(Des A. Theobald (1p to 27p), J. Nicholson (30p, 40p, 50p, £1), Colleen Corlett (£2, £5). Litho Questa (£2), Walsall (£5) (hologram by Applied Holographics), Enschedé (others))

1993 (4 JAN)–**97**. Perf 14½ (£2), 14½×14 (£5) or 13½×13 (others), all comb

539	**508**	1p multicoloured (*a*)	. . . .	10	10
540	**509**	2p multicoloured (*a*)	. . . .	10	10
541	**510**	4p multicoloured (*a*)	. . . .	10	10
		a. Booklet pane. Nos. 541, 544 and 548 each ×2 (g)	. . . . . .	3·50	
542	**511**	5p multicoloured (*a*)	. . . .	10	10
543	**512**	20p multicoloured (*ae*)	. . . .	40	25
		a. Booklet pane. Nos. 542×2 and 547×3	. . . .	3·00	
		b. Booklet pane. Nos. 543×4 and 547×6	. . . .	5·50	
544	**513**	21p multicoloured (*ag*)	. . . .	50	50
545	**514**	22p multicoloured (*a*)	. . . .	50	50
546	**515**	23p multicoloured (*a*)	. . . .	66	55
547	**516**	24p multicoloured (*aH*)	. . . .	50	36
548	**517**	25p multicoloured (*ag*)	. . . .	60	60
549	**518**	26p multicoloured (*a*)	. . . .	65	65
550	**519**	27p multicoloured (*a*)	. . . .	65	65
551	**520**	30p multicoloured (*b*)	. . . .	75	75
552	**520a**	35p multicoloured (*f*)	. . . .	85	85
553	**521**	40p multicoloured (*b*)	. . . .	1·00	90
554	**522**	50p multicoloured (*b*)	. . . .	1·25	1·10
555	**523**	£1 multicoloured (*bg*)	. . . .	2·50	2·40
556	**523a**	£2 multicoloured (*c*)	. . . .	3·75	4·00
557	**523b**	£5 multicoloured (*d*)	. . . .	10·00	11·00
539/57		*Set of 19*	. . . .	22·00	22·00
		First Day Covers (6)	. . . . . .		30·00
		Presentation Packs (6)	. . . . .	30·00	
		Stamp Cards (Nos. 539/51, 553/5)	. . . .	8·00	22·00
		Souvenir Folder (Nos. 539/51, 553/5)	. . . .	12·00	

For 4p, 20p and 24p in similar designs, but smaller, see Nos. 687/93.

Printings: (*a*) 4.1.93. Inscribed '1993'; (*b*) 15.9.93. Inscribed '1993'; (*c*) 12.1.94. Inscribed '1994'; (*d*) 5.7.94. Inscribed '1994'; (*e*) 8.2.95. Inscribed '1995'; (*f*) 11.1.1996. Inscribed '1996'; (*g*) 14.5.97. Inscribed '1997'

Plate Nos.: £2, £5 1A, 1B (each ×4); others 1A, 1B, 1C, 1D (each ×4)

Sheets: 25 (5×5) (£2), 10 (5×2) (£5) or 50 (5×10) (others). In addition to stamp booklets Nos. 543*a*/*b* also come from a special booklet sheet of 50 (5×10) which provides either 10 examples of No. 543*a* or 5 of 543*b*. No. 541*a* comes from a special booklet sheet of 30 (5×6)

Imprint: Central, bottom margin (£2, £5) or right-hand corner, bottom margin (others)

Withdrawn: 30.11.98 1p to £1; 12.1.99 £2; 5.7.99 £5

524 No. 1 Motor Car and No. 13 Trailer at Groudle Glen Hotel

525 No. 9 Tunnel Car and No. 19 Trailer at Douglas Bay Hotel

526 No. 19 Motor Car and No. 59 Royal Trailer Special at Douglas Bay

527 No. 33 Motor Car, No. 45 Trailer and No. 13 Van at Derby Castle

Centenary of Manx Electric Railway

(Des A. Theobald. Litho B.D.T.)

1993 (3 FEB). Perf 14 (C)

559	**524**	20p multicoloured	60	60
		a. Boolet pane. Nos. 559/62 . .	3·50	
560	**525**	24p multicoloured	90	90
561	**526**	28p multicoloured	1·00	1·00
562	**527**	39p multicoloured	1·40	1·40
559/62		Set of 4	3·50	3·50
		First Day Cover		3·75
		Presentation Pack	3·75	

Booklet pane No. 559a exists in four versions, which differ in the order of the stamps within the block of four and in the information printed on the pane margin.

Plate Nos.: All values 1A, 1B (each ×4)

Sheets: 10 (2×5)

Imprint: Central, left-hand margin

Withdrawn: 2.2.94

528 'Sir Hall Caine' (statue)

529 'The Brass Bedstead' (painting)

530 Abstract Bronze Sculpture

531 'Polar Bear Skeleton' (drawing)

Europa. Contemporary Art by Bryan Kneale

(Des Colleen Corlett. Litho B.D.T.)

1993 (14 APR). Perf 14 (C)

563	**528**	20p multicoloured	60	60
		a. Horiz pair. Nos. 563/4	1·25	1·25
564	**529**	20p multicoloured	60	60

565	**530**	28p multicoloured	1·00	1·00
		a. Horiz pair. Nos. 565/6	2·00	2·00
566	**531**	28p multicoloured	1·00	1·00
563/6		Set of 4	3·00	3·00
		First Day Cover		3·50
		Presentation Pack	3·50	

Plate Nos.: Both values 1A, 1B, 1C (each ×4)

Sheets: 20 (4×5). The two designs for each value printed together, se-tenant, in horizontal pairs throughout the sheets

Imprint: Central, right-hand margin

Withdrawn: 13.4.94

532 Graham Oates and Bill Marshall (1933 International Six Day Trial) on Ariel Square Four

533 Sergeant Geoff Duke (1947 Royal Signals Display Team) on Triumph 3T Twin

534 Dennis Parkinson (1953 Senior Manx Grand Prix) on Manx Norton

535 Richard Swallow (1991 Junior Classic MGP) on Aermacchi

536 Steve Colley (1992 Scottish Six Day Trial) on Beta Zero

Manx Motor Cycling Events

(Des C. Abbott. Litho Walsall)

1993 (3 JUNE). Perf 13½×14 (C)

567	**532**	20p multicoloured	35	35
568	**533**	24p multicoloured	45	45
569	**534**	28p multicoloured	70	60
570	**535**	33p multicoloured	90	90

571	**536**	39p multicoloured	. . . .	1·00	95
567/71		Set of 5	. . . .	3·00	3·00
		First Day Cover	. . . .		4·00
		Presentation Pack	. . . . . .	4·50	
		Stamp Cards (set of 5)	. . . .	3·00	6·00
MS572		165×120 mm. Nos. 567/71	. . . . . .	4·50	4·50
		Souvenir Folder	. . . .	4·75	

Plate Nos.: All values 1A, 1B, 1C, 1D (each ×4)

Sheets: 20 (4×5)

Imprint: Right-hand corner, bottom margin

Withdrawn: 2.6.94

537 *Inachis io*
(Peacock)

538 *Argynnis aglaja*
(Dark Green
Fritillary)

539 *Cynthia cardui*
(Painted Lady)

540 *Celastrina argiolus*
(Holly Blue)

541 *Vanessa atalanta* (Red Admiral)

Butterflies

(Des Colleen Corlett. Litho Questa)

1993 (15 SEPT). Perf 14½ (C)

573	**537**	24p multicoloured	. . . .	75	65
		a. Horiz strip of 5. Nos. 573/7	.	3·50	
574	**538**	24p multicoloured	. . . .	75	65
575	**539**	24p multicoloured	. . . .	75	65
576	**540**	24p multicoloured	. . . .	75	65
577	**541**	24p multicoloured	. . . .	75	65
573/7		Set of 5	. . . .	3·50	3·00
		First Day Cover	. . . .		4·25
		Presentation Pack	. . . .	4·00	

Examples of Nos. 573/7 sold at 'Philakorea '94' and 'Singpex '94' come with commemorative cachets on the bottom margin.

Plate Nos.: 1A, 1B (each ×4)

Sheets: 20 (5×4). The five designs for each value printed together, *se-tenant*, in horizontal strips throughout the sheets

Imprint: Right-hand corner, bottom margin

Withdrawn: 14.9.94

542 Children
decorating
Christmas
Tree

543 Girl with
Snowman

544 Boy opening
Presents

545 Girl with
Teddy Bear

546 Children with Toboggan

Christmas

(Des Christine Haworth. Litho Questa)

1993 (12 OCT). Perf 14 (C)

578	**542**	19p multicoloured	. . . .	50	50
579	**543**	23p multicoloured	. . . .	60	60
580	**544**	28p multicoloured	. . . .	70	70
581	**545**	39p multicoloured	. . . .	1·10	1·10
582	**546**	40p multicoloured	. . . .	1·10	1·10
578/82		Set of 5	. . . .	3·50	3·50
		First Day Cover	. . . .		4·00
		Presentation Pack	. . . .	4·25	
		Set of 5 Gutter Pairs	. . . . . .	7·00	

Plate Nos.: All values 1A, 1B, 1C, 1D (each ×4)
Sheets: 40 (2 panes 4×5)
Imprint: Bottom, right-hand margin of each pane
Withdrawn: 11.10.94

Year Pack 1993
1993 (12 OCT). *Comprises Nos. 539/51, 553/5, 559/71 and 573/82*

Year Pack .... 32·00

Withdrawn: 31.12.94

Post Office Yearbook
1993 (12 OCT). *Comprises Nos. 539/51, 553/5, 559/71 and 573/82*

Yearbook .... 40·00

Sold out: 8.95

547 White-throated Robin

548 Black-eared Wheatear

549 Goldcrest

550 Northern Oriole

551 River Kingfisher

552 Hoopoe

553 Black-billed Magpie
(illustration reduced. Actual size 100×71 mm)

Calf of Man Bird Observatory
(Des Colleen Corlett. Litho B.D.T.)

1994 (18 FEB). Perf 13½×13 (No. **MS**589) or 14 (others), both comb

583	**547**	20p multicoloured	50	60
		a. Pair. Nos. 583/4	1·00	1·25
584	**548**	20p multicoloured	50	60
585	**549**	24p multicoloured	80	90
		a. Pair. Nos. 585/6	1·60	1·75
586	**550**	24p multicoloured	80	90
587	**551**	30p multicoloured	1·00	1·10
		a. Pair. Nos. 587/8	2·00	2·25
588	**552**	30p multicoloured	1·00	1·10
583/8		Set of 6	4·25	4·75
		First Day Cover		5·00
		Presentation Pack	5·00	
		Souvenir Folder (complete sheets)		20·00
MS589		100×71 mm. **553** £1 multicoloured	3·00	3·50
		First Day Cover		4·50
		Presentation Pack	3·50	

No. **MS**589 also commemorates the 'Hong Kong '94' philatelic exhibition.

Plate Nos.: All values 1A, 1B (each ×4)
Sheets: 10 (2×5). The two designs for each value printed together, *se-tenant*, in horizontal and vertical pairs throughout the sheets
Imprint: Central, right-hand margin
Withdrawn: 17.2.95

554 Gaiety Theatre, Douglas **555** Sports

556 Artist at work and Yachts racing

557 T.T. Races and British Aerospace Hawk T.1s of Red Arrows

558 Musical Instruments

559 Laxey Wheel and Manx Cat

560 Tower of Refuge, Douglas, with Bucket and Spade

561 Cyclist

562 Tynwald Day and Classic Car

563 Santa Mince Pie Train, Groudle Glen

Booklet Stamps. Manx Tourism Centenary

(Des Colleen Corlett. Litho Cartor)

1994 (18 FEB). Perf 13½ (C)

590	**554**	24p multicoloured	65	60
		a. Booklet pane. Nos. 590/9		
		with margins all round	6·00	
591	**555**	24p multicoloured	65	60
592	**556**	24p multicoloured	65	60
593	**557**	24p multicoloured	65	60
594	**558**	24p multicoloured	65	60
595	**559**	24p multicoloured	65	60
596	**560**	24p multicoloured	65	60
597	**561**	24p multicoloured	65	60
598	**562**	24p multicoloured	65	60
599	**563**	24p multicoloured	65	60
590/9		Set of 10	6·00	5·50
		First Day Cover		6·50
		Presentation Pack	6·50	
		Stamp Cards (set of 3)	1·50	

Nos. 590/9 were only issued in £2.40 stamp booklets.

Withdrawn: 17.2.95

564 Eubranchus tricolor (sea slug)

565 Loligo forbesii (common squid)

566 Edward Forbes and Signature

567 Solaster moretonis (fossil starfish)

568 Adamsia carciniopados (anemone) on Hermit Crab

569 Solaster endeca (starfish)

Europa. Discoveries of Edward Forbes (marine biologist)

(Des Jennifer Toombs. Litho Enschedé)

1994 (5 MAY). Perf 13×14½ (C)

600	**564**	20p multicoloured	50	50
		a. Horiz strip of 3. Nos. 600/2 .	1·50	
601	**565**	20p multicoloured	50	50
602	**566**	20p multicoloured	50	50
603	**567**	30p multicoloured	90	90
		a. Horiz strip of 3. Nos. 603/5 .	2·75	
604	**568**	30p multicoloured	90	90
605	**569**	30p multicoloured	90	90
600/5		Set of 6	3·75	3·75
		First Day Cover		4·25
		Presentation Pack	4·50	

Plate Nos.: Both values 1A, 1B (each ×4)

Sheets: 15 (3×5). The three designs for each value printed together, se-tenant, in horizontal strips of 3 throughout the sheets

Imprint: Central, bottom margin

Withdrawn: 4.5.95

570 Maj.-Gen. Bedell Smith and Naval Landing Force including Ben-My-Chree IV (ferry)

571 Admiral Ramsay and Naval Ships including Victoria and Lady of Man (ferries)

186

572 Gen. Motgomery and British Landings

573 Lt.-Gen. Dempsey and 2nd Army Landings

574 Air Chief Marshal Leigh-Mallory, U.S. Paratroops and Aircraft

575 Air Chief Marshal Tedder, British Paratroops and Aircraft

576 Lt.-Gen. Bradley and U.S. 1st Army Landings

577 Gen. Eisenhower and American Landings

50th Anniversary of D-Day

(Des A. Theobald. Litho Questa)

1994 (6 JUNE). Perf 14 (C)

606	**570**	4p multicoloured	15	15
		a. Horiz pair. Nos. 606/7	30	30
607	**571**	4p multicoloured	15	15
608	**572**	20p multicoloured	70	70
		a. Horiz pair. Nos. 608/9	1·40	1·40
609	**573**	20p multicoloured	70	70
610	**574**	30p multicoloured	1·00	1·00
		a. Horiz pair. Nos. 610/11	2·00	2·00
611	**575**	30p multicoloured	1·00	1·00
612	**576**	41p multicoloured	1·25	1·25
		a. Horiz pair. Nos. 612/13	2·50	2·50
613	**577**	41p multicoloured	1·25	1·25
606/13		Set of 8	5·50	5·50
		First Day Cover		6·00
		Presentation Pack	6·25	
		Souvenir Folder (complete sheets)	26·00	

Plate Nos.: All values 1A, 1B (each ×5)

Sheets: 8 (2×4). The two designs for each value printed together, *setenant*, in horizontal pairs throughout the sheets

Imprint: Central, left-hand margin

Withdrawn: 5.6.95

578 Postman Pat, Jess and Ffinlo at Sea Terminal, Douglas

579 Laxey Wheel

580 Cregneash

581 Manx Electric Railway Trains

582 Peel Harbour

583 Douglas Promenade

584 Postman Pat, Jess, Policeman and Children at Zebra Crossing
(*illustration reduced. Actual size* 110×85 mm)

Postman Pat visits the Isle of Man

(Des Colleen Corlett. Litho B.D.T.)

1994 (14 SEPT). Perf 13 (No. **MS**620) or 15×14 (others), both comb

614	**578**	1p multicoloured	15	15
		a. Booklet pane of 2 with margins all round	50	
615	**579**	20p multicoloured	60	60
		a. Booklet pane of 2 with margins all round	1·75	
616	**580**	24p multicoloured	80	80
		a. Booklet pane of 2 with margins all round	2·25	
617	**581**	30p multicoloured	90	90
		a. Booklet pane of 2 with margins all round	2·50	
618	**582**	36p multicoloured	1·10	1·10
		a. Booklet pane of 2 with margins all round	2·75	
619	**583**	41p multicoloured	1·25	1·25
		a. Booklet pane of 2 with margins all round	3·25	
614/19		*Set of 6 . . . .*	4·25	4·25
		First Day Cover		4·50
		Presentation Pack	4·50	
		Stamp Cards (set of 6)	3·00	7·50
MS620		110×85 mm. **584** £1 multicoloured	2·25	2·25
		First Day Cover		3·00
		Presentation Pack	3·00	

Examples of No. **MS**620 from stamp booklets show a line of roulettes at left.

Plate Nos.: All values 1A, 1B (each ×4)

Sheets: 10 (2×5)

Imprint: Right-hand corner, bottom margin

Withdrawn: 13.9.95

585 Cycling

586 Downhill Skiing

587 Swimming

588 Hurdling

589 Centenary Logo

Centenary of International Olympic Committee

(Des D. Miller. Litho Walsall)

1994 (11 OCT). Perf 14×14½ (C)

621	**585**	10p multicoloured	35	25
622	**586**	20p multicoloured	55	50
623	**587**	24p multicoloured	70	65
624	**588**	35p multicoloured	95	90
625	**589**	48p multicoloured	1·60	1·25
621/5		*Set of 5 . . . .*	3·75	3·25
		First Day Cover		3·75
		Presentation Pack	4·00	

Plate Nos.: 10p 1A (×4); 20p 1B (×4); 24p 1C (×4); 35p 1D (×4); 48p 1E (×4)

Sheets: 20 (5×4)

Imprint: Central, left-hand margin

Withdrawn: 10.10.95

590 Santa Train to Santon

591 Father Christmas and Postman Pat on Mini Tractor, Douglas

592 Father Christmas and Majorettes in Sleigh, Port St. Mary

Christmas. Father Christmas in the Isle of Man

(Des Colleen Corlett. Litho Cartor)

1994 (11 OCT). Perf 13½×14 (23p) or 14×13½ (others), all comb

626	**590**	19p multicoloured	60	60
627	**591**	23p multicoloured	80	80
628	**592**	60p multicoloured	2·00	2·00
626/8		*Set of 3 . . . .*	3·00	3·00
		First Day Cover		3·50
		Presentation Pack	3·75	
		Set of 3 Gutter Pairs	6·00	

Plate Nos.: All values 1A, 1B, 1C, 1D (each ×4)

Sheets: 40 (2 panes 5×4)

Imprint: Central, side margins of each pane

Withdrawn: 10.10.95

Year Pack 1994

1994 (11 OCT). *Comprises Nos. 556 and 583/628, with or without No. 557*

> Year Pack with No. 557 . . . . 50·00
> Year Pack without No. 557 . 40·00

Withdrawn: 31.12.95

Post Office Yearbook

1994 (NOV). *Comprises Nos. 556/7 and 583/628*

> Yearbook . . . . 55·00

Sold out: 3.96

593 Foden Steam Wagon, Highway Board Depot, Douglas

594 Clayton and Shuttleworth and Fowler engines pulling Dead Whale

595 Wallis and Steevens at Ramsey Harbour

596 Marshall Engine with Threshing Machine, Ballarhenny

597 Marshall Convertible Steam Roller

Steam Traction Engines

(Des A. Peck. Litho Enschedé)

1995 (8 FEB). Perf 13½×13 (C)

629	**593**	20p multicoloured	. . . .	55	60
630	**594**	24p multicoloured	. . . .	60	70
631	**595**	30p multicoloured	. . . .	80	85
632	**596**	35p multicoloured	. . . .	1·10	1·10
633	**597**	41p multicoloured	. . . .	1·10	1·25
629/33		*Set of 5*		3·75	4·00
		First Day Cover			4·50
		Presentation Pack	4·50		

Plate Nos.: 35p 1A, 1B, 1C, 1D (each ×4); others 1A, 1B (each ×4)

Sheets: 20 (4×5)

Withdrawn: 7.2.96

598 Car No. 2 and First Train, 1895

599 Car No. 4 in Green Livery and Car No. 3 in Laxey Valley

600 Car No. 6 and Car No. 5 in 1971

601 Goods Car No. 7 and *Caledonia* Steam Locomotive pulling Construction Train

602 Passenger Car and Argus Char-a-banc at Bungalow Hotel (*illustration reduced. Actual size 110×87 mm*)

603 Peace Doves forming Wave and Tower of Refuge, Douglas Bay

604 Peace Dove breaking Barbed Wire

Centenary of Snaefell Mountain Railway

(Des A. Theobald. Litho B.D.T.)

1995 (8 FEB). Perf 14 (C)

634	**598**	20p multicoloured	70	70
		a. Booklet pane. Nos. 634/7 with margins all round	3·50	
635	**599**	24p multicoloured	80	80
636	**600**	35p multicoloured	1·10	1·10
637	**601**	42p multicoloured	1·25	1·25
634/7		Set of 4	3·50	3·50
		First Day Cover		4·25
		Presentation Pack	4·50	
MS638		110×87 mm. **602** £1 multicoloured	3·25	3·25
		a. Booklet pane. As No. **MS**638 with additional margins all round showing further inscriptions at right and left .	3·75	
		First Day Cover		3·75
		Presentation Pack	4·00	

Booklet pane No. 634*a* exists in three versions which differ in the order of the stamps within the block of four.

Examples of No. **MS**638 from booklet No. SB39 show a white margin, description of the design and line of roulettes at left and an additional inscription, '1895. CENTENARY SNAEFELL MOUNTAIN RAILWAY. 1995', vertically in the margin at right.

Plate Nos.: All values 1A, 1B (each ×4)

Sheets: 10 (2×5)

Imprint: Central, left-hand margin

Withdrawn: 7.2.96

Europa. Peace and Freedom

(Des Colleen Corlett and M. Magleby (20p), Colleen Corlett (30p). Litho Enschedé)

1995 (28 APR). Perf 14×13½ (C)

639	**603**	20p multicoloured	60	75
640	**604**	30p multicoloured	1·00	1·00
639/40		Set of 2	1·60	1·75
		First Day Cover		2·25
		Presentation Pack	2·40	

Plate Nos.: Both values 1A, 1B (each ×5)

Sheets: 10 (5×2)

Imprint: Central, bottom margin

Withdrawn: 27.4.96

605 Spitfire, Tank and Medals

606 Typhoon, Anti-aircraft Gun and Medals

607 Lancaster, H.M.S. *Biter* (escort carrier) and Medals

608 U.S. Navy Aircraft, Jungle Patrol and Medals

609 Celebrations in Parliament Square

610 V.E. Day Bonfire

611 Street Party

612 King George VI and Queen Elizabeth on Isle of Man in July, 1945

50th Anniversary of End of Second World War

(Des A. Theobald. Litho B.D.T.)

1995 (8 MAY). Perf 14 (C)

641	**605**	10p multicoloured	30	30
		a. Horiz pair. Nos. 641/2	60	60
642	**606**	10p multicoloured	30	30
643	**607**	20p multicoloured	55	55
		a. Horiz pair. Nos. 643/4	1·10	1·10
644	**608**	20p multicoloured	55	55
645	**609**	24p multicoloured	70	70
		a. Horiz pair. Nos. 645/6	1·40	1·40
646	**610**	24p multicoloured	70	70
647	**611**	40p multicoloured	1·10	1·10
		a. Horiz pair. Nos. 647/8	2·25	2·25
648	**612**	40p multicoloured	1·10	1·10
641/8		Set of 8	4·75	4·75
		First Day Cover		5·50
		Presentation Pack	5·50	
		Souvenir Folder (complete sheets)	19·00	

Plate Nos.: All values 1A, 1B, 1C (each ×4)

Sheets: 8 (2×4). The two designs for each value printed together, *se-tenant*, in horizontal pairs throughout the sheets

Imprint: Central, left-hand margin

Withdrawn: 7.5.96

613 Reg Parnell in Maserati '4 CLT', 1951

614 Stirling Moss in Frazer Nash, 1951

615 Richard Seaman in Delage, 1936

616 Prince Bira in ERA R2B 'Romulus', 1937

617 Kenelm Guinness in Sunbeam 1, 1914

618 Freddie Dixon in Riley, 1934

619 John Napier in Arrol Johnston, 1905 (*illustration reduced. Actual size* 103×73 mm)

90th Anniversary of Motor Racing on Isle of Man

(Des N. Sykes. Litho Questa)

1995 (8 MAY). Perf 14 (C)

649	**613**	20p multicoloured	65	60
650	**614**	24p multicoloured	80	75
651	**615**	30p multicoloured	90	85
652	**616**	36p multicoloured	1·10	1·00
653	**617**	41p multicoloured	1·25	1·10
654	**618**	42p multicoloured	1·25	1·10
649/54		Set of 6	5·50	5·00
		First Day Cover		5·50
		Presentation Pack	6·00	
MS655		103×73 mm. **619** £1 multicoloured	3·00	3·00
		First Day Cover		3·25
		Presentation Pack	3·25	

Plate Nos.: All values 1A, 1B (each ×5)

Sheets: 20 (5×4)

Imprint: Right hand corner, bottom margin

Withdrawn: 7.5.96

620 Thomas the Tank Engine and Bertie Bus being Unloaded

621 Mail Train

622 Bertie and Engines at Ballasalla

623 Viking the Diesel Engine, Port Erin

624 Thomas and Railcar at Snaefell Summit

625 Engines racing past Laxey Wheel

50th Anniversary of Thomas the Tank Engine Stories by Revd. Awdry. 'Thomas the Tank Engine's Dream

(Des O. Bell. Litho B.D.T.)

1995 (15 AUG). Perf 14 (C)

656	**620**	20p multicoloured	65	60
		a. Booklet pane. Nos. 656/7 with margins all round	1·50	
		b. Booklet pane. Nos. 656 and 661 with margins all round	2·00	
657	**621**	24p multicoloured	80	75
		a. Booklet pane. Nos. 657/8 with margins all round	1·50	
658	**622**	30p multicoloured	90	85
		a. Booklet pane. Nos. 658/9 with margins all round	1·75	
659	**623**	36p multicoloured	1·10	1·00
		a. Booklet pane. Nos. 659/60 with margins all round	2·00	
660	**624**	41p multicoloured	1·25	1·10
		a. Booklet pane. Nos. 660/1 with margins all round	2·25	

661	**625**	45p multicoloured	1·50	1·25
656/61		Set of 6	5·50	5·00
		First Day Cover		5·50
		Presentation Pack	6·00	
		Stamp Cards (set of 6)	3·00	9·00

Plate Nos.: All values 1A, 1B (each ×4)

Sheets: 10 (2×5)

Imprint: Central, bottom margin

Withdrawn: 14.8.96

626 Amanita muscaria

627 Boletus edulis

628 Coprinus disseminatus

629 Pleurotus ostreatus

630 Geastrum triplex

631 Shaggy Ink and Bee Orchid
(illustration reduced. Actual size 100×71 mm)

192

Fungi

(Des Colleen Corlett. Litho Enschedé)

1995 (1 SEPT). Perf 13½ (C)

662	**626**	20p multicoloured	40	40
663	**627**	24p multicoloured	50	50
664	**628**	30p multicoloured	60	60
665	**629**	35p multicoloured	75	75
666	**630**	45p multicoloured	1·25	1·25
662/6		Set of 5	3·25	3·25
		First Day Cover		4·00
		Presentation Pack	4·75	
MS667		100×71 mm. **631** £1 multicoloured	3·00	3·50
		First Day Cover		3·50
		Presentation Pack	3·50	

No. **MS**667 is inscribed 'Singapore World Stamp Exhibition 1st–10th September 1995' on the sheet margin.

Plate Nos.: All values 1A, 1B, 1C (each ×4)

Sheets: 20 (4×5)

Imprint: Right-hand corner, bottom margin

Withdrawn: 31.8.96

632 St. Catherine's Church, Port Erin

633 European Robin on Holly Branch

634 St. Peter's Church and Wild Flowers

635 Hedgehog hibernating under Farm Machinery

Christmas

(Des Colleen Corlett. Litho B.D.T.)

1995 (10 OCT). Perf 14 (C)

668	**632**	19p multicoloured	55	55
669	**633**	23p multicoloured	70	70
670	**634**	42p multicoloured	1·50	1·50
671	**635**	50p multicoloured	1·75	1·75
668/71		Set of 4	4·00	4·00
		First Day Cover		4·50
		Presentation Pack	4·50	
		Set of 4 Gutter Pairs	8·00	

Plate Nos.: All values 1A, 1B, 1C (each ×4)

Sheets: 40 (2 panes 5×4)

Imprint: Right-hand corner, bottom margin

Withdrawn: 9.10.96

Year Pack 1995

1995 (10 OCT). Comprises Nos. 629/71

Year Pack . . . . 42·00

Withdrawn: 31.12.96

Post Office Yearbook

1995 (OCT). Comprises Nos. 629/38, 639/40 in sheets of 10 and 641/71

Yearbook . . . . 45·00

Sold out: By 5.97

636 Langness Lighthouse

637 Point of Ayre Lighthouse

638 Chicken Rock Lighthouse

639 Calf of Man Lighthouse

640 Douglas Head Lighthouse

641 Maughold Head Lighthouse

Lighthouses

(Des D. Swinton. Litho Questa)

1996 (24 JAN). Perf 14 (C)

672	**636**	20p multicoloured	50	50
		a. Booklet pane. No. 672×4 with margins all round	2·25	
673	**637**	24p multicoloured	60	60
		a. Booklet pane. No. 673×4 with margins all round	3·00	
674	**638**	30p multicoloured	90	90
		a. Booklet pane. Nos. 674 and 676, each ×2, with margins all round	3·75	
675	**639**	36p multicoloured	1·00	1·00
		a. Booklet pane. Nos. 675 and 677, each ×2, with margins all round	4·00	
676	**640**	41p multicoloured	1·10	1·10
677	**641**	42p multicoloured	1·25	1·25
672/7		Set of 6	5·00	5·00
		First Day Cover		5·50
		Presentation Pack	5·50	
		Set of 6 Gutter Pairs	10·00	

Plate Nos.: All values 1A, 1B (each ×5)

Sheets: 40 (2 panes 4×5) 20p, 30p, 41p; (2 panes 5×4) others

Imprint: Central, left-hand margin (20p, 30p, 41p) or central, bottom margin (others)

Withdrawn: 22.1.97

642 White Manx Cat and Celtic Interlaced Ribbons

643 Cat and Union Jack Ribbons

644 Cat on Rug in German Colours, Mouse and Brandenburg Gate

645 Cat, U.S.A. Flag and Statue of Liberty

646 Cat, Map of Australia and Kangaroo

647 Cat and Kittens
(*illustration reduced. Actual size 100×71 mm*)

Manx Cats

(Des Nancy Corkish. Litho B.D.T.)

1996 (14 MAR). Perf 13×13 (No. **MS**683) or 14 (others), both comb

678	**642**	20p multicoloured	50	50
679	**643**	24p multicoloured	60	60
680	**644**	36p multicoloured	90	90
681	**645**	42p multicoloured	1·10	1·10
682	**646**	48p multicoloured	1·25	1·25
678/82		Set of 5	4·00	4·00
		First Day Cover		5·00
		Presentation Pack	5·00	
		Stamp Cards (set of 5)	2·50	6·50
MS683		100×71 mm. **647** £1.50, mult	3·50	3·50
		First Day Cover		4·50
		Presentation Pack	4·50	

For No. **MS**683 with 'CAPEX '96' logo see No. **MS**712.

Plate Nos.: All values 1A, 1B (each ×4)

Sheets: 10 (2×5)

Imprint: Central, left-hand margin

Withdrawn: 13.3.97

648 Douglas Borough Arms

Centenary of Douglas Borough

(Des Colleen Corlett. Litho B.D.T.)

1996 (14 MAR). Self-adhesive. Die-cut perf 9×10

684	**648**	(20p) multicoloured	70	1·00
		First Day Cover		1·50
		Presentation Pack	1·50	

No. 684 was printed in sheets of 40, each stamp surrounded by white backing paper divided by roulettes. The actual stamps are separated from the backing paper by die-cut perforations. It was initially sold for 20p and was only valid for postage within the Isle of Man.

Plate Nos.: 1A, 1B (each ×4)

Sheets: 40 (8×5)

Imprint: Right-hand corner, bottom margin

Withdrawn: 30.11.98

651 *Sir Winston Churchill* (cadet schooner)

653 *Tynwald I* (paddle-steamer), 1846

657 *Francis Drake* (ketch)

Ships

(Des A. Theobald. Litho Walsall)

1996 (21 APR). *As Nos. 541, 543 and 547, but smaller as T* **651/7**. Perf 14 (C)

687	**651**	4p multicoloured	20	15
		a. Booklet pane. Nos. 687, 689 and 693, each ×2	6·75	
689	**653**	20p multicoloured	60	70
693	**657**	24p multicoloured	90	90
687/93		Set of 3	1·50	1·60
		First Day Cover	2·00	
		Presentation Pack	2·00	

The 20p and 24p show the positions of the face value and Queen's head reversed.

Plate Nos.: All values 1A, 1B (each ×4)

Sheets: 100 (10×10)

Imprint: Right-hand corner, bottom margin

Withdrawn: 30.11.98

665 Princess Anne (President, Save the Children Fund) and Children

666 Queen Elizabeth II and People of the Commonwealth

Europa. Famous Women

(Des D. Miller. Litho B.D.T.)

1996 (21 APR). Perf 14 (C)

701	**665**	24p multicoloured	70	75
702	**666**	30p multicoloured	90	1·00
701/2		Set of 2	1·60	1·75
		First Day Cover		2·25
		Presentation Pack	3·50	

The background designs of Nos. 701/2 continue onto the vertical sheet margins.

Plate Nos.: Both values 1A, 1B (each ×4)

Sheets: 10 (2×5)

Withdrawn: 20.4.97

667 Alec Bennett

668 Stanley Woods

669 Artie Bell

670 Joey and Robert Dunlop

671 R.A.F. Red Arrows Display Team (*illustration reduced. Actual size* 100×70 *mm*)

Tourist Trophy Motorcycle Races. Irish Winners

(Des J. Dunne. Litho Questa)

1996 (30 MAY). Perf 14 (C)

703	**667**	20p multicoloured	50	45
704	**668**	24p multicoloured	60	60
705	**669**	45p multicoloured	90	90
706	**670**	60p multicoloured	1·40	1·40
703/6		Set of 4	3·00	3·00
		First Day Cover		3·75
		Presentation Pack	4·00	
		Souvenir Folder	12·00	
		Set of 4 Gutter Pairs	6·00	
MS707		100×70 mm. **671** £1 multicoloured	3·00	3·00
		First Day Cover		4·00
		Presentation Pack	4·00	

The souvenir folder contains Nos. 703/7, together with the stamps and miniature sheet in similar designs issued by Ireland.

Plate Nos.: 20p 1A, 1B (each ×4); 24p 1A (×4); 45p 1C (×4); 60p 1D (×4)

Sheets: 40 (2 panes 2×10)

Imprint: Right-hand corner, bottom margin

Withdrawn: 29.5.97

672 National Poppy Appeal Trophy

673 Manx War Memorial, Braddan

674 Poppy Appeal Collection Box

675 Royal British Legion Badge

75th Anniversary of Royal British Legion

(Des C. Abbott. Litho B.D.T.)

1996 (8 JUNE). Perf 14 (C)

708	**672**	20p multicoloured	65	55
709	**673**	24p multicoloured	70	60
710	**674**	42p multicoloured	1·10	1·00
711	**675**	75p multicoloured	2·00	2·00
708/11		Set of 4	4·00	3·75
		First Day Cover		4·25
		Presentation Pack	4·50	

Plate Nos.: 75p 1A, 1B, 1C (each ×4); others 1A (×4)

Sheets: 40 (8×5)

Imprint: Right hand cornor, bottom margin

Withdrawn: 7.6.97

'CAPEX '96' International Stamp Exhibition, Toronto

1996 (8 JUNE). No. **MS**683 additionally inscribed with 'CAPEX '96' exhibition logo on sheet margin.

MS712	100×71 mm. **647** £1.50, mult	6·00	6·50
	First Day Cover		8·00

Withdrawn: 31.7.97

676 U.N.I.C.E.F. Projects in Mexico

677 Projects in Sri Lanka

678 Projects in Colombia

679 Projects in Zambia

680 Projects in Afghanistan

681 Projects in Vietnam

50th Anniv of U.N.I.C.E.F.

(Des C. Abbott. Litho Enschedé)

1996 (18 SEPT). Perf 13½×14 (C)

713	**676**	24p multicoloured	65	60
		a. Horiz pair. Nos. 713/14	1·25	1·25
714	**677**	24p multicoloured	65	60
715	**678**	30p multicoloured	85	75
		a. Horiz pair. Nos. 715/16	1·60	1·50
716	**679**	30p multicoloured	85	75
717	**680**	42p multicoloured	1·25	1·10
		a. Horiz pair. Nos. 717/18	2·50	2·25
718	**681**	42p multicoloured	1·25	1·10
713/18		Set of 6	4·75	4·50
		First Day Cover		5·00
		Presentation Pack	5·25	

Plate Nos.: All values 1A, 1B (each ×4)

Sheets: 40 (10×4). The two designs for each value printed together, *se-tenant*, in horizontal pairs throughout the sheets

Imprint: Right-hand corner, bottom margin

Withdrawn: 17.9.97

682 Labrador

683 Border Collie

684 Dalmatian

685 Mongrel

686 English Setter

687 Alsatian

688 Dogs at Work
(*illustration reduced. Actual size 100×71 mm*)

Dogs

(Des Colleen Corlett. Litho Questa)

1996 (18 SEPT). Perf 13½×14 (No. **MS**725) or 14½ (others), both comb

719	**682**	20p multicoloured	60	55
		a. Booklet pane. No. 719×4 with margins all round	1·60	
720	**683**	24p multicoloured	70	65
		a. Booklet pane. No. 720×4 with margins all round	2·00	
721	**684**	31p multicoloured	1·00	90
		a. Booklet pane. Nos. 721/4 with margins all round	3·50	
722	**685**	38p multicoloured	1·10	1·00
723	**686**	43p multicoloured	1·50	1·25
724	**687**	63p multicoloured	2·00	1·75
719/24		Set of 6	6·25	5·50
		First Day Cover		6·00
		Presentation Pack	6·75	
MS725		100×71 mm. **688** £1.20, mult	3·75	3·75
		a. Booklet pane. As No. **MS**725, but with additional white margins all round separated by roulette	3·75	
		First Day Cover		4·25
		Presentation Pack	4·50	

Plate Nos.: All values 1A (×4)

Sheets: 10 (2×5)

Imprint: Left-hand corner, bottom margin

Withdrawn: 17.9.97

689 'Snowman and Pine Trees' (David Bennett)

690 'Three-legged Father Christmas' (Louis White)

691 'Family around Christmas Tree' (Robyn Whelan)

692 'Father Christmas in Sleigh' (Claire Bradley)

Christmas. Children's Paintings

(Adapted Colleen Corlett. Litho Walsall)

1996 (2 NOV). Perf 14×14½ (C)

726	**689**	19p multicoloured	55	50
727	**690**	23p multicoloured	70	65

728	**691**	50p multicoloured	. . . .	1·60	1·40
729	**692**	75p multicoloured	. . . .	2·10	1·90
728/9		*Set of 4*		4·50	4·00
		First Day Cover			4·50
		Presentation Pack		5·00	

Plate Nos.: All values 1A, 1B (each ×4)

Sheets: 40 (5×8)

Imprint: Right-hand corner, bottom margin

Withdrawn: 1.11.97

Year Pack 1996

1996 (NOV). *Comprises Nos.* 552 *and* 672/729
Year Pack . . . . 45·00

Withdrawn: 30.11.98

Post Office Yearbook

1996 (NOV). *Comprises Nos.* 552 *and* 672/729
Yearbook . . . . 48·00

Withdrawn: 30.11.98

693 Primroses and
Cashtyl ny Ard

694 Lochtan Sheep
and Lambs

695 Daffodils,
Mallard and
Ducklings

696 Little Grebe with
Young and Frog
on Lily Pad

Spring in Man

(Des Colleen Corlett. Litho B.D.T.)

1997 (12 FEB). Perf 14 (C)

730	**693**	20p multicoloured	. . . .	50	50
731	**694**	24p multicoloured	. . . .	70	70
732	**695**	43p multicoloured	. . . .	1·10	1·10
733	**696**	63p multicoloured	. . . .	1·60	1·60
730/3		*Set of 4*		3·50	3·50
		First Day Cover			4·25
		Presentation Pack		4·25	
		Set of 4 Gutter Pairs		7·00	

Plate Nos.: All values 1A, 1B (each ×4)

Sheets: 40 (2 panes 5×4)

Imprint: Right-hand corner, bottom margin

Withdrawn: 11.2.98

697 Barn Owl

698 Short-eared Owl

699 Long-eared Owl

700 Little Owl

701 Snowy Owl

702 Eurasian Tawny Owl

703a Long-eared Owl
(*illustration reduced. Actual size* 100×71 *mm*)

Owls

(Des J. Paul. Litho B.D.T.)

1997 (12 FEB). Perf 13 (No. **MS**740) or 14 (others), both comb

734	**697**	20p multicoloured		65	60
		a. Booklet pane. No. 734×4 with margins all round	1·60		
735	**698**	24p multicoloured		80	75
		a. Booklet pane. No. 735×4 with margins all round	2·00		
736	**699**	31p multicoloured		1·00	90
		a. Booklet pane. Nos. 736/9 with margins all round	3·50		
737	**700**	36p multicoloured		1·25	1·10
738	**701**	43p multicoloured		1·40	1·25
739	**702**	56p multicoloured		1·60	1·50
734/9		Set of 6		6·00	5·50
		First Day Cover			6·00
		Presentation Pack		6·75	
		Stamp Cards (set of 6)		2·75	7·00
MS740		100×71 mm. **703a** £1.20, mult . .		4·00	4·25
		a. Booklet pane. As No. **MS**740 but with additional white margins all round and with line of roulettes at left	4·50		
		First Day Cover			6·00
		Presentation Pack		4·75	

No. **MS**740 includes the 'HONG KONG' '97' International Stamp Exhibition logo on the sheet margin.

Plate Nos.: All values 1A, 1B (each ×4)

Sheets: 10 (5×2)

Imprint: Bottom, right-hand margin

Withdrawn: 11.2.98

704 Moddey Dhoo, Peel Castle

705 Fairies in Tree and Cottage

706 Fairies at Fairy Bridge

707 Giant Finn Maccoil and Calf of Man

708 The Buggane of St. Trinian's

709 Fyonderee and Farm

Europa. Tales and Legends

(Des Colleen Corlett. Litho Enschedé)

1997 (24 APR). Perf 13½×14 (C)

741	**704**	24p multicoloured		55	55
742	**705**	25p multicoloured		65	65
743	**706**	31p multicoloured		85	85
744	**707**	36p multicoloured		1·10	1·10
745	**708**	37p multicoloured		1·10	1·10
746	**709**	43p multicoloured		1·40	1·40
741/6		Set of 6		5·00	5·00
		First Day Cover			5·50
		Presentation Pack		5·50	

Nos. 742/3 include the 'EUROPA' emblem.

Plate Nos.: All values 1A, 1B, 1C, 1D (each ×4)

Sheets: 10 (2×5)

Withdrawn: 23.4.98

710 Sopwith Tabloid

711 Grumman Tiger (1996 Schneider Trophy)

712 BAe ATP (15th anniv of Manx Airlines)

713 BAe 146-200 (15th anniv of Manx Airlines)

714 Boeing 757-200 (largest aircraft to land on Isle of Man)

715 Farman Biplane (1st Manx flight, 1911)

716 Spitfire

717 Hawker Hurricane

Manx Aircraft

(Des R. Carter. Litho Questa)

1997 (24 APR). Perf 14 (C)

747	**710**	21p multicoloured	45	45
		a. *Horiz pair. Nos.* 747/8	90	90
748	**711**	21p multicoloured	45	45
749	**712**	25p multicoloured	55	55
		a. *Horiz pair. Nos.* 749/50	1·10	1·10
750	**713**	25p multicoloured	55	55
751	**714**	31p multicoloured	70	70
		a. *Horiz pair. Nos.* 751/2	1·50	1·40
752	**715**	31p multicoloured	70	70
753	**716**	36p multicoloured	80	80
		a. *Horiz pair. Nos.* 753/4	1·70	1·60
754	**717**	36p multicoloured	80	80
747/54		*Set of 8*	5·00	4·50
		First Day Cover		5·50
		Presentation Pack	5·25	
		Souvenir Folder (*complete sheets*)	18·00	

No. 752 is inscribed 'EARMAN' in error.

Plate Nos.: All values 1A (×4)

Sheets: 8 (2×4) the two designs for each value printed together, *se-tenant*, in horizontal pairs throughout the sheets, the backgrounds forming composite designs

Withdrawn: 23.4.98

718 14th Hole, Ramsey Golf Club

719 15th Hole, King Edward Bay Golf and Country Club

720 17th Hole, Rowany Golf Club

721 8th Hole, Castletown Golf Links

722a Golf Ball
(*illustration reduced. Actual size* 100×71 *mm*)

Golf

(Des D. Swinton. Litho Questa)

1997 (29 MAY). Perf 14 (C)

755	**718**	21p multicoloured	50	50
		a. *Booklet pane. No.* 755×3 with margins all round	1·50	
756	**719**	25p multicoloured	60	60
		a. *Booklet pane. No.* 756×3 with margins all round	1·75	
757	**720**	43p multicoloured	1·10	1·10
		a. *Booklet pane. Nos.* 757/8 each ×2 with margins all round	4·00	
758	**721**	50p multicoloured	1·50	1·50
755/8		*Set of 4*	3·25	3·25
		First Day Cover		4·00
		Presentation Pack	4·00	
		Set of 4 Gutter Pairs	6·50	
MS759		100×71 mm. **722a** £1·30, mult	3·50	3·50
		a. *Booklet pane. As No.* **MS**759, *but with additional white margins all round*	3·50	
		First Day Cover		3·75
		Presentation Pack	3·75	

No. **MS**759 includes the 'PACIFIC 97' International Stamp Exhibition logo on the sheet margin.

Plate Nos.: All values 1A, 1B (each ×4)

Sheets: 40 (2 panes 5×4)

Imprint: Right-hand corner, bottom margin of each pane

Withdrawn: 28.5.98

To mark the return of Hong Kong to China, 1st July 1997 香港回歸中國專集-1.7.1997 11-11

723a Royal Yacht *Britannia*
(*illustration reduced. Actual size* 130×90 *mm*)

Return of Hong Kong to China

(Litho Walsall)

1997 (1 JULY). *Sheet* 130×90 *mm containing stamp as No. 546 with changed imprint date. Wmk Mult Crown CA Diagonal.* Perf 13×13½ (C)

MS760	**723a**	23p multicoloured	1·40	1·60
		First Day Cover		6·50

Withdrawn: 30.6.98

724 Steve Colley

725 Steve Saunders

726 Sammy Miller

727 Don Smith

F.I.M. 'Trial des Nations' Motorcycle Team Trials

(Des R. Organ. Litho Cartor)

1997 (17 SEPT). Perf 13½ (C)

761	**724**	21p multicoloured	55	50
762	**725**	25p multicoloured	65	60

763	**726**	37p multicoloured	1·25	1·00
764	**727**	44p multicoloured	1·50	1·25
761/4		Set of 4	3·50	3·00
		First Day Cover		4·00
		Presentation Pack	4·50	
		Set of 4 Gutter Pairs	7·00	

Plate Nos.: All values 1A, 1B (each ×4)

Sheets: 40 (2 panes 5×4) 21p, 44p; (2 panes 4×5) 25p, 37p

Imprint: Central, gutter margin

Withdrawn: 16.9.98

728 Angel and Shepherd

729 Angel and King

730 The Nativity

Christmas

(Des Jennifer Toombs. Litho B.D.T.)

1997 (3 NOV). Perf 14 (C)

765	**728**	20p multicoloured	65	55
766	**729**	24p multicoloured	75	70
767	**730**	63p multicoloured	1·60	1·50
765/7		Set of 3	3·00	2·50
		First Day Cover		3·00
		Presentation Pack	3·50	

Plate Nos.: 20p, 24p 1A (×5); 63p 1A, 1B (each ×5)

Sheets: 40 (8×5) 20p, 24p; 20 (4×5) 63p

Imprint: Central, left-hand margin

Withdrawn: 2.11.98

731 Engagement of Princess Elizabeth and Lieut. Philip Mountbatten, 1947

732 Wedding Photograph, 1947

733 At Ascot, 1952

734 Golden Wedding Photograph, 1997

735a Queen Elizabeth and Prince Philip at Peel, 1989

Golden Wedding of Queen Elizabeth and Prince Philip

(Des Colleen Corlett. Litho and die-stamped Questa)

1997 (3 NOV). Perf 14 (No. **MS**772) or 14×14½, both comb

768	**731**	50p sepia and gold	1·40	1·40
		a. Strip of 4. Nos. 768/71	5·00	
769	**732**	50p multicoloured	1·40	1·40
770	**733**	50p multicoloured	1·40	1·40
771	**734**	50p multicoloured	1·40	1·40
768/71		Set of 4	5·00	5·00
		First Day Cover		5·50
		Presentation Pack	5·50	
		Souvenir Folder (complete sheet and **MS**772)	21·00	
MS772		100×72 mm. **735a** £1 multicoloured	3·00	3·00
		First Day Cover		3·50

Plate Nos.: 1A (×5)

Sheets: 16 (4×4). Nos. 768/71 were printed together, *se-tenant*, as horizontal or vertical strips of 4 throughout the sheets

Imprint: Right-hand corner, bottom margin

Withdrawn: 2.11.98

Year Pack 1997

1997 (3 NOV). *Comprises Nos. 730/72*
Year Pack . . . . 37·00

Withdrawn: 30.11.98

Post Office Yearbook

1997 (3 NOV). *Comprises Nos. 730/72*
Yearbook . . . . 40·00

Sold out: By 8.2001

736 Bearded Iris

737 Daisy

738 Shamrock

739 Silver Jubilee Rose

740 Oriental Poppy

741 Heath Spotted Orchid

742 Cushag

743 Gorse

744 Princess of Wales Rose

745 Dog Rose

746 Fuchsia 'Lady Thumb'

747 Daffodil

748 Spear Thistle

753 Queen Elizabeth II and Queen Elizabeth the Queen Mother

Two Types of 4p:—

   I. 'WSP' imprint aligns with 'N' of 'MAN' (sheet stamps and 1998 booklet)

   II. 'WSP' ends to right of 'N' of 'MAN' (1999 booklet)

Flowers

(Des Colleen Corlett (1p to £1). Litho Cartor (£2.50), Walsall (others))

1998 (12 FEB)–**99**. Perf 13 (1p, 2p, 10p, 20p, 30p) or 13×13½ (others), both comb

773	**736**	1p multicoloured (b)	10	10
774	**737**	2p multicoloured (b)	10	10
775	**738**	4p multicoloured (I) (a)	10	10
		a. Booklet pane. Nos. 775, 779 and 781, each ×2 (a)	3·25	
		b. Type II (c)	50	60
		ba. Booklet pane. Nos. 775b×2, 780×3 and 782 (c)	3·00	
776	**739**	5p multicoloured (c)	10	15
777	**740**	10p multicoloured (b)	20	25
778	**741**	20p multicoloured (b)	40	30
779	**742**	21p multicoloured (a)	40	45
780	**743**	22p multicoloured (c)	45	50
781	**744**	25p multicoloured (a)	50	40
782	**745**	26p multicoloured (c)	50	40
783	**746**	30p multicoloured (b)	60	60
784	**747**	50p multicoloured (a)	1·00	1·00
785	**748**	£1 multicoloured (a)	2·00	2·00
790	**753**	£2·50 multicoloured (b)	5·00	4·75
773/90		Set of 14	10·50	10·00
		First Day Covers (4)		13·50
		Presentation Packs (4)	13·50	
		Souvenir Folder (Nos. 773/85)	8·00	
		Gutter Pair (No. 790)	10·00	

Printings: (a) 12.2.98. Inscribed '1998'; (b) 2.7.98. Inscribed '1998'; (c) 26.4.99. Inscribed '1999'

Plate Nos.: 4p, 21p, 25p, 50p, £1, £2.50 1A, 1B (each ×4); others 1A (×4)

Sheets: 40 (2 panes 5×4) £2.50, 50 (10×5) (others). In addition to stamp booklets Nos. 775a and 775ba also come from separate special booklet sheets of 36 (6×5), each containing five strips

Imprint: Central, bottom margin

756 Viking Figurehead

757 Viking Longship at Sea

758 Viking Longship on Beach

759 Stern of Ship

760a Viking Ship at Peel Castle

   (illustration reduced. Actual size 100×71 mm)

Viking Longships

(Des A. Bell. Litho B.D.T.)

1998 (14 FEB). Perf 14 (C)

793	**756**	21p multicoloured	55	50
794	**757**	25p multicoloured	75	70
795	**758**	31p multicoloured	90	80
796	**759**	75p multicoloured	2·25	2·00

793/G		Set of 4	4·00	3·50	
		First Day Cover		4·25	
		Presentation Pack	5·00		
		Set of 4 Gutter Pairs	8·00		
MS797		100×71 mm. **760a** £1 multicoloured	3·00	3·00	
		First Day Cover		4·50	
		Presentation Pack	4·25		

Plate Nos.: All values 1A, 1B (each ×4)
Sheets: 40 (2 panes 4×5)
Imprint: Central, right-hand margin
Withdrawn: 13.2.99

761 Bottle-nosed Dolphins

762 Basking Shark

763 Front View of Basking Shark

764 Minke Whale

765 Killer Whale and Calf

U.N.E.S.C.O. International Year of the Ocean
(Des J. Paul. Litho Questa)

1998 (14 MAR). Perf 14 (C)

798	**761**	10p multicoloured		30	30
		a. Booklet pane. Nos. 798/9, each ×3 and 3 labels with margins all round		2·75	
		b. Booklet pane. Nos. 798/9 and 800/2, each ×2, and 1 central label with margins all round		7·00	
799	**762**	21p multicoloured		50	50
800	**763**	25p multicoloured		65	65
801	**764**	31p multicoloured		75	75
802	**765**	63p multicoloured		1·60	1·60
798/802		Set of 5		3·50	3·50
		First Day Cover			4·25
		Presentation Pack		4·25	
		Souvenir Folder		25·00	
		Stamp Cards (set of 5)		3·00	6·00

Plate Nos.: All values 1A, 1B (each ×4)
Sheets: 10 (2×5)
Withdrawn: 13.3.99

766 Locomotive No. 12 *Hutchinson*

767 Locomotive No. 10 *G. H. Wood*

768 Locomotive No. 11 *Maitland*

769 Locomotive No. 4 *Loch*

770a Pillar Box and Train at Douglas Station (25p); Locomotive No. 4 *Sutherland* (£1)
(*illustration reduced. Actual size* 120×54 *mm*)

125th Anniversary of Isle of Man Steam Railway
(Des A. Peck. Litho Questa)

1998 (2 MAY). Perf 14½×14 (C)

803	**766**	21p multicoloured		60	50
		a. Booklet pane. Nos. 803/6 with margins all round		3·50	
804	**767**	25p multicoloured		70	60
805	**768**	31p multicoloured		90	80
806	**769**	63p multicoloured		1·60	1·60
803/6		Set of 4		3·50	3·25
		First Day Cover			3·50
		Presentation Pack		4·00	
		Souvenir Folder		25·00	
MS807		199×54 mm. **770a** 25p mult; £1 mult		3·00	3·00
		a. Booklet pane. As No. **MS**807, but with additional margins showing diagram all round . .		3·00	
		First Day Cover			3·50
		Presentation Pack		3·50	

Booklet pane No. 803a exists in two versions, which differ in the order of the stamps within the block of four.

Plate Nos.: All values 1A (×4)
Sheets: 40 (5×8)
Imprints: Right-hand corner, bottom margin
Withdrawn: 31.5.99

771 Purple Helmets Display Team

772 Joey Dunlop

773 Dave Molyneux

774 Naomi Taniguchi

775 Mike Hailwood

Isle of Man T.T. Races and 50th Anniversary of Honda (motorcycle manufacturer)

(Des The Agency. Litho B.D.T.)

1998 (1 JUNE). Perf 14 (C)

808	**771**	21p multicoloured	40	45
809	**772**	25p multicoloured	50	55
810	**773**	31p multicoloured	65	65
811	**774**	43p multicoloured	1·00	1·00
812	**775**	63p multicoloured	1·40	1·50
808/12		Set of 5	3·50	3·75
		First Day Cover		4·50
		Presentation Pack	4·50	
		Souvenir Folder	20·00	
		Set of 5 Gutter Pairs	7·00	

Plate Nos.: All values 1A (×4)

Sheets: 40 (2 panes 5×4 with double gutter)

Withdrawn: 31.5.99

776 Princess Diana wearing Protective Clothing, Angola

777 Receiving Award from United Cerebral Palsy Charity, New York, 1995

778 With Children, South Korea, 1992

779 Wearing Blue Jacket, July 1993

Diana, Princess of Wales Commemoration

(Litho Cartor)

1998 (19 JUNE). Perf 13½×13 (C)

813	**776**	25p multicoloured	55	55
		a. Strip of 4. Nos. 813/16	2·25	
814	**777**	25p multicoloured	55	55
815	**778**	25p multicoloured	55	55
816	**779**	25p multicoloured	55	55
813/16		Set of 4	2·25	2·00
		First Day Cover		3·00
		Presentation Pack	3·00	
		Souvenir Folder	20·00	

Plate Nos.: 1A (×4)

Sheets: 16 (4×4). Nos. 813/16 were printed together, se-tenant, as horizontal or vertical strips of 4 throughout the sheet

Withdrawn: 18.6.99

780 Tynwald Day Ceremony

781 Traditional Dancers, Tynwald Fair

Europa. Festivals

(Des M. Thompson. Litho Cartor)

1998 (2 JULY). Perf 13×13½ (C)

817	**780**	25p multicoloured	50	45
818	**781**	30p multicoloured	75	65
817/18		Set of 2	1·25	1·10
		First Day Cover		2·00
		Presentation Pack	2·25	

Plate Nos.: Both values 1A (×4)

Sheets: 10 (2×5)

Withdrawn: 30.10.99

782 Father Christmas at
North Pole

783 Father Christmas
checking List

784 Flying over Spring
Valley Sorting Office

785 Passing through
Baldrine Village

786 Father Christmas delivering
Presents

Christmas. 'A Very Special Delivery'

(Des A. Bell. Litho Enschedé)

1998 (25 Sept). Perf 14½×14 (C)

819	**782**	20p multicoloured	40	30
820	**783**	24p multicoloured	50	45
821	**784**	30p multicoloured	75	60
822	**785**	43p multicoloured	95	85
823	**786**	63p multicoloured	1·40	1·25
819/23		Set of 5	3·75	3·50
		First Day Cover		4·50
		Presentation Pack	4·50	
		Set of 5 Gutter Pairs	7·50	

Plate Nos.: All values 1A (×4)

Sheets: 40 (2 panes 5×4)

Imprint: Right-hand corner, bottom margin

Withdrawn: 30.10.99

Year Pack 1998

1998 (25 SEPT). Comprises Nos. 773/823
Year Pack . . . . 36·00

Sold out: 9.99

Post Office Yearbook

1998 (25 SEPT). Comprises Nos. 773/823
Yearbook . . . . 42·00

Sold out: 8.2000

787 Large Oval Pillar
Box, Kirk Onchan

788 Wall Box,
Ballaterson

789 King Edward VII Pillar
Box, Laxey Station

790 Wall Box, Spaldrick

791 Small Oval Pillar
Box, Derby Road,
Douglas

792 Wall Box, Baldrine
Station

Local Post Boxes

(Des The Agency. Litho Walsall)

1999 (4 MAR). Perf 14 (C)

824	**787**	10p multicoloured	25	25
825	**788**	20p multicoloured	45	45
826	**789**	21p multicoloured	50	50
827	**790**	25p multicoloured	60	55
828	**791**	44p multicoloured	1·00	95
829	**792**	63p multicoloured	1·50	1·40
824/9		Set of 6	4·00	4·00
		First Day Cover		4·50
		Presentation Pack	4·50	
		Set of 6 Gutter Pairs	8·00	

Plate Nos.: All values 1A, 1B (each ×4)

Sheets: 50 (2 panes 5×5)

Imprint: Right-hand corner, bottom margin

Withdrawn: 3.3.2000

793 Cottage,
Ballaglass
Glen

794 Glen Maye
Waterfall

Europa. Parks and Gardens

(Des Julia Ashby-Smyth. Litho B.D.T.)

1999 (4 MAR). Perf 14 (C)

830	**793**	25p multicoloured	....	50	50
831	**794**	30p multicoloured	....	75	60
830/1		Set of 2	....	1·25	1·10
		First Day Cover	....		1·90
		Presentation Pack	....	1·90	

Plate Nos.: Both values 1A, 1B (each ×4)

Sheets: 10 (5×2)

Withdrawn: 3.3.2000

795 Ann and James Ritchie,
Ramsey

796 Sir William Hillary,
Douglas

797 Ruby Clery, Peel

798 Herbert and Edith
(inshore lifeboat), Port
Erin

799 1974 150th Anniversary
8p Stamp

800 Gough Ritchie II, Port
St. Mary

801 1991 Manx Lifeboats 21p
Stamp

802a Sir William Hillary (founder)
(illustration reduced. Actual size 100×70 mm)

175th Anniversary of Royal National Lifeboat Institution

(Des Mainstream Media (No. **MS**839), R. Tomlinson (others).
Litho Questa)

1999 (4 MAR). Perf 13½×14 (No. **MS**839) or 14, both comb

832	**795**	21p multicoloured	....	50	50
		a. Booklet pane. Nos. 832/5 and 837, plus four printed labels, with margins all round		5·00	
		b. Booklet pane. Nos. 832/4, 836 and 838, plus four printed labels, with margins all round		5·00	
833	**796**	25p multicoloured	....	55	55
834	**797**	37p multicoloured	....	80	80
835	**798**	43p multicoloured	....	90	90
836	**799**	43p multicoloured	....	2·25	3·00
837	**800**	56p multicoloured	....	1·25	1·25
838	**801**	56p multicoloured	....	2·50	3·00
832/8		Set of 7	....	8·00	8·75
		First Day Cover (Nos. 832/5, 837)	....		4·50
		Presentation Pack (Nos. 832/5, 837)	....	4·50	
		Set of 5 Gutter Pairs (Nos. 832/5, 837)	....	8·00	

MS839   100×70 mm. **802a** £1 multicoloured   3·00   3·00
        a. Booklet pane. As No. **MS**839,
           but with additional margins
           showing lifeboats all round   2·50
           First Day Cover . . . .   4·00
           Presentation Pack . . . .   3·00

Nos. 836 and 838 were only available in £4.64 stamp booklets.

No. 832*b* includes an 'iBRA' Stamp Exhibition label and No. **MS**839 the 'Australia '99' World Stamp Exhibition emblem on the sheet margin.

Plate Nos.: All values 1A (×4)

Sheets: 40 (2 panes 5×4)

Withdrawn: 3.3.2000

Geurey ❈ Winter

803 Winter

Arragh ❈ Spring

804 Spring

Sourey ❈ Summer

805 Summer

Fouyr ❈ Autumn

806 Autumn

Centenary of Yn Cheshaght Ghailckagh (Manx Gaelic Society). The Seasons

(Des C. Alexander. Litho Walsall)

1999 (11 MAY). Perf 14½×14 (C)
840   **803**   22p multicoloured   60   60
841   **804**   26p multicoloured   65   65
842   **805**   50p multicoloured . . . .   1·10   1·10
843   **806**   63p multicoloured . . . .   1·60   1·60
840/3   Set of 4 . . . .   3·50   3·50
             First Day Cover . . . .   4·25
             Presentation Pack . . . .   4·25
             Set of 4 Gutter Pairs . . . . . .   7·00

Nos. 840/3 are inscribed 'Ellan Vannin', the Manx name for the Isle of Man.

Plate Nos.: All values 1A, 1B (each ×4)

Sheets: 50 (2 panes 5×5)

Imprint: Right-hand corner, bottom margin

Withdrawn: 10.5.2000

807a Queen Victoria; King Edward VII; King George V; King Edward VIII; King George VI; Queen Elizabeth II (*illustration reduced. Actual size 170×75 mm*)

British Monarchs of the 20th Century

(Des Colleen Corlett. Litho Walsall)

1999 (2 JUNE). *Sheet* 170×75 mm. Perf 14 (C)
MS844   **807a**   26p×6, multicoloured . . . . .   3·25   3·25
                 First Day Cover . . . .   4·00
                 Presentation Pack . . . .   4·00
                 Souvenir Folder (*Nos. 824/9,*
                    MS844) . . . .   25·00

Withdrawn: 1.6.2000

808 Tilling-Stevens Double Deck Bus, 1922

809 Thornycroft BC Single Deck, 1928

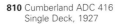

810 Cumberland ADC 416 Single Deck, 1927

811 Straker-Squire Single Deck, 1914

812 Thornycroft A2 Single Deck, 1927

813 Leyland Lion LT9 Single Deck, 1938

Manx Buses

(Des P. Hearsey. Litho B.D.T.)

1999 (18 JUNE). Perf 14 (C)

845	**808**	22p multicoloured	50	50
		a. *Booklet pane. Nos. 845/6 and 847×2, with margins all round*	2·40	
		b. *Booklet pane. Nos. 845/6 and 848×2, with margins all round*	2·75	
		c. *Booklet pane. Nos. 845/6 and 849×2, with margins all round*	3·00	
		d. *Booklet pane. Nos. 845/6 and 850×2, with margins all round*	3·00	
846	**809**	26p multicoloured	55	55
847	**810**	28p multicoloured	65	65
848	**811**	37p multicoloured	80	80
849	**812**	38p multicoloured	90	90
850	**813**	40p multicoloured	1·00	1·00
845/50		*Set of 6*	4·00	4·00
		First Day Cover		4·50
		Presentation Pack	4·50	
		Stamp Cards (set of 6)	3·00	7·50

Plate Nos.: All values 1A (×4)

Sheets: 25 (5×5)

Imprint: Central, bottom margin

Withdrawn: 17.6.2000

814 Miss Sophie Rhys-Jones

815 Leaving St. George's Chapel, Windsor

816 Prince Edward

817 Miss Sophie Rhys-Jones and Prince Edward

818 In Landau

Royal Wedding

(Des Catherine James. Litho B.D.T.)

1999 (19 JUNE–1 SEPT). Perf 14 (C)

851	**814**	22p multicoloured (a)	55	55
852	**815**	26p multicoloured (b)	55	55
853	**816**	39p multicoloured (a)	80	80
854	**817**	44p multicoloured (a)	1·10	1·10
855	**818**	53p multicoloured (b)	1·25	1·25
851/5		*Set of 5*	3·75	3·75
		First Day Covers (2)		5·00
		Presentation Pack	4·50	

Printings: (a) 19.6.99; (b) 1.9.99

Plate Nos.: All values 1A, 1B (each ×4)

Sheets: 25 (5×5)

Imprint: Central, bottom margin

Withdrawn: 31.8.2000

'PhilexFrance 99' International Stamp Exhibition, Paris

1999 (2 JULY). No. MS807 additionally inscribed with 'PhilexFrance' exhibition logo on sheet margin.

MS856   119×54 mm.   **770a** 25p mult; £1 mult   3·50   3·75

Withdrawn: 1.7.2000

819 St. Luke's Church, Baldwin

820 St. Mark's Chapel, Malew

821 St. German's
Parish
Church and
Cathedral,
Peel

822 Kirk Christ
Church,
Rushen

Christmas. Churches

(Des N. Sayle. Litho Cartor)

1999 (22 SEPT). Perf 13½ (C)

857	**819**	21p multicoloured	45	45
858	**820**	25p multicoloured	60	60
859	**821**	30p multicoloured	70	70
860	**822**	64p multicoloured	1·50	1·50
857/60		Set of 4	3·00	3·00
		First Day Cover		3·50
		Presentation Pack	3·75	
		Set of 4 Gutter Pairs	6·00	

Plate Nos.: All values 1A (×4)
Sheets: 40 (2 panes 4×5)
Imprint: Central, bottom margin
Withdrawn: 21.9.2000

823 'Massachusetts', 1967

824 'Words', 1968

825 'I've Gotta Get a
Message to You', 1968

826 'Ellan Vannin', 1998

827 'You Win Again', 1987

828 'Night Fever', 1978

829a 'Immortality', 1998
(*illustration reduced. Actual size* 119×108 *mm*)

830a 'Stayin' Alive', 1978
(*illustration reduced. Actual size* 119×108 *mm*)

Legends of Music. The Bee Gees (pop group)

(Des The Agency. Litho Cartor (Nos. 861/6), Walsall (No.
MS867))

1999 (12 OCT). Perf 15 (No. **MS**867) or 13½, both comb

861	**823**	22p multicoloured	60	50
862	**824**	26p multicoloured	70	65
863	**825**	29p multicoloured	70	65
864	**826**	37p multicoloured	90	85
865	**827**	38p multicoloured	90	85
866	**828**	66p multicoloured	1·50	1·50
861/6		Set of 6	4·75	4·50
		First Day Cover		5·50
		Presentation Pack	5·50	
		Souvenir Folder (complete		
		sheets)	45·00	

MS867 Two sheets, each 119×108 mm. (a) **829a** 60p multicoloured (*circular, 40 mm diam*). (b) **830a** 90p multicoloured, (*circular 40 mm diam*)

Set of 2 sheets	3·00	3·50
First Day Cover		9·00

Sheets: 9 stamps and three labels, arranged 3×4, with the labels in the third horizontal row

Withdrawn: 11.10.2000

Year Pack 1999

1999 (12 OCT). *Comprises Nos. 776, 780, 782, 824/35, 837 and* 840/67

Year Pack .... 50·00

Withdrawn: 2.8.2001

Post Office Yearbook

1999 (12 OCT). *Comprises Nos. 776, 780, 782, 824/35, 837 and* **MS**839/67

Yearbook .... 58·00

Sold out: 8.2000

831a Sky at Sunset over Calf of Man (50p); Sky at Dawn over Maughold Head (50p); Constellations over Man at Start of New Millennium (£2)
(*illustration reduced. Actual size* 169×74 mm)

New Millennium

(Des H. Parkin and R. Berry. Litho Questa)

1999 (31 DEC). *Sheet* 169×74 mm. Perf 14½ (C)

MS868	**831a**	50p, 50p, £2 multicoloured	6·50	6·75
		First Day Cover		9·00
		Presentation Pack		7·00

The first day cover has three cancellations, one on each stamp, running in a two minute sequence from 23.59 on 31 Dec 99 to 00.01 on 01 Jan 00.

Withdrawn: 30.12.2000

832 Harrison's Chronometer, 1735, and Map

833 Daniel's Chronometer, 2000, and Clock Face

834 Harrison's Chronometer, 1767, Map and Clock

835 Mudge's Chronometer, 1769, and Steam Locomotives

836 Arnold's Chronometer, 1779, and Map of Africa

837 Earnshaw's Chronometer, 1780, and Map of Caribbean

'The Story of Time'

(Des E. Cassidy. Litho Cartor)

2000 (24 JAN). Perf 13×13½ (C)

869	**832**	22p multicoloured	....	50	55
870	**833**	26p multicoloured	....	55	60
871	**834**	29p multicoloured	....	65	70
872	**835**	34p multicoloured	....	75	80

873	**836**	38p multicoloured	80	85
874	**837**	44p multicoloured	95	1·00
060/74		Set of 6	3·75	4·00
		First Day Cover		5·00
		Presentation Pack	4·75	

Plate Nos.: 29p, 38p 1A, 1B (each ×4); others 1A (×4)

Sheets: 25 (5×5)

Imprint: Top left-hand margin and bottom right-hand margin

Withdrawn: 23.1.2001

838 Duke and Duchess of York on Wedding Day, 1923

839 Queen Elizabeth with Princess Elizabeth, 1940

840 King George VI and Queen Elizabeth visiting Troops, 1944

841 Queen Mother and Queen Elizabeth, 1954

842 Queen Mother with Prince Charles, 1985

843 Queen Mother, 1988

844a Queen Mother visiting Isle of Man

'Queen Elizabeth the Queen Mother's Century'

(Des E.D.L. Litho B.D.T.)

2000 (29 FEB). Perf 14 (C)

875	**838**	22p multicoloured	50	55
		a. Horiz strip of 3. Nos. 875/7 .	1·75	
876	**839**	26p sepia and black	55	60
877	**840**	30p sepia and black	65	70
878	**841**	44p multicoloured	95	1·00
		a. Horiz strip of 3. Nos. 878/80	3·50	
879	**842**	52p multicoloured	1·10	1·25
880	**843**	64p multicoloured	1·40	1·50
875/80		Set of 6	4·75	5·00
		First Day Cover		5·75
		Presentation Pack	5·50	
		Souvenir Folder (complete sheets and **MS**881)	21·00	
MS881		100×70 mm. **844a** £1 multicoloured	2·25	2·25
		First Day Cover		3·00
		Presentation Pack	3·00	

Plate Nos.: All values 1A (×4)

Sheets: 12 (3×4). Nos. 875/7 and 878/80 were each printed together, *se-tenant*, as horizontal strips of 3 throughout the sheets

Withdrawn: 28.2.2001

845 Barn Swallow

846 Spotted Flycatcher

847 Eurasian Sky Lark

848 Yellowhammer

Endangered Species. Song Birds

(Des Catherine James. Litho Walsall)

2000 (5 MAY). Perf 14½ (C)

882	**845**	22p multicoloured	50	55
		a. Strip of 4. Nos. 882/5	4·00	
883	**846**	26p multicoloured	55	60
884	**847**	64p multicoloured	1·50	1·50
885	**848**	77p multicoloured	1·75	1·75
882/5		Set of 4	4·00	4·00
		First Day Cover		4·75
		Presentation Pack	4·75	

Plate Nos.: All values 1A (×4)

Sheets: 20 (4×5). Nos. 882/5 were printed together, *se-tenant*, both horizontally and vertically, within the sheets

Withdrawn: 4.5.2001

'The Stamp Show 2000' International Stamp Exhibition, London

2000 (22 May). As No. **MS**881, *but with 'The Stamp Show 2000' multicoloured logo added to the bottom sheet margin.* Perf 14 (C)

MS886 100×70 mm. **844a** £1 multicoloured   2·40   2·50

Withdrawn: 21.5.2001

849 Lieut. John Quilliam and Admiral Lord Nelson, Battle of Trafalgar

850 Ensign Caesar Bacon and Duke of Wellington, Battle of Waterloo

851 Col. Thomas Leigh Goldie and Earl of Cardigan, Crimea

852 Bugler John Dunne and Sir Robert Baden Powell, Boer War

853 George Kneale and Viscount Kitchener of Khartoum, First World War

854 First Officer Alan Watterson and Sir Winston Churchill, Second World War

855a Two Supermarine Spitfires (60p); Spitfire on Ground, Battle of Britain (60p)
(*illustration reduced. Actual size* 170×75 *mm*)

Isle of Man at War

(Des P. Hannon (Nos. 887/92), P. Hearsey (No. **MS**893). Litho B.D.T.)

2000 (22 MAY). Perf 15×14 (No. **MS**893) or 13, both comb

887	**849**	22p multicoloured	50	55
		a. Booklet pane. Nos. 887/91 .	3·75	
		b. Booklet pane. Nos. 887 and 890/2	4·00	
888	**850**	26p multicoloured	55	60
889	**851**	36p multicoloured	75	80
890	**852**	48p multicoloured	1·00	1·10
891	**853**	50p multicoloured	1·10	1·25
892	**854**	77p multicoloured	1·50	1·60
887/92		Set of 6	4·75	5·25
		First Day Cover		6·00
		Presentation Pack	6·00	

MS893 170×75 mm. **855a** 60p multi-
coloured; 60p multicoloured   2·75   2·75
First Day Cover   3·50
Presentation Pack   3·50

Plate Nos.: All values A1 (×4)

Sheets: 8 (2×4). Nos. 887/8, 889/90 and 891/2 were each printed in sheets containing vertical strips of the two designs separated by a gutter margin

Imprint: Lower left-hand margin

Withdrawn: 21.5.2001

856a Prince William as a Child (22p); With Queen Mother (26p); As a teenager (45p); With Prince Charles and Prince Harry (52p); Wearing ski-suit (56p) (*illustration reduced. Actual size* 170×75 *mm*)

18th Birthday of Prince William

(Des The Agency. Litho B.D.T.)

2000 (21 JUNE). Sheet 170×75 *mm.* Perf 14 (C)

MS894 **856a** 22p, 26p, 45p, 52p, 56p multi-
coloured   4·50   4·50
First Day Cover   5·25
Presentation Pack   5·25

Withdrawn: 20.6.2001

857 Ballet Shoes and Painted Ceiling

858 Comedy Mask and Box Decoration

859 Drama Mask and Statue

860 Pantomime Dame with Wig and Mosaic

861 Opera Glasses and Decoration

862 Top Hat with Cane and Painted Ceiling

Centenary of Gaiety Theatre, Douglas

(Des The Agency. Litho B.D.T.)

2000 (16 JULY). Perf 14 (C)

895	**857**	22p multicoloured	. . . .	50	55
896	**858**	26p multicoloured	. . . .	55	60
897	**859**	36p multicoloured	. . . .	75	80
898	**860**	45p multicoloured	. . . .	95	1·00
899	**861**	52p multicoloured	. . . .	1·10	1·25
900	**862**	65p multicoloured	. . . .	1·40	1·50
895/900		Set of 6	. . . .	4·75	5·25
		First Day Cover	. . . .		6·25
		Presentation Pack	. . . .	6·25	
		Stamp Cards (set of 6)	. . . .	3·50	9·50

Plate Nos.: All values 1A (×4)

Sheets: 20 (4×5) with enlarged illustrated margin at left

Imprint: Central, right-hand margin

Withdrawn: 14.7.2001

863 Map of Great Britain, Union Jack and Liner

864 Sydney Opera House, Australian Flag and Map

865 New Zealand Map and Flag

866 Map of Buenos Aires and Waterfront

867 U.S. Flag, Map of Boston and Harbour

868 South African Flag, Map and Table Mountain

'BT Global Challenge' Round the World Yacht Race

(Des The Agency. Litho Cartor)

2000 (10 SEPT). Perf 13½ (C)

901	**863**	22p multicoloured	. . . .	50	55
902	**864**	26p multicoloured	. . . .	55	60
903	**865**	36p multicoloured	. . . .	75	80
904	**866**	40p multicoloured	. . . .	85	90
905	**867**	44p multicoloured	. . . .	95	1·00
906	**868**	65p multicoloured	. . . .	1·40	1·50
901/6		Set of 6	. . . .	4·50	4·75
		First Day Cover	. . . .		5·75
		Presentation Pack	. . . .	5·75	
		Set of 6 Gutter Pairs	. . . . . .	9·00	

Plate Nos.: All values 1A (×4)

Sheets: 40 (2 panes 2×10)

Imprint: Centre, side margins

Withdrawn: 8.9.2001

869 Sailing and Holiday Tours Poster, 1925

870 'Isle of Man for Happy Holidays'

871 Woman in Swimsuit standing on Isle of Man, 1929

872 Stewardess and Ferry

873 'Isle of Man for Holidays 1931' and Ferry

170th Anniversary of Steam Packet Company. Tourism Posters

(Litho Cartor)

2000 (6 OCT). Perf 13½ (C)

907	**869**	22p multicoloured	50	55
908	**870**	26p multicoloured	55	60
909	**871**	36p multicoloured	75	80
910	**872**	45p multicoloured	95	1·00
911	**873**	65p multicoloured	1·40	1·50
907/11		Set of 5	3·75	4·00
		First Day Cover		5·00
		Presentation Pack	5·00	

Plate Nos.: All values 1A (×4)

Sheets: 20 (5×4)

Imprint: Centre, side margins

Withdrawn: 5.10.2001

874 Girl with Christingle Candle

875 Children dancing around Christmas Tree

876 'Building Europe'

877 Girl hugging Teddy Bear

878 Children with Stars

Christmas and Europa

(Des R. Wetherall (36p after J.-P. Cousin). Litho Questa)

2000 (7 NOV). Perf 14 (C)

912	**874**	21p multicoloured	45	50
913	**875**	25p multicoloured	55	60
914	**876**	36p multicoloured	75	80
		a. Sheetlet of 10	7·50	
915	**877**	45p multicoloured	95	1·00
916	**878**	65p multicoloured	1·40	1·50
912/16		Set of 5	3·75	4·00
		First Day Cover		5·00
		Presentation Pack	5·00	
		Set of 5 Gutter Pairs	7·50	

Plate Nos.: All values 1A (×4)

Sheets: 40 (2 panes 4×5); 36p also 10 (5×2)

Imprint: Right-hand corner, bottom margin

Withdrawn: 6.11.2001

Year Pack 2000

2000 (7 NOV). Comprises Nos. **MS**868/85 and 887/916

Year Pack .... 55·00

Sold out: By 10.2002

Post Office Yearbook

2000 (7 NOV). Comprises Nos. **MS**868/85 and 887/916

Yearbook .... 58·00

Sold out: By 10.2003

879 Wyon Medal, Penny Black and Queen Victoria

880 Great Exhibition Medal and Albert Tower, Ramsey

881 Silver Coin and *Great Britain* (early steamship)

882 Manx Coin of 1839, *Oliver Twist* and St. Thomas' Church, Douglas

883 Silver Coin of 1887, Arrival of First Train at Vancouver and Jubilee Lamp Standard

884 Silver Coin of 1893, Joe Mylchreest at Kimberley Diamond Mine and Foxdale Clock Tower

Death Centenary of Queen Victoria

(Des Mannin Design. Litho Walsall)

2001 (22 JAN). Perf 13½ (C)

917	**879**	22p multicoloured	50	55
918	**880**	26p multicoloured	55	60
919	**881**	34p multicoloured	75	80
920	**882**	39p multicoloured	85	90
921	**883**	40p multicoloured	85	90
922	**884**	52p multicoloured	1·10	1·25
917/22		Set of 6	4·25	4·50
		First Day Cover		5·50
		Presentation Pack	5·50	

Plate Nos.: All values 1A (×4)

Sheets: 20 (4×5)

Imprint: Right-hand corner, bottom margin

Withdrawn: 21.1.2002

885a St. Patrick and Snakes
(*illustration reduced. Actual size* 110×85 *mm*)

Chinese New Year ('Year of the Snake')

(Des The Agency. Litho and die-stamped Questa)

2001 (22 JAN). *Sheet* 110×85 *mm*. Perf 13½×14 (C)

MS923	**885a**	£1 multicoloured	2·25	2·40
		First Day Cover		3·25
		Presentation Pack	3·25	

No. **MS**923 includes the 'Hong Kong 2001' logo on the sheet margin.

Withdrawn: 21.1.2002

886 White-tailed Bumble Bee

887 Seven-spot Ladybird

888 Lesser Mottled Grasshopper

889 Manx Robber Fly

Elephant Hawkmoth, Deilephila elpenor

890 Elephant Hawkmoth

Insects

(Des R. Lewington. Litho Questa)

2001 (1 FEB). Perf 14 (C)

924	**886**	22p multicoloured	50	55
925	**887**	26p multicoloured	55	60
926	**888**	29p multicoloured	65	70
927	**889**	59p multicoloured	1·25	1·40
928	**890**	66p multicoloured	1·40	1·50
924/8		Set of 5	4·00	4·25
		First Day Cover		5·00
		Presentation Pack	5·00	

Plate Nos.: All values 1A, 1B (each ×4)

Sheets: 10 (5×2)

Imprint: Right-hand corner, bottom margin

Withdrawn: 31.1.2002

891 Letter-carrier, 1805

892 Postman, 1859

893 Postman, 1910

894 Postman, 1933

895 Postman, 1983

896 Postman, 2001

Postal Uniforms

(Des Colleen Corlett. Litho B.D.T.)

2001 (18 APR). Perf 14 (C)

929	**891**	22p multicoloured	50	55
930	**892**	26p multicoloured	55	60
931	**893**	36p multicoloured	75	80
932	**894**	39p multicoloured	85	90
933	**895**	40p multicoloured	85	90
934	**896**	66p multicoloured	1·40	1·50
929/34		Set of 6	4·50	4·75
		First Day Cover		5·50
		Presentation Pack	5·50	

Plate Nos.: All values 1A (×4)

Sheets: 20 (5×4)

Imprint: Central, bottom margin

Withdrawn: 17.4.2002

897a 1967–70 Great Britain ½d. Machin (29p);
1952–1954 Great Britain 6d. Wilding
(34p); 1971 Isle of Man 2½p. Regional (37p);
1958–68 Isle of Man 4d. Regional (50p)
(*illustration reduced. Actual size* 170×75 *mm*)

75th Birthday of Queen Elizabeth II

(Des The Agency. Litho B.D.T.)

2001 (18 APR). *Sheet* 170×75 *mm*. Perf 14 (C)

MS935	**897a**	29p, 34p, 37p, 50p multi-coloured	3·50	3·75
		First Day Cover		4·25
		Presentation Pack	4·25	

Withdrawn: 17.4.2002

898 Joey Dunlop on Rea
Yamaha, Parliament
Square, 1977 TT Races

899 At Governor's, 1983
TT Races

904 'The Manx Derby,
1627' (Johnny Jonas)

905 'Post Haste' (Johnny
Jonas)

900 Leaving Ramsey, 1988
TT Races

901 On Honda motorbike,
1991

906 'Red Rum' (Hamilton-
Rennick)

907 'Hyperion' (Sir
Alfred Munnings)

902 On 250cc Honda at
Ballaspur, 1999

903 On the Mountain

908 'Isle of Man' (Johnny Jonas)

Joey Dunlop (motorcycle champion) Commemoration

(Des Ruth Sutherland. Litho B.D.T.)

2001 (17 MAY). Perf 14 (C)

936	**898**	22p multicoloured	50	55
937	**899**	26p multicoloured	55	60
938	**900**	36p multicoloured	75	80
939	**901**	45p multicoloured	95	1·00
940	**902**	65p multicoloured	1·40	1·50
941	**903**	77p multicoloured	1·60	1·75
936/41		*Set of 6*	5·25	5·75
		First Day Cover		6·50
		Presentation Pack	6·50	
		Souvenir Folder (containing		
		5 sets of Nos. 936/41,		
		6 Postcards (PC20/5) and		
		special commemorative		
		cover)	40·00	
		Set of 6 Gutter Pairs	10·50	

Sheets: 20 (2 panes 2×5)

Withdrawn: 16.5.2002

Horse Racing Paintings

(Des The Agency. Litho Cartor)

2001 (18 MAY). Perf 13½ (C)

942	**904**	22p multicoloured	50	55
943	**905**	26p multicoloured	55	60
944	**906**	36p multicoloured	85	80
945	**907**	52p multicoloured	1·20	1·25
946	**908**	63p multicoloured	1·50	1·50
942/6		*Set of 5*	4·00	4·25
		First Day Cover		5·00
		Presentation Pack	5·00	

Plate Nos: All values 1A (×4)

Sheets: 20 (4×5)

Withdrawn: 17.5.2002

909 Beef

910 Queenies with Salmon Caviar

911 Seafood

912 Lamb

913 Kipper Tart

914 Lemon Tart with Raspberries

Europa. Local Dishes prepared by Kevin Woodford

(Des The Agency. Litho B.D.T.)

2001 (10 AUG). Perf 14 (C)			
947	**909**	22p multicoloured	50	55
948	**910**	26p multicoloured	55	60
		a. Panel at foot of stamp in pale lilac (R. 2/1)	20·00	
		b. Sheetlet of 10	5·50	
949	**911**	36p multicoloured	75	80
		b. Sheetlet of 10	7·75	
950	**912**	45p multicoloured	95	1·00
951	**913**	50p multicoloured	1·10	1·25
952	**914**	66p multicoloured	1·40	1·50
947/52		Set of 6	4·75	5·25
		First Day Cover		6·00
		Presentation Pack	6·00	
		Recipe Cards (set of 6)	20·00	

The 26p and 36p show the inscription 'EUROPA 2001' at bottom right.

On Nos. 947/52 the panel at the foot of each stamp, on which the designer and printer imprints occur, is normally white. On R. 2/1 of the 26p in sheets of 25 this panel is in pale lilac.

The set of recipe cards show a strip of 4 stamps plus label and first day of issue postmark.

Plate Nos.: All values 1A (×4)

Sheets: 30 (6×5) containing 25 stamps and 5 stamp-size labels, different for each value, in the first vertical row; 26p, 36p also 10 (2×10)

Withdrawn: 9.8.2002

915 Castletown Police Station

916 'Leafield' (semi-detached house)

917 'The Red House' (Baillie Scott's home)

918 'Ivydene' (detached house)

919 Onchan Village Hall

The Architecture of Mackay Hugh Baillie Scott

(Des Tracey Harding. Litho Cartor)

2001 (3 SEPT). Perf 13½ (C)			
953	**915**	22p multicoloured	50	55
954	**916**	26p multicoloured	55	60
955	**917**	37p multicoloured	80	85
956	**918**	40p multicoloured	85	90
957	**919**	80p multicoloured	1·75	1·90
953/7		Set of 5	4·00	4·25
		First Day Cover		5·00
		Presentation Pack	5·00	

Nos. 953/7 are inscribed 'HUGH MACKAY' in error.

Plate Nos.: All values 1A (×4)

Sheets: 20 (4×5) with a further view of the building depicted on the sheet margins

Withdrawn: 2.9.2002

'Hafnia '01' International Stamp Exhibition, Denmark

2001 (16 OCT). No. **MS**935 *additionally inscribed with* 'Hafnia '01' *logo in red on sheet margin*
MS958 170×75 mm. **897a** 29p, 34p, 37p
50p multicoloured . . . . 3·00 3·25
First Day Cover . . . . 4·25

Sold out: By 8.2003

920 Royal Refreshments at Glasgow

921 Queen on Visit to Lancaster

922 Queen with Labradors, Sandringham

923 Queen meeting Scottish Korean War Veterans

924 Queen at Desk, Sandringham

925 Queen with Bouquet, Oxford

Golden Jubilee (1st issue). 'The Daily Life of the Queen—An Artist's Diary' (paintings by Michael Noakes)

(Adapted The Agency. Litho Questa)

2001 (29 OCT) **02**. Perf 14 (C)
959 **920** 22p multicoloured (a) . . . . 50 bb
a. Booklet pane. Nos. 959/61 with margins all round (b) . . 1·75
960 **921** 26p multicoloured (a) 55 60
961 **922** 39p multicoloured (a) 85 90
962 **923** 40p multicoloured (a) 85 90
a. Booklet pane. Nos. 962/4 with margins all round (b) . . 3·00
963 **924** 45p multicoloured (a) . . . . 95 1·00
964 **925** 65p multicoloured (a) . . . . 1·40 1·50
959/64 Set of 6 . . . . 4·50 5·00
First Day Cover . . . . 5·75
Presentation Pack . . . . 5·75
Souvenir Folder (complete sheets) . . . . 42·00

See also Nos. 970/5.

Printings: (a) 29.10.2001; (b) 6.2.2002

Plate Nos.: All values 1A (×4)

Sheets: 8 (4×2) with enlarged illustrated margin at left

Withdrawn: 28.10.2002 (sheets)

926 Christmas Tree Wall Decoration

927 Traditional Wreath

928 Table Decoration

929 Topiary Tree

930 Contemporary Wreath

Christmas. Decorations by Isle of Man Floreat Workshop

(Des The Agency. Litho Questa)

2001 (5 NOV). Perf 14×14½ (C)

965	**926**	21p multicoloured	45	50
966	**927**	25p multicoloured	55	60
967	**928**	37p multicoloured	80	85
968	**929**	45p multicoloured	95	1·00
969	**930**	65p multicoloured	1·40	1·50
965/9		Set of 5	3·75	4·00
		First Day Cover		4·75
		Presentation Pack	5·00	

Plate Nos.: All values 1A, 1B (each ×4)

Sheets: 25 (5×5) with horizontal rows of stamps interspersed by rows of inscribed greetings labels. The 21p and 25p values were also available with personal photographs shown on these labels

Withdrawn: 4.11.2002

Year Folder 2001

2001 (5 NOV). Comprises Nos. 917/57 and 959/69

Year Folder . . . . 45·00

Sold out: By 11.2003

Year Pack 2001

2001 (5 NOV). Comprises Nos. 917/57 and 959/69

Year Pack . . . . 55·00

Sold out: By 11.2003

Post Office Yearbook

2001 (5 NOV). Comprises Nos. 917/57 and 959/69

Yearbook . . . . 60·00

Sold out: By 4.2002

931 'The Coronation, 1953' (Terence Cuneo)

932 'Queen Elizabeth II as Colonel-in-Chief of Grenadier Guards on Imperial, 1962' (Terence Cuneo)

933 'Queen Elizabeth II in Evening Dress, 1981' (June Mendoza)

934 'Queen Elizabeth II in Garter Robes, 2000' (Chen Yan Ning)

935 'Royal Succession' (John Wonnacott)

936a Sculpture of Queen Elizabeth II by David Cregeen (illustration reduced. Actual size 110×85 mm)

Golden Jubilee (2nd issue). Royal Paintings

(Des The Agency. Litho and die-stamped Questa)

2002 (6 FEB). Perf 14½×14 (No. **MS**975) or 14 (others), both comb

970	**931**	50p multicoloured	1·00	1·10
		a. Vert strip of 5. Nos. 970/4 . .	5·00	
		b. Booklet pane. Nos. 970/2 with margins all round	3·00	
971	**932**	50p multicoloured	1·00	1·10
972	**933**	50p multicoloured	1·00	1·10
973	**934**	50p multicoloured	1·00	1·10
		b. Booklet pane. Nos. 973/4 with margins all round	2·00	

974	**935**	50p multicoloured	1·00	1·10
970/4		Set of 5	5·00	5·50
		First Day Cover		6·00
		Presentation Pack	6·00	
		Souvenir Folder (*complete*		
		sheet)	20·00	
		Gutter Strip	10·50	
MS975		110×85 mm. **936a** £1 multicoloured	2·00	2·10
	b.	Booklet pane. As No.		
		MS975, *but* 152×97 mm		
		with a line of roulettes at left	2·00	2·10
		First Day Cover		3·00
		Presentation Pack	3·00	

Plate Nos.: 1A (×4)

Sheets: 20 (2 panes 2×5). Nos. 970/4 were printed together, *se-tenant*, as vertical strips of 5. The panes are separated by an enlarged vertical gutter illustrated with further royal portraits

Withdrawn: 5.2.2003

937 Cycling

938 Running

939 Javelin and High Jump

940 Swimming

941 Decathlon

942 Wheelchair Racing

17th Commonwealth Games, Manchester. Photographic Montages

(Des The Agency. Litho B.D.T.)

2002 (11 MAR). Perf 14 (C)

976	**937**	22p multicoloured	45	50
977	**938**	26p multicoloured	50	55
978	**939**	29p multicoloured	60	65
979	**940**	34p multicoloured	70	75
980	**941**	40p multicoloured	80	85

981	**942**	45p multicoloured	90	95
976/81		Set of 6	3·75	4·25
		First Day Cover		4·75
		Presentation Pack	5·00	

Plate Nos.: All values 1A (×4)

Sheets: 9 (3×3) with an illustrated gutter between the second and third horizontal rows, and an enlarged right margin

Withdrawn: 10.3.2003

943 'Queen Elizabeth the Queen Mother' (Johnny Jonas)

Queen Elizabeth the Queen Mother Commemoration

(Des The Agency. Litho Cartor)

2002 (23 APR). Perf 13×13½ (C)

982	**943**	£3 multicoloured	6·00	6·25
		First Day Cover		7·00
		Presentation Pack	7·00	

Plate Nos.: 1A (×4)

Sheets: 10 (5×2)

944 Ireland v Czech Republic

945 England v Greece

946 Italy v Belgium

947 France v Portugal

948 England v Brazil   **949** France v Japan

World Cup Football Championship, Japan and Korea

(Des E. Cassidy. Litho Cartor)

2002 (1 MAY). Perf 13½ (C)

983	**944**	22p multicoloured	. . . .	45	50
984	**945**	26p multicoloured	. . . .	50	55
985	**946**	39p multicoloured	. . . .	80	85
986	**947**	40p multicoloured	. . . .	80	85
987	**948**	66p multicoloured	. . . .	1·25	1·40
988	**949**	68p multicoloured	. . . .	1·40	1·50
983/8		Set of 6	. . . .	5·00	5·50
		First Day Cover	. . . .		6·00
		Presentation Pack	. . . .	6·25	

Plate Nos.: All values 1A (×4)

Sheets: 25 (5×5)

Withdrawn: 30.4.2003

950 'Monk's Bridge, Ballasalla'

951 'Laxey'

952 'Langness Lighthouse'

953 'King William's College'

954 'The Mull Circle and Bradda Head'

Watercolours by Toni Onley

(Des The Agency. Litho Cartor)

2002 (1 MAY). Perf 13½ (C)

989	**950**	22p multicoloured	. . . .	45	50
990	**951**	26p multicoloured	. . . .	50	55
991	**952**	37p multicoloured	. . . .	75	80
992	**953**	45p multicoloured	. . . .	90	95
993	**954**	65p multicoloured	. . . .	1·25	1·40
989/93		Set of 5	. . . .	3·75	4·00
		First Day Cover	. . . .		4·75
		Presentation Pack	. . . .	5·00	

Plate Nos.: All values 1A (×4)

Sheets: 25 (5×5)

Withdrawn: 30.4.2003

Golden Jubilee Celebrations

2002 (4 JUNE). *No.* **MS**975 *additionally inscribed* 'THE ISLE OF MAN CELEBRATES THE JUBILEE 4th JUNE 2002' *in purple on the sheet margin*

MS994   110×85 mm. **935a** £1 multicoloured   2·00   2·10

Withdrawn: 3.6.2003

955 Magenta Flower on Yellow Background

956 Green Flower on Pink Background

957 Purple Flower on Green Background

958 Maroon Flower on Brown Background

959 Red Flower on Blue Background

960 Orange Flower on Yellow Background

Memories of the Isle of Man

(Des Sir Paul McCartney. Litho Walsall)

2002 (1 JULY). Perf 13½×13 (C).

995	**955**	22p multicoloured	45	50
996	**956**	26p multicoloured	50	55
997	**957**	29p multicoloured	60	65
998	**958**	52p multicoloured	1·00	1·10
999	**959**	63p multicoloured	1·25	1·40
1000	**960**	77p multicoloured	1·50	1·60
995/1000		Set of 6	5·25	5·75
		First Day Cover		6·25
		Presentation Pack	6·50	
		Souvenir Folder (complete sheets and first day cover)	50·00	

Plate Nos.: All values 1A (×4)

Sheets: 8 (4×2) with inscribed margins and a photograph of Sir Paul McCartney at left

Withdrawn: 30.6.2003

961 Manx Milestone
(Mrs. B. Trimble)

962 Plough Horses
(Miss D. Flint)

963 Manx Emblem
(Ruth Nicholls)

964 Loaghtan Sheep
(Diana Burford)

965 Fishing Fleet,
Port St. Mary
(Phil Thomas)

966 Peel
(Michael Thompson)

967 Daffodils
(Michael Thompson)

968 Millennium Sword
(Mr. F. K. Smith)

969 Peel Castle
(Kathy Brown)

970 Snaefell Railway
(Joan Burgess)

971 Laxey Wheel
(Kathy Brown)

972 Sheep at Druidale
(John Brown)

973 Carousel at Silverdale
(Colin Edwards)

974 Grandma
(Stephanie Corkhill)

975 Manx Rock
(Ruth Nicholls)

976 T.T. Riders at
Signpost
(Neil Brew)

977 Groudle Railway
(Albert Lowe)

978 Royal Cascade
(Brian Speedie)

979 St. Johns
(John Hall)

980 Niarbyl Cottages
with Poppies
(Cathy Galbraith)

Photography – The People's Choice. Competition Winners

(Des The Agency. Litho Walsall)

2002 (30 AUG–1 OCT). (a) *PVA gum.* Perf 14 (C)

1001	**961**	23p multicoloured (b)	. . . .	45	50
		a. Block of 10. Nos. 1001/10	.	4·50	
1002	**962**	23p multicoloured (b)	. . . .	45	50
1003	**963**	23p multicoloured (b)	. . . .	45	50
1004	**964**	23p multicoloured (b)	. . . .	45	50
1005	**965**	23p multicoloured (b)	. . . .	45	50
1006	**966**	23p multicoloured (b)	. . . .	45	50
1007	**967**	23p multicoloured (b)	. . . .	45	50
1008	**968**	23p multicoloured (b)	. . . .	45	50
1009	**969**	23p multicoloured (b)	. . . .	45	50
1010	**970**	23p multicoloured (b)	. . . .	45	50
1011	**971**	27p multicoloured (a)	. . . .	55	60
		a. Block of 10. Nos. 1011/20	.	5·50	
1012	**972**	27p multicoloured (a)	. . . .	55	60
1013	**973**	27p multicoloured (a)	. . . .	55	60
1014	**974**	27p multicoloured (a)	. . . .	55	60
1015	**975**	27p multicoloured (a)	. . . .	55	60
1016	**976**	27p multicoloured (a)	. . . .	55	60
1017	**977**	27p multicoloured (a)	. . . .	55	60
1018	**978**	27p multicoloured (a)	. . . .	55	60
1019	**979**	27p multicoloured (a)	. . . .	55	60
1020	**980**	27p multicoloured (a)	. . . .	55	60
1001/20		Set of 20	. . . .	10·00	11·00
		First Day Covers (2)	. . . . . .		12·00
		Presentation Packs (2)	. . . .	12·00	

(b) *Booklet stamps. Self-adhesive.* Perf 6½ (die-cut)

1021	**961**	23p multicoloured (b)	. . . .	45	50
		a. Booklet pane. Nos. 1021/30	4·50		
1022	**962**	23p multicoloured (b)	. . . .	45	50
1023	**963**	23p multicoloured (b)	. . . .	45	50
1024	**964**	23p multicoloured (b)	. . . .	45	50
1025	**965**	23p multicoloured (b)	. . . .	45	50

1026	**966**	23p multicoloured (b)	. . . .	45	50
1027	**967**	23p multicoloured (b)	. . . .	45	50
1028	**968**	23p multicoloured (b)	. . . .	45	50
1029	**969**	23p multicoloured (b)	. . . .	45	50
1030	**970**	23p multicoloured (b)	. . . .	45	50
1031	**971**	27p multicoloured (b)	. . . .	55	60
		a. Booklet pane. Nos. 1031/40	5·50		
1032	**972**	27p multicoloured (b)	. . . .	55	60
1033	**973**	27p multicoloured (b)	. . . .	55	60
1034	**974**	27p multicoloured (b)	. . . .	55	60
1035	**975**	27p multicoloured (b)	. . . .	55	60
1036	**976**	27p multicoloured (b)	. . . .	55	60
1037	**977**	27p multicoloured (b)	. . . .	55	60
1038	**978**	27p multicoloured (b)	. . . .	55	60
1039	**979**	27p multicoloured (b)	. . . .	55	60
1040	**980**	27p multicoloured (b)	. . . .	55	60
1021/40		Set of 20	. . . .	10·00	11·00

Nos. 1021/30 and 1031/40 were only available in £2.30 and £2.70 stamp booklets with the surplus self-adhesive paper around each stamp retained.

Printings: (a) 30.8.02; (b) 1.10.02

Plate Nos.: Both values 1A (×5)

Sheets: 40 (5×8) Nos. 1001/10 and 1011/20 were each printed together, *se-tenant*, as blocks of 10, in sheets of 40.

Withdrawn: 29.8.2003 27p sheets; 30.9.2003 23p sheets

981 Father Christmas

982 Virgin Mary
and Jesus

983 Clown

984 Bandsman
playing
Cymbals

985 Fairy

986a 'CHRISTMAS' and Festive Characters
(*illustration reduced. Actual size* 123×55 *mm*)

Christmas. Entertainment

(Des Anthea Radcliffe. Litho Questa)

2002 (5 NOV). Perf 15×14½ (No. **MS**1046) or 14×14½ (others), both comb

1041	**981**	22p multicoloured	45	50
1042	**982**	26p multicoloured	50	55
1043	**983**	37p multicoloured	75	80
1044	**984**	47p multicoloured	95	1·00
1045	**985**	68p multicoloured	1·40	1·50
1041/5		Set of 5	4·00	4·25
		First Day Cover		5·00
		Presentation Pack	5·00	
MS1046		123×55 mm. **986a** £1.30, multicoloured	2·50	2·75
		First Day Cover		3·50
		Presentation Pack	3·75	

The 37p value includes the 'EUROPA' emblem.

Plate Nos.: All values 1A (each ×4)

Sheets: 40 (5×8)

Withdrawn: 4.11.2003

Year Folder 2002

2002 (5 NOV). *Comprises Nos.* 970/93, 995/1020 *and* 1041/5
Year Folder . . . . 45·00

Sold out: By 31.7.2004

Year Pack 2002

2002 (5 NOV). *Comprises Nos.* 970/93, 995/1020 *and* 1041/5
Year Pack . . . . 55·00

Sold out: By 31.7.2004

Post Office Yearbook

2002 (5 NOV). *Comprises Nos.* 970/93, 995/1020 *and* 1041/5
Yearbook . . . . 60·00

987 Dish Aerial and Peel Castle

988 Dish aerial Tromode Teleport

989 Camp on Moon and lunar vehicle

990 Astronaut exploring lunar surface

991 *Sea Launch Odyssey* (marine launch platform)

992 *Sea Launch Commander* (assembly and command ship)

993 Loral Telstar 1 satellite

994 Loral Telstar 8 satellite

995a Phobos and American Spaceship (75p); Mars, Astronauts and Transfer Vehicle (75p)
(*illustration reduced. Actual size* 110×85 *mm*)

Isle of Man Involvement in Space Exploration

(Des E. McCall (27p, 75p), E. Gignac (others). Litho Cartor)

2003 (14 FEB). Perf 13½×13 (**MS**1055) or 13½ (others), both comb

1047	**987**	23p multicoloured	45	50
		a. Horiz pair. Nos. 1047/8	90	1·00
1048	**988**	23p multicoloured	45	50

1049	**989**	27p multicoloured	55	60
		a. Horiz pair. Nos. 1049/50 . . .	1·10	1·10
1050	**990**	27p multicoloured	55	60
1051	**991**	37p multicoloured	75	80
		a. Horiz pair. Nos. 1051/2 . . .	1·50	1·60
1052	**992**	37p multicoloured	75	80
1053	**993**	42p multicoloured	85	90
		a. Horiz pair. Nos. 1053/4 . . .	1·60	1·75
1054	**994**	42p multicoloured	85	90
		Set of 8	5·50	5·50
		First Day Cover		6·00
		Presentation Pack	6·25	
MS1055	110×85 mm. **995a** 75p multi-			
coloured			1·50	1·60
		First Day Cover		4·00
		Presentation Pack	4·00	

Plate Nos.: All values 1A (×4)

Sheets: 8 (2×4). Nos. 1047/8, 1049/50, 1051/2 and 1053/4 were each printed together, as horizontal se-tenant pairs forming composite designs, in sheets with enlarged illustrated right margins

Withdrawn: 13.2.2004

Post Office Vehicles

(Des P. Hearsey. Litho Questa)

2003 (14 FEB). Perf 14½ (C)

1056	**996**	23p multicoloured	45	50
1057	**997**	27p multicoloured	55	60
1058	**998**	37p multicoloured	75	80
1059	**999**	42p multicoloured	85	90
1060	**1000**	89p multicoloured	1·75	1·90
		Set of 5	4·25	4·50
		First Day Cover		5·25
		Presentation Pack	5·25	

Plate Nos.: All values 1A (×4)

Sheets: 25 (5×5)

Imprint: Right-hand side, bottom margin

Withdrawn: 13.2.2004

996 Delivery Handcart (1900–45)

997 Morris Z Van (1942)

998 Morris L Diesel Van (1960s)

999 DI BSA Bantam Telegraph Delivery Motorbikes

1000 Ford Escort 55 Van

1001 Queen Elizabeth II wearing St. Edward's Crown

1002 The Ring

1003 The Orb

1004 Royal Sceptre and Rod of Equity and Mercy

1005 Queen Elizabeth II
wearing Imperial
State Crown

1006 State Coach

50th Anniversary of Coronation

(Des Diane Fawcett. Litho Walsall)

2003 (12 APR). Perf 13½ (C)

1061	**1001**	50p multicoloured	1·00	1·10
		a. Block of 6. Nos. 1061/6 . .	6·00	
1062	**1002**	50p multicoloured	1·00	1·10
1063	**1003**	50p multicoloured	1·00	1·10
1064	**1004**	50p multicoloured	1·00	1·10
1065	**1005**	50p multicoloured	1·00	1·10
1066	**1006**	50p multicoloured	1·00	1·10
		Set of 6	6·00	6·50
		First Day Cover		7·00
		Presentation Pack	7·00	
		Souvenir Folder	25·00	

Plate Nos.: 1A (×5)

Sheets: 24. Nos. 1061/6 were printed together, *se-tenant*, as four blocks of six with Nos. 1061 and 1065 at either end, 1062/4 in the top row and 1066 at the bottom

Withdrawn: 10.4.2004

1007 De Havilland
D.H.83 Fox Moth
and Saro Cloud
(amphibian)

1008 De Havilland
D.H.61 Giant
Moth and D.H.80
Puss Moth

1009 Avro Type 652
and Boeing B-17
Flying Fortress

1010 Eurofighter
Typhoon and
Avro Vulcan

1011 Handley Page Herald
and Bristol Wayfarer

1012 Aerospatiale
Concorde and
projected Airbus
Industrie A380

Centenary of Powered Flight

(Des K. Woodcock. Litho B.D.T.)

2003 (9 MAY). Perf 13½ (C)

1067	**1007**	23p multicoloured	45	50
		a. Horiz strip of 3. Nos. 1067/9	1·75	
1068	**1008**	27p multicoloured	55	60
1069	**1009**	37p multicoloured	75	80
1070	**1010**	40p multicoloured	80	85
		a. Horiz strip of 3. Nos. 1070/2	3·75	
1071	**1011**	67p multicoloured	1·40	1·50
1072	**1012**	89p multicoloured	1·75	1·90
		Set of 6	5·50	6·00
		First Day Cover		6·50
		Presentation Pack	6·75	
		Souvenir Folder (complete sheets and **MS**1073)	28·00	

Plate Nos.: All values 1A (×4)

Sheets: 12 (2 panes 3×2). Nos. 1067/9 and 1070/2 were each printed together, *se-tenant*, as horizontal strips of three, within sheets containing two blocks of six separated by large illustrated gutters.

Withdrawn: 8.5.2004

1012a Avro Lancaster attacking Mohne Dam
(*illustration reduced. Actual size* 78×50 *mm*)

60th Anniversary of Attack on German Dams by No. 617 ('Dambusters') Squadron

(Des R. Taylor. Litho B.D.T.)

2003 (9 MAY). *Sheet* 170×75 *mm.* Perf 13 (C)

MS1073	**1012a**	£2 multicoloured	4·00	4·25
		First Day Cover		5·00
		Presentation Pack		5·00

Withdrawn: 8.5.2004

1013 Prince William   **1014** Prince William

1015 Prince William   **1016** Prince William

21st Birthday of Prince William of Wales

(Des The Agency Ltd. Litho Cartor)

2003 (9 JUNE). Perf 13½ (C)

1074	**1013**	42p black and grey	85	90
1075	**1014**	47p black and grey	95	1·00
1076	**1015**	52p black and grey	1·00	1·10
1077	**1016**	68p black and grey	1·40	1·50
		Set of 4	4·00	4·50
		First Day Cover		5·00
		Presentation Pack		5·25

Plate Nos.: All values 1A (×4)

Sheets: 25 (5×5)

Imprint: Central, side margins

Withdrawn: 8.6.2004

Trilaterale Ticino Exhibition, Locarno, Switzerland

2003 (18 JUNE). *No.* **MS**1073 *additionally inscribed with* 'Ticino 2003' *logo in blue on sheet margin.*

MS1078   £2 multicoloured . . . .   4·00   4·25

Withdrawn: 17.6.2004

1017 *Manx
Gold*
(Agatha
Christie)

1018 *Quatermass
and the Pit*
(Nigel
Kneale)

1019 *Flashman at
the Charge*
(George
MacDonald
Fraser)

1020 *The Eternal
City* (Hall
Caine)

1021 *Peveril of
the Peak*
(Sir Walter
Scott)

1022 *Emma's
Secret*
(Barbara
Taylor
Bradford)

'The Manx Bookshelf'. Book Covers

(Des D. Macdonald. Litho Walsall)

2003 (5 JULY). Perf 13½ (C)

1079	**1017**	23p multicoloured	45	50
1080	**1018**	27p multicoloured	55	60
1081	**1019**	30p multicoloured	60	65
1082	**1020**	38p multicoloured	75	80

1083	**1021**	40p multicoloured	80	85
1084	**1022**	53n multicoloured	1·00	1·10
		Set of 6	4·00	4·50
		First Day Cover		5·25
		Presentation Pack	5·25	

The 38p. value includes the 'EUROPA 2003' emblem.

Plate Nos: All values 1A (×4)

Sheets: 20 (5×4) with small *se-tenant* label giving the author's name at the foot of each stamp; 38p also 10 (5×2)

Withdrawn: 3.7.2004

1023 King Henry VII and Henry Tudor crowned by Sir Thomas Stanley on Bosworth Battlefield

1024 King Henry VIII and Manx Church (Dissolution of the Monasteries)

1025 Queen Elizabeth I and Globe showing Route of Drake's Circumnavigation

1026 King Henry VIII, Cardinal Wolsey and Hampton Court Palace

1027 Queen Mary I and Tudor Rose

1028 Queen Elizabeth I and Ships of Spanish Armada

400th Anniversary of End of the Tudor Reign

(Des D. Kearney. Litho BDT)

2003 (15 SEPT). Perf 14 (C)

1085	**1023**	23p multicoloured	45	50
1086	**1024**	27p multicoloured	55	60
1087	**1025**	38p multicoloured	75	80
1088	**1026**	40p multicoloured	80	85

1089	**1027**	47p multicoloured	95	1·00
1090	**1028**	67p multicoloured	1·40	1·50
		Set of 6	4·75	5·25
		First Day Cover		5·75
		Presentation Pack	6·00	
		Stamp Cards (set of 6) . . .	4·25	10·00

Plate Nos.: All values 1A (×4)

Sheets: 25 (5×5)

Withdrawn: 14.9.2004

1029 Henry Bloom Noble and Orphanage Boys

1030 Nurse and Ramsey Cottage Hospital

1031 Children and Children's Home

1032 Bathers at Noble's Baths

1033 Scout and Headquarters

1034 Noble's Hospital, c. 1912

1035 Villa Marina

1036 Noble's Park

1037 St. Ninian's
Church

1038 Noble's
Library

1039 Boy tying Scarf
on Snowman

1040 Snowman
(wearing black
hat and scarf)

1041 Boy and
Snowman
holding Hands

1042 Snowman
(wearing brown
hat and scarf)

1043 Boy flying with Snowman

Centenary of Henry Bloom Noble Trust

(Des Tracey Harding. Litho Walsall)

2003 (1 OCT). (*a*) *PVA gum.* Perf 14 (C)

1091	**1029**	23p multicoloured	45	50
		a. Horiz strip of 5. Nos.		
		1091/5	2·25	
1092	**1030**	23p multicoloured	45	50
1093	**1031**	23p multicoloured	45	50
1094	**1032**	23p multicoloured	45	50
1095	**1033**	23p multicoloured	45	50
1096	**1034**	27p multicoloured	55	60
		a. Horiz strip of 5. Nos.		
		1096/1100	2·75	
1097	**1035**	27p multicoloured	55	60
1098	**1036**	27p multicoloured	55	60
1099	**1037**	27p multicoloured	55	60
1100	**1038**	27p multicoloured	55	60
1091/1100		*Set of 10*	5·00	5·50
		First Day Cover		6·00
		Presentation Pack	6·00	

(*b*) *Self-adhesive booklet stamps.* Roul 6½

1101	**1029**	23p multicoloured	45	50
		a. Booklet pane. Nos.		
		1101/5, *each × 2*	4·50	
1102	**1030**	23p multicoloured	45	50
1103	**1031**	23p multicoloured	45	50
1104	**1032**	23p multicoloured	45	50
1105	**1033**	23p multicoloured	45	50
1106	**1034**	27p multicoloured	55	60
		a. Booklet pane. Nos.		
		1106/1110, *each × 2*	11·00	
1107	**1035**	27p multicoloured	55	60
1108	**1036**	27p multicoloured	55	60
1109	**1037**	27p multicoloured	55	60
1110	**1038**	27p multicoloured	55	60
1101/10		*Set of 10*	5·00	5·50

Plate Nos.: Both values 1A (×4)

Sheets: 50 (5×10). Nos. 1091/5 and 1096/1100 were each printed together, *se-tenant,* in horizontal strips of 5 throughout the sheets Nos. 1101/5 and 1106/1110 were only issued in £2.30 and £2.70 booklets, Nos. SB57/8.

Withdrawn: 30.9.2004 (sheets)

Christmas. The Snowman by Raymond Briggs

(Litho DLR)

2003 (5 NOV). Perf 14½ (C)

1111	**1039**	22p multicoloured	45	50
1112	**1040**	26p multicoloured	50	55
1113	**1041**	38p multicoloured	75	80
1114	**1042**	47p multicoloured	95	1·00
1115	**1043**	68p multicoloured	1·40	1·50
		Set of 5	4·00	4·25
		First Day Cover		5·00
		Presentation Pack	5·25	

Plate Nos.: All values 1A (×4)

Sheets: 40 (5×8)

Withdrawn: 4.11.2004

Year Folder 2003

2003 (12 NOV). *Comprises Nos. 1047/77, 1079/1100 and* 1111/15

Year Folder . . . . 50·00

2003 (12 NOV). *Comprises Nos.* 1047/77, 1079/1100 *and* 1111/15

Year Pack . . . . 60·00

Post Office Yearbook

2003 (12 NOV). *Comprises Nos.* 1047/77, 1079/1100 *and* 1111/15

Yearbook . . . . 60·00

1044 Aragorn

1045 Gimli

1046 Gandalf

1047 Legolas on Horseback

1048 Gollum

1049 Frodo and Sam

1050 Legolas drawing Bow

1051 Aragorn on Horseback

1052a The Ring
(*illustration reduced. Actual size* 120×78 mm)

Making of The Lord of the Rings Film Trilogy: The Return of the King

(Des The Agency Ltd. Litho BDT)

2003 (17 DEC). Perf 13½ (C)

1116	**1044**	23p multicoloured		
1117	**1045**	27p multicoloured	45	50
1118	**1046**	30p multicoloured	55	60
1119	**1047**	38p multicoloured	60	65
1120	**1048**	42p multicoloured	75	80
1121	**1049**	47p multicoloured	85	90
1122	**1050**	68p multicoloured	95	1·00
1123	**1051**	85p multicoloured	1·40	1·50
1116/23		Set of 8	1·75	1·90
		First Day Cover	7·25	7·75
		Presentation Pack		8·25
		Souvenir Folder (complete sheets and **MS**1124)	8·25 50·00	
		Stamp Cards (pre-paid) (set of 8)	9·50	9·50

MS1124 120×78 mm. **1052a** £2 The Ring (44×40 mm) . . . . 4·00 4·25

First Day Cover . . . . 5·00

Presentation Pack . . . . 5·00

Plate Nos.: All values 1A (×4)

Sheets: 6 (3×2) with enlarged illustrated margins

Withdrawn: 16.12.2004

1053 *Maitland* (Simon Hall)

1054 *Evening Star* (Terence Cuneo)

1055 Pen-y-Darren Tramroad Locomotive (Terence Cuneo)

1056 *Duchess of Hamilton* (Craig Tiley)

1057 *City of Truro* (B. J. Freeman)

1058 *Mallard* (Terence Cuneo)

Bicentenary of Running of First Steam Locomotive. Paintings of Steam Locomotives

(Des Fusion Graphics from paintings. Litho Cartor)

2004 (21 FEB). Perf 13×13½ (C)

1125	**1053**	23p multicoloured	75	75
1126	**1054**	27p multicoloured	90	90
1127	**1055**	40p multicoloured	1·30	1·30
1128	**1056**	57p multicoloured	1·80	1·80
1129	**1057**	61p multicoloured	2·00	2·00
1130	**1058**	90p multicoloured	3·00	3·00
1125/30		*Set of 6*	9·75	9·75
		First Day Cover		11·00
		Presentation Pack	11·50	

Plate Nos.: All values 1A (×4)

Sheets: 25 (5×5)

1059 Troops on Landing Craft and Tanks going Ashore

1060 Troops leaving Landing Craft and Tanks going Ashore

1061 Troops leaving Landing Craft

1062 Landing Craft and Troops wading Ashore

1063 *Lady of Mann* (ferry used as landing craft carrier)

1064 *Ben-my-Chree* (ferry used as landing craft carrier)

1065 Consolidated B-24 Liberators (bombers) and North American P-51 Mustang (fighter)

1066 Airspeed A.S.51 Horsa Gliders (troop carriers)

1067a Winston Churchill; Troops and Aircraft; Military Vehicles on Street; Soldiers with *France* Guidebook
(*illustration reduced. Actual size 170×75 mm*)

60th Anniversary of D-Day

(Des B. Sanders (Nos. 1131/8 only) and The Agency Ltd. Litho DLR (Nos. 1131/8) or Enschedé (**MS**1139))

2004 (6 APR). Perf 14 (C)

1131	**1059**	23p multicoloured	75	75
		a. Horiz pair. Nos. 1131/2 . . .	1·50	1·50
1132	**1060**	23p multicoloured	75	75
1133	**1061**	27p multicoloured	90	90
		a. Horiz pair. Nos. 1133/4 . . .	1·80	1·80
1134	**1062**	27p multicoloured	90	90
1135	**1063**	47p multicoloured	1·50	1·50
		a. Horiz pair. Nos. 1135/6 . . .	3·00	3·00
1136	**1064**	47p multicoloured	1·50	1·50
1137	**1065**	68p multicoloured	2·20	2·20
		a. Horiz pair. Nos. 1137/8 . . .	4·25	4·25
1138	**1066**	68p multicoloured	2·20	2·20
1131/8		*Set of 8*	10·50	10·50
		First Day Cover		12·50
		Presentation Pack	12·50	
		Collectors Folder (complete sheets and **MS**1139)	40·00	

MS1139 170×75 mm. **1067a** 50p×4,
multicoloured. Perf 13½×14 (C) . . . . . 6·50 6·50
First Day Cover . . . . 8·00
Presentation Pack . . . . . . 8·25

Plate Nos.: All values 1A (×4)

Sheets: 10 Nos. 1131/2, 1133/4, 1135/6 and 1137/8 were each
printed together, *se-tenant*, in horizontal pairs throughout the
sheets, each pair forming a composite design.

1068 Lesser
Celandine

1069 Red Campion

1070 Devil's-bit
Scabious

1071 Northern
Harebell

1072 Wood
Anemone

1073 Common
Spotted Orchid

Bicentenary of Royal Horticultural Society. Wild Flowers

(Des The Agency Ltd. Litho Cartor)

2004 (3 MAY). Perf 13½ (C)
1140	**1068**	25p multicoloured	85	85
1141	**1069**	28p multicoloured	95	95
1142	**1070**	37p multicoloured	1·20	1·20
1143	**1071**	40p multicoloured	1·30	1·30
1144	**1072**	68p multicoloured	2·20	2·20
1145	**1073**	85p multicoloured	2·75	2·75
1140/5		Set of 6	9·25	9·25
		First Day Cover		11·00
		Presentation Pack	11·00	

Plate Nos.: All values 1A (×4)

Sheets: 40 (5×8)

1074 In *No Limit*,
1936

1075 Pushing
Motorcycle

1076 Riding in TT
Race

1077 With Florence
Desmond

1078 On Motorcycle

1079 Close-up of
George Formby

Birth Centenary of George Formby (entertainer). Scenes from No Limit *(film)*

(Des Ruth Sutherland. Litho BDT)

2004 (26 MAY). Perf 13½ (C)
1146	**1074**	25p multicoloured	80	80
1147	**1075**	28p multicoloured	90	90
1148	**1076**	40p multicoloured	1·30	1·30
1149	**1077**	43p multicoloured	1·40	1·40
1150	**1078**	50p multicoloured	1·70	1·70
1151	**1079**	74p multicoloured	2·40	2·40
1146/51		Set of 6	8·50	8·50
		First Day Cover		10·00
		Presentation Pack	10·00	

Sheets: 25 (5×5)

1080 Johnny Weissmuller
(gold, 100m & 400m
freestyle), Paris,
1924

1081 Jesse Owens (gold,
100m, 200m, long
jump), Berlin, 1936

1082 John Mark carrying Olympic Flame, London, 1948

1083 Fanny Blankers-Koen (gold, 100m, 200m, 80m hurdles), London, 1948

1084 James Cracknell, Steven Redgrave, Tim Foster and Matthew Pinsent (gold, men's coxless fours), Sydney, 2000

Olympic Games, Athens. 'Olympic Legends'

(Des Fusion Graphics. Litho BDT)

2004 (1 JULY). Perf 14 (C)

1152	**1080**	25p multicoloured	85	85
1153	**1081**	28p multicoloured	95	95
1154	**1082**	43p multicoloured	1·40	1·40
1155	**1083**	55p multicoloured	1·80	1·80
1156	**1084**	91p multicoloured	3·00	3·00
1152/6		Set of 5	8·00	8·00
		First Day Cover		9·75
		Presentation Pack	10·00	

Plate Nos.: All values 1A (×4)

Sheets: 25 (5×5)

Imprint: Central, bottom margin

1085 Celtic Islanders and Viking Invaders

1086 Fisherman ('Ships and the Sea')

1087 Miner and Laxey Wheel ('Laxey Miners')

1088 Soldier with Longbow and Castle ('Kings and Lords of Mann')

1089 Woman with Spinning Wheel ('Farmers and Crofters')

1090 Calf of Man

1091 Peel Castle

1092 Laxey Wheel

1093 Castle Rushen

1094 Cregneash

Manx National Heritage 'The Story of Mann'

(Des The Agency Ltd. Litho BDT)

2004 (3 AUG). (a) PVA gum. Perf 14 (C)

1157	**1085**	(25p) multicoloured	80	80
		a. Horiz strip of 5. Nos. 1157/61	4·00	
1158	**1086**	(25p) multicoloured	80	80
1159	**1087**	(25p) multicoloured	80	80
1160	**1088**	(25p) multicoloured	80	80
1161	**1089**	(25p) multicoloured	80	80
1162	**1090**	(28p) multicoloured	90	90
		a. Horiz strip of 5. Nos. 1162/6	4·50	
1163	**1091**	(28p) multicoloured	90	90
1164	**1092**	(28p) multicoloured	90	90
1165	**1093**	(28p) multicoloured	90	90
1166	**1094**	(28p) multicoloured	90	90
1157/66		Set of 10	8·50	8·50
		First Day Cover		10·50
		Presentation Pack	10·50	

(b) Self-adhesive booklet stamps. Perf 12½ (die-cut)

1167	**1085**	(25p) multicoloured	80	80
		a. Booklet pane. Nos. 1167/71, each ×2	8·00	

1168	**1086**	(25p) multicoloured	80	80
1169	**1087**	(25p) multicoloured	80	80
1170	**1088**	(25p) multicoloured	80	80
1171	**1089**	(25p) multicoloured	80	80
1172	**1090**	(28p) multicoloured	90	90
		a. Booklet pane. Nos. 1172/6, each ×2	9·00	
1173	**1091**	(28p) multicoloured	90	90
1174	**1092**	(28p) multicoloured	90	90
1175	**1093**	(28p) multicoloured	90	90
1176	**1094**	(28p) multicoloured	90	90
1167/76		Set of 10	8·50	8·50

Nos. 1157/61 and 1167/71 are inscribed 'IOM' and were initially sold at 25p. Nos. 1162/6 and 1172/6 are inscribed 'UK' and were initially sold at 28p.

Plate Nos. Both values 1A (×4)

Sheets: 50 (5×10). Nos. 1157/61 and 1162/6 were each printed together, *se-tenant*, in horizontal strips of 5 throughout the sheets. Nos. 1167/71 and 1172/6 were only issued in £2.50 and £2.80 booklets, Nos. SB59/60.

1095a Laxey Wheel
(*illustration reduced. Actual size* 120×78 *mm*)

150th Anniversary of the Great Laxey Wheel

(Des The Agency Ltd. Litho BDT)

2004 (3 AUG). Perf 14 (C)
MS1177	**1095a**	£2 multicoloured	6·50	6·50
		First Day Cover		8·50
		Presentation Pack	8·50	

1096 'Maughold Church'

1097 'Port St. Mary'

1098 'Ballaugh Old Church'

1099 'Douglas Bay (A Midsummer's Night)'

1100 'Point of Ayre'

1101 'Peel Harbour and Castle'

The Isle of Man Watercolours by Alfred Heaton Cooper

(Des The Agency Ltd. Litho Enschedé)

2004 (21 OCT). Perf 13½×13 (C)
1178	**1096**	25p multicoloured	80	80
1179	**1097**	28p multicoloured	90	90
1180	**1098**	40p multicoloured	1·30	1·30
1181	**1099**	41p multicoloured	1·30	1·30
1182	**1100**	43p multicoloured	1·40	1·40
1183	**1101**	74p multicoloured	2·40	2·40
1178/83		Set of 6	8·00	8·00
		First Day Cover		10·00
		Presentation Pack	10·00	

The 28p and 40p values include the 'EUROPA 2004' emblem.

Plate Nos.: All values 1A (×4)

Sheets: 25 (5×5); 28p and 40p also 10 (2×5)

Sindelfingen International Stamp Exhibition, Sindelfingen, Germany

2004 (29 OCT). No. **MS**1177 additionally inscribed with SINDELFINGEN logo on the sheet margin.
MS1184	**1095a**	£2 multicoloured	6·50	6·50

1102 Robin on Flower Pot

1103 Robin at Foot of Tree

236

1104 Robin perched on Branch among Bracken

1105 Robin on Window Ledge

1106 Robin on Snowy Logs

1107 Harry Potter (Daniel Radcliffe), Ron Weasley (Rupert Grint) and Hermione Granger (Emma Watson)

1108 Snowy Owl delivering Owl Post

1109 Harry Potter and White Stag

1110 Hogwarts Express

Robins—'Winter's Friends'

(Des Dr. J. Paul. Litho Lowe-Martin, Canada)

2004 (9 NOV). Perf 12½×13 (C)

1185	**1102**	25p multicoloured	80	80
1186	**1103**	28p multicoloured	90	90
1187	**1104**	40p multicoloured	1·30	1·30
1188	**1105**	47p multicoloured	1·50	1·50
1189	**1106**	68p multicoloured	2·30	2·30
1185/9		Set of 5	6·75	6·75
		First Day Cover		8·75
		Presentation Pack	8·75	
MS1190	148×200 mm. Nos. 1185/9×2		6·75	6·75

Plate Nos.: All values 1A (×7)

Sheets: 40 (5×8)

Year Folder 2004

2004 (9 NOV). *Comprises Nos.* 1116/66, **MS**1177/83 *and* 1185/9

Year Folder . . . . 60·00

Year Pack 2004

2004 (9 NOV) *Comprises Nos.* 1116/66, **MS**1177/83 *and* 1185/9

Year Pack . . . . 75·00

Post Office Yearbook

2004 (9 NOV) *Comprises Nos.* 1116/66, **MS**1177/83 *and* 1185/9

Yearbook . . . . 60·00

1111 Rubeus Hagrid (Robbie Coltrane)

1112 Purple Triple-decker Bus

1113 Dementor and Harry Potter flying

1114 Harry Potter on the Hippogriff Buckbeak

Harry Potter and the Prisoner of Azkaban *(film)*

(Des The Agency Ltd. Litho Enschedé)

2004 (7 DEC). Perf 13½ (C)

1191	**1107**	25p multicoloured	80	80
1192	**1108**	28p multicoloured	90	90
1193	**1109**	39p multicoloured	1·30	1·30
1194	**1110**	40p multicoloured	1·30	1·30
1195	**1111**	49p multicoloured	1·60	1·60
1196	**1112**	55p multicoloured	1·80	1·80
1197	**1113**	57p multicoloured	1·90	1·90
1198	**1114**	68p multicoloured	2·20	2·20
1191/8		Set of 8	11·75	11·75
		First Day Cover		13·50
		Presentation Pack	13·75	
		Collectors Folder (contains complete sheets and 'Owl Post Office' first day cover)	50·00	
		Stamp Cards (pre paid) (set of 8)	11·75	11·75

Plate Nos.: All values 1A (×5)

Sheets: 5 (1×5)

SOUVENIR POSTAL STATIONERY POSTCARDS

The following postcards were issued by the Isle of Man Postal Authority often in connection with various philatelic exhibitions and, with the exception of Nos. PC8, PC11 and PC15/16 show imprinted stamp designs.

'San Marino 82'

1982 (1 SEPT). *Card showing imprinted stamp design as No. 217. Sold at 30p*

PC1   19½p multicoloured . . . . 1·00   1·25

Withdrawn: 30.4.84

'Tembal 83', Basel

1983 (21 MAY). *Card showing imprinted stamp design as No. 250. Sold at 30p*

PC2   20½p multicoloured . . . . 1·00   1·60

Withdrawn: 20.5.84

'Espana 84', Madrid

1984 (27 APR). *Card showing imprinted stamp design as No. 266. Sold at 30p*

PC3   20½p multicoloured . . . . 1·50   1·75

Withdrawn: 26.4.85

'Ausipex 84', Melbourne

1984 (21 SEPT). *Card showing imprinted stamp design as No. 278. Sold at 40p*

PC4   33p multicoloured . . . . 1·50   2·75

Withdrawn: 20.9.85

'Italia 85', Rome

1985 (25 OCT). *Card showing imprinted stamp designs as Nos. 292/3. Sold at 40p*

PC5 14p+14p multicoloured . . . . 1·50   3·25

Withdrawn: 24.10.86

'Ameripex 86', Chicago

1986 (22 MAY). *Card showing imprinted stamp design as No. 302. Sold at 40p*

PC6   34p multicoloured . . . . 2·25   2·75

Withdrawn: 21.5.87

'Stockholmia 86', Stockholm

1986 (28 AUG). *Card showing imprinted stamp designs as Nos. 305/6. Sold at 40p*

PC7   15p+15p multicoloured . . . . 1·25   2·00

Withdrawn: 27.8.87

'Hafnia 87', Copenhagen

1987 (16 OCT). *Card with Nos. 358/9 affixed. Sold at 50p*

PC8   12p+15p multicoloured . . . . 1·25   1·75

Withdrawn: 15.10.88

'Finlandia 88', Helsinki

1988 (1 JUNE). *Card showing imprinted stamp designs as Nos. 371 and 375. Sold at 50p*
PC9   14p+18p multicoloured . . . .   1·25   1·50

    Withdrawn: 31.5.89

'Sydpex 88', Sydney

1988 (30 JULY). *Card showing imprinted stamp designs as Nos. 386/7. Sold at 60p*
PC10   29p +31p multicoloured . . . .   1·50   1·75

    Withdrawn: 29.7.89

'Filacept 88', The Hague

1988 (18 OCT). *Card with Nos. 383/4 affixed. Sold at 50p*
PC11   22p+22p multicoloured . . . .   1·25   2·00

    Withdrawn: 17.10.89

'Belgica 90', Brussels

1990 (2 JUNE). *Card showing imprinted stamp designs as Nos. 442 and 446. Sold at 50p*
PC12   1p+37p multicoloured . . . .   1·25   1·50

    Withdrawn: 2.93

'Essen 94', Centenary of Picture Postcards

1994 (5 MAY). *Cards showing imprinted stamp design as No. 338. Sold at 80p the pair*
PC13   31p multicoloured (Douglas) . . . .   1·25   1·50
PC14   31p multicoloured (Ramsey) . . . .   1·25   1·50

    Withdrawn: 4.5.95

'Jakarta 95'

1995 (19 AUG). *Sold at 15p*
PC15   Komodo Dragon   75   1·00

    Withdrawn: 6.98

'Beijing 95'

1995 (16 SEPT). *Sold at 15p*
PC16   Great Wall of China   75   1·00

    Withdrawn: 6.98

Isle of Man T.T. Races and 50th Anniversary of Honda

1998 (1 JUNE). *Card showing imprinted stamp design as No. 809. Sold at 50p*
PC17   25p multicoloured . . . .   1·00   1·25

    Withdrawn: 6.99

'Espana 2000', Madrid

2000 (6 OCT). *Card showing imprinted stamp design as No. 910*
PC18   45p multicoloured . . . .   1·50   1·50

    Withdrawn: 6.2002

'Sindelfingen', Germany

2000 (6 OCT). *Card showing imprinted stamp design as No. 911*
PC19   65p multicoloured . . . .   1·50   1·50

    Withdrawn: 6.2002

Joey Dunlop (motorcycle champion) Commemoration

2001 (17 MAY). *Cards showing stamp designs and enlarged photographs on the front and Douglas postage paid impression on the reverse. Sold at £5.71*
PC20/5   Set of 6 cards . . . .   11·50   11·50

    Withdrawn: 16.5.2002

MANX POSTAL MUSEUM POSTCARDS

1987 (23 MAR). *Sold at 10p*
PM1   Reopening of Regent Street Post Office, Douglas   30   1·00

    Sold out: By 2.90

1989 (28 APR). *Sold at 15p*
PM2   Bicentenary of the Mutiny on the Bounty   40   1·50

    Sold out: By 1.93

1990 (10 APR). *Sold at 18p*
PM3   'CUNARD 150' Exhibition, Liverpool. Sinking of *Lusitania* (as No. 191)   50   1·50

    Sold out: By 2.94

POSTAGE DUE STAMPS

D **1**

D **2**

D **3** Badge of
Post Office
Authority

(Des and litho Questa)

1973 (5 JULY). Perf 14×13½ (C)

D1	D **1**	½p red, black & bistre-yellow (ab)	1·50	1·10
D2		1p red, black and cinnamon (ab)	50	60
D3		2p red, black & lt apple-green (ab)	15	20
		a. Positive offset of red ptg on back		
D4		3p red, black and grey (ab)	20	20
D5		4p red, black & carmine-rose (ab)	30	35
D6		5p red, black and cobalt (ab)	30	35
D7		10p red, black & light lavender (ab)	40	40
D8		20p red, black & pale turq-grn (ab)	75	60
D1/8		Set of 8	3·75	3·50
		Presentation Pack (ptg b)	5·00	

Printings: (a) 5.7.73; (b) 1.9.73. Examples of printing (b) are known used from mid-August onwards.

Prices quoted above are for printing (b), which can be identified by the letter 'A' added after '1973' at the foot of the stamp. Collectors should beware of spurious examples with the 'A' removed. Price for set of 8 from printing (a) £24 mint or used

Plate Nos.: All values 1A, 1B (each ×3)

Sheets: 100 (10×10)

Imprint: Right-hand corner, bottom margin, and left-hand corner, top margin

Sold out: Printing (a) between 13.8.73 and 10.9.73. Printing (b) ½p by 12.74; 1p by 2.75; 2p and 3p by 5.75; others by 31.12.75

(Des and litho Questa)

1975 (8 JAN). Perf 14×13½ (C)

D9	D **2**	½p black, red & greenish yellow	10	10
D10		1p black, red and flesh	10	10
D11		4p black, red and rose-lilac	10	15
D12		7p black, red & lt greenish blue	15	20
D13		9p black, red and brownish grey	25	30
D14		10p black, red and bright mauve	25	20
D15		50p black, red and orange-yellow	90	90
D16		£1 black, red & turquoise-green	1·50	1·60
D9/16		Set of 8	3·00	3·25
		First Day Cover		4·50
		Presentation Pack	3·50	

Plate Nos.: All values 1A, 1B (each ×3)

Sheets: 100 (10×10)

Imprint: Left-hand corner, bottom margin

Withdrawn: 31.12.82 (1p to £1); 31.12.85 ½p

(Litho B.D.T.)

1982 (5 OCT). Centres multicoloured; background colour given. Perf 14½×14 (C)

D17	D **3**	1p turquoise-green	10	10
D18		2p mauve	10	10
D19		5p greenish blue	10	10
D20		10p reddish lilac	20	25
D21		20p grey	40	45
D22		50p buff	90	1·10
D23		£1 salmon	1·60	2·10
D24		£2 bright blue	3·25	4·25
D17/24		Set of 8	6·00	7·75
		First Day Cover		12·00
		Presentation Pack	8·00	

Plate Nos.: All values 1A (×5)

Sheets: 50 (10×5)

Imprint: Right-hand corner, bottom margin

D **4**

(Des Colleen Corlett. Litho B.D.T.)

1992 (18 SEPT). Perf 13×13½ (C)

D25	D **4**	£5 multicoloured	8·00	8·50
		First Day Cover		12·00
		Presentation Pack	9·50	

Plate Nos.: 1A, 1B (each ×4)

Sheets: 50 (10×5)

Imprint: Right-hand corner, bottom margin

STAMP BOOKLETS

PRICES. Prices are given for complete booklets. All booklets to No. SB7 are stitiched.

B **1** Derbyhaven

1973 (5 JULY–17 OCT). *Coloured covers as Type B* **1**, *printed in black*

Type B **1**. *Yellow cover*
SB1   10p booklet containing 2×2½p (No. 16), 2×2p (No. 15) and 2×½p (No. 12) (*ab*) . . . . 14·00

Ballaugh Church. Green cover
SB2   25p booklet containing 10×2½p (No. 16) (*ab*) .   3·00

Peel Castle. Stone cover
SB3   30p booklet containing 10×3p (No. 17) (*a*) . . 19·00
SB3*a* As SB3 but cover in buff (*b*) . . . . 17·00

Quayside, Douglas. Lavender-grey cover
SB4   50p booklet containing 8×2½p (No. 16) and
       10×3p (No. 17) (*a*) . . . .   8·00
SB4*a* As SB4 but grey-green cover (*b*) . . . .   4·50

Nos. SB1/4 were made up from ordinary sheets, the stamps being in vertical pairs with stitching through the side margins. Stamps from both sides of the sheets were used, so that panes come either upright or inverted.

Printings: (*a*) 5.7.73: (*b*) 17.10.73

STAMP SACHETS. These are cardboard covers, with stamps loose inside, contained in clear plastic sachets.

B **2**

1973 (5 JULY–1 NOV). *Stamp Sachets. Covers as Type B* **2**
10p sachet containing 5×½p (No. 12) and 3×2½p (No. 16)
10p sachet containing 2×½p (No. 12) and 3×3p (No. 17)
   (1 Nov) (*Price 1·00 each*)

B **3** Old Laxey Bridge
   (*illustration reduced. Actual size* 89×51 *mm*)

1974 (1 APR). *Coloured covers as Type B* **3**, *printed in black*

Type B **3**. *Buff cover*
SB5   30p booklet containing 8×½p (No. 12), 4×3p
       (No. 17) and 4×3½p (No. 18) . . . . 1·40

Monk's Bridge, Ballasalla. Green cover
SB6   40p booklet containing 4×½p (No. 12), 8×3p
       (No. 17) and 4×3½p (No. 18) . . . . 1·40

St. Michael's Chapel, Langness. Red cover
SB7   50p booklet containing 12×3p (No. 17) and
       4×3½p (No. 18) . . . . 1·40

Nos. SB5/7 contain panes of four, and were produced in the same way as Nos. SB1/4.

1974 (29 JULY). *Stamp Sachets. Cover designs as Nos. SB5/7, but inscriptions redrawn. Contents unchanged*
30p sachet. Pink cover (*Price 1·50*)
40p sachet. Green cover (*Price 1·60*)
50p sachet. Yellow cover (*Price 1·90*)

1975 (25 APR–16 JUNE). *Stamp Sachets. Blue cover showing Post Office badge*
20p sachet containing 3×2p (No. 15) and 4×3½p (No. 18) attached to cover by the selvedge (*Price 2·20*)
20p sachet containing 1×½p (No. 12), 2×1½p (No. 14) and 3×5½p (No. 22), loose or attached to selvedge (28 May) (*Price 2·70*)
20p sachet containing 4×½p (No. 12), 2×1½p (No. 14) and 3×5p (No. 21), loose or attached to selvedge (16 June) (*Price 2·70*)

1976 (20 SEPT)–**79**. *Stamp Sachet. Blue cover similar to Type* B **3**, *showing Rushen and Castletown Harbour*
20p sachet containing 2×1p (No. 13) and 3×6p (No. 23) (*Price 1·10*)
20p sachet containing 2×1p (No. 13) and 3×6p (No. 139) (3.79) (*Price 2·40*)

B **4** Viking Longship
(*illustration reduced. Actual size* 81×49 mm)

Millennium of Tynwald

1979 (16 MAY). *Folded card covers as Type* B **4**
SB8   20p booklet containing 4×3p and 2×4p (No.
        150*ab*) (blue cover) . . . .   1·25
SB9   40p booklet containing 8×3p and 4×4p (No.
        150*a*×2) (pink cover) . . . .   1·25
SB10 60p booklet containing 12×3p and 6×4p
        (No. 150*a*×3) (yellow cover) . . . .   2·00

Examples of Nos. SB8/9 are known containing the wrong
pane.

Withdrawn: 28.9.80

1980 (29 SEPT). *Folded card covers as Type* B **4**
SB11 40p booklet containing 2×1p, 4×3p, 4×4p
        and 2×5p (Nos. 150*ba* and 188*a*) (pink cover
        showing Manx Loaghtyn Ram) . . . .   1·00
SB12 80p booklet containing 4×1p, 8×3p, 8×4p
        and 4×5p (Nos. 150*ba* and 188*a* each ×2)
        (green cover showing Peregrine Falcon) . . . .   2·00

Withdrawn: 9.4.86

1985 (12 JUNE). *Booklet No.* SB11 *with cover surcharged*
50*p and an additional loose* 10*p stamp inside*
SB13 50p booklet containing Nos. 150*ba*, 188*a* and
        one 10p (No. 236) . . . .   4·50

Withdrawn: 9.4.86

B **5** Celtic Cross Logo
(*illustration reduced.
Actual size
80×48 mm*)

Manx Heritage Year

1986 (10 APR). *Folded card covers as Type* B **5**
SB14 50p booklet containing 2×1p, 2×4p, 2×5p
        and 3×10p (Nos. 188*a* and 316*a*) olive-green
        cover) . . . .   2·00
SB15 £1.14 booklet containing 2×1p, 2×2p, 4×3p,
        4×4p, 2×5p and 7×10p (Nos. 150*ba*, 188*a*,
        315*a* and 316*a*) (greenish blue cover) . . . . . .   4·00

Withdrawn: 25.3.87

B **6** Loch Promenade
(*illustration reduced. Actual size* 82×48 mm)

Victorian Douglas

1987 (26 MAR). *Folded card covers as Type* B **6**
SB16 50p booklet containing either No. 334*a* or
        334*ab* (orange-brown and deep yellow-green
        cover Type B **6**) . . . .   1·75
SB17 £1.10 booklet containing either Nos. 334*a* or
        334*ab*, and 334*b* (orange-brown and bright
        scarlet cover showing The Breakwater) . . . .   3·50

Withdrawn: 15.3.88

B **7** Baldwin Reservoir Tramway Steam Locomotive *Injebreck* (*illustration reduced. Actual size* 82×48 *mm*)

Manx Railways and Tramways

1988 (16 MAR). *Folded multicoloured card covers as Type* B **7**

SB18   50p booklet containing No. 367*a* (cover Type B **7**) .... 3·00

SB19   £1.99 booklet containing Nos. 367*a* and 370*a* (cover showing Manx Electric Railway train at Maughold Head) .... 7·00

Withdrawn: 15.10.89

B **8** 'Mutineers casting Bligh adrift' (Robert Dodd) (*illustration reduced. Actual size* 155×100 *mm*)

Bicentenary of The Mutiny on the Bounty

1989 (28 APR). *Multicoloured cover as Type* B **8**. *Booklet contains text and illustrations on interleaving pages. Stitched*

SB20   £5.30 booklet containing Nos. 408*a*/*b*, 410*a* and **MS**415 .... 14·00

Examples of No. **MS**415 from the booklet have wider margins than the normal miniature sheets.

Withdrawn: 2.92

Manx Railways and Tramways

1989 (16 OCT). *Folded multicoloured covers as Type* B **7**

SB21   50p booklet containing No. 367*b* (cover showing Port Erin Breakwater Tramway Locomotive *Henry B. Loch*) .... 2·50

SB22   £2.09 booklet containing Nos. 367*b* and 371*a* (cover showing Douglas Cable Tramway) .... 6·50

Withdrawn: 13.2.90

Manx Railways and Tramways

1990 (14 FEB). *Folded multicoloured covers as Type* B **7**

SB23   50p booklet containing No. 372*a* (cover showing Marine Drive Tramway) .... 2·75

SB24   £1.74 booklet containing No. 372*b* (cover showing Ramsey Harbour Tramway) .... 6·25

Withdrawn: 8.1.91

B **9** Penny Black (*illustration reduced. Actual size* 125×75 *mm*)

150th Anniversary of the Penny Black and 'Stamp World London 90' International Stamp Exhibition, London

1990 (3 MAY). *Black and ochre cover as Type* B **9**. *Booklet contains text and illustrations on interleaving pages. Stapled*

SB25   £3.50 booklet containing Nos. 442*c*, 443*a* and **MS**447 .... 9·00

Withdrawn: 23.9.93

Manx Railway and Tramways

1991 (9 JAN). *Folded multicoloured covers as Type* B **7**

SB26   50p booklet containing No. 367*ca* (cover, 80×48 mm, showing Groudle Glen Railway steamlocomotive *Polar Bear*) .... 4·00

SB27   £1 booklet containing No. 367*cb* (cover, 56×43 mm, showing I.M.R. No. 11 *Maitland* pulling Royal Train, 1963) .... 4·75

Withdrawn: 7.1.92

B **10** Three Kings
  (*illustration reduced. Actual size* 150×105 *mm*)

Christmas

1991 (14 OCT). *Deep violet cover as Type* B **10**. *Stitched*
SB28   £4.16 booklet containing No. 500a×2 . . . . . .   12·50

  Withdrawn: 23.9.93

Manx Railways and Tramways

1992 (8 JAN*). Folded multicoloured covers as Type* B **7**, *but*
  56×43 *mm*
SB29   £1 booklet containing No. 375ab (cover
    showing double-decker horse tram, Douglas)   4·00
SB30   £2 booklet containing No. 375ac (cover
    showing T.P.O. Special) . . . .   7·00

  Withdrawn: 3.1.93

B **11** Union Pacific No. 119, 1869
  (*illustration reduced. Actual size* 119×74 *mm*)

Construction of Union Pacific Railroad

1992 (22 MAY). *Multicoloured cover as Type* B **11**. *Pane
  attached by selvedge*
SB31   £4.38 booklet containing pane No. 522b . . . .   10·00

  Withdrawn: 27.4.94

B **12** *Francis Drake*
  (ketch)

Ships

1993 (4 JAN). *Multicoloured covers as Type* B **12**. *Panes
  attached by selvedge*
SB32   £1.10 booklet containing pane No. 543a
    (cover Type B **12** . . . .   3·00
SB33   £2.20 booklet containing pane No. 543b
    (cover showing *Tynwald I*) . . . .   5·50

  Withdrawn: 20.4.96

B **13** No. 9 Tunnel Car and Crew
  (*illustration reduced. Actual size* 160×98 *mm*)

Centenary of Manx Electric Railway

1993 (3 FEB). *Multicoloured cover as Type* B **13**. *Stitched*
SB34   £4.44 booklet containing pane No. 559a×4   .   14·00

  Withdrawn: 27.4.94

B **14** (*illustration reduced.
  Actual size* 62×95 *mm*)

Christmas

1993 (12 OCT). *Folded multicoloured covers as Type B* **14**. *Panes attached by selvedge*

SB35 £1.90 booklet containing No. 578×10 (cover Type B **14**) . . . . 4·50

SB36 £2.30 booklet containing No. 579×10 (cover showing No. 579) . . . . 5·50

Withdrawn: 10.10.95

B **15** (*illustration reduced. Actual size* 134×85 *mm*)

Manx Tourism Centenary

1994 (18 FEB). *Multicoloured cover as Type B* **15**. *Pane attached by selvedge*

SB37 £2.40 booklet containing pane No. 590a and pane of 12 (3×4) greetings labels . . . . 6·00

Sold out: By 9.95

B **16** Postman Pat, Jess, Ferry and Aircraft
(*illustration reduced. Actual size* 152×85 *mm*)

Postman Pat visits the Isle of Man

1994 (14 SEPT). *Multicoloured cover as Type B* **16** *cut out to show stamps from first pane. Booklet contains text and illustrations on labels attached to panes. Stitched*

SB38 £4.04 booklet containing Nos. 614a/19a, **MS**620 and pane of 8 character labels . . . . . 12·00

Withdrawn: By 2.97

B **17** Car and Passengers at Snaefell Summit
(*illustration reduced. Actual size* 162×97 *mm*)

Centenary of Snaefell Mountain Railway

1995 (8 FEB). *Black, scarlet and grey cover as Type B* **17**. *Booklet contains text and illustrations on labels attached to panes. Stitched.*

SB39 £4.63 booklet containing No. 634a×3 and **MS**638a . . . . 14·00

Withdrawn: By 2.97

B **18** Thomas the Tank Engine
(*illustration reduced. Actual size* 151×80 *mm*)

50th Anniversary of Thomas the Tank Engine Stories by Revd. Awdry. 'Thomas the Tank Engine's Dream'

1995 (15 AUG). *Multicoloured cover as Type B* **18** *cut out to show stamps from first pane. Stitched*

SB40 £3.92 booklet containing Nos. 656a/b, 657a, 658a, 659a and 660a . . . . 11·00

Withdrawn: By 2.97

B **19** Aerial view of Langness Lighthouse
(*illustration reduced. Actual size* 130×82 *mm*)

Lighthouses

1996 (24 JAN). *Multicoloured cover as Type* B **19.** *Booklet contains text and illustrations on interleaving pages. Stitched*
SB41 £4.74 booklet containing Nos. 672a/5a . . . . . 12·00

Withdrawn: By 5.97

Ships

1996 (21 APR). Multicoloured cover as Type B **12.** Pane attached by selvedge
SB42 96p booklet containing pane No. 687a (cover showing *Sir Winston Churchill*) . . . . 6·75

Sold out: 5.97

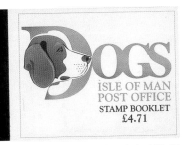

B **20** (*illustration reduced. Actual size* 118×81 *mm*)

Dogs

1996 (18 SEPT). *Multicoloured cover as Type* B **20.** *Booklet contains text and illustrations on interleaving pages. Stitched*
SB43 £4.71 booklet containing Nos. 719a, 720a, 721a and **MS**725a . . . . 10·00

Withdrawn: 17.9.97

B **21** Tawny Owl
(*illustration reduced. Actual size* 152×80 *mm*)

Owls

1997 (12 FEB). *Multicoloured cover as Type* B **21.** *Booklet contains text and illustrations on interleaving pages. Stitched*
SB44 £4.62 booklet containing Nos. 734a/6a and **MS**740a . . . . 10·50

Withdrawn: 11.2.98

Ships

1997 (14 MAY). *Multicoloured cover as Type* B **12.** *Pane attached by selvedge*
SB45 £1 booklet containing pane No. 541a (cover showing Royal Yacht *Britannia*) . . . . 4·00
a. With extra loose 4p stamp and optd inside front cover . . . . 5·00

No. SB45a was issued from booklet machines until 1 July 1997 when the postal rates were revised. The overprint inside the front cover was applied by handstamp.

Withdrawn: 31.12.97 No. SB45a; 30.11.98 No. SB45

B **22** King Edward Bay Golf and Country Club
(*illustration reduced. Actual size* 160×96 *mm*)

Golf

1997 (29 MAY). *Multicoloured cover as Type* B **22.** *Booklet contains text and illustrations on panes and interleaving pages. Stitched*
SB46 £4.54 booklet containing Nos. 755a/7a and **MS**759a . . . . 10·00

Withdrawn: 28.5.98

B **23** Cushag

Flowers

1998 (12 FEB). *Multicoloured cover as Type* B **23.** *Pane attached by selvedge*
B47 £1 booklet containing No. 775a . . . . 3·25

Withdrawn: 31.8.99

B **24** Basking Shark
(illustration reduced. Actual size 157×105 mm)

U.N.E.S.C.O. International Year of the Ocean

1998 (16 MAR). *Multicoloured cover as Type B* **24**. *Booklet contains text and illustrations on interleaving pages. Stitched*
B48   £3.62 booklet containing No. 798a/b . . . .   9·75

Withdrawn: 13.3.99

B **25** Steam Train at Douglas Station
(illustration reduced. Actual size 157×105 mm)

125th Anniversary of Isle of Man Steam Railway

1998 (2 MAY). *Multicoloured cover as Type B* **25**. *Booklet contains text and illustrations on interleaving pages. Stitched*
B49   £4.05 booklet containing Nos. 803a×2 and
         MS807a . . . .   10·00

Sold out: 6.2000

B **26** *Manchester & Salford, 1868–1887*
(illustration reduced. Actual size 158×108 mm)

175th Anniversary of Royal National Lifeboat Institution

1999 (4 MAR). *Multicoloured cover as Type B* **26**. *Booklet contains text and illustrations on interleaving pages. Stitched*
SB50   £4.64 booklet containing Nos. 832a/b and
         MS839a . . . .   13·00

Withdrawn: 3.3.2000

Flowers

1999 (26 APR). *Multicoloured cover as Type B* **23**. *Pane attached by selvedge*
SB51   £1 booklet containing pane No. 775ba (cover
         showing Dog Rose) . . . .   2·70

Sold out: By 31.8.2004

B **27** Bus Radiator and Headlights
(illustration reduced. Actual size 158×100 mm)

Manx Buses

1999 (18 JUNE). *Multicoloured cover as Type B* **27**. *Booklet contains text and illustrations on panes and interleaving pages. Stitched*
SB52   £4.78 booklet containing panes Nos. 845a/d .   11·50

Sold out: 8.2001

B **28** Flags, Weapons and Military Headgear
(illustration reduced. Actual size 180×75 mm)

Isle of Man at War

2000 (22 MAY). *Multicoloured cover as Type B* **28**. *Booklet contains text and illustrations on interleaving pages. Stitched*
SB53   £4.99 booklet containing Nos. 887a/b and
         MS893 . . . .   10·00

Sold out: By 6.2003

247

B **29** 'The Coronation, 1953' (Terence Cuneo)
(*illustration reduced. Actual size* 165×95 *mm*)

Golden Jubilee

2002 (6 FEB). *Multicoloured cover as Type* B **29**. *Booklet contains text and illustrations on panes and interleaving pages. Stitched*
SB54   £5.87 booklet containing panes Nos. 959*a*,
962*a*, 970*b*, 973*b* and **MS**975*b* . . . .   11·50

Withdrawn: 30.4.2004

B **30** Aspects of Isle of Man
(*illustration reduced. Actual size* 105×70 *mm*)

Photography – The People's Choice

2002 (1 OCT). Multicoloured covers as Type B **30**. Self-adhesive
SB55   £2.30 booklet containing No. 1021*a* . . . .   4·50
SB56   £2.70 booklet containing No. 1031*a* . . . .   5·25

Withdrawn: 30.4.2004

B **31** Henry Bloom Noble and Original Villa Marina
(*illustration reduced. Actual size* 104×70 *mm*)

Centenary of Henry Bloom Noble Trust

2003 (1 OCT). *Multicoloured covers as Type* B **31**. *Self-adhesive.*
SB57   £2.30 booklet containing No. 1101*a* . . . .   4·50
SB58   £2.70 booklet containing No. 1106*a* . . . . .   11·00

Withdrawn: 31.12.2004

B **32** Soldier, Viking, Miner, Spinner and Fisherman
(*illustration reduced. Actual size* 102×70 *mm*)

Manx National Heritage 'The Story of Mann'

2004 (3 AUG). *Multicoloured covers as Type* B **32**. *Self-adhesive.*
SB59   (£2.50) booklet containing pane No. 1167*a*
(*cover as Type* B **32**) . . . .   8·00
SB60   (£2.80) booklet containing pane No. 1172*a*
(*cover showing Cregneash, Calf of Man, Castle Rushen, Laxey Wheel and Peel Castle*) . . . .   9·00

JERSEY

THE GERMAN OCCUPATION 1940–1945

Soon after the commencement of the occupation of Jersey by German forces on 1 July 1940 orders were given by the German Commandant to the Island's Postmaster for stocks of the currently available stamps to be forwarded to the Jersey printers, J. T. Bigwood, for overprinting with a swastika and 'JERSEY 1940'. All values of the 1937–8 definitives from ½d to 10s, excluding the 1d, were so overprinted as were the 1940 Postal Centenary stamps, excluding the 1d, but whilst this was in progress the Bailiff of Jersey protested to the German Commandant who referred the matter to Berlin and was ordered to destroy the stocks. Four complete sets to 1s, and a few singles, however, are known to exist. At the same time Bigwoods prepared a local 1d. stamp incorporating the arns of Jersey and the words 'ETATS DE JERSEY'. These were printed in imperforate sheets of thirty (10×3) and are known with and without a swastika and '1940' overprint. These also were destroyed with the exception of two sheets of each which have been cut up for collectors and a damaged sheet with the overprint which is complete. There is also a complete sheet of the unoverprinted stamp in the National Postal Museum.

Jersey eventually issued locally printed ½d and 1d stamps, the 1d on 1 April 1941 and the ½d on 29 January 1942. No distinct shades exist though both values come on newsprint paper and, in addition, the 1d is known on chalk-surfaced paper.

In June 1943 a pictorial set of six stamps from ½d to 3d was issued, the designer being the well-known Jersey artist Edmund Blampied. Two values, the 1d and 2½d, are known on newsprint paper.

Both these and the earlier issues remained on sale until 13 April 1946 after which date they could no longer be used.

1   **2**

The Swastika Overprints
1940. *Prepared for use but not issued. Stamps of Great Britain overprinted by J. T. Bigwood, States' Printers*

(a) *On 1937–9 definitive issue*

Cat. No.	Type No.		Unused
SW1	**1**	½d. green	£1700
SW2		1½d. red-brown	£1700
SW3		2d. orange	£1700
SW4		2½d. ultramarine	£1700
SW5		3d. violet	£1700
SW6		4d. grey-green	£1700
SW7		5d. brown	£1700
SW8		6d. purple	£1700
SW9		7d. emerald-green	£1700
SW10		8d. bright carmine	£1700
SW11		9d. deep olive-green	£1700
SW12		10d. turquoise-blue	£1700
SW13		1s. bistre-brown	£1700

(b) *On 1940 Stamp Centenary issue*

SW14	**2**	½d. green	£1700
SW15		1½d. red-brown	£1700
SW16		2d. orange	£1700
SW17		2½d. ultramarine	£1700
SW18		3d. violet	£1700

3   **4**

(Des R. W. Cutland. Typo J. T. Bigwood)

1940. *Prepared for use but not issued. No wmk. Imperforate*

SW19	**3**	1d. scarlet	£1700
SW20	**4**	1d. scarlet	£1700

5 Arms of Jersey

Stamps issued during the German Occupation

(Des Major N. V. L. Rybot. Typo *Jersey Evening Post*, St. Helier)

1941–43. *White paper. No wmk. Perf 11 (L)*

1	**5**	½d bright green (29.1.42)	4·00	3·25
		a. *Imperf between* (vertical pair)	£800	
		b. *Imperf between* (horizontal pair)	£700	
		c. *Imperf* (pair)	£250	
		d. *On greyish paper* (1.43)	5·50	5·50
2		1d scarlet (1.4.41)	4·50	2·50
		a. *Imperf between* (vertical pair)	£800	
		b. *Imperf between* (horizontal pair)	£700	
		c. *Imperf* (pair)	£275	
		d. *On chalk-surfaced paper* (9.41)	42·00	38·00
		e. *On greyish paper* (1.43)	5·50	5·75
1		*First Day Cover* (plain)		7·00
2		*First Day Cover* (plain)		7·00

Sheets: 60 (6×10)

Imprint: ½d 'EVENING POST', JERSEY, JANUARY, 1942
1d 'EVENING POST', JERSEY, 17/3/41

Quantities printed: ½d 703,500; 1d 1,030,620

Withdrawn and invalidated: 13.4.46

6 Old Jersey Farm

7 Portelet Bay

8 Corbière Lighthouse

9 Elizabeth Castle

10 Mont Orgueil Castle

11 Gathering Vraic (seaweed)

Pictorial Issue

(Des E. Blampied. Eng H. Cortot. Typo French Govt Printing Works, Paris)

1943 (1 JUNE)–**44**. *No wmk. Perf 13½ (C)*

3	**6**	½d green	7·50	5·50
		a. Rough, grey paper (6.10.43)	7·50	5·50
4	**7**	1d scarlet	2·00	75
		a. On newsprint (28.2.44)	2·50	75
5	**8**	1½d brown (8.6.43)	3·50	3·25
6	**9**	2d orange-yellow (8.6.43)	4·75	3·25
7	**10**	2½d blue (29.6.43)	2·00	1·00
		a. On newsprint (25.2.44)	1·00	1·10
		ba. Thin paper (design shows through on reverse)	£225	
8	**11**	3d violet (29.6.43)	1·25	3·00
3/8		Set of 6	18·00	15·00
		First Day Covers (3)		32·00
		Set of 6 Gutter Pairs	40·00	

Printings: The sheets of the various printings were dated in the sheet corners as follows:

½d 1st Printing 1/5/43
2nd Printing 3/6/43
3rd Printing 6/10/43
1d 1st Printing 7/5/43
2nd Printing 8/5/43
3rd Printing 7/10/43
4th Printing 28/2/44
1½d 1st Printing 17/5/43
2nd Printing 18/5/43
2d 1st Printing 20/5/43
2nd Printing 21/5/43
2½d 1st Printing 31/5/43
2nd Printing 25/2/44
3d 1st Printing 4/6/43
2nd Printing 5/6/43

Sheets: 60 (2 panes 3×10)

Imprint: None

Quantities printed: ½d (No. 3) 360,000; ½d (No. 3a) 120,000; 1d (No. 4) 960,000; 1d (No. 4a) 240,000; 1½d 360,000; 2d 360,000; 2½d (No. 7) 360,000; 2½d (Nos. 7a/b) 360,000; 3d 360,000

Withdrawn and invalidated: 13.4.46

REGIONAL ISSUES

Although specifically issued for regional use, these issues were initially valid for use throughout Great Britain. However, they ceased to be valid in Jersey and Guernsey from 1 October 1969 when these islands each established their own independent postal administration and introduced their own stamps.

DATES OF ISSUE. Conflicting dates of issue have been announced for some of the regional issues, partly explained by the stamps being released on different dates by the Philatelic Bureau in Edinburgh or the Philatelic Counter in London and in the regions. We have adopted the practice of giving the earliest known dates, since once released the stamps could have been used anywhere in the U.K.

INVALIDATION. The regional issues of Jersey were invalidated for use in Jersey and Guernsey on 1 November 1969 (although Guernsey granted a further extension for British and regional stamps till the end of March 1970). The stamps continued to be valid for use in the rest of the United Kingdom until 29 February 1972. Those still current remained on sale at philatelic sales counters until 30 September 1970.

11a Multiple Crowns

12

13

(Des E. Blampied (Type **12**), W. Gardner (Type **13**). Portrait by Dorothy Wilding Ltd. Photo Harrison)

1958–67 *Wmk Type* **11a**. *Perf* 15×14 (C)

9	**12**	2½d carmine-red (8.6.64)	20	45
		a. *Imperf three sides* (*pair*) £2000		
10	**13**	3d deep lilac (18.8.58)	20	25
		p. *One centre phosphor band* (9.6.67)	15	15
11		4d ultramarine (7.2.66)	25	30
		p. *Two phosphor bands* (5.9.67) .	15	25
9/11		*Set of 3*	45	75
9		*First Day Cover*		30·00
10		*First Day Cover*		17·00
11		*First Day Cover*		8·00

Cylinder Nos.: 2½d 1; 3d (ord) 1, 2; 3d (phos) 2; 4d (ord) 1; 4d (phos) 1

Sheets: 240 (12×20)

Quantities sold (ordinary only); 2½d 4,770,000; 3d 35,169,720; 4d 6,623,040

Withdrawn: 31.8.66 2½d

Sold out: 10.67 3d (ordinary); 11.67 4d (ordinary); 10.68 3d and 4d (phosphor)

1968–69. *No wmk. Chalk–surfaced paper. One centre phosphor band* (4*d values*) *or two phosphor bands* (5*d*). *Perf* 15×14 (C)

12	**13**	4d olive-sepia (4.9.68)	15	25
13		4d bright vermilion (26.2.69)	15	35
14		5d Royal blue (4.9.68)	15	50
12/14		*Set of 3*	45	1·00
12, 14		*First Day Cover*		3·00

Cylinder Nos.: 4d (olive-sepia) 1; 4d (bright vermilion) 1; 5d 1

Withdrawn: 30.9.69 (locally), 30.9.70 (British Philatelic Counters) 4d olive-sepia, 4d bright vermilion and 5d

INDEPENDENT POSTAL ADMINISTRATION

Jersey established their own independent postal administration on 1 October 1969 and introduced their own stamps.

NO WATERMARK. All the following issues are on unwatermarked paper.

14 Elizabeth Castle

15 La Hougue Bie (Prehistoric Tomb)

16 Portelet Bay

17 La Corbière Lighthouse

18 Mont Orgueil Castle by Night

19 Arms and Royal Mace

20 Jersey Cow

21 Chart of the English Channel

22 Mont Orgueil Castle by Day

23 Queen Elizabeth II (after Cecil Beaton)

24 Jersey Airport

25 Legislative Chamber

26 The Royal Court

27 Queen Elizabeth II (after Cecil Beaton)

(Des V. Whiteley. Photo Harrison (½d to 1s9d), Courvoisier (others))

1969 (1 OCT)–**70**. *Granite paper (2s6d to £1). Multicoloured; frame colours given.* Perf 14 (½d to 1s9d) or 12 (others), all comb

15	**14**	½d ochre (a)	10	60
		a. Thick paper (a)	30	60
16	**15**	1d brown (abc)	10	10
		a. Booklet stamp with blank margins* (a)	75	
		b. Thick paper (a)	80	90
17	**16**	2d claret (a)	10	10
		a. Thinner paper (bc)	25	25
18	**17**	3d ultramarine (a)	10	10
		a. Thinner paper (d)	50	25
		b. Orange omitted	£120	
19	**18**	4d yellow-olive (a)	10	10
		a. Booklet stamp with blank margins* (a)	40	
		b. Thinner paper (c)	10	15
20	**19**	5d bistre (a)	10	10
		a. Thinner paper (c)	15	30
21	**20**	6d yellow-brown (ab)	10	10
		a. Thinner paper (e)	6·50	7·00
22	**21**	9d orange-brown (a)	10	20
		a. Thinner paper (d)	2·25	2·75
23	**22**	1s reddish lilac (a)	25	25
		a. Thinner paper (c)	1·75	1·75
24	**21**	1s6d myrtle-green (a)	80	75
		a. Thinner paper (d)	2·50	2·75
25	**23**	1s9d pale myrtle-green (a)	80	75
		a. Thinner paper (c)	10·00	10·00
26	**24**	2s6d black and pale mauve (a) . . .	1·25	1·00
27	**25**	5s black and pale blue (a)	4·75	3·50
28	**26**	10s black and pale slate-blue (a) . .	12·00	9·00
		a. Error. Green border†	£4500	
29	**27**	£1 pale bistre (af)††	1·75	1·50
15/29		Set of 15	20·00	16·00
		First Day Cover		20·00
15/29		Presentation Packs (3) . . . . . . 24·00		

*Nos. 16a and 19a are on medium paper. No. 16b on thick paper comes from 7s and 10s booklets.

†During the final printing of the 10s a sheet was printed in the colours of the 50p, No. 56, ie. green border instead of slate.

††Printing (f) is the decimal issue which can be positively distinguished by the inscriptions in the left sheet margin which read 'Sheet value £25' at bottom and 'Value per row £5' at top instead of 'Sheet value £25 0s. 0d.' and 'Value per row £5 0s. 0d.' respectively. It exists with more blue in the Queen's dress and less red in the drapery but this printing also includes intermediate shades close to printing (a).

The thinner paper varieties result from a deliberate change as the thicker paper did not adhere well. The two types may be further distinguished by the gum which is creamy on the thicker paper and white on the thinner.

There are a number of shades in this issue which are in part due to the variation in the paper.

There was no postal need for the ½d value as the ½d coin had been withdrawn prior to its issue in anticipation of decimalisation.

Printings: (a) 1.10.69; (b) 18.2.70; (c) 15.4.70; (d) 5.5.70; (e) 27.5.70; (f) 3.73

Cylinder Nos.: ½d, 1d, 2d, 4d, 1s 1A (×5); 3d 1A (×7); 5d, 6d, 9d, 1s6d, 1s9d 1A (×6); 2s6d to £1 None

Sheets: 60 (6×10) ½d to 1s6d; (10×6) 1s9d; 25 (5×5) 2s6d to £1

Quantities sold: ½d 999,439; 1d 1,050,124; 2d 726,837; 3d 635,019; 4d 7,148,849; 5d 4,886,016; 6d 550,766; 9d 954,649; 1s 577,086; 1s6d 419,872; 1s9d 306,674; 2s6d 244,894; 5s 206,629; 10s 179,981; £1 271,194

Withdrawn: 14.2.72 (except ½d, sold out 10.69, and £1 withdrawn 31.8.77)

Invalidated: 14.2.72 (except £1)

28 First Day Cover

Inauguration of Post Office

(Des R. Sellar. Photo Harrison)

1969 (1 OCT). *Multicoloured; background colours given.* Perf 14 (C)

30	**28**	4d magenta	10	10
31		5d new blue	20	10
32		1s6d red-brown	50	75
33		1s9d bright emerald	80	1·00
30/3		Set of 4	1·40	1·75
		First Day Cover		4·50
		Presentation Pack . . . . 2·00		

Cylinder Nos.: All values 1A (×4)

Sheets: 60 (6×10)

Quantities sold: 4d 1,483,686; 5d 742,820; 1s6d 272,155; 1s9d 238,856

Withdrawn: 1.10.70

Invalidated: 14.2.72

29 'Lord Coutanche' (Sir James Gunn)

30 'Sir Winston Churchill' (Van Praag)

31 'Liberation' (Edmund Blampied)

32 S.S. *Vega* (unknown artist)

25th Anniversary of Liberation

(Des Rosalind Dease from paintings. Photo Courvoisier)

1970 (9 MAY). *Granite paper*. Perf 11½ (C)

34	**29**	4d multicoloured	20	20
35	**30**	5d multicoloured	20	20
36	**31**	1s6d multicoloured	90	1·00
37	**32**	1s9d multicoloured	90	1·00
34/7		Set of 4	2·00	2·25
		First Day Cover		3·00
		Presentation Pack	2·75	

A special Presentation Pack in gold, red and blue-green on olive was given to Jersey schoolchildren (Price £15). The normal Presentation Pack is printed in gold and blue-green.

Sheets: 50 (10×5) 4d, 5d; (5×10) 1s6d, 1s9d

Quantities sold: 4d 1,617,751; 5d 1,296,678; 1s6d 334,468; 1s9d 319,893

Withdrawn: 9.5.71

Invalidated: 14.2.72

33 'A Tribute to Enid Blyton'

34 'Rags to Riches'

35 'Gourmet's Delight'

36 'We're the Greatest'

'Battle of Flowers' Parade

(Des Jennifer Toombs. Photo Courvoisier)

1970 (28 JULY). *Granite paper*. Perf 11½ (C)

38	**33**	4d multicoloured	20	10
39	**34**	5d multicoloured	20	20
40	**35**	1s6d multicoloured	2·75	2·25
41	**36**	1s9d multicoloured	2·75	2·25
38/41		Set of 4	5·25	4·25
		First Day Cover		4·25
		Presentation Pack	7·50	

Sheets: 50 (5×10)

Quantities sold: 4d 1,905,109; 5d 1,498,301; 1s6d 262,072; 1s9d 231,077

Withdrawn: 27.7.71

Invalidated: 14.2.72

37 Martello Tower, Archirondel

253

Decimal Currency

(Des V. Whiteley. Photo Harrison ($\frac{1}{2}$ to 9p), Courvoisier (others))

1970–74. *Designs as Typo 37 etc., but with values inscribed in decimal currency and new design (6p). Chalk surfaced paper (4$\frac{1}{2}$p, 5$\frac{1}{2}$p, 8p), granite paper (10p, 20p, 50p)*

42	**14**	$\frac{1}{2}$p multicoloured (*bgk*)	10	10
		a. Booklet stamp with blank margins (*b*)	20	
43	**17**	1p multicoloured (*bn*)	10	10
		a. Orange omitted		
44	**20**	1$\frac{1}{2}$p multicoloured (*b*)	10	10
45	**18**	2p multicoloured (*b*)	10	10
		a. Booklet stamp with blank margins	60	
46	**19**	2$\frac{1}{2}$p multicoloured (*bk*)	10	10
		a. Booklet stamp with blank margins (*b*)	20	
		ab. Gold (Mace) omitted	£375	
		ac. Gold (Mace) ptg double	£300	
47	**15**	3p multicoloured (*bch*)	10	10
		a. Booklet stamp with blank margins (*e*)	60	
48	**16**	3$\frac{1}{2}$p multicoloured (*bh*)	10	10
		a. Booklet stamp with blank margins (*h*)	25	
49	**21**	4p multicoloured (*bfimo*)	10	10
49a	**19**	4$\frac{1}{2}$p multicoloured (*j*)*	20	20
		ab. Uncoated paper	£400	
50	**22**	5p multicoloured (*blmo*)	10	10
50a	**20**	5$\frac{1}{2}$p multicoloured (*j*)	40	30
51	**37**	6p multicoloured (*b*)	20	10
52	**21**	7$\frac{1}{2}$p multicoloured (*b*)	20	15
52a	**18**	8p multicoloured (*j*)	15	15
53	**23**	9p multicoloured (*b*)	25	20
54	**24**	10p multicoloured (*adh*)	40	30
55	**25**	20p multicoloured (*adh*)	90	80
56	**26**	50p multicoloured (*al*)	1·50	1·25
42/56		*Set of 18*	4·50	3·75
		First Day Cover (3)		6·00
42/56, 29		*Presentation Packs (4)*		6·50

Gum: From 1974 printings appeared with dextrin added to the PVA gum giving a bluish-green tinge and mottled appearance. These are on the $\frac{1}{2}$, 2$\frac{1}{2}$, 3 and 3$\frac{1}{2}$p. The 4$\frac{1}{2}$ and 5$\frac{1}{2}$p only come with dextrin, and the 10, 20 and 50p only with gum arabic.

The Presentation Packs for this series exist in two different sizes, 4$\frac{1}{4}$ in×5$\frac{1}{2}$ in of the initial supply and 8$\frac{1}{2}$×4$\frac{1}{2}$ in for replacement stock.

Printings: (*a*) 1.10.70; (*b*) 15.2.71; (*c*) 1.8.72; (*d*) 15.11.72; (*e*) 1.12.72; (*f*) 1.10.73; (*g*) 3.12.73; (*h*) 1.7.74; (*i*) 12.8.74; (*j*) 31.10.74; (*k*) 1.11.74; (*l*) 28.1.75; (*m*) 1.4.75; (*n*) 21.4.75; (*o*) 30.10.75

Plate Nos.: $\frac{1}{2}$p, 2p, 3$\frac{1}{2}$p, 6p, 8p 1A (×5); 1p 1A (×7), 2A–1A (×6) (*n*); 1$\frac{1}{2}$p, 2$\frac{1}{2}$p, 4$\frac{1}{2}$p, 5$\frac{1}{2}$p, 7$\frac{1}{2}$p, 9p 1A (×6); 3p 1A (×5), 1A (×4)–2A (*h*); 4p 1A (×6), 2A–1A (×5) (*mo*); 5p 1A (×5), 2A–1A (×4) (*mo*); 10p to 50p None

Sheets: 50 (5×10) $\frac{1}{2}$p to 8p; (10×5) 9p; 25 (5×5) 10p to 50p

Quantities sold: $\frac{1}{2}$p 2,247,128; 1p 1,654,860; 1$\frac{1}{2}$p 817,871; 2p 2,305,239; 2$\frac{1}{2}$p 5,096,912; 3p 4,780,836; 3$\frac{1}{2}$p 2,069,095; 4p 3,908,727; 4$\frac{1}{2}$p 349,157; 5p 3,593,226; 5$\frac{1}{2}$p 333,125; 6p 1,072,224; 7$\frac{1}{2}$p 538,810; 8p 329,361; 9p 458,977; 10p 862,524; 20p 765,524; 50p 490,675

Withdrawn: 31.1.77 ($\frac{1}{2}$p to 9p); 31.8.77 (others)

38 White Eared-Pheasant

39 Thick-billed Parrot

40 Western Black and White Colobus Monkey

41 Ring-tailed Lemur

Wildlife Preservation Trust (First Series)

(Des Jennifer Toombs. Photo Courvoisier)

1971 (12 MAR). *Granite paper. Perf 11$\frac{1}{2}$ (C)*

57	**38**	2p multicoloured	20	10
58	**39**	2$\frac{1}{2}$p multicoloured	20	15
59	**40**	7$\frac{1}{2}$p multicoloured	2·20	1·50
60	**41**	9p multicoloured	3·00	1·50
57/60		*Set of 4*	5·00	3·00
		First Day Cover		6·00
		Presentation Pack	6·00	

See also Nos. 73/6, 217/21, 324/9, 447/51 and 824/9.

Sheets: 50 (5×10) 2p, 9p; (10×5) others

Quantities sold: 2p 1,025,544; 2$\frac{1}{2}$p 1,363,427; 7$\frac{1}{2}$p 233,147; 9p 220,710

Withdrawn: 11.3.72

42 Royal British Legion Badge

43 Poppy Emblem and Field

44 Jack Counter VC, and Victoria Cross

45 Crossed Tricolour and Union Jack

50th Anniversary of Royal British Legion

(Des G. Drummond. Litho Questa)

1971 (15 JUNE). Perf 14 (C)

61	**42**	2p multicoloured	20	10
62	**43**	2½p multicoloured	20	10
63	**44**	7½p multicoloured	1·00	1·10
64	**45**	9p multicoloured	1·00	1·10
61/4		Set of 4	2·10	2·10
		First Day Cover		3·50
		Presentation Pack	3·25	

Plate Nos.: 2p, 2½p 1A, 1B (each ×4); others 1A, 1B (each ×5)

Sheets: 50 (5×10)

Imprint: Right-hand corner, bottom margin

Quantities sold: 2p 1,381,873; 2½p 1,529,866; 7½p 239,477; 9p 226,407

Withdrawn: 14.6.72

46 'Tante Elizabeth' (E. Blampied)

47 'English Fleet in the Channel' (P. Monamy)

48 'The Boyhood of Raleigh' (Millais)

49 'The Blind Beggar' (W. W. Ouless)

Paintings

(Des and photo Courvoisier)

1971 (5 OCT). *Granite paper*. Perf 11½ (C)

65	**46**	2p multicoloured	15	10
66	**47**	2½p multicoloured	20	10
67	**48**	7½p multicoloured	1·25	1·40
68	**49**	9p multicoloured	1·40	1·50
65/8		Set of 4	2·75	2·75
		First Day Cover		4·00
		Presentation Pack	3·50	

See also Nos. 115/18 and 213/16.

Sheets: 50 (5×10) 2p, 9p; (10×5) others

Quantities sold: 2p 1,243,198; 2½p 1,490,595; 7½p 264,532; 9p 251,770

Withdrawn: 4.10.72

50 Jersey Fern

51 Jersey Thrift

52 Jersey Orchid

53 Jersey Viper's Bugloss

Wild Flowers of Jersey

(Des G. Drummond. Photo Courvoisier)

1972 (18 JAN). *Granite paper*. Perf 11½ (C)

69	**50**	3p multicoloured	20	10
70	**51**	5p multicoloured	30	20
71	**52**	7½p multicoloured	1·25	1·40
72	**53**	9p multicoloured	1·25	1·40
69/72		Set of 4	2·75	2·75
		First Day Cover		3·50
		Presentation Pack	3·25	

Sheets: 50 (5×10)

Quantities sold: 3p 1,124,878; 5p 332,764; 7½p 202,404; 9p 196,998

Withdrawn: 17.1.73

54 Cheetah

55 Rothschild's Mynah

56 Spectacled Bear

57 Tuatara

Wildlife Preservation Trust (Second Series)

(Des Jennifer Toombs. Photo Courvoisier)

1972 (17 MAR). *Granite paper.* Perf 11½ (C)

73	**54**	2½p multicoloured	30	10
74	**55**	3p multicoloured	25	20
75	**56**	7½p multicoloured	50	70
76	**57**	9p multicoloured	80	90
73/6		Set of 4	1·60	1·75
		First Day Cover		4·50
		Presentation Pack	2·50	

Sheets: 50 (10×5) 3p; (5×10) others

Quantities sold: 2½p 1,223,916; 3p 1,631,752; 7½p 279,935; 9p 235,968

Withdrawn: 16.3.73

58 Artillery Shako

59 Shako (2nd North Regt)

60 Shako (5th South-West Regt)

61 Helmet (3rd Jersey Light Infantry)

Royal Jersey Militia

(Des and photo Courvoisier)

1972 (27 JUNE). *Granite paper.* Perf 11½ (C)

77	**58**	2½p multicoloured	10	10
78	**59**	3p multicoloured	10	10
79	**60**	7½p multicoloured	30	20
80	**61**	9p multicoloured	50	60
77/80		Set of 4	90	90
		First Day Cover		3·00
		Presentation Pack	1·75	

Sheets: 50 (10×5)

Quantities sold: 2½p 1,240,393; 3p 1,857,224; 7½p 300,554; 9p 271,832

Withdrawn: 26.6.73

62 Princess Anne

63 Queen Elizabeth and Prince Philip

64 Prince Charles

65 The Royal Family

Royal Silver Wedding

(Des G. Drummond from photographs by D. Groves. Photo Courvoisier)

1972 (1 NOV). *Granite paper*. Perf 11½ (C)

81	**62**	2½p multicoloured		10	10
82	**63**	3p multicoloured		10	10
83	**64**	7½p multicoloured		35	35
84	**65**	20p multicoloured		35	35
81/4		*Set of 4*		80	80
		First Day Cover		1·50	
		Presentation Pack	1·10		

Sheets: 25 (5×5)

Quantities sold: 2½p 1,743,240; 3p 1,638,566; 7½p 424,029; 20p 418,824

Sold out: by 23.1.73 (7½p, 20p); 16.5.73 (3p)

Withdrawn: 31.10.73 (2½p)

66 Silver Wine Cup and Christening Cup

67 Gold Torque

68 Royal Seal of Charles II

69 Armorican Bronze Coins

Centenary of La Société Jersiaise

(Des G. Drummond. Photo Courvoisier)

1973 (23 JAN). *Granite paper*. Perf 11½ (C)

85	**66**	2½p violet-blue, new blue and black	10	10
86	**67**	3p bright cerise, orange-yellow and black	10	10
87	**68**	7½p multicoloured	25	20
88	**69**	9p multicoloured	30	30
85/8		*Set of 4*	70	60
		First Day Cover	1·25	
		Presentation Pack	1·25	

Sheets: 50 (10×5) 3p, 7½p; (5×10) others

Quantities sold: 2½p 2,008,923; 3p 2,437,421; 7½p 363,543; 9p 327,917

Sold out: by 31.10.73 (7½p)

Withdrawn: 22.1.74 (2½p, 3p, 9p)

70 Balloon *L'Armee de La Loire* and Letter, Paris, 1870

71 Astra Seaplane, 1912

72 Supermarine Sea Eagle

73 De Havilland D.H.86 Dragon Express *Giffard Bay*

Jersey Aviation History

(Des and photo Courvoisier)

1973 (16 MAY). *Granite paper*. Perf 11½ (C)

89	**70**	3p multicoloured		10	10
90	**71**	5p multicoloured		10	10
91	**72**	7½p multicoloured		35	35
92	**73**	9p multicoloured		45	45
89/92		*Set of 4*		90	90
		First Day Cover		1·50	
		Presentation Pack	1·25		

Sheets: 50 (5×10)

Quantities sold: 3p 3,085,497; 5p 641,583; 7½p 368,069; 9p 356,379

Sold out: by 31.10.73 (7½p)

Withdrawn: 15.5.74 (3p, 5p, 9p)

74 *North Western*, 1870

75 *Calvados*, 1873

76 *Carteret at Grouville Station*, 1898

77 *Caesarea*, 1873, and Route Map

Centenary of Jersey Eastern Railway

(Des G. Drummond. Photo Courvoisier)

1973 (6 AUG). *Granite paper*. Perf 11½ (C)

93	**74**	2½p multicoloured	10	10
94	**75**	3p multicoloured	10	10
95	**76**	7½p multicoloured	25	35
96	**77**	9p multicoloured	35	45
93/6		Set of 4	70	90
		First Day Cover		1·40
		Presentation Pack	1·25	

Sheets: 50 (5×10)

Quantities sold: 2½p 1,591,063; 3p 3,051,097; 7½p 396,919; 9p 365,310

Sold out: by 31.10.73 (7½p)

Withdrawn: 5.8.74 (2½p, 3p, 9p)

78 Princess Anne and Captain Mark Phillips

Royal Wedding

(Des and photo Courvoisier)

1973 (14 NOV). *Granite paper*. Perf 11½ (C)

97	**78**	3p multicoloured	10	10
98		20p multicoloured	50	50
97/8		Set of 2	60	60
		First Day Cover		80
		Presentation Pack	95	

Sheets: 25 (5×5)

Quantities sold: 3p 1,988,407; 20p 522,793

Withdrawn: 30.11.74

79 Spider Crab

80 Conger Eel

81 Lobster

82 Tuberculate Ormer

Marine Life

(Des Jennifer Toombs. Photo Courvoisier)

1973 (15 NOV). *Granite paper*. Perf 11½ (C)

99	**79**	2½p multicoloured	10	10
100	**80**	3p multicoloured	10	10
101	**81**	7½p multicoloured	30	35
102	**82**	20p multicoloured	40	45
99/102		Set of 4	80	90
		First Day Cover		1·25
		Presentation Pack	1·40	

Sheets: 50 (5×10)

Quantities sold: 2½p 1,596,526; 3p 1,243,541; 7½p 501,541; 20p 517,440

Sold out: by 28.2.74 (7½p)

Withdrawn: 30.11.74 (2½p, 3p, 20p)

83 Freesias

84 Anemones

85 Carnations and Gladioli

86 Daffodils and Iris

Spring Flowers

(Des G. Drummond. Photo Courvoisier)

1974 (13 FEB). *Granite paper*. Perf 11½ (C)

103	**83**	3p multicoloured	10	10
104	**84**	5½p multicoloured	15	15
105	**85**	8p multicoloured	25	30
106	**86**	10p multicoloured	30	35
103/6		Set of 4	70	80
		First Day Cover		1·10
		Presentation Pack	1·25	

Sheets: 50 (10×5)

Quantities sold: 3p 1,239,968; 5½p 590,376; 8p 475,665; 10p 507,542

Withdrawn: 28.2.75

87 First U.K. Pillar-box and Contemporary Cover

88 Jersey Postmen, 1862 and 1969

89 Modern Pillar-box and Cover

90 Mail Transport, 1874 and 1974

Centenary of Universal Postal Union

(Des G. Drummond. Photo Courvoisier)

1974 (7 JUNE). *Granite paper.* Perf 11½ (C)

107	**87**	2½p multicoloured	. . . .	10	10
108	**88**	3p multicoloured	. . . .	10	15
109	**89**	5½p multicoloured	. . . .	25	20
110	**90**	20p multicoloured	. . . .	35	40
107/10		*Set of 4*	. . . .	70	75
		First Day Cover	. . . .		95
		Presentation Pack	. . . .	1·25	

Sheets: 50 (5×10)

Quantities sold: 2½p 461,174; 3p 1,380,018; 5½p 421,674; 20p 386,348

Withdrawn: 30.6.75

91 John Wesley

92 Sir William Hillary

93 Canon Wace

94 Sir Winston Churchill

Anniversaries. Events described on stamps

(Des recess and litho De La Rue)

1974 (31 JULY). Perf 13×14 (C)

111	**91**	3p agate and light cinnamon	. . .	10	10
112	**92**	3½p blackish violet & light azure	. .	10	10
113	**93**	8p blue-black and pale rose-lilac	.	20	20
114	**94**	20p black and pale buff	. . . .	45	45
		a. *Pale buff* (*background omitted*)			
111/14		*Set of 4*	. . . .	75	75
		First Day Cover	. . . .		90
		Presentation Pack	. . . .	1·25	

Plate Nos.: 3p and 20p 1A–1A, 1B–1B; 3½p and 8p 1A–1A, 1B–1B, 2A–1A, 2B–1B

Sheets: 50 (10×5)

Imprint: Right-hand corner, bottom margin

Quantities sold: 3p 908,852; 3½p 2,355,391; 8p 338,397; 20p 409,291

Withdrawn: 31.7.75

95 *Catherine* and *Mary* (royal yachts)

96 French Two-decker

97 Dutch Vessel

98 Battle of Cap La Hague, 1692

Marine Paintings by Peter Monamy

(Des and photo Courvoisier)

1974 (22 NOV). *Granite paper.* Perf 11½ (C)

115	**95**	3½p multicoloured	....	10	10
116	**96**	5½p multicoloured	....	15	10
117	**97**	8p multicoloured	....	25	20
118	**98**	25p multicoloured	....	55	55
115/18		*Set of 4*	....	95	90
		First Day Cover	....		2·00
		Presentation Pack	....	1·75	

Sheets: 50 (10×5) 8p; (5×10) others

Quantities sold: 3½p 1,670,994; 5½p 448,137; 8p 416,296; 25p 415,991

Withdrawn: 30.11.75

99 Potato Digger

100 Cider Crusher

101 Six-Horse Plough

102 Hay Cart

Nineteenth-Century Farming

(Des G. Drummond. Photo Courvoisier)

1975 (25 FEB). *Granite paper.* Perf 11½ (C)

119	**99**	3p multicoloured	....	10	10
120	**100**	3½p multicoloured	....	10	10
121	**101**	8p multicoloured	....	20	20
122	**102**	10p multicoloured	....	35	30
119/22		*Set of 4*	....	70	65
		First Day Cover	....		85
		Presentation Pack	....	90	

Sheets: 50 (5×10)

Quantities sold: 3p 588,185; 3½p 1,025,295; 8p 432,432; 10p 457,196

Withdrawn: 28.2.76

103 H.M. Queen Elizabeth, the Queen Mother (photograph by Cecil Beaton)

Royal Visit

(Des and photo Courvoisier)

1975 (30 MAY). *Granite paper.* Perf 11½ (C)

123	**103**	20p multicoloured	....	50	45
		First Day Cover	....		1·75
		Presentation Pack	....	90	

Cylinder Nos.: A1–1–1–1–1, B1–1–1–1–1

Sheets: 25 (5×5)

Quantity sold: 572,675

Withdrawn: 31.5.76

104 Nautilus Shell

105 Parasol

106 Deckchair

107 Sandcastle with flags of Jersey and the U.K.

Jersey Tourism

(Des A. Games. Photo Courvoisier)

1975 (6 JUNE). *Designs based on holiday posters. Granite paper.* Perf 11½ (C)

124	**104**	5p multicoloured	....	10	10
125	**105**	8p multicoloured	....	10	10
126	**106**	10p multicoloured	....	30	25
127	**107**	12p multicoloured	....	40	35
124/7		*Set of 4*	....	80	70
		First Day Cover	....		1·10
		Presentation Pack	....	1·75	
MS128		147×69 mm. Nos. 124/7	....	90	1·10
		First Day Cover	....		2·75

Cylinder Nos.: All values A1–1–1–1–1, B1–1–1–1–1

Sheets: 50 (10×5)

Quantities sold: 5p 1,377,519; 8p 368,521; 10p 467,278; 12p 389,574; miniature sheet 298,689

Withdrawn: 30.6.76

108 Common Tern

109 British Storm Petrel

110 Brent Geese

111 Shag

Sea Birds

(Des Jennifer Toombs. Photo Courvoisier)

1975 (28 JULY). *Granite paper.* Perf 11½ (C)

129	**108**	4p multicoloured	....	10	10
130	**109**	5p multicoloured	....	15	10
131	**110**	8p multicoloured	....	40	25
132	**111**	25p multicoloured	....	70	50
129/32		Set of 4	....	1·25	85
		First Day Cover	....		1·40
		Presentation Pack	....	1·60	

Sheets: 50 (10×5)

Quantities sold: 4p 872,260; 5p 2,871,390; 8p 384,550; 25p 362,160

Withdrawn: 31.7.76

112 Armstrong Whitworth Siskin IIIA

113 Supermarine Southampton 1 Flying Boat

114 Supermarine Spitfire Mk I

115 Folland Fo. 141 Gnat T 1

50th Anniversary of Royal Air Forces Association, Jersey Branch

(Des A. Theobald. Photo Courvoisier)

1975 (30 OCT). *Granite paper.* Perf 11½ (C)

133	**112**	4p multicoloured	....	10	10
134	**113**	5p multicoloured	....	15	10
135	**114**	10p multicoloured	....	40	25
136	**115**	25p multicoloured	....	70	50
133/6		Set of 4	....	1·25	85
		First Day Cover	....		1·60
		Presentation Pack	....	1·50	

Cylinder Nos.: All values A1–1–1–1–1, B1–1–1–1–1

Sheets: 50 (5×10)

Quantities sold: 4p 1,496,640; 5p 1,805,624; 10p 581,627; 25p 407,423

Withdrawn: 30.10.76

116 Map of Jersey Parishes

117 Zoological Park

118 St. Mary's Church

119 Seymour Tower

120 La Corbière Lighthouse

121 St. Saviour's Church

122 Elizabeth Castle

123 Gorey Harbour

124 Jersey Airport

125 Grosnez Castle

126 Bonne Nuit Harbour

127 Le Hocq Tower

128 Morel Farm

129 Parish Arms and Island Scene

130 Flag and Map

131 Postal H.Q. and Badge

132 Parliament, Royal Court and Arms

133 Lieutenant-Governor's Flag and Government House

134 Queen Elizabeth II (photograph by Alex Wilson)

Parish Arms and Views

(Des Courvoisier (£2), G. Drummond (others). Litho Questa (½p to 15p). Photo Courvoisier (others))

1976–80. *Granite paper (20p to £2). Perf 14½ (½p to 15p) or 12 (others), all comb*

137	**116**	½p multicoloured (*af*)	10	10
138	**117**	1p multicoloured (*af*)	10	10
		a. Booklet pane of 4 (No. 138×2 plus 2 se-tenant labels) (*b*)	70	
		b. Booklet pane. No. 138×4 (*begh*)	80	
139	**118**	5p multicoloured (*ad*)	10	10
		a. Booklet pane of 4 (*b*)	40	
140	**119**	6p multicoloured (*ad*)	10	10
		a. Booklet pane of 4 (*eg*)	40	
141	**120**	7p multicoloured (*ad*)	10	10
		a. Booklet pane of 4 (*bh*)	40	
142	**121**	8p multicoloured (*ad*)	15	10
		a. Booklet pane of 4 (*eg*)	80	
143	**122**	9p multicoloured (*a*)	15	10
		a. Booklet pane of 4 (*h*)	60	
144	**123**	10p multicoloured (*af*)	20	10
145	**124**	11p multicoloured (*a*)	25	25
146	**125**	12p multicoloured (*a*)	25	20
147	**126**	13p multicoloured (*a*)	25	20
148	**127**	14p multicoloured (*a*)	30	20
149	**128**	15p multicoloured (*a*)	30	25
150	**129**	20p multicoloured (*c*)	45	35
151	**130**	30p multicoloured (*c*)	55	40
152	**131**	40p multicoloured (*c*)	80	50
153	**132**	50p multicoloured (*c*)	1·00	70
154	**133**	£1 multicoloured (*c*)	3·00	1·50
155	**134**	£2 multicoloured (*d*)	4·00	2·50
137/55		Set of 19	11·00	7·00
		First Day Covers (4)		10·50
		Presentation Packs (4) . . . . . 13·00		

Printings: (*a*) 29.1.76; (*b*) 5.4.76; (*c*) 20.8.76; (*d*) 16.11.77; (*e*) 28.2.78; (*f*) 31.8.78; (*g*) 1.10.79; (*h*) 6.5.80

Plate or cylinder Nos.: ½p to 9p, 13p, 14p 1A, 1B, 1C, 1D (each ×4), 10p 1A, 1B, 1C, 1D (each ×4), 1B–1B–1B–2B, 2A–1A–1A–2A, 2B–1B–1B–2B, 2C–1C–1C–2C, 2D–1D–1D–2D; 11p 1A, 1B, 1C, 1D (each ×5); 12p 1A, 1B, 1C, 1D (each ×4), 1A–1A–2A–2A, 1B–1B–2B–2B, 1C–1C–2C–2C, 1D–1D–2D–2D; 15p 1A, 1B, 1C, 1D (each ×4), 1A–2A–1A–1A, 1B–2B–1B–1B, 1C–2C–1C–1C, 1D–2D–1D–1D, 1A–2A–2A–1A, 1B–2B–2B–1B, 1C–2C–2C–1C, 1D–2D–2D–1D, 1A–3A–2A–1A, 1B–3B–2B–1B, 1C–3C–2C–1C,

1D–3D–2D–1D; 20p A1–1–1–1–1, B1–1–1–1–1, C1–1–1–1–1, D1–1–1–1–1; 30p, £1 A1–1–1–1–1, B1–1–1–1–1; 40p, 50p A1–1–1–1, B1–1–1–1; £2 A1–1–1–1–1–1, B1–1–1–1–1–1–1, C1–1–1–1–1–1–1, D1–1–1–1–1–1–1

Sheets: 50 (5×10) ½p to 15p; 25 (5×5) others

Imprint: Right-hand corner, bottom margin (½p to 15p); central, bottom margin (others)

Withdrawn: 27.2.82 ½p to 9p (sheets); 20.4.82 1p, 5p to 9p (booklets); 31.7.82 10p to 15p; 28.2.83 20p to £1; 31.3.92 £2

135 Sir Walter Ralegh and Map of Virginia

136 Sir George Carteret and Map of New Jersey

137 Philippe D'Auvergne and Long Island Landing

138 John Copley and Sketch

'Links with America'

(Des M. Orbell. Photo Courvoisier)

1976 (29 MAY). *Granite paper.* Perf 11½ (C)

160	**135**	5p multicoloured	10	10
161	**136**	7p multicoloured	15	10
162	**137**	11p multicoloured	40	25
163	**138**	13p multicoloured	50	40
160/3		*Set of 4*	1·00	75
		First Day Cover		1·25
		Presentation Pack	1·40	

Cylinder Nos.: 5p, 11p A1–1–1–1–1, B1–1–1–1–1; others A1–1–1–1, B1–1–1–1

Sheets: 25 (5×5)

Quantities sold: 5p 980,029; 7p 1,352,629; 11p 582,706; 13p 435,561

Withdrawn: 31.5.77

139 Dr. Grandin and Map of China

140 Sampan on the Yangtze

141 Overland Trek

142 Dr. Grandin at Work

Birth Centenary of Dr. Lilian Grandin (medical missionary)

(Des Jennifer Toombs. Photo Courvoisier)

1976 (25 NOV). *Granite paper.* Perf 11½ (C)

164	**139**	5p multicoloured	10	10
165	**140**	7p lt yellow, yellow-brown & blk	10	10
166	**141**	11p multicoloured	35	25
167	**142**	13p multicoloured	50	40
164/7		*Set of 4*	95	75
		First Day Cover		1·25
		Presentation Pack	1·40	

Cylinder Nos.: 7p A1–1–1, B1–1–1; 13p A1–1–1–1–1, B1–1–1–1–1; others A1–1–1–1, B1–1–1–1

Sheets: 50 (5×10)

Quantities sold: 5p 757,843; 7p 1,043,198; 11p 384,436; 13p 354,096

Withdrawn: 30.11.77

143 Coronation, 1953 (photograph by Cecil Beaton)

144 Visit to Jersey, 1957

145 Queen Elizabeth II (photograph by Peter Grugeon)

Silver Jubilee

(Des G. Drummond. Photo Courvoisier)

1977 (7 FEB). *Granite paper*. Perf 11½ (C)

168	**143**	5p multicoloured		15	10
169	**144**	7p multicoloured		20	15
170	**145**	25p multicoloured		40	35
168/70		*Set of 3*		70	55
		First Day Cover		1·25	
		Presentation Pack		1·25	

Cylinder Nos.: All values A1–1–1–1–1, B1–1–1–1–1

Sheets: 25 (5×5)

Imprint: Central, bottom margin

Quantities sold: 5p 1,220,986; 7p 1,212,639; 25p 681,241

Withdrawn: 28.2.78

146 Coins of 1871 and 1877

147 One-twelfth Shilling, 1949

148 Silver Crown, 1966

149 £2 Piece, 1972

Centenary of Currency Reform

(Des D. Henley. Litho Questa)

1977 (25 MAR). Perf 14 (C)

171	**146**	5p multicoloured		10	10
172	**147**	7p multicoloured		15	10
173	**148**	11p multicoloured		30	30
174	**149**	13p multicoloured		35	35
171/4		*Set of 4*		80	75
		First Day Cover		1·10	
		Presentation Pack		1·40	

Plate Nos.: 7p 1A, 1B (each ×5), 1A–2A–1A (×3), 1B–2B–1B (×3); others 1A, 1B (each ×5)

Sheets: 50 (5×10)

Imprint: Right-hand corner, bottom margin

Quantities sold: 5p 1,029,661; 7p 923,950; 11p 383,834; 13p 368,249

Withdrawn: 31.3.78

150 Sir William Weston and *Santa Anna*, 1530

151 Sir William Drogo and Ambulance, 1877

152 Duke of Connaught and Ambulance, 1917

153 Duke of Gloucester and Stretcher-team, 1977

St. John Ambulance Centenary

(Des A. Theobald. Litho Questa)

1977 (24 JUNE). Perf 14×13½ (C)

175	**150**	5p multicoloured		10	10
176	**151**	7p multicoloured		10	10
177	**152**	11p multicoloured		25	20
178	**153**	13p multicoloured		30	25
175/8		*Set of 4*		70	60
		First Day Cover		1·10	
		Presentation Pack		1·25	

Plate Nos.: 5p 1A, 1B, 1C (each ×5); 7p, 11p 1A, 1B, 1C (each ×6); 13p 1A, 1B, 1C (each ×5), 1B–2B–1B–1B–1B

Sheets: 40 (8×5)

Imprint: Bottom corner, right-hand margin

Quantities sold: 5p 849,532; 7p 1,089,526; 11p 421,039; 13p 370,887

Withdrawn: 30.6.78

154 Arrival of Queen Victoria, 1846

155 Victoria College, 1852

156 Sir Galahad Statue, 1924

157 College Hall

125th Anniversary of Victoria College

(Des R. Granger Barrett. Litho Questa)

1977 (29 SEPT). Perf 14½ (C)

179	**154**	7p multicoloured	. . . .	15	10
180	**155**	10½p multicoloured	. . . .	20	15
		a. Black ptg double	. . . .		
181	**156**	11p multicoloured	. . . .	25	25
182	**157**	13p multicoloured	. . . .	30	25
179/82		Set of 4	. . . .	80	70
		First Day Cover	. . . .		1·10
		Presentation Pack	. . . .	1·40	

Plate Nos.: 7p 1A, 1B (each ×6), 1A–1A–2A–1A–1A–1A, 1B–1B–2B–1B–1B–1B; 13p 1A, 1B (each ×6); others 1A, 1B (each ×5)

Sheets: 50 (5×10) 7 and 10½p, (10×5) others

Imprint: Right-hand corner, bottom margin

Quantities sold: 7p 1,496,997; 10½p 906,669; 11p 528,293; 13p 371,251

Withdrawn: 30.9.78

158 Harry Vardon Statuette and Map of Royal Jersey Course

159 Harry Vardon's Grip and Swing

160 Harry Vardon's Putt

161 Golf Trophies and Book by Harry Vardon

Centenary of Royal Jersey Golf Club

(Des Jennifer Toombs. Litho Questa)

1978 (28 FEB). Perf 14 (C)

183	**158**	6p multicoloured	. . . .	10	10
184	**159**	8p multicoloured	. . . .	15	10
185	**160**	11p multicoloured	. . . .	35	25
186	**161**	13p multicoloured	. . . .	40	35
183/6		Set of 4	. . . .	90	70
		First Day Cover	. . . .		1·10
		Presentation Pack	. . . .	1·40	

Plate Nos.: 6p 1A, 1B (each ×5); 8p, 11p 1A, 1B (each ×4); 13p 1A, 1B (each ×4), 2A–1A–1A–1A, 2B–1B–1B–1B

Sheets: 50 (5×10)

Imprint: Right-hand corner, bottom margin

Quantities sold: 6p 837,427; 8p 851,904; 11p 466,343; 13p 368,648

Withdrawn: 28.2.79

162 Mont Orgueil Castle

163 St. Aubin's Fort

164 Elizabeth Castle

Europa. Fortifications

(Des from paintings by Thomas Philips. Photo Courvoisier)

1978 (1 MAY). Granite paper. Perf 11½ (C)

187	**162**	6p multicoloured	10	10
188	**163**	8p multicoloured	15	15
189	**164**	10½p multicoloured	35	25
187/9		Set of 3	55	45
		First Day Cover		70
		Presentation Pack	80	

Cylinder Nos.: All values A1–1–1–1–1, B1–1–1–1–1, C1–1–1–1–1, D1–1–1–1–1

Sheets: 20 (5×4)

Imprint: Central, bottom margin

Quantities sold: 6p 2,602,412; 8p 2,592,722; 10½p 2,564,535

Withdrawn: 31.5.79

165 'Gaspé Basin' (P. J. Ouless)

166 Map of Gaspé Peninsula

167 Century (brigantine)

168 Early Map of Jersey

169 St. Aubin's Bay, Town and Harbour

Links with Canada

(Des R. Granger Barrett. Litho Questa)

1978 (9 JUNE). Perf 14½ (C)

190	**165**	6p multicoloured	10	10
191	**166**	8p multicoloured	15	10
192	**167**	10½p multicoloured	20	15
193	**168**	11p multicoloured	40	25
194	**169**	13p multicoloured	45	40
190/4		Set of 5	1·10	90
		First Day Cover		1·10
		Presentation Pack	1·50	

Plate Nos.: 6p 1A, 1B, 1C, 1D (each ×5); others 1A, 1B, 1C, 1D (each ×6)

Sheets: 50 (5×10)

Imprint: Right-hand corner, bottom margin

Quantities sold: 6p 1,047,825, 8p 1,096,489, 10½p 699,002; 11p 443,932; 13p 367,472

Withdrawn: 30.6.79

170 Queen Elizabeth and Prince Philip

171 Hallmarks of 1953 and 1977

25th Anniversary of Coronation

(Des and photo Courvoisier)

1978 (26 JUNE). Granite paper. Perf 11½ (C)

195	**170**	8p silver, black and cerise	20	10
196	**171**	25p silver, black and new blue	50	45
195/6		Set of 2	70	55
		First Day Cover		90
		Presentation Pack	95	

Cylinder Nos.: Both values A1–1–1, B1–1–1

Sheets: 50 (10×5)

Quantities sold: 8p 1,060,259; 25p 459,558

Withdrawn: 30.6.79

172 Mail Cutter, 1778–1827

173 Flamer, 1831–37

174 Diana, 1877–90

175 Ibex, 1891–1925

176 *Caesarea*, 1960–75

Bicentenary of England–Jersey Government Mail Packet Service

(Des Jersey P.O. Litho Harrison)

1978 (18 OCT). Perf 14½×14 (C)

197	**172**	6p black, yellow-brown and greenish yellow	10	10
198	**173**	8p black, dull yellowish green and pale yellow-green	15	10
199	**174**	10½p black, ultramarine & cobalt .	30	20
200	**175**	11p blk, purple & pale rose-lilac	35	30
201	**176**	13p black, Venetian red and pink	40	40
197/201		Set of 5	1·10	1·00
		First Day Cover		1·40
		Presentation Pack	1·50	

Plate Nos.: All values 1A, 1B (each ×3)

Sheets: 50 (5×10)

Imprint: Right-hand corner, bottom margin

Quantities sold: 6p 1,157,597; 8p 1,149,500; 10½p 528,170; 11p 468,589; 13p 371,210

Withdrawn: 31.10.79

177 Jersey Calf

178 'Ansom Designette' (calf presented to the Queen, 27 June 1978)

9th World Jersey Cattle Bureau Conference

(Des Jersey P.O. and Questa. Litho Questa)

1979 (1 MAR). Perf 13½ (C)

202	**177**	6p multicoloured	10	10
		a. Gold ptg double	£400	
203	**178**	25p multicoloured	50	45
		a. Gold ptg double	£400	
202/3		Set of 2	60	55
		First Day Cover		95
		Presentation Pack	1·10	

Plate Nos.: Both values 1A, 1B, 1C, 1D, 1E, 1F (each ×8)

Sheets: 20 (4×5)

Imprint: Right-hand corner, bottom margin

Withdrawn: 29.2.80

179 Jersey Pillar Box, c. 1860

180 Clearing a Modern Jersey Post Box

181 Telephone Switchboard, c. 1900

182 Modern S.P.C. Telephone System

Europa. Communications

(Des Jennifer Toombs. Litho Questa)

1979 (1 MAR). Thin paper. Perf 14 (C)

204	**179**	8p multicoloured	25	25
		a. Horiz pair. Nos. 204/5	50	50
		b. Thick paper	40	40
		ba. Horiz pair. Nos. 204b/5b . . .	80	90
		c. Perf 14½ (thick paper)	30	30
		ca. Horiz pair. Nos. 204c/5c . . .	60	70
205	**180**	8p multicoloured	25	25
		b. Thick paper	40	40
		c. Perf 14½ (thick paper)	30	30
206	**181**	10½p multicoloured	25	25
		a. Horiz pair. Nos. 206/7	50	70
		b. Thick paper	70	70
		ba. Horiz pair. Nos. 206b/7b . . .	1·40	1·50
		c. Perf 14½	70	70
		ca. Horiz pair. Nos. 206c/7c . . .	1·40	1·50
207	**182**	10½p multicoloured	25	25
		b. Thick paper	70	70
		c. Perf 14½	70	70
		ca. Greenish blue omitted	£400	
204/7		Set of 4	90	90
		First Day Cover (Nos. 204/5, 206c/7c)		1·10
		First Day Cover (Nos. 204/7)		
		Presentation Pack (either perforation)	1·10	

Although both perforations were supplied to Jersey at the same time the 8p perforated 14½ is not known used before early April.

Plate Nos.: Both values 1A, 1B, 1C, 1D, 1E, 1F, 1G, 1H (each ×8)

Sheets: 20 (4×5) the two designs of each value were printed together, *so tenant*, in horizontal pairs throughout

Imprint: Central, bottom margin

Quantities sold: 8p 5,149,852; 10½p 3,047,039

Withdrawn: 29.2.80

183 Percival Mew Gull
Golden City

184 De Havilland D.H.C.1
Chipmunk

185 Druine D.31 Turbulent

186 De Havilland D.H.82A
Tiger Moth

187 North American AT-6
Harvard

25th Anniversary of International Air Rally

(Des A. Theobald. Photo Courvoisier)

1979 (24 APR). *Granite paper.* Perf 11½ (C)

208	**183**	6p multicoloured	10	10
209	**184**	8p multicoloured	25	15
210	**185**	10½p multicoloured	25	20
211	**186**	11p multicoloured	30	25
212	**187**	13p multicoloured	40	35
208/12		*Set of 5*	1·10	95
		First Day Cover		1·50
		Presentation Pack	1·60	

Cylinder Nos.: 13p A1–1–1–1–1, B1–1–1–1–1, C1–1–1–1–1, D1–1–1–1–1; others A1–1–1–1, B1–1–1–1, C1–1–1–1, D1–1–1–1

Sheets 20 (5×4)

Imprint: Central, bottom margin

Quantities sold: 6p 1,327,279; 8p 1,338,234; 10½p 433,127; 11p 457,566; 13p 426,528

Withdrawn: 30.4.80

188 'My First Sermon'

189 'Orphans'

190 'The Princes in the Tower'

191 'Christ in the House of His Parents'

International Year of the Child and 150th Birth Anniversary of Millais

(Des Jersey P.O. and Courvoisier. Photo Courvoisier)

1979 (13 AUG). *Granite paper.* Perf 12×12½ (25p) or 12×11½ (others), all comb

213	**188**	8p multicoloured	20	15
214	**189**	10½p multicoloured	30	20
215	**190**	11p multicoloured	30	30
216	**191**	25p multicoloured	50	40
213/16		*Set of 4*	1·25	95
		First Day Cover		1·40
		Presentation Pack	1·60	

Cylinder Nos.: 25p A1–1–1–1–1, B1–1–1–1–1; others A1–1–1–1–1, B1–1–1–1–1, C1–1–1–1–1, D1–1–1–1–1

Sheets: 20 (4×5) 25p or (5×4) others

Quantities sold: 8p 1,187,969; 10½p 953,826; 11p 508,316; 25p 463,234

Withdrawn: 30.8.80

192 Pink Pigeon

193 Orang-utan

194 Waldrapp

195 Lowland Gorilla

196 Rodriguez Flying Fox

Wildlife Preservation Trust (Third Series)

(Des Jennifer Toombs. Photo Courvoisier)

1979 (8 NOV). *Granite paper.* Perf 11½ (C)

217	**192**	6p multicoloured	10	10
218	**193**	8p multicoloured	20	15
219	**194**	11½p multicoloured	30	30
220	**195**	13p multiocoloured	30	30
221	**196**	15p multicoloured	45	35
217/21		*Set* of 5	1·25	1·10
		First Day Cover		1·40
		Presentation Pack	1·60	

Cylinder Nos.: All values A1–1–1–1–1, B1–1–1–1–1, C1–1–1–1–1,
D1–1–1–1–1

Sheets: 20 (11½p 4×5; others 5×4)

Imprint: Right-hand corner, bottom margin

Quantities sold: 6p 1,128,144; 8p 1,080,889; 11½p 559,534; 13p 443,140; 15p 433,115

Withdrawn: 30.11.80

197 Plan of Mont Orgueil

198 Plan of La Tour de St. Aubin

199 Plan of Elizabeth Castle

200 Map of Jersey showing Fortresses

Fortresses. Drawings by Thomas Phillips

(Litho Enschedé)

1980 (5 FEB). Perf 13×13½ (25p) or 13½×13 (others), all comb

222	**197**	8p multicoloured	20	15
223	**198**	11½p multicoloured	30	30
224	**199**	13p multicoloured	30	30
225	**200**	25p multicoloured	50	45
222/5		*Set of 4*	1·25	1·10
		First Day Cover		1·40
		Presentation Pack	1·60	

Sheets: 20 (4×5)

Imprint: Right-hand corner, bottom margin

Quantities sold: 8p 665,647; 11½p 363,246; 13p 415,790; 25p 379,743

Withdrawn: 28.2.81

201 Sir Walter Ralegh and Paul Ivy **202** engineer) discussing Elizabeth Castle

203 Sir George Carteret receiving rights **204** to Smith's Island, Virginia, from King Charles II

269

Europa. Personalities. Links with Britain

(Des Jersey Post Office and Questa. Litho Questa)

1980 (6 MAY). Perf 14 (C)

226	**201**	9p multicoloured	15	15
		a. Horiz pair. Nos. 226/7	40	50
227	**202**	9p multicoloured	15	15
228	**203**	13½p multicoloured	30	30
		a. Horiz pair. Nos. 228/9	60	70
229	**204**	13½p multicoloured	30	30
226/9		Set of 4	90	80
		First Day Cover		1·25
		Presentation Pack	1·40	

Plate Nos.: Both values 1A, 1B, 1C, 1D, 1E, 1F (each ×4)

Sheets: 20 (4×5). The two designs of each value were printed together, *se-tenant*, in horizontal pairs throughout, forming composite designs.

Imprint: Central, left-hand margin

Quantities sold: 9p 4,793,980; 13½p 2,638,136

Withdrawn: 31.5.81

205 Planting

206 Digging

207 Weighbridge

Centenary of Jersey Royal Potato

(Des R. Granger Barrett. Litho Questa)

1980 (6 MAY). Perf 14 (C)

230	**205**	7p multicoloured	15	10
231	**206**	15p multicoloured	30	25
232	**207**	17½p multicoloured	30	35
230/2		Set of 3	65	65
		First Day Cover		95
		Presentation Pack	1·25	

Plate Nos.: All values 1A, 1B, 1C, 1D, 1E, 1F (each ×6)

Sheets: 20 (4×5)

Imprint: Central, left-hand margin

Quantities sold: 7p 1,379,048; 15p 383,956; 17½p 375,082

Withdrawn: 31.5.83

208 Three Lap Event

209 Jersey International Road Race

210 Scrambling

211 Sand Racing (saloon cars)

212 National Hill Climb

60th Anniversary of Jersey Motor-cycle and Light Car Club

(Des A. Theobald. Photo Courvoisier)

1980 (24 JULY). *Granite paper.* Perf 11½ (C)

233	**208**	7p multicoloured	15	15
234	**209**	9p multicoloured	20	15
235	**210**	13½p multicoloured	30	25
236	**211**	15p multicoloured	30	30
237	**212**	17½p multicoloured	35	35
233/7		Set of 5	1·25	1·10
		First Day Cover		1·60
		Presentation Pack	1·75	

Cylinder Nos.: 7p, 15p A1–1–1–1–1, B1–1–1–1–1, C1–1–1–1–1, D1–1–1–1–1; others A1–1–1–1, B1–1–1–1, C1–1–1–1, D1–1–1–1

Sheets: 20 (5×4)

Imprint: Left-hand corner, bottom margin

Quantities sold: 7p 1,452,280; 9p 1,426,548; 13½p 384,861; 15p 350,608; 17½p 338,658

Withdrawn: 31.7.81

213 *Eye of the Wind*

214 Diving from Inflatable Dinghy

215 Exploration of Papua New Guinea

216 Captain Scott's *Discovery*

217 Using Aerial Walkways, Conservation Project, Sulawesi

218 *Eye of the Wind*, and Goodyear Aerospace Airship *Europa*

Operation Drake and 150th Anniversary of Royal Geographical Society (14p)

(Des G. Drummond. Litho Questa)

1980 (1 OCT). Perf 14 (C)

238	**213**	7p multicoloured	15	15
239	**214**	9p multicoloured	20	20
240	**215**	13½p multicoloured	30	25
241	**216**	14p multicoloured	30	30
242	**217**	5p multicoloured	35	35
		a. Black (*face value and inscr*) ptg double		
243	**218**	17½p multicoloured	40	40
		a. Black (*face value and inscr*) ptg double		
238/43		Set of 6	1·50	1·50
		First Day Cover		1·75
		Presentation Pack	2·00	

Plate Nos.: All values 1A, 1B, 1C, 1D, 1E, 1F (each ×6)

Sheets: 20 (5×4)

Imprint: Upper left-hand margin

Quantities sold: 7p 1,631,558; 9p 1,071,684; 13½p 432,201; 14p 357,109; 15p 357,922; 17½p 351,215

Withdrawn: 31.10.81

219

220

221

222

Bicentenary of Battle of Jersey. Details of painting 'The Death of Major Peirson' by J. S. Copley

(Photo Courvoisier)

1981 (6 JAN). *Granite paper*. Perf 12½×12 (C)

244	**219**	7p multicoloured	15	15
245	**220**	10p multicoloured	25	20
246	**221**	15p multicoloured	35	30
247	**222**	17½p multicoloured	40	35
244/7		Set of 4	1·00	90
		First Day Cover		1·40
		Presentation Pack	1·50	
MS248		144×97 mm. Nos. 244/7	1·40	1·60
		First Day Cover		4·50

Stamps from No. **MS**248 are without white margins.

Cylinder Nos.: All values A1–1–1–1–1, B1–1–1–1–1

Sheets: 20 (5×4)

Imprint: Right-hand corner, bottom margin

Quantities sold: 7p 997,416; 10p 1,107,456; 15p 367,971; 17½p 359,794; miniature sheet 469,953

Withdrawn: 31.1.82

223 De Bagot

224 De Carteret

225 La Cloche

226 Dumaresq   **227** Payn   **228** Janvrin

229 Poingdestre   **230** Pipon   **231** Marett

232 Le Breton   **233** Le Maistre   **234** Bisson

235 Robin   **236** Herault   **237** Messervy

238 Fiott   **239** Malet   **240** Mabon

241 De St. Martin   **242** Hamptonne   **243** Badier

244 L'Arbalestier   **245** Journeaulx   **246** Lempriere

247 Auvergne   **248** Remon

249 Jersey Crest and Map of Channel   **250** 'Queen Elizabeth II' (Norman Hepple)

Arms of Jersey Families

(Des Courvoisier (£5), G. Drummond (others). Litho Questa (½p to £1). Photo Courvoisier (£5))

1981 (24 FEB)–**88**. *Granite paper* (£5). Perf 15×14 (16p, 17p, 18p, 19p, 26p, 75p), 12½×12 (£5) or 14 (others), all comb

249	**223**	½p black, silver & turq-grn (a) ..	20	20
250	**224**	1p multicoloured (a)	10	10
		a. Booklet pane of 6 (acf)	40	
		b. Perf 15×14 (o)	30	30
251	**225**	2p multicoloured (a)	10	10
		a. Booklet pane of 6 (cf)	70	
		b. Perf 15×14 (io)	20	20
		ba. Booklet pane of 6 (l)	1·00	
252	**226**	3p multicoloured (a)	10	15
		a. Booklet pane of 6 (a)	80	
		b. Perf 15×14 (ik)	15	15
		ba. Booklet pane of 6 (h)	1·00	
253	**227**	4p black, silver and mauve (a) ..	15	15
		a. Perf 15×14 (k)	20	20
		ab. Booklet pane of 6 (mq)	1·00	
254	**228**	5p multicoloured (a)	15	15
		a. Perf 15×14 (k)	30	30
255	**229**	6p multicoloured (a)	20	20
		a. Perf 15×14 (k)	40	40
256	**230**	7p multicoloured (a)	25	25
		a. Booklet pane of 6 (ac)	1·40	
257	**231**	8p multicoloured (a)	30	30
		a. Booklet pane of 6 (f)	1·75	
258	**232**	9p multicoloured (ae)	30	25
		a. Perf 15×14 (h)	40	40
		ab. Booklet pane of 6 (h)	2·50	
		ac. 'Ghost impression' from No. 261a*		

272

259	**233**	10p multicoloured (*a*)	25	25
		a. *Booklet pane of 6* (*ac*)	1·50	
		b. *Perf* 15×14 (*l*)	40	40
		ba. *Booklet pane of 6* (*l*)	1·60	
260	**234**	11p multicoloured (*be*)	30	30
		a. *Booklet pane of 6* (*f*)	1·90	
		b. *Perf* 15×14 (*m*)	45	45
		ba. *Booklet pane of 6* (*m*)	1·75	
261	**235**	12p multicoloured (*be*)	35	30
		a. *Perf* 15×14 (*hg*)	50	50
		ab. *Booklet pane of 6* (*hq*)	3·00	
262	**236**	13p multicoloured (*b*)	35	35
		a. *Perf* 15×14 (*i*)	50	50
263	**237**	14p multicoloured (*b*)	40	40
		a. *Perf* 15×14 (*i*)	40	40
		ab. *Booklet pane of 6* (*l*)	2·40	
264	**238**	15p multicoloured (*b*)	40	40
		a. *Perf* 15×14 (*mo*)	45	45
		ab. *Booklet pane of 6* (*m*)	2·25	
265	**239**	16p multicoloured (*jo*)	35	35
		a. *Booklet pane of 6* (*q*)	2·25	
266	**240**	17p multicoloured (*j*)	45	45
266*a*	**241**	18p multicoloured (*p*)	50	50
266*b*	**242**	19p multicoloured (*p*)	60	60
267	**243**	20p black, silver and lemon (*b*) . .	50	50
		a. *Perf* 15×14 (*k*)	80	80
268	**244**	25p black and dull blue (*d*)	45	45
268*a*	**223**	26p black, silver and carmine (*p*)	50	50
269	**245**	30p multicoloured (*d*)	50	60
		a. *Perf* 15×14 (*k*)	1·00	1·00
270	**246**	40p multicoloured (*d*)	80	80
		a. *Perf* 15×14 (*m*)	1·50	1·40
271	**247**	50p multicoloured (*d*)	1·00	1·00
		a. *Perf* 15×14 (*m*)	1·90	1·90
272	**248**	75p multicoloured (*n*)	1·50	1·50
273	**249**	£1 multicoloured (*d*)	2·00	2·00
274	**250**	£5 multicoloured (*g*)	10·00	10·00
249/74		*Set of 29*	20·00	20·00
		First Day Covers (7)		22·00
		Presentation Packs (4)	25·00	

*Examples of No. 258*ac* show an impression of the blue (shield) plate from the 12p value. The error was caused by an impression of the 12p plate remaining on the transfer roller.

No. 258*a* only occurs in the £2.16 stamp booklet issued 27 April 1984, No. 259*b* from the £3.12 booklet of 1 April 1986, No. 260*b* from the £3.60 booklet of 6 April 1987 and No. 261*a* from the £2.16 booklet of 27 April 1984 and the £3.84 booklet of 17 May 1988.

No. 252*b* first occurred in the £2.16 stamp booklet of 27 April 1984, but was subsequently issued in sheets.

Printings: (*a*) 24.2.81; (*b*) 28.7.81; (*c*) 1.12.81; (*d*) 23.2.82; (*e*) 11.6.82; (*f*) 19.4.83; (*g*) 17.11.83; (*h*) 27.4.84; (*i*) 15.11.84; (*j*) 25.10.85; (*k*) 4.3.86; (*l*) 1.4.86; (*m*) 6.4.87; (*n*) 23.4.87; (*o*) 12.1.88; (*p*) 26.4.88; (*q*) 17.5.88

Plate and Cylinder Nos.: ½p, 20p 1A, 1B, 1C, 1D, 1E, 1F, 1G, 1H (each ×3); 6p, 11p, 12p, 13p, 14p, 50p, 75p 1A, 1B, 1C, 1D, 1E, 1F, 1G, 1H (each ×5); 10p 1A, 1B, 1C, 1D, 1F, 1G, 1H (each ×5), 2A–1A (×4), 2B–1B (×4), 2C–1C (×4), 2D–1D (×4), 2E–1E (×4), 2F–1F (×4), 2G–1G (×4), 2H–1H (×4); 25p 1A–1A, 1B–1B, 1C–1C, 1D–1D, 1E–1E, 1F–1F, 1G–1G, 1H–1H; 26p 1A, 1B, 1C, 1D, 1E, 1F, 1G, 1H (each ×3); £1 1A, 1B, 1C, 1D, 1E, 1F, 1G, 1H (each ×6); £5 A1–1–1–1, B1–1–1–1, C1–1–1–1, D1–1–1–1; others 1A,

1B, 1C, 1D, 1E, 1G, 1H (each ×4)

Sheets: £1 25 (5×5); £5 10 (5×2); others 50 (10×5)

Imprint: Right–hand corner, bottom margin

Withdrawn: 31.12.85 ½p; 30.4.87 £1; 31.3.90 1p to 10p; 31.1.91 11p to 20p; 31.3.91 25p to 75p; 30.4.97 £5

251 Knight of Hambye slaying Dragon

252 Servant slaying Knight and awaiting Execution

253 St. Brelade celebrating Easter on Island

254 Island revealing itself as Huge Fish

Europa. Folklore

(Des Jennifer Toombs. Litho Questa)

1981 (7 APR). Perf 14½ (C)

275	**251**	10p multicoloured	25	25
		a. *Horiz pair. Nos.* 275/6	60	60
276	**252**	10p multicoloured	25	25
277	**253**	18p multicoloured	50	45
		a. *Horiz pair. Nos.* 277/8	1·40	1·50
278	**254**	18p multicoloured	50	45
275/8		*Set of 4*	1·75	1·25
		First Day Cover		1·50
		Presentation Pack	2·00	

Legends: 10p, Slaying of the Dragon of Lawrence by the Knight of Hambye; 18p. Voyages of St. Brelade.

Plate Nos.: 10p 1A, 1B, 1C, 1D, 1E, 1F, 1G, 1H (each ×6); 18p 1A, 1B, 1C, 1D, 1E, 1F, 1G, 1H (each ×5)

Sheets: 20 (4×5). The two designs of each value were each printed together, *se-tenant*, in horizontal pairs throughout

Imprint: Central, left-hand margin

Quantities sold: 10p 3,459,902; 18p 2,494,444

Withdrawn: 30.4.82

255 Harbour by Gaslight

256 Quay

257 Royal Square

258 Halkett Place

259 Central Market

150th Anniversary of Gas Lighting in Jersey

(Des R. Granger Barrett. Photo Courvoisier)

1981 (22 MAY). *Granite paper.* Perf 11½ (C)

279	**255**	7p multicoloured	. . . .	20	15
280	**256**	10p multicoloured	. . . .	25	25
281	**257**	18p multicoloured	. . . .	40	40
282	**258**	22p multicoloured	. . . .	45	45
283	**259**	25p multicoloured	. . . .	55	55
279/83		Set of 5	. . . .	1·60	1·60
		First Day Cover	. . . .		1·75
		Presentation Pack	. . . .	2·00	

Cylinder Nos.: All values A1–1–1–1–1, B1–1–1–1–1, C1–1–1–1–1, D1–1–1–1–1

Sheets: 20 (5×4)

Imprint: Left-hand corner, bottom margin

Quantities sold: 7p 1,433,090; 10p 1,416,051; 18p 384,043; 22p 417,191; 25p 333,402

Withdrawn: 31.5.82

260 Prince Charles and Lady Diana Spencer

Royal Wedding

(Des Jersey P.O. and Courvoisier. Photo Courvoisier)

1981 (28 JULY). *Granite paper.* Perf 11½ (C)

284	**260**	10p multicoloured	. . . .	20	20
285		25p multicoloured	. . . .	75	90
284/5		Set of 2	. . . .	95	1·10
		First Day Cover	. . . .		2·50
		Presentation Pack	. . . .	2·00	

Cylinder Nos.: Both values A1–1–1–1–1, B1–1–1–1–1

Sheets: 20 (5×4)

Imprint: Left-hand corner, bottom margin

Quantities sold: 10p 935,571; 25p 580,597

Withdrawn: 31.7.82

261 Christmas Tree in Royal Square

262 East Window, Parish Church, St. Helier

263 Boxing Day Meet of Jersey Drag Hunt

Christmas

(Des A. Copp. Litho Questa)

1981 (29 SEPT). Perf 14½ (C)

286	**261**	7p multicoloured	. . . .	15	10
287	**262**	10p multicoloured	. . . .	25	25
		a. Black *(face value, inscr and choir)* printed double	. . . . . .		
288	**263**	18p multicoloured	. . . .	30	30
286/8		Set of 3	. . . .	60	60
		First Day Cover	. . . .		95
		Presentation Pack	. . . .	1·25	
		Postcards *(set of 3)*	. . . .	1·10	2·50

Plate Nos.: All values 1A, 1B, 1C, 1D, 1E, 1F, 1G, 1H (each ×5)

Sheets: 20 (4×5)

Imprint: Central, left-hand margin

Quantities sold: 7p 1,437,626; 10p 1,386,934; 18p 422,693

Withdrawn: 30.9.82

264 Jersey, 16,000 B.C.

265 10,000 B.C.

274

266 7,000 B.C.

267 4,000 B.C.

Europa. Historic Events

(Des A. Copp. Litho Questa)

1982 (20 APR). Perf 14 (C)

289	**264**	11p multicoloured	20	20
290	**265**	11p multicoloured	20	20
291	**266**	19½p multicoloured	45	45
292	**267**	19½p multicoloured	45	45
289/92		*Set of 4*	1·10	1·10
		First Day Cover		1·50
		Presentation Pack	1·50	

Plate Nos.: All values 1A, 1B, 1C, 1D, 1E, 1F (each ×6)

Sheets: 20 (Nos. 289, 292, 4×5; others 5×4)

Imprint: Central, left-hand margin

Quantities sold: 11p (both designs) 3,414,424; 19½p (both designs) 2,307,769

Withdrawn: 30.4.83

268 Rollo, Duke of Normandy, William the Conqueror and 'Clameur de Haro'

269 John of England, Philippe Auguste of France and Siege of Rouen

270 Jean Martell (brandy merchant), early Still and view of Cognac

271 Victor Hugo, 'Le Rocher des Proscrits' (rock where he used to meditate) and Marine Terrace

272 Pierre Teilhard de Chardin (philosopher) and 'Maison Saint Louis' (science institute)

273 Père Charles Rey (scientist), anemo-tachymeter and The Observatory, St. Louis

Links with France

(Des R. Granger Barrett. Litho Questa)

1982 (11 JUNE–7 SEPT). Perf 14 (C)

293	**268**	8p multicoloured	20	15
		a. Horiz pair. Nos. 293/4	50	50
		b. Booklet pane. Nos. 293/4 each ×2 (7.9.82)	1·00	
294	**269**	8p multicoloured	20	15
295	**270**	11p multicoloured	30	30
		a. Horiz pair. Nos. 295/6	60	60
		b. Booklet pane. Nos. 295/6 each ×2 (7.9.82)	1·50	
296	**271**	11p multicoloured	30	30
297	**272**	19½p multicoloured	45	45
		a. Horiz pair. Nos. 297/8	90	90
		b. Booklet pane. Nos. 297/8 each ×2 (7.9.82)	2·25	
		c. Black (face value and inscr) printed double		
298	**273**	19½p multicoloured	45	45
		c. Black (face value and inscr) printed double		
293/8		*Set of 6*	1·75	1·60
		First Day Cover		1·75
		Presentation Pack	2·25	

Each booklet pane has margins all round and text, in English or French, printed on the binding selvedge.

Nos. 297c and 298c come from an example of booklet pane No. 297b.

Plate Nos.: All values 1A, 1B, 1C, 1D (each ×4)

Sheets: 20 (4×5). The two designs of each value were printed together, *se-tenant*, in horizontal pairs throughout

Imprint: Central, left-hand margin

Quantities sold (sheet stamps): 8p (both designs) 2,019,854; 11p (both designs) 1,914,536; 19½p (both designs) 828,272

Withdrawn: 30.6.83 (sheets)

274 Sir William Smith and Proclamation of King George V, Jersey, 1910

275 Sir William Smith and Lord Baden-Powell at Boys' Brigade Display, 1903

276 Boys' Brigade Band, Jersey Liberation Parade, 1945

277 Lord and Lady Baden-Powell in St. Helier, 1924

278 Scouts in Summer Camp, Jersey

Youth Organizations

(Des A. Theobald. Photo Courvoisier)

1982 (18 NOV). *Granite paper.* Perf 11½ (C)

299	**274**	8p multicoloured	20	15
300	**275**	11p multicoloured	20	15
301	**276**	24p multicoloured	45	40
302	**277**	26p multicoloured	60	50
303	**278**	29p multicoloured	75	60
299/303		Set of 5	2·00	1·60
		First Day Cover		1·90
		Presentation Pack	2·25	

Nos. 299/303 were issued on the occasion of the 75th anniversary of the Boy Scout Movement, the 125th birth anniversary of Lord Baden-Powell and the centenary of the Boys' Brigade (1983).

Cylinder Nos.: All values A1–1–1–1–1, B1–1–1–1–1, C1–1–1–1–1, D1–1–1–1–1

Sheets: 20 (11p, 26p 5×4; others 4×5)

Imprint: Lower left-hand margin

Quantities sold: 8p 1,006,110; 11p 1,006,206; 24p 242,482; 26p 255,359; 29p 244,746

Withdrawn: 30.11.83

279 H.M.S. *Tamar* with H.M.S. *Dolphin* at Port Egmont

280 H.M.S. *Dolphin* and H.M.S. *Swallow* off Magellan Strait

281 Discovering Pitcairn Island

282 Carteret taking possession of English Cove, New Zealand

283 H.M.S. *Swallow* sinking a Pirate, Macassar Strait

284 H.M.S. *Endymion* leading Convoy from West Indies

Jersey Adventurers (First Series). 250th Birth Anniv of Philippe de Carteret

(Des R. Granger Barrett. Litho Questa)

1983 (15 FEB). Perf 14×14½ (C)

304	**279**	8p multicoloured	20	15
		a. Black (face value and inscr) printed double		
305	**280**	11p multicoloured	25	15
		a. Black (face value and inscr) printed double		
306	**281**	19½p multicoloured	40	35
307	**282**	24p multicoloured	45	45
		a. Black (face value and inscr) printed double		
308	**283**	26p multicoloured	50	50
		a. Black (face value and inscr) printed double		
309	**284**	29p multicoloured	65	60
304/9		Set of 6	2·25	2·00
		First Day Cover		2·75
		Presentation Pack	3·50	

See also Nos. 417/21 and 573/8.

Plate Nos.: All values 1A, 1B, 1C, 1D, 1E, 1F (each ×6)

Sheets: 20 (4×5)

Imprint: Central, left-hand margin

Quantities sold: 8p 983,227; 11p 979,640; 19½p 377,535; 24p 264,595; 26p 279,424; 29p 254,023

Withdrawn: 29.2.84

285 1969 5s. Legislative
Chamber Definitive

286 Royal Mace

287 1969 10s. Royal Court
Definitive showing
Green Border Error

288 Bailiff's Seal

Europa

(Des G. Drummond. Litho Questa)

1983 (19 APR). Perf 14½ (C)

310	**285**	11p multicoloured	35	30
		a. Horiz pair. Nos. 310/11	70	80
311	**286**	11p multicoloured	35	30
312	**287**	19½p multicoloured	45	40
		a. Horiz pair. Nos. 312/13	90	90
313	**288**	19½p multicoloured	45	40
310/13		Set of 4	1·50	1·25
		First Day Cover		2·00
		Presentation Pack	2·25	

Plate Nos.: Both values 1A, 1B, 1C, 1D, 1E, 1F (each ×6)

Sheets: 20 (4×5). The two designs of each value were printed together, se-tenant, in horizontal pairs throughout

Imprint: Central, left-hand margin

Quantities sold: 11p (both designs) 2,973,691; 19½p (both designs) 1,301,579

Withdrawn: 30.4.84

289 Charles Le Geyt and
Battle of Minden

290 London to Weymouth
Mail Coach

291 P.O. Mail Packet
Chesterfield attacked
by French Privateer

292 Mary Godfray and the
Hue Street Post Office

293 Mail Steamer leaving St.
Helier Harbour

World Communications Year and 250th Birth Anniversary of Charles Le Geyt (first Jersey postmaster)

(Des A. Copp. Litho Questa)

1983 (21 JUNE). Perf 14 (C)

314	**289**	8p multicoloured	20	20
315	**290**	11p multicoloured	30	30
316	**291**	24p multicoloured	55	55
317	**292**	26p multicoloured	65	65
318	**293**	29p multicoloured	80	80
314/18		Set of 5	2·25	2·25
		First Day Cover		2·50
		Presentation Pack	2·75	

Plate Nos.: All values 1A, 1B, 1C, 1D (each ×5)

Sheets: 20 (4×5)

Imprint: Central, left-hand margin

Quantities sold: 8p 1,136,008; 11p 961,725; 24p 244,690; 26p 247,654; 29p 230,325

Withdrawn: 30.6.84

294 Assembly Emblem

13th General Assembly of the A.I.P.L.F. (Association Internationale des Parlementaires de Langue Francaise)

(Des A. Copp. Litho Questa)

1983 (21 JUNE). Perf 14½ (C)

319	**294**	19½p multicoloured	50	50
		First Day Cover		95
		Presentation Pack	1·25	

Plate Nos.: 1A, 1B, 1C, 1D (each ×5)

Sheets: 20 (4×5)

Imprint: Central, left-hand margin

Quantity sold: 312,304

Withdrawn: 30.6.84

295 'Cardinal Newman'

296 'Incident in the French Revolution'

297 'Thomas Hardy'

298 'David with the Head of Goliath'

50th Death Anniversary of Walter Ouless (artist)

(Des and photo Courvoisier)

1983 (20 Sept). *Granite paper.* Perf 11½ (C)

320	**295**	8p multicoloured	20	20
321	**296**	11p multicoloured	30	30
322	**297**	20½p multicoloured	50	50
323	**298**	31p multicoloured	80	80
320/3		*Set of 4*	1·60	1·60
		First Day Cover		2·00
		Presentation Pack	2·25	

Cylinder Nos.: All values 1A, 1B (each ×5)

Sheets: 20 (4×5) 31p or (5×4) others

Imprint: Central, left-hand margin

Quantities sold: 8p 1,054,200; 11p 1,055,429; 20½p 424,049; 31p 216,128

Withdrawn: 30.9.84

299 Golden Lion Tamarin

300 Snow Leopard

301 Jamaican Boa

302 Round Island Gecko

303 Coscoroba Swan

304 St. Lucia Amazon

Wildlife Preservation Trust (Fourth Series)

(Des W. Oliver. Litho Questa)

1984 (17 JAN). Perf 13½×14 (C)

324	**299**	9p multicoloured	25	10
325	**300**	12p multicoloured	25	15
326	**301**	20½p multicoloured	45	40
327	**302**	26p multicoloured	75	65
328	**303**	28p multicoloured	80	70
329	**304**	31p multicoloured	1·00	90
324/9		*Set of 6*	*3·25	2·50
		First Day Cover		4·25
		Presentation Pack	3·75	

Plate Nos.: 20½p, 28p 1B, 1C, 1E, 1F (each ×4); others 1A, 1B, 1C, 1D, 1E, 1F (each ×4)

Sheets: 20 (5×4)

Imprint: Central, left-hand margin

Quantities sold: 9p 1,229,713; 12p 1,365,973; 20½p 266,444; 26p 239,180; 28p 255,205; 31p 221,422

Withdrawn: 31.1.85

305 C.E.P.T. 25th Anniversary Logo

Europa

(Des J. Larrivière. Litho Questa)

1984 (12 MAR). Perf 14½×15 (C)

330	**305**	9p cobalt, ultramarine & black .	20	15
331		12p light green, green and black	30	25
332		20½p rose-lilac, dp magenta & blk	60	50
330/2		Set of 3	1·00	80
		First Day Cover		1·50
		Presentation Pack	1·60	

Plate Nos.: All values 1A, 1B, 1C, 1D, 1E, 1F (each ×3)

Sheets: 20 (4×5)

Imprint: Central, left-hand margin

Quantities sold: 9p 1,352,245; 12p 1,388,802; 20½p 742,046

Withdrawn: 31.3.85

306 Map showing Commonwealth

Links with the Commonwealth

(Des A. Copp. Litho Questa)

1984 (12 MAR). Sheet 108×74 mm. Perf 15×14½ (C)

MS333	**306**	75p multicoloured	2·00	2·00
		First Day Cover		2·50
		Presentation Pack	2·75	

Quantity sold: 215,566

Withdrawn: 31.3.85

307 Sarah Bloomshoft at Demie de Pas Light, 1906

308 Hearts of Oak and Maurice Georges, 1949

309 Elizabeth Rippon and Hanna, 1949

310 Elizabeth Rippon and Santa Maria, 1951

311 Elizabeth Rippon and Bacchus, 1973

312 Thomas James King and Cythara, 1983

Centenary of the Jersey R.N.L.I. Lifeboat Station

(Des G. Palmer. Litho Questa)

1984 (1 JUNE). Perf 14½ (C)

334	**307**	9p multicoloured	25	15
335	**308**	9p multicoloured	25	15
336	**309**	12p multicoloured	35	30
337	**310**	12p multicoloured	35	30
338	**311**	20½p multicoloured	60	60
339	**312**	20½p multicoloured	60	60
334/9		Set of 6	2·10	1·90
		First Day Cover		3·00
		Presentation Pack	3·25	
		Postcard (as No. 339)	1·25	2·25

Plate Nos.: All values 1A, 1B, 1C, 1D, 1E, 1F (each ×5)

Sheets: 20 (4×5)

Imprint: Central, left-hand margin

Quantities sold: 9p (No. 334) 485,538; 9p (No. 335) 435,647; 12p (No. 336) 534,920; 12p (No. 337) 518,807; 20½p (No. 338) 298,935; 20½p (No. 339) 290,945

Withdrawn: 30.6.85

313 Bristol Type 170 Freighter Mk 32

314 Airspeed A.S.57 Ambassador 2

315 De Havilland D.H.114 Heron 1B

316 De Havilland D.H.89A Dragon Rapide

40th Anniversary of International Civil Aviation Organization

(Des G. Drummond. Litho Questa)

1984 (24 JULY). Perf 14 (C)

340	**313**	9p multicoloured	20	15
341	**314**	12p multicoloured	35	35

342	**315**	26p multicoloured	. . . .	75	75
343	**316**	31p multicoloured	. . . .	1·00	1·00
340/3		Set of 4	. . . .	2·10	2·00
		First Day Cover	. . .		2·75
		Presentation Pack	. . . .	3·25	

Plate Nos.: All values 1A, 1B, 1C, 1D (each ×4)

Sheets: 20 (4×5)

Imprint: Central, left-hand margin

Quantities sold: 9p 563,394; 12p 751,072; 26p 262,640; 31p 193,703

Withdrawn: 31.7.85

317 'Robinson Crusoe leaves the Wreck'

318 'Edinburgh Castle'

319 'Maori Village'

320 'Australian Landscape'

321 'Waterhouse's Corner, Adelaide'

322 'Captain Cook at Botany Bay'

Links with Australia. Paintings by John Alexander Gilfillan

(Des R. Granger Barrett. Photo Courvoisier)

1984 (21 SEPT). *Granite paper.* Perf 11½×12 (C)

344	**317**	9p multicoloured	. . . .	25	20
345	**318**	12p multicoloured	. . . .	30	20
346	**319**	20½p multicoloured	. . . .	60	50
347	**320**	26p multicoloured	. . . .	70	60
348	**321**	28p multicoloured	. . . .	80	80
349	**322**	31p multicoloured	. . . .	80	80
344/9		Set of 6	. . . .	3·00	2·75
		First Day Cover	. . . .		3·75
		Presentation Pack	. . . .	3·75	
		Postcards (Set of 3 as Nos. 347/9)	. . . .	1·75	4·50

Cylinder Nos.: All values A1, B1 (each ×6)

Sheets: 20 (4×5)

Imprint: Central, left-hand margin

Quantities sold: 9p 541,384; 12p 635,192; 20½p 210,119; 26p 234,836; 28p 188,052; 31p 192,353

Withdrawn: 30.9.85

323 'B.L.C. St. Helier'

324 'Oda Mt Bingham'

Christmas. Jersey Orchids (First Series)

(Photo Courvoisier)

1984 (15 NOV). *Granite paper.* Perf 12×11½ (C)

350	**323**	9p multicoloured	. . . .	25	20
351	**324**	12p multicoloured	. . . .	50	50
350/1		Set of 2	. . . .	75	70
		First Day Cover	. . . .		1·50
		Presentation Pack	. . . .	1·50	

See also Nos. 433/7, 613/17 and 892/7.

Cylinder Nos.: Both values A1, B1, C1, D1 (each ×6)

Sheets: 20 (4×5)

Imprint: Central, left-hand margin

Quantities sold: 9p 1,197,796; 12p 1,116,097

Withdrawn: 30.11.85

325 'Hebe off Corbière, 1874'

326 'The Gaspe engaging the Diomede'

327 'The Paddle-steamer London entering Naples, 1856'

328 'The Rambler entering Cape Town, 1840'

329 'St. Aubin's Bay from Mount Bingham, 1872'

Death Centenary of Philip John Ouless (artist)

(Photo Harrison)

1985 (26 FEB). Perf 14×15 (C)

352	**325**	9p multicoloured	....	25	20
353	**326**	12p multicoloured	....	30	30
354	**327**	22p multicoloured	....	65	60
355	**328**	31p multicoloured	....	1·00	90
356	**329**	34p multicoloured	....	1·25	1·00
352/6		*Set of* 5	....	3·00	2·75
		First Day Cover	....		3·50
		Presentation Pack	....	4·00	

Cylinder Nos.: 31p 1B (×5); others 1A, 1B (each ×5)

Sheets: 20 (4×5)

Imprint: Central, left-hand margin

Quantities sold: 9p 463,589; 12p 405,133; 22p 407,598; 31p 193,772; 34p 185,467

Withdrawn: 28.2.86

330 John Ireland (composer) and Faldouet Dolmen

331 Ivy St. Helier (actress) and His Majesty's Theatre, London

332 Claude Debussy (composer) and Elizabeth Castle

Europa. European Music Year

(Des Jennifer Toombs. Litho Questa)

1985 (23 APR). Perf 14 (C)

357	**330**	10p multicoloured	....	30	30
358	**331**	13p multicoloured	....	45	45
359	**332**	22p multicoloured	....	80	80
357/9		*Set of* 3	....	1·40	1·40
		First Day Cover	....		1·90
		Presentation Pack	....	2·00	

Plate Nos.: 10p 1A, 1B, 1C, 1D, 1E, 1F (each ×5); 13p 1A, 1C, 1D, 1E, 1F (each ×5); 22p 1A, 1B, 1D, 1E, 1F (each ×5)

Sheets: 20 (4×5)

Imprint: Central, left-hand margin

Quantities sold: 10p 916,040; 13p 766,179; 22p 620,375

Withdrawn: 30.4.86

Plate Nos.: All values 1A, 1B, 1C, 1D, 1E, 1F (each ×4)

Sheets: 20 (5×4)

Imprint: Central, left-hand margin

Quantities sold: 10p 943,351; 13p 944,724; 29p 175,365; 31p 183,591; 34p 179,842

Withdrawn: 30.5.86

333 Girls' Brigade

334 Girl Guides (75th anniversary)

335 Prince Charles and Jersey Youth Service Activities Base

336 Sea Cadet Corps

337 Air Training Corps

International Youth Year

(Des A. Theobald. Litho Questa)

1985 (30 MAY). Perf 14½×14 (C)

360	**333**	10p multicoloured	30	30
361	**334**	13p multicoloured	40	40
362	**335**	29p multicoloured	70	70
363	**336**	31p multicoloured	75	75
364	**337**	34p multicoloured	90	90
360/4		Set of 5	2·75	2·75
		First Day Cover		3·25
		Presentation Pack		3·75

338 *Duke of Normandy* at Cheapside

339 Saddletank at First Tower

340 *La Moye* at Millbrook

341 *St Heliers* at St. Aubin

342 *St Aubyns* at Corbière

Jersey Western Railway

(Des G. Palmer. Photo Courvoisier)

1985 (16 JULY). *Granite paper*. Perf 11½ (C)

365	**338**	10p multicoloured	45	45
366	**339**	13p multicoloured	50	50
367	**340**	22p multicoloured	90	90
368	**341**	29p multicoloured	95	95
369	**342**	34p multicoloured	1·00	1·00
365/9		Set of 5	3·50	3·50
		First Day Cover		3·75
		Presentation Pack	4·00	

Cylinder Nos.: 10p, 13p A1, B1 (each ×5); others A1 (×5)

Sheets: 20 (4×5)

Imprint: Central, left-hand margin

Quantities sold: 10p 708,912; 13p 706,189; 22p 249,659; 29p 179,849; 34p 179,977

Withdrawn: 31.7.86

343 Memorial Window to Revd. James Hemery (former Dean) and St. Helier Parish Church

344 Judge Francis Jeune, Baron St. Helier, and Houses of Parliament

345 Silverware by Pierre Amiraux

346 Francis Voisin (merchant) and Russian Port

347 Robert Brohier, Schweppes Carbonation Plant and Bottles

348 George Ingouville, V.C., R.N., and Attack on Viborg

300th Anniversary of Huguenot Immigration

(Des R. Granger Barrett. Litho Questa)

1985 (10 SEPT). Perf 14 (C)

370	**343**	10p multicoloured	30	30
		a. *Booklet pane of 4*	1·25	
371	**344**	10p multicoloured	30	30
		a. *Booklet pane of 4*	1·25	
372	**345**	13p multicoloured	40	40
		a. *Booklet pane of 4*	1·60	
373	**346**	13p multicoloured	40	40
		a. *Booklet pane of 4*	1·60	
		ab. *Black (face value and inscr)*		
		printed double		
374	**347**	22p multicoloured	55	50
		a. *Booklet pane of 4*	2·25	
		b. *Black (inscr) printed double* .		
375	**348**	22p multicoloured	55	50
		a. *Booklet pane of 4*	2·25	
370/5		*Set of 6*	2·25	2·10
		First Day Cover		2·75
		Presentation Pack	2·75	

Each booklet pane has margins all round and text printed on the binding selvedge.

Plate Nos.: 13p (No. 372) 1A, 1B, 1C, 1D (each ×4); 22p (No. 375) 1A, 1C, 1D (each ×5); others 1A, 1B, 1C, 1D (each ×5)

Sheets: 20 (4×5)

Imprint: Central, left-hand margin

Quantities sold (sheets): 10p (No. 370) 308,085; 10p (No. 371) 310,475; 13p (No. 372) 488,224; 13p (No. 373) 477,764; 22p (No. 374) 259,921; 22p (No. 375) 253,607

Withdrawn: 30.9.86 (sheets)

349 Howard Davis Hall, Victoria College

350 Schooner *Westward*

351 Howard Davis Park, St. Helier

352 Howard Davis Experimental Farm, Trinity

Thomas Davis (philanthropist) Commemoration

(Des A. Copp. Litho Cartor)

1985 (25 OCT). Perf 13½ (C)

376	**349**	10p multicoloured	35	35
377	**350**	13p multicoloured	50	50
378	**351**	31p multicoloured	70	70
379	**352**	34p multicoloured	85	85
376/9		*Set of 4*	2·25	2·25
		First Day Cover		2·75
		Presentation Pack	3·00	

Plate Nos.: 10p 1A, 1B, 1C, 1D (each ×5); 13p 2A, 2B, 2C, 2D (each ×5); 31p 3A, 3B, 3C, 3D (each ×5); 34p 4A, 4B, 4C, 4D (each ×5)

Sheets: 20 (4×5)

Imprint: Central, left hand margin

Quantities sold: 10p 939,104; 13p 831,351; 31p 170,020; 34p 156,653

Withdrawn: 31.10.86

357 Aspects of Communications in 1910 and 1986 on TV Screens

353 'Amaryllis belladonna' (Pandora Sellars)

354 'A Jersey Lily' (Lily Langtry) (Sir John Millais)

Jersey Lilies

(Des C. Abbott. Litho Questa)

1986 (28 JAN). Perf 15×14½ (C)
380	**353**	13p multicoloured	45	45
381	**354**	34p multicoloured	1·00	1·10
380/1		Set of 2	1·40	1·50
		First Day Cover		2·00
		Presentation Pack	2·25	
MS382	140×96 mm. Nos. 380×4 and 381		2·75	3·00
		First Day Cover		6·00
		Presentation Pack	4·00	

Plate Nos.: 13p 1A, 1B, 1C, 1D, 1E, 1F, 1G, 1H (each ×6); 34p 1A, 1B, 1C, 1D (each ×5)

Sheets: 20 (4×5); (5×4) 34p

Imprint: Central, left-hand margin

Quantities sold: 13p 444,175; 34p 169,811; miniature sheet 157,575

Withdrawn: 31.1.87

Appearance of Halley's Comet

(Des Jennifer Toombs. Litho Cartor)

1986 (4 MAR). Perf 13½×13 (C)
383	**355**	10p multicoloured	35	35
384	**356**	22p multicoloured	80	85
385	**357**	31p multicoloured	1·00	1·10
383/5		Set of 3	1·90	2·10
		First Day Cover		2·25
		Presentation Pack	2·75	

Plate Nos.: All values 1A, 1B, 1C, 1D (each ×5)

Sheets: 20 (4×5)

Imprint: Central, left-hand margin

Quantities sold: 10p 552,062; 22p 245,111; 31p 182,390

Withdrawn: 31.3.87

358 Dwarf Pansy

359 Sea Stock

360 Sand Crocus

Europa. Environmental Conservation

(Des Pandora Sellars. Litho Questa)

1986 (21 APR). Perf 14½×14 (C)
386	**358**	10p multicoloured	35	35
387	**359**	14p multicoloured	45	45
388	**360**	22p multicoloured	70	70
386/8		Set of 3	1·40	1·40
		First Day Cover		1·75
		Presentation Pack	2·25	

355 King Harold, William of Normandy and Halley's Comet, 1066 (Bayeux Tapestry)

356 Lady Carteret, Edmond Halley, Map and Comet

Plate Nos.: 22p 1A, 1B, 1C, 1E, 1F (each ×5); others 1A, 1B, 1C, 1D, 1E, 1F (each ×5)

Sheets: 20 (5×4)

Imprint: Central, left-hand margin

Quantities sold: 10p 892,977; 14p 892,631; 22p 612,513

Withdrawn: 30.4.87

361 Queen Elizabeth II (from photo by Karsh)

60th Birthday of Queen Elizabeth II

(Photo Courvoisier)

1986 (21 APR). *Granite paper*. Perf 14½ (C)
389 **361** £1 multicoloured . . . . 2·50 1·50
              First Day Cover . . . .   3·25
              Presentation Pack . . . . 3·00

No. 389 was retained in use as part of the current definitive series until replaced by No. 500.
For a £2 value in this design see No. 491*b*.

Cylinder Nos.: 1A, 1B, 1C, 1D (each ×6)

Sheets: 20 (4×5)

Imprint: Central, left-hand margin

Quantity sold: 431,591

Withdrawn: 31.5.90

362 Le Rât Cottage

363 The Elms (Trust Headquarters)

364 Morel Farm

365 Quétivel Mill

366 La Vallette

50th Anniversary of the National Trust for Jersey

(Des A. Copp. Litho Cartor)

1986 (17 JUNE). Perf 13½×13 (C)
390 **362** 10p multicoloured 25   20
391 **363** 14p multicoloured 35   30
392 **364** 22p multicoloured 65   65
393 **365** 29p multicoloured 70   70
394 **366** 31p multicoloured 75   75
390/4   *Set of 5* . . . . 2·40 2·40
             First Day Cover . . . .   2·75
             Presentation Pack . . . . 3·75

Plate Nos.: All values 1A, 1B, 1C, 1D (each ×5)

Sheets: 20 (4×5)

Imprint: Central, left-hand margin

Quantities sold: 10p 946,735; 14p 919,823; 22p 427,370; 29p 173,763; 31p 178,353

Withdrawn: 30.6.87

367 Prince Andrew and Miss Sarah Ferguson

Royal Wedding

(Des A. Copp. Litho Cartor)

1986 (23 JULY). Perf 13½ (C)
395 **367** 14p multicoloured 35   35
396   40p multicoloured . . . . 1·25 1·25
395/6   *Set of 2* . . . . 1·60 1·60
             First Day Cover . . . .   2·00
             Presentation Pack . . . . 2·25

Plate Nos.: Both values 1A, 1B, 1C, 1D (each ×6)

Sheets: 20 (5×4)

Imprint: Central, left-hand margin

Quantities sold: 14p 991,943; 40p 267,312

Withdrawn: 31.7.87

JERSEY

10ᴾ   _Blampied_ "Gathering Vraic"

368 'Gathering Vraic'

JERSEY

14ᴾ   Blampied "Driving home in the rain"

369 'Driving Home in the Rain'

JERSEY

29ᴾ   _Blampied_ "The Miller"

370 'The Miller'

JERSEY

31ᴾ   Blampied "The Joy Ride"

371 'The Joy Ride'

JERSEY

34ᴾ   _Blampied_ "Tante Elizabeth"   **372** 'Tante Elizabeth'

Birth Centenary of Edmund Blampied (artist)

(Des A. Copp. Litho Questa)

1986 (28 AUG). Perf 14 (C)

397	**368**	10p multicoloured	25	25
398	**369**	14p black, brownish grey & lt bl .	40	40
399	**370**	29p multicoloured	75	75
400	**371**	31p black, brownish grey and pale orange	90	90
401	**372**	34p multicoloured	95	95
397/401		Set of 5	3·00	3·00
		First Day Cover		3·75
		Presentation Pack	4·00	

Plate Nos.: 14p, 31p 1A, 1B, 1C, 1D (each ×3); others 1A, 1B, 1C, 1D (each ×5)

Sheets: 20 (4×5)

Imprint: Central, left-hand margin

Quantities sold: 10p, 885,979; 14p 675,290; 29p 163,085; 31p 157,559; 34p 151,128

Withdrawn: 31.8.87

JERSEY 10p

373 Island Map on Jersey Lily, and Dove holding Olive Branch

JERSEY 14p

374 Mistletoe Wreath encircling European Robin and Dove

JERSEY 34p

375 Christmas Cracker releasing Dove

Christmas. International Year of Peace

(Des G. Taylor. Litho Questa)

1986 (4 NOV). Perf 14½×14 (C)

402	**373**	10p multicoloured	20	20
403	**374**	14p multicoloured	40	40
404	**375**	34p multicoloured	95	95
402/4		Set of 3	1·40	1·40
		First Day Cover		2·00
		Presentation Pack	2·00	

Plate Nos.: All values 1A, 1B, 1C, 1D, 1E, 1F (each ×6)

Sheets: 20 (5×4)

Imprint: Central, left-hand margin

Quantities sold: 10p 947,614; 14p 940,123; 34p 169,269

Withdrawn: 30.11.87

Post Office Yearbook

1986 (4 NOV). Comprises Nos. 380/404

Yearbook . . . . 45·00

Withdrawn: 31.1.88

JERSEY 10ᴾ

376 *Westward* under Full Sail

JERSEY 14ᴾ

377 T. B. Davis at the Helm

378 *Westward* overhauling *Britannia*

379 *Westward* fitting-out at St. Helier

Racing Schooner **Westward**

(Des A. Copp. Litho Cartor)

1987 (15 JAN). Perf 13½ (C)

405	**376**	10p multicoloured	. . . .	40	35
406	**377**	14p multicoloured	. . . .	50	55
407	**378**	31p multicoloured	. . . .	95	95
408	**379**	34p multicoloured	. . . .	95	95
405/8		Set of 4	. . . .	2·50	2·50
		First Day Cover	. . . .		2·75
		Presentation Pack	. . . .	3·75	

Plate Nos.: All values 1A, 1B, 1C, 1D (each ×5)

Sheets: 20 (4×5)

Imprint: Central, left-hand margin

Quantites sold: 10p 519,330; 14p 370,229; 31p 173,046; 34p 158,754

Withdrawn: 31.1.88

380 De Havilland D.H.86 Dragon Express *Belcraute Bay*

381 Boeing 757 and Douglas DC-9-15

382 Britten Norman 'long nose' Trislander and Islander

383 Shorts 330 and Vickers Viscount 800

384 B.A.C. One Eleven 500 and Handley Page H.P.R.7 Dart Herald

50th Anniversary of Jersey Airport

(Des G. Palmer. Litho Questa)

1987 (3 MAR). Perf 14 (C)

409	**380**	10p multicoloured	. . . .	25	25
410	**381**	14p multicoloured	. . . .	40	45
411	**382**	22p multicoloured	. . . .	55	50
412	**383**	29p multicoloured	. . . .	90	90
413	**384**	31p multicoloured	. . . .	95	95
409/13		Set of 5	. . . .	2·75	2·75
		First Day Cover	. . . .		3·50
		Presentation Pack	. . . .	3·75	

Plate Nos.: All values 1A, 1B, 1C, 1D (each ×4)

Sheets: 20 (4×5)

Imprint: Central, left-hand margin

Quantities sold: 10p 313,733; 14p 281,226; 22p 368,486; 29p 155,159; 31p 167,709

Withdrawn: 31.3.88

385 St. Mary and St. Peter's Roman Catholic Church

386 Villa Devereux, St. Brelade

387 Fort Regent Leisure Centre, St. Helier

Europa. Modern Architecture

(Des A. Copp. Litho Questa)

1987 (23 APR). Perf 15×14 (C)

414	**385**	11p multicoloured	. . . .	40	40
415	**386**	15p multicoloured	. . . .	50	45
416	**387**	22p multicoloured	. . . .	75	75
414/16		Set of 3	. . . .	1·50	1·40
		First Day Cover	. . . .		2·00
		Presentation Pack	. . . .	2·25	

Plate Nos.: 11p, 15p 1A, 1B, 1C, 1D, 1E, 1F, 1G, 1H, 1I, 1J (each ×6); 22p 1A, 1B, 1C, 1D, 1E, 1F, 1G, 1H (each ×6)

Sheets: 10 (2×5)

Imprint: Central, left-hand margin

Quantities sold: 11p 847,735; 15p 883,825; 22p 467,615

Withdrawn: 30.4.88

388 H.M.S. *Racehorse* and H.M.S. *Carcass* (bomb-ketches) trapped in Arctic

389 H.M.S. *Alarm* on Fire, Rhode Island

390 H.M.S. *Arethusa* wrecked off Ushant

391 H.M.S. *Rattlesnake* stranded on Isle de Trinidad

392 Mont Orgueil Castle and Fishing Boats

Jersey Adventurers (Second Series). Philippe D'Auvergne

(Des R. Granger Barrett. Litho Questa)

1987 (9 JULY). Perf 14 (C)

417	**388**	11p multicoloured	. . . .	30	35
418	**389**	15p multicoloured	. . . .	40	45
419	**390**	29p multicoloured	. . . .	70	75
420	**391**	31p multicoloured	. . . .	80	90
421	**392**	34p multicoloured	. . . .	85	95
417/21		*Set* of 5	. . . .	2·75	3·00
		First Day Cover	. . . .		3·25
		Presentation Pack	. . . .	4·25	

See also Nos. 501/6 and 539/44.

Plate Nos.: All values 1A, 1B, 1C, 1D (each ×4)

Sheets: 20 (4×5)

Imprint: Central, left-hand margin

Quantities sold: 11p 694,506; 15p 897,162; 29p 138,711; 31p 144,518; 34p 140,968

Withdrawn: 31.7.88.

393 Grant of Lands to Normandy, 911 and 933

394 Edward the Confessor and Duke Robert I of Normandy landing on Jersey, 1030

395 King William's Coronation, 1066, and Fatal Fall, 1087

396 Death of William Rufus, 1100, and Battle of Tinchebrai, 1106

397 Civil War between Matilda and Stephen, 1135–41

398 Henry inherits Normandy, 1151: John asserts Ducal Rights in Jersey, 1213

900th Death Anniversary of William the Conqueror

(Des Jennifer Toombs, Litho Cartor)

1987 (9 SEPT–16 OCT). Perf 13½ (C)

422	**393**	11p multicoloured (*a*)	. . . .	30	30
		a. Booklet pane of 4 (*b*)	. . . . . .	1·25	
423	**394**	15p multicoloured (*a*)	. . . .	35	35
		a. Booklet pane of 4 (*b*)	. . . . . .	1·40	
424	**395**	22p multicoloured (*a*)	. . . .	70	65
		a. Booklet pane of 4 (*b*)	. . . . . .	2·75	

425	**396**	29p multicoloured (a)	75	65
		a. Booklet pane of 4 (b)	3·00	
426	**397**	31p multicoloured (a)	85	75
		a. Booklet pane of 4 (b)	3·25	
427	**398**	34p multicoloured (a)	95	90
		a. Booklet pane of 4 (b)	3·75	
422/7		Set of 6	3·50	3·25
		First Day Cover		3·75
		Presentation Pack	4·50	

Each booklet pane has margins all round and text printed on the binding selvedge.

Printings: (a) 9.9.87; (b) 16.10.87

Plate Nos.: All values 1A, 1B, 1C, 1D (each ×6)

Imprint: Central, left-hand margin

Quantities sold (sheets): 11p 869,726; 15p 968,815; 22p 217,160; 29p 139,905; 31p 147,527; 34p 143,684

Withdrawn: 30.9.88 (sheets)

399 'Grosnez Castle'

400 'St. Aubin's Bay'

401 'Mont Orgueil Castle'

402 'Town Fort and Harbour, St. Helier'

403 'The Hermitage'

Christmas. Paintings by John Le Capelain

(Photo Courvoisier)

1987 (3 NOV). Granite paper. Perf 11½ (C)

428	**399**	11p multicoloured	35	30
429	**400**	15p multicoloured	50	50
430	**401**	22p multicoloured	65	65
431	**402**	31p multicoloured	90	90
432	**403**	34p multicoloured	1·00	1·00
428/32		Set of 5	3·00	3·00
		First Day Cover		3·75
		Presentation Pack	4·00	

Cylinder Nos.: 11p, 15p, 22p 1A, 1B (each ×6); 31p, 34p 1A (×6)

Sheets: 20 (5×4)

Imprint: Central, left-hand margin

Quantities sold: 11p 951,916; 15p 874,209; 22p 371,992; 31p 154,824; 34p 145,550

Withdrawn: 30.11.88

Post Office Yearbook

1987 (3 NOV). Comprises Nos. 272 and 405/32
Yearbook . . . . 38·00

Withdrawn: 28.2.89

404 Cymbidium pontac

405 Odontioda Eric Young

406 Lycaste auburn Seaford and Ditchling

407 Odontoglossum St. Brelade

408 Cymbidium mavourneen Jester

Jersey Orchids (Second Series)

(Litho Questa)

1988 (12 JAN). Perf 14 (C)

433	**404**	11p multicoloured	40	35
434	**405**	15p multicoloured	45	45
435	**406**	29p multicoloured	70	70
436	**407**	31p multicoloured	80	80
437	**408**	34p multicoloured	95	95
433/7		Set of 5	3·00	3·00
		First Day Cover		3·50
		Presentation Pack	3·75	

Plate Nos.: All values 1A, 1B, 1C, 1D (each ×5)

Sheets: 20 (4×5) 11p, 20p, 34p; (5×4) 15p, 31p

Imprint: Central, left hand margin

Quantities sold: 11p 558,185; 15p 374,117; 29p 143,613; 31p 162,096; 34p 151,193

Withdrawn: 31.1.89

JERSEY 11ᴾ

409 Labrador Retriever

JERSEY 15ᴾ

410 Wire-haired Dachshund

JERSEY 22ᴾ

411 Pekingese

JERSEY 31ᴾ

412 Cavalier King Charles Spaniel

JERSEY 34ᴾ **413** Dalmatian

Centenary of Jersey Dog Club

(Des P. Layton. Litho Questa)

1988 (2 MAR). Perf 14 (C)

438	**409**	11p multicoloured	. . . .	40	30
439	**410**	15p multicoloured	. . . .	60	30
440	**411**	22p multicoloured	. . . .	80	75
441	**412**	31p multicoloured	. . . .	90	95
442	**413**	34p multicoloured	. . . .	1·00	1·00
438/42		Set of 5	. . . .	3·25	3·00
		First Day Cover	. . . .		3·75
		Presentation Pack	. . . .	4·25	

Plate Nos.: All values 1A, 1B, 1C, 1D (each ×4)

Sheets: 20 (4×5)

Imprint: Central, left-hand margin

Quantities sold: 11p 371,583; 15p 374,953; 22p 178,132; 31p 154,530; 34p 146,628

Withdrawn: 31.3.89

414 De Havilland D.H.C.7 Dash Seven, London Landmarks and Jersey Control Tower

415 Weather Radar and Jersey Airport Landing System

416 Hydrofoil, St. Malo, and Elizabeth Castle, St. Helier

417 Port Control Tower and Jersey Radio Maritime Communication Centre, La Moye

Europa. Transport and Communications

(Des A. Copp. Litho Cartor)

1988 (26 APR). Perf 14×13½ (horiz) or 13½×14 (vert), both comb

443	**414**	16p multicoloured	. . . .	40	45
444	**415**	16p multicoloured	. . . .	40	45
445	**416**	22p multicoloured	. . . .	75	75
446	**417**	22p multicoloured	. . . .	75	75
443/6		Set of 4	. . . .	2·10	2·40
		First Day Cover	. . . .		2·75
		Presentation Pack	. . . .	3·00	

Plate Nos.: Nos. 443/4, 446 1A, 1B, 1C, 1D (each ×5); No. 445 1A, 1B, 1C, 1D (each ×6)

Sheets: 20 (4×5) Nos. 443, 445; (5×4) Nos. 444, 446

Imprint: Central, left-hand margin

Quantities sold: 16p (No. 443) 881,324; 16p (No. 444) 865,868; 22p (No. 445) 509,086; 22p (No. 446) 510,104

Withdrawn: 30.4.89

418 Rodriguez Fody

419 Volcano Rabbit

420 White-faced Marmoset

421 Ploughshare Tortoise

422 Mauritius Kestrel

423 Rain Forest Leaf Frog, Costa Rica

424 Archaeological Survey, Peru

425 Climbing Glacier, Chile

426 Red Cross Centre, Solomon Islands

427 Underwater Exploration, Australia

428 *Zebu* (brigantine) returning to St. Helier

Wildlife Preservation Trust (Fifth Series)

(Des W. Oliver. Litho Cartor)

1988 (6 JULY). Perf 13½×14 (vert) or 14×13½ (horiz), both comb

447	**418**	12p multicoloured	45	45
448	**419**	16p multicoloured	55	50
449	**420**	29p multicoloured	90	1·00
450	**421**	31p multicoloured	1·10	1·10
451	**422**	34p multicoloured	1·25	1·25
447/51		Set of 5	3·75	3·75
		First Day Cover		4·50
		Presentation Pack	4·50	

Plate Nos.: All values 1A, 1B, 1C, 1D (each ×6)

Sheets: 20 (5×4) 12p, 29p, 34p; (4×5) 16p, 31p

Imprint: Central, left-hand margin

Quantities sold: 12p 875,722; 16p 969,800; 29p 146,567; 31p 155,348; 34p 151,723

Withdrawn: 31.7.89

Operation Raleigh

(Des V. Ambrus. Photo Courvoisier)

1988 (27 SEPT). *Granite paper.* Perf 12 (C)

452	**423**	12p multicoloured	35	25
453	**424**	16p multicoloured	40	40
454	**425**	22p multicoloured	60	60
455	**426**	29p multicoloured	70	70
456	**427**	31p multicoloured	80	80
457	**428**	34p multicoloured	90	90
452/7		Set of 6	3·50	3·25
		First Day Cover		3·75
		Presentation Pack	4·50	

No. 455 also commemorates the 40th anniversary of the World Health Organization.

Cylinder Nos.: All values 1A (×5)

Sheets: 20 (5×4)

Imprint: Central, left-hand margin

Quantities sold: 12p 706,594; 16p 507,077; 22p 226,791; 29p 127,647; 31p 127,658; 34p 128,055

Withdrawn: 30.9.89

429 St. Clement

430 St. Ouen

431 St. Brelade

 (St. Lawrence image)

432 St. Lawrence

435 Austin 7 'Chummy', 1926

436 Ford 'Model T', 1926

437 Bentley 8 Litre, 1930

438 Cadillac '452A-V16 Fleetwood Sports Phaeton', 1931

Christmas. Jersey Parish Churches (First Series)

(Des P. Layton. Litho B.D.T.)

1988 (15 NOV). Perf 13½ (C)

458	**429**	12p multicoloured	30	15
459	**430**	16p multicoloured	45	30
460	**431**	31p multicoloured	90	80
461	**432**	34p multicoloured	85	85
458/61		Set of 4	2·25	1·90
		First Day Cover		2·75
		Presentation Pack	3·75	
		Postcards (set of 4)	2·00	5·50

See also Nos. 535/8 and 597/600.

Plate Nos.: All values 1A, 1B, 1C, 1D (each ×5)

Sheets: 20 (4×5)

Imprint: Central, left-hand margin

Quantities sold: 12p 964,161; 16p 917,883; 31p 170,477; 34p 159,688

Withdrawn: 30.11.89

Post Office Yearbook

1988 (15 NOV). Comprises Nos. 266a/b, 268a and 433/61

Yearbook . . . . 40·00

Withdrawn: 23.10.89

433 Talbot 'Type 4 CT Tourer', 1912

434 De Dion 'Bouton Type 1-D', 1920

Vintage Cars (First Series)

(Des A. Copp. Litho Questa)

1989 (31 JAN). Perf 14 (C)

462	**433**	12p multicoloured	35	30
463	**434**	16p multicoloured	50	45
464	**435**	23p multicoloured	60	55
		a. Black (inscr etc) printed double		
465	**436**	30p multicoloured	80	80
466	**437**	32p multicoloured	1·00	1·00
467	**438**	35p multicoloured	1·00	1·00
462/7		Set of 6	3·75	3·75
		First Day Cover		4·25
		Presentation Pack	4·50	

See also Nos. 591/6 and 905/10.

Plate Nos.: 12p, 30p 1A, 1B (each ×4); 16p, 32p 1C, 1D (each ×4); 23p, 35p 1A, 1B, 1C, 1D (each ×4)

Sheets: 20 (4×5)

Imprint: Central, left-hand margin

Quantities sold: 12p 253,257; 16p 230,695; 23p 228,895; 30p 130,974; 32p 144,798; 35p 148,189

Withdrawn: 31.1.90

439 Belcroute Bay

440 High Street, St. Aubin

441 Royal Jersey Golf Course

442 Portelet Bay

443 Les Charrières D'Anneport

444 St. Helier Marina

445 Sand Yacht
Racing, St.
Ouen's Bay

446 Rozel Harbour

447 St. Aubin's
Harbour

448 Jersey Airport

449 Corbière
Lighthouse

450 Val de la
Mare

451 Elizabeth
Castle

452 Greve de
Lecq

453 Samarès
Manor

454 Bonne Nuit
Harbour

455 Grosnez
Castle

456 Augrès
Manor

457 Central
Market

458 St. Brelade's
Bay

459 St. Ouen's
Manor

460 La Hougue
Bie

461 Mont Orgueil
Castle

462 Royal
Square, St.
Helier

463 Queen Elizabeth II
(from photo by
Karsh)

464 Arms of King George VI

293

Jersey Scenes

(Des G. Drummond (1p to 75p). Photo Courvoisier (£2),
Litho Questa (£4), B.D.T. (others))

1989 (21 MAR)–**95**. Perf 11½×12 (£2), 15×14 (£4) or 13×13½
(others), all comb

468	**439**	1p multicoloured (a)	10	10
469	**440**	2p multicoloured (a)	10	10
470	**441**	4p multicoloured (a)	10	10
		a. Booklet pane of 6 with margins all round (d)	60	
471	**442**	5p multicoloured (a)	10	15
		a. Booklet pane of 6 with margins all round (f)	75	
472	**443**	10p multicoloured (a)	30	30
473	**444**	13p multicoloured (a)	40	45
474	**445**	14p multicoloured (ae)	40	45
		a. Booklet pane of 6 with margins all round (d)	2·00	
		b. Booklet pane of 8 with margins all round (i)	2·75	
475	**446**	15p multicoloured (ae)	45	50
		a. Booklet pane of 6 with margins all round (f)	2·00	
476	**447**	16p multicoloured (ah)	50	55
		a. Booklet pane of 8 with margins all round (i)	3·50	
477	**448**	17p multicoloured (aj)	50	55
478	**449**	18p multicoloured (akm)	55	60
		a. Booklet pane of 6 with margins all round (d)	2·50	
479	**450**	19p multicoloured (ano)	55	60
480	**451**	20p multicoloured (ae)	45	45
		a. Booklet pane of 6 with margins all round (f)	3·00	
481	**452**	21p multicoloured (b)	50	55
482	**453**	22p multicoloured (bh)	45	50
		a. Booklet pane of 8 with margins all round (i)	4·50	
483	**454**	23p multicoloured (bjkmo)	75	55
484	**455**	24p multicoloured (b)	60	60
485	**456**	25p multicoloured (b)	70	75
486	**457**	26p multicoloured (bh)	75	80
487	**458**	27p multicoloured (b)	80	90
488	**459**	30p multicoloured (c)	85	90
489	**460**	40p multicoloured (c)	1·00	1·00
490	**461**	50p multicoloured (c)	1·25	1·40
491	**462**	75p multicoloured (c)	2·00	1·90
491b	**463**	£2 multicoloured (g)	4·00	3·25
491c	**464**	£4 multicoloured (l)	7·00	6·75
468/91c		Set of 26 . . . . 22·00		22·00
		First Day Covers (5)		26·00
		Presentation Packs (5) . . . . 27·00		

For £1 value as No. 491b see No. 389.

Printings: (a) 21.3.89; (b) 16.1.90; (c) 13.3.90; (d) 3.5.90; (e) 13.11.90;
(f) 12.2.91; (g) 19.3.91; (h) 7.1.92; (i) 22.5.92; (j) 11.1.93; (k) 18.2.94;
(l) 24.1.95; (m) 21.3.95; (n) 1.9.95; (o) 12.11.96

Cylinder or Plate Nos.: £2 A1, B1, C1, D1 (each ×6); £4 1A (×5);
others 1A, 1B, 1C, 1D, 1E, 1F (each ×4)

Sheets: £2 20 (4×5); £4 10 (5×2); others 50 (5×10)

Imprint: Left-hand corner, bottom margin (£4) or central, left-hand
margin (others)

Withdrawn: 31.3.99 1p to £2

465 Agile Frog

466 *Heteropterus morpheus* (butterfly)

467 Barn Owl

468 Green Lizard

Endangered Jersey Fauna

(Des W. Oliver. Litho Cartor)

1989 (25 APR). Perf 13½×13 (Nos. 492 and 495), 13×13½ (No. 493) or 13½×14 (No. 494), all comb

492	**465**	13p multicoloured	. . . .	80	85
493	**466**	13p multicoloured	. . . .	80	85
494	**467**	17p multicoloured	. . . .	80	85
495	**468**	17p multicoloured	. . . .	80	85
492/5		*Set of 4*	. . . .	2·75	3·00
		First Day Cover	. . . .		4·00
		Presentation Pack	. . . .	3·75	

Plate Nos.: All designs 1A, 1B, 1C, 1D (each ×5)

Sheets: 20 (4×5) Nos. 492 and 495; (5×4) Nos. 493/4

Imprint: Central, left-hand margin

Quantities sold: 13p (No. 492) 650,061; 13p (No. 493) 589,329; 17p (No. 494) 552,582; 17p (No. 495) 515,262

Withdrawn: 30.4.90

469 Toddlers' Toys

470 Playground Games

JERSEY 23P

471 Party Games

JERSEY 23P

472 Teenage Sports

Europa. Children's Toys and Games

(Des from clay plaques by Clare Luke. Litho Questa)

1989 (25 APR). Perf 14 (C)

496	**469**	17p multicoloured	. . . .	45	45
497	**470**	17p multicoloured	. . . .	45	45
498	**471**	23p multicoloured	. . . .	80	80
499	**472**	23p multicoloured	. . . .	80	80
496/9		*Set of 4*	. . . .	2·25	2·25
		First Day Cover	. . . .		2·50
		Presentation Pack	. . . .	2·75	

Plate Nos.: All designs 1A, 1B, 1C, 1D, 1E, 1F (each ×4)

Sheets: 20 (4×5)

Imprint: Central, left-hand margin

Quantities sold: 17p (No. 496) 473,930; 17p (No. 497) 471,124; 23p (No. 498) 424,212; 23p (No. 499) 424,340

Withdrawn: 30.4.90

473 Queen Elizabeth II and Royal Yacht *Britannia* in Elizabeth Harbour

Royal Visit

(Des A. Copp. Litho Questa)

1989 (24 MAY). Perf 14½ (C)

500	**473**	£1 multicoloured	. . . .	2·50	2·00
		First Day Cover	. . . .		3·00
		Presentation Pack	. . . .	3·00	

No. 500 was retained in use as part of the current definitive series until replaced by No. 634.

Sheets: 20 (4×5)

Imprint: Central, left-hand margin

Withdrawn: 30.6.94

JERSEY 13

JERSEY 17

474 Philippe D'Auvergne presented to Louis XVI, 1786

475 Storming the Bastille, 1789

476 Marie de Bouillon and Revolutionaries, 1790

477 Auvergne's Headquarters at Mont Orgueil, 1795

478 Landing Arms for Chouan Rebels, 1796

479 The Last Chouan Revolt, 1799

Bicentenary of the French Revolution. Philippe D'Auvergne

(Des V. Ambrus. Litho Cartor)

1989 (7 JULY). Perf 13½ (C)

501	**474**	13p multicoloured	40	30
		a. Booklet pane of 4	1·25	
502	**475**	17p multicoloured	50	40
		a. Booklet pane of 4	2·00	
503	**476**	23p multicoloured	60	50
		a. Booklet pane of 4	2·25	
504	**477**	30p multicoloured	95	90
		a. Booklet pane of 4	3·75	
505	**478**	32p multicoloured	1·00	90
		a. Booklet pane of 4	4·00	
506	**479**	35p multicoloured	1·25	1·00
		a. Booklet pane of 4	5·00	
501/6		Set of 6	4·25	3·50
		First Day Cover		4·25
		Presentation Pack	4·50	

Each booklet pane has margins all round and text printed on the binding selvedge.
See also Nos. 539/44.

Plate Nos.: All values 1A, 1B, 1C, 1D (each ×4)

Sheets: 20 (5×4)

Imprint: Central, left-hand margin

Quantities sold: 13p 637,422; 17p 840,904; 23p 408,967; 30p 133,642; 32p 148,474; 35p 151,639

Withdrawn: 31.7.90

480 St. Helier off Elizabeth Castle

481 Caesarea II off Corbière Lighthouse

482 Reindeer in St. Helier Harbour

483 Ibex racing Frederica off Portelet

484 Lynx off Noirmont

Centenary of Great Western Railway Steamer Service to Channel Islands

(Des G. Palmer. Litho Questa)

1989 (5 SEPT). Perf 13½×14 (C)

507	**480**	13p multicoloured	30	30
508	**481**	17p multicoloured	35	35
509	**482**	27p multicoloured	80	75
510	**483**	32p multicoloured	95	95
511	**484**	35p multicoloured	1·10	1·00
507/11		Set of 5	3·25	3·00
		First Day Cover		3·75
		Presentation Pack	4·00	

Plate Nos.: 13p, 27p 1A, 1B (each ×4); 17p, 32p 1C, 1D (each ×4); 35p 1A, 1B, 1C, 1D (each ×4)

Sheets: 20 (4×5)

Imprint: Central, left-hand margin

Quantities sold: 13p 265,382; 17p 294,992; 27p 135,226; 32p 128,966; 35p 134,800

Withdrawn: 28.9.90

JERSEY Gorey Harbour **13P**

485 Gorey Harbour

JERSEY La Corbière **17P**

486 La Corbière

JERSEY Grève de Lecq **23P**

487 Grève de Lecq

JERSEY Bouley Bay **32P**

488 Bouley Bay

JERSEY Mont Orgueil **35P**

JERSEY ●

EUROPA **18P**

490 Head Post
Office, Broad
Street, 1969

JERSEY ●

EUROPA **18P**

491 Postal Headquarters,
Mont Millais, 1990

489 Mont Orgueil

JERSEY — EUROPA **24P**

492 Hue Street Post Office,
1815

JERSEY — EUROPA **24P**

493 Head Post Office,
Halkett Place, 1890

150th Birth Anniversary of Sarah Louisa Kilpack (artist)

(Litho Enschedè)

1989 (24 OCT). Perf 13×12½ (C)

512	**485**	13p multicoloured	25	25
513	**486**	17p multicoloured	30	30
514	**487**	23p multicoloured	80	75
515	**488**	32p multicoloured	85	85
516	**489**	35p multicoloured	90	1·00
512/16		Set of 5	2·75	2·75
		First Day Cover		3·25
		Presentation Pack	4·00	

Plate Nos.: 13p, 17p, 1A, 1B, 1C (each ×5); 23p, 32p, 35p 1A, 1B (each ×5)

Sheets: 20 (4×5)

Imprint: Central, left-hand margin

Quantities sold: 13p 649,308; 17p 571,503; 23p 159,487; 32p 138,562; 35p 137,950

Withdrawn: 31.10.90

Post Office Yearbook

1989 (24 OCT). *Comprises Nos. 462/80 and 492/516*
Yearbook . . . . 35·00

Sold out: 12.11.90

Europa. Post Office Buildings

(Des P. Layton. Litho Cartor)

1990 (13 MAR). Perf 13½×14 (vert) or 14×13½ (horiz), both comb

517	**490**	18p multicoloured	50	40
518	**491**	18p multicoloured	50	50
519	**492**	24p multicoloured	65	65
520	**493**	24p multicoloured	65	65
517/20		Set of 4	2·10	2·00
		First Day Cover		2·50
		Presentation Pack	2·50	

Plate Nos.: All designs 1A, 1B, 1C, 1D (each ×5)

Sheets: 20 (5×4) 18p; (4×5) 24p

Imprint: Central, left-hand margin

Quantities sold: 18p (No. 517) 596,221; 18p (No. 518) 595,918; 24p (No. 519) 400,441; 24p (No. 520) 406,656

Withdrawn: 31.3.91

494 'Battle of Flowers'
Parade

495 Sports

496 Mont Orgueil Castle and German Underground Hospital Museum

497 Salon Culinaire

500 Radio Jersey Broadcaster

501 Channel Television Studio Cameraman

Festival of Tourism

(Des A. Copp. Litho Enschedè)

1990 (3 MAY). Perf 14×13½ (C)

521	**494**	18p multicoloured	....	55	55
522	**495**	24p multicoloured	....	70	70
523	**496**	29p multicoloured	....	85	85
524	**497**	32p multicoloured	....	90	90
521/4		Set of 4	....	2·75	2·75
		First Day Cover	....		3·25
		Presentation Pack	....	4·00	
MS525	151×100 mm. Nos. 521/4	....		2·75	3·00
		First Day Cover	....		4·50
		Presentation Pack	....	4·50	

Plate Nos.: 18p 1A, 1B, 1C, 1D, 1E (each ×5); 24p 1A, 1B, 1C, 1D (each ×5); 29p 1A (×5); 32p 1A, 1B (each ×5)

Sheets: 20 (5×4)

Imprint: Central, left-hand margin

Quantities sold: 18p 630,610; 24p 252,670; 29p 168,528; 32p 127,334; miniature sheet 110,177

Withdrawn: 31.5.91

International Literacy Year. Jersey News Media

(Des A. Copp. Litho Cartor)

1990 (26 JUNE). Perf 13½ (C)

526	**498**	14p multicoloured	....	45	45
527	**499**	18p multicoloured	....	45	45
528	**500**	34p multicoloured	....	90	90
529	**501**	37p multicoloured	....	95	95
526/9		Set of 4	....	2·50	2·50
		First Day Cover	....		2·75
		Presentation Pack	....	3·50	

Plate Nos.: All values 1A, 1B, 1C, 1D (each ×4)

Sheets: 20 (4×5)

Imprint: Central, left-hand margin

Quantities sold: 14p 926,906; 18p 795,733; 34p 121,842; 37p 129,468

Withdrawn: 30.6.91

498 Early Printing Press and Jersey Newspaper Mastheads

499 Modern Press, and Offices of *Jersey Evening Post* in 1890 and 1990

502 British Aerospace Hawk T.1

503 Supermarine Spitfire

504 Hawker Hurricane MK I

505 Vickers-Armstrong Wellington

37P 50th Anniversary Battle of Britain **506** Avro Type 683 Lancaster

50th Anniversary of Battle of Britain

(Des G. Palmer. Litho Questa)

1990 (4 SEPT). Perf 14 (C)

530	**502**	14p multicoloured	....	40	45
531	**503**	18p multicoloured	....	55	60
532	**504**	24p multicoloured	....	85	85
533	**505**	34p multicoloured	....	1·50	1·60
534	**506**	37p multicoloured	....	1·60	1·60
530/4		Set of 5	....	4·50	4·50
		First Day Cover	....		5·25
		Presentation Pack	....	5·25	

Plate Nos.: 14p, 34p 1A, 1B (each ×5); 18p, 37p 1C, 1D (each ×5); 24p 1A, 1B, 1C, 1D (each ×5)

Sheets: 20 (4×5)

Imprint: Central, left-hand margin

Quantities sold: 14p 495,815; 18p 519,684; 24p 206,541; 34p 136,330; 37p 134,747

Withdrawn: 30.9.91

507 St. Helier

508 Grouville

509 St. Saviour

510 St. John

Christmas. Jersey Parish Churches (Second Series)

(Des P. Layton. Litho B.D.T.)

1990 (13 NOV). Perf 13½ (C)

535	**507**	14p multicoloured	....	45	40
536	**508**	18p multicoloured	....	45	40

537	**509**	34p multicoloured	....	1·00	1·10
538	**510**	37p multicoloured	....	1·25	1·40
535/8		Set of 4	....	3·00	3·00
		First Day Cover			3·50
		Presentation Pack	....	4·00	
		Postcards (set of 4)	....	2·25	5·00

Plate Nos.: All values 1A, 1B, 1C, 1D (each ×5)

Sheets: 20 (4×5)

Imprint: Central, left-hand margin

Quantities sold: 14p 948,076; 18p 690,282; 34p 141,514; 37p 147,768

Withdrawn: 30.11.91

Post Office Yearbook

1990 (13 NOV). Comprises Nos. 481/91 and 517/38

Yearbook .... 37·00

Withdrawn: 30.11.91

511 Prince's Tower, La Hougue Bie

512 Auvergne's Arrest in Paris

513 Auvergne plotting against Napoleon

514 Execution of George Cadoudal

515 H.M.S. *Surly* (cutter) attacking French Convoy

516 Auvergne's Last Days in London

175th Death Anniversary of Philippe d'Auvergne

(Des V. Ambrus. Litho Cartor)

1991 (22 JAN). Perf 13½ (C)

539	**511**	15p multicoloured	....	45	40
540	**512**	20p multicoloured	....	55	55
541	**513**	26p multicoloured	....	70	75

542	**514**	31p multicoloured	. . . .	90	90
543	**515**	37p multicoloured	. . . .	1·10	1·10
544	**516**	44p multicoloured	. . . .	1·25	1·25
539/44		Set of 6	. . . .	4·50	4·50
		First Day Cover	. . . .		4·75
		Presentation Pack	. . . .	5·00	

Plate Nos.: All values 1A, 1B, 1C, 1D (each ×4)

Sheets: 20 (4×5)

Imprint: Central, left-hand margin

Quantities sold: 15p 709,403; 20p 454,921; 26p 159,902; 31p 140,379; 37p 341,103; 44p 153,157

Withdrawn: 31.1.92

517 'Landsat 5' and Thematic Mapper Image over Jersey

518 'ERS-1' Earth Resources Remote Sensing Satellite

519 'Meteosat' Weather Satellite

520 'Olympus Direct Broadcasting Satellite

Europa. Europe in Space

(Des A. Copp. Litho Enschedé)

1991 (19 MAR). Perf 14½×13 (C)

545	**517**	20p multicoloured	. . . .	50	50
546	**518**	20p multicoloured	. . . .	50	50
547	**519**	26p multicoloured	. . . .	80	85
548	**520**	26p multicoloured	. . . .	80	85
545/8		Set of 4	. . . .	2·40	2·40
		First Day Cover	. . . .		2·75
		Presentation Pack	. . . .	3·00	

Plate Nos.: All designs 1A, 1B, 1C (each ×5)

Sheets: 20 (5×4)

Imprint: Central, left-hand margin

Quantities sold: 20p (No. 545) 682,799; 20p (No. 546) 690,871; 26p (No. 547) 442,476; 26p (No. 548) 439,415

Withdrawn: 31.3.92

521 1941 1d. Stamp (50th anniv of first Jersey postage stamp)

522 Steam Train (centenary of Jersey Eastern Railway extension to Gorey Pier)

523 Jersey Cow and Herd Book (125th anniv of Jersey Herd Book)

524 Stone-laying Ceremony (painting by P. Ouless) (150th anniv of Victoria Harbour)

525 Marie Bartlett and Hospital (250th anniversary of Marie Bartlett's hospital bequest)

Anniversaries

(Des A. Copp. Litho Cartor)

1991 (16 MAY). Perf 13½ (C)

549	**521**	15p multicoloured	. . . .	30	30
550	**522**	20p multicoloured	. . . .	50	55
551	**523**	26p multicoloured	. . . .	60	70
552	**524**	31p multicoloured	. . . .	75	80
553	**525**	53p multicoloured	. . . .	1·75	1·75
549/53		Set of 5	. . . .	3·50	3·75
		First Day Cover	. . . .		4·25
		Presentation Pack	. . . .	4·50	

Plate Nos.: All values 1A, 1B, 1C, 1D (each ×4)

Sheets: 20 (5×4)

Imprint: Central, left-hand margin

Quantities sold: 15p 618,479; 20p 608,585; 26p 245,772; 31p 133,604; 53p 135,394

Withdrawn: 30.5.92

526 *Melitaea cinxia*

527 *Euplagia quadripunctaria*

528 *Deilephila porcellus*

529 *Inachis io*

Butterflies and Moths

(Des W. Oliver. Litho Enschedé)

1991 (9 JULY). Perf 13×12½ (C)

554	**526**	15p multicoloured	35	35
555	**527**	20p multicoloured	45	30
556	**528**	37p multicoloured	1·40	1·50
557	**529**	57p multicoloured	1·75	1·90
554/7		*Set of 4*	3·50	3·75
		First Day Cover		4·50
		Presentation Pack	4·50	

Plate Nos.: All values 1A, 1B, 1C (each ×4)

Sheets: 20 (4×5)

Imprint: Central, left-hand margin

Quantities sold: 15p 489,632; 20p 646,607; 37p 130,494; 57p 142,646

Withdrawn: 31.7.92

530 Drilling for Water, Ethiopia

531 Building Construction, Rwanda

532 Village Polytechnic, Kenya

533 Treating Leprosy, Tanzania

534 Ploughing, Zambia

535 Immunisation Clinic, Lesotho

Overseas Aid

(Des A. Theobald. Litho B.D.T.)

1991 (3 SEPT). Perf 13½×14 (C)

558	**530**	15p multicoloured	45	40
559	**531**	20p multicoloured	50	45
560	**532**	26p multicoloured	70	70
561	**533**	31p multicoloured	85	90
562	**534**	37p multicoloured	1·10	1·10
563	**535**	44p multicoloured	1·25	1·40
558/63		*Set of 6*	4·50	4·50
		First Day Cover		5·00
		Presentation Pack	5·00	

Plate Nos.: All values 1A, 1B (each ×4)

Sheets: 20 (4×5)

Imprint: Central, left-hand margin

Quantities sold: 15p 517,917; 20p 644,721; 26p 177,179; 31p 115,769; 37p 111,112; 44p 142,024

Withdrawn: 30.9.92

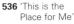

536 'This is the Place for Me'

537 'The Island Come True'

538 'The Never Bird'

539 'The Great White Father'

543 Northern Lapwing

544 Fieldfare

Christmas. Illustrations by Edmund Blampied for J. M. Barrie's 'Peter Pan'

(Litho Questa)

1991 (5 NOV). Perf 14 (C)

564	**536**	15p multicoloured	40	40
565	**537**	20p multicoloured	65	65
566	**538**	37p multicoloured	1·25	1·25
567	**539**	53p multicoloured	1·60	1·60
564/7		Set of 4	3·50	3·50
		First Day Cover		3·75
		Presentation Pack	4·25	

Sheets: 20 (5×4)

Imprint: Central, left-hand margin

Quantities sold: 15p 917,860; 20p 693,203; 37p 128,585; 53p 117,877

Withdrawn: 30.11.92

Post Office Yearbook

1991 (5 NOV). *Comprises Nos. 491b and 539/67*
Yearbook .... 32·00

Sold out: By 9.93

540 Pied Wagtail

541 Firecrest

542 Common Snipe

Winter Birds

(Des W. Oliver. Litho Cartor)

1992 (7 JAN). Perf 13½×14 (C)

568	**540**	16p multicoloured	50	25
569	**541**	22p multicoloured	70	55
570	**542**	28p multicoloured	80	85
571	**543**	39p multicoloured	1·25	1·25
572	**544**	57p multicoloured	1·75	1·75
568/72		Set of 5	4·50	4·25
		First Day Cover		4·75
		Presentation Pack	5·00	

See also Nos. 635/9.

Plate Nos.: All values 1A, 1B, 1C, 1D (each ×4)

Sheets: 20 (5×4)

Imprint: Central, left-hand margin

Quantities sold: 16p 481,678; 22p 462,647; 28p 268,973; 39p 151,671; 57p 132,065

Withdrawn: 30.1.93

545 Shipping at Shanghai, 1860

546 Mesny's Junk running Taiping Blockade, 1862

547 General Mesny outside River Gate, 1874

548 Mesny in Burma, 1877

301

549 Mesny and Governor Chang, 1882

550 Mesny in Mandarin's Sedan Chair, 1886

Jersey Adventures (Third Series). 150th Birth Anniversary of William Mesny

(Des V. Ambrus. Litho Cartor)

1992 (25 FEB). Perf 13½ (C)

573	**545**	16p multicoloured	40	45
		a. Black printed double		
		b. Booklet pane of 4	1·50	
574	**546**	16p multicoloured	40	45
		a. Booklet pane of 4	1·50	
575	**547**	22p multicoloured	65	65
		a. Booklet pane of 4	2·00	
576	**548**	22p multicoloured	65	65
		a. Booklet pane of 4	2·00	
577	**549**	33p multicoloured	90	95
		a. Booklet pane of 4	3·00	
578	**550**	33p multicoloured	90	95
		a. Booklet pane of 4	3·00	
573/8		Set of 6	3·50	3·75
		First Day Cover		4·25
		Presentation Pack	4·50	

Each booklet pane has margins all round and text printed on the binding selvedge.

Plate Nos.: All values 1A, 1B, 1C, 1D (each ×4)

Sheets: 20 (4×5)

Imprint: Central, left-hand margin

Quantities sold: 16p (No. 573) 346,732; 16p (No. 574) 336,655; 22p (No. 575) 377,299; 22p (No. 576) 360,220; 33p (No. 577) 129,904; 33p (No. 578) 130,637

Withdrawn: 27.2.93 (sheets)

551 Tickler (brigantine)

552 Hebe (brig)

553 Gemini (barque)

554 Percy Douglas (full-rigged ship)

Jersey Shipbuilding

(Des A. Copp. Litho Questa)

1992 (14 APR). Perf 14 (C)

579	**551**	16p multicoloured	45	40
580	**552**	22p multicoloured	70	75
581	**553**	50p multicoloured	1·40	1·50
582	**554**	57p multicoloured	1·60	1·75
579/82		Set of 4	3·75	4·00
		First Day Cover		4·50
		Presentation Pack	4·50	
MS583		148×98 mm. Nos. 579/82	4·00	4·25
		First Day Cover		4·50
		Presentation Pack	4·50	

Plate Nos.: 16p 1A, 1B, 1C, 1D, 1E, 1F (each ×4); 22p, 57p 1A, 1B, 1C, 1D (each ×4); 50p 1A, 1B (each ×4)

Sheets: 20 (5×4)

Imprint: Central, left-hand margin

Quantities sold: 16p 673,830; 22p 462,972; 50p 138,158; 57p 111,044; miniature sheet 126,594

Withdrawn: 30.4.93

555 John Bertram (ship owner) and Columbus

556 Sir George Carteret (founder of New Jersey)

557 Sir Walter Ralegh (founder of Virginia)

Europa. 500th Anniversary of Discovery of America by Columbus

(Des V. Ambrus. Litho Questa)

1992 (14 APR). Perf 14×14½ (C)

584	**555**	22p multicoloured	65	50
585	**556**	28p multicoloured	75	80
586	**557**	39p multicoloured	1·10	1·40
584/6		Set of 3	2·25	2·40
		First Day Cover		3·00
		Presentation Pack	3·25	

Plate Nos.: 22p 1A, 1B (each ×5); 28p 1A, 1B, 1C, 1D (each ×5); 39p 1C, 1D (each ×5)

Sheets: 20 (4×5)

Imprint: Central, left-hand margin

Quantities sold: 22p 459,817; 28p 664,537; 39p 298,597

Withdrawn: 30.4.93

558 'Snow Leopards' (Allison Griffiths)

559 'Three Elements' (Nataly Miorin)

560 'Three Men in a Tub' (Amanda Crocker)

561 'Cockatoos' (Michelle Millard)

Batik Designs

(Litho Questa)

1992 (23 JUNE). Perf 14½ (C)

587	**558**	16p multicoloured	....	45	40
588	**559**	22p multicoloured	....	65	45
589	**560**	39p multicoloured	....	1·10	1·25
590	**561**	57p multicoloured	....	1·50	1·75
587/90		Set of 4	....	3·25	3·50
		First Day Cover	....		4·00
		Presentation Pack	....	4·25	

Plate Nos.: 16p, 39p 1A, 1B (each ×4); 22p, 57p 1C, 1D (each ×4)

Sheets: 20 (5×4)

Imprint: Central, left-hand margin

Quantities sold: 16p 427,970; 22p 472,443; 39p 112,188; 57p 113,465

Withdrawn: 30.6.93

562 Morris Cowley 'Bullnose', 1925

563 Rolls Royce 20/25, 1932

564 Chenard and Walcker T5, 1924

565 Packard 900 series Light Eight, 1932

566 Lanchester 21, 1927

567 Buick 30 Roadster, 1913

Vintage Cars (Second Series)

(Des A. Copp. Litho Enschedé)

1992 (8 SEPT). Perf 13×12½ (C)

591	**562**	16p multicoloured	....	30	30
592	**563**	22p multicoloured	....	45	45
593	**564**	28p multicoloured	....	70	75
594	**565**	33p multicoloured	....	90	95
595	**566**	39p multicoloured	....	1·00	1·10
596	**567**	50p multicoloured	....	1·50	1·75
591/6		Set of 6	....	4·50	4·75
		First Day Cover	....		5·00
		Presentation Pack	....	5·25	

Plate Nos.: All values 1A, 1B (each ×4)

Sheets: 20 (4×5)

Imprint: Central, left-hand margin

Quantities sold: 16p 434,984; 22p 426,734; 28p 290,202; 33p 134,477; 39p 124,759; 50p 127,917

Withdrawn: 30.9.93

568 Trinity

569 St. Mary

570 St. Martin   **571** St. Peter

Christmas. Jersey Parish Churches (Third Series)

(Des P. Layton. Litho B.D.T.)

1992 (3 NOV). Perf 13½ (C)

597	**568**	16p multicoloured	40	30
598	**569**	22p multicoloured	55	50
599	**570**	39p multicoloured	1·10	1·00
600	**571**	57p multicoloured	1·50	1·40
597/600		Set of 4	3·25	3·00
		First Day Cover		3·75
		Presentation Pack	4·00	
		Postcards (set of 4)	2·00	5·00

Plate Nos.: All values 1A, 1B, 1C, 1D (each ×5)

Sheets: 20 (4×5)

Imprint: Central, left-hand margin

Quantities sold: 16p 894,098; 22p 729,413; 39p 93,764; 57p 95,936

Withdrawn: 30.11.93

Post Office Yearbook

1992 (3 NOV). Comprises Nos. 568/600
Yearbook .... 30·00

Sold out: By 10.95

572 Farmhouse   **573** Trinity Church   **574** Daffodils and Cows

575 Jersey Cows   **576** Sunbathing   **577** Windsurfing

578 Crab (Queen's head at left)   **579** Crab (Queen's head at right)   **580** 'Singin' in the Rain' Float

581 'Dragon Dance' Float   **582** 'Bali, Morning of the World' Float   **583** 'Zulu Fantasy' Float

Booklet Stamps

(Des A. Copp. Litho B.D.T.)

1993 (11 JAN). Perf 13 (C)

601	**572**	(–) multicoloured	60	70
		a. Booklet pane. Nos. 601/4, each ×2, with margins all round	5·00	
602	**573**	(–) multicoloured	60	70
603	**574**	(–) multicoloured	60	70
604	**575**	(–) multicoloured	60	70
605	**576**	(–) multicoloured	70	60
		a. Booklet pane. Nos. 605/8, each ×2, with margins all round	5·50	
606	**577**	(–) multicoloured	70	60
607	**578**	(–) multicoloured	70	60
608	**579**	(–) multicoloured	70	60
609	**580**	(–) multicoloured	85	80
		a. Booklet pane. Nos. 609/12, each ×2, with margins all round	7·00	
610	**581**	(–) multicoloured	85	80
611	**582**	(–) multicoloured	85	80
612	**583**	(–) multicoloured	85	80
601/12		Set of 12	7·75	7·50
		First Day Cover		16·00
		Presentation Pack	10·00	

The above do not show face values, but are inscribed 'BAILIWICK POSTAGE PAID' (Nos. 601/4), 'U.K. MINIMUM POSTAGE PAID' (Nos. 605/8) or 'EUROPE POSTAGE PAID' (Nos. 609/12). They were initially sold at 17p, 23p or 28p, but Nos. 601/4 and 609/12 were increased to 18p and 30p on 10 January 1994 and Nos. 601/4 to 19p on 4 July 1995. On 10 March 1997 Nos. 601/4 were increased to 20p, Nos. 605/8 to 24p and Nos. 609/12 to 31p.

Withdrawn: 30.9.99

584 Phragmipedium Eric Young 'Jersey'   **585** Odontoglossum Augres 'Trinity'

586 *Miltonia* St. Helier 'Colomberie'

587 *Phragmipedium pearcei*

588 *Calanthe* Grouville 'Gorey'

Jersey Orchids (Third Series)

(Litho Enschedé)

1993 (26 JAN). Perf 14×13 (C)

613	**584**	17p multicoloured	45	35
		a. Black printed double		
614	**585**	23p multicoloured	70	65
		a. Black printed double		
615	**586**	28p multicoloured	80	75
		a. Black printed double		
616	**587**	39p multicoloured	1·25	1·40
617	**588**	57p multicoloured	1·75	1·90
		a. Black printed double		
613/17		Set of 5	4·50	4·50
		First Day Cover		5·00
		Presentation Pack	4·75	

Plate Nos.: 17p, 23p 1A, 1B, 1C (each ×5); 28p, 39p, 57p 1A, 1B (each ×5)

Sheets: 20 (5×4)

Imprint: Central, left-hand margin

Quantities sold: 17p 391,802; 23p 391,444; 28p, 188,149; 39p 141,610; 57p 141,463

Withdrawn: 31.1.94

589 Douglas DC-3 Dakota

590 Wight Seaplane

591 Avro Shackleton A.E.W.2

592 Gloster Meteor Mk III and De Havilland D.H.100 Vampire FB.5

593 Hawker Siddeley Harrier GR.1A

594 Panavia Tornado F Mk 3

75th Anniversary of Royal Air Force

(Des A. Theobald. Litho Questa)

1993 (1 APR). Perf 14 (C)

618	**589**	17p multicoloured	45	30
619	**590**	23p multicoloured	60	65
620	**591**	28p multicoloured	70	70
621	**592**	33p multicoloured	80	85
622	**593**	39p multicoloured	1·00	1·10
623	**594**	57p multicoloured	1·50	1·60
618/23		Set of 6	4·50	4·75
		First Day Cover		6·00
		Presentation Pack	5·25	
MS624		147×98 mm. Nos. 619 and 623	4·50	4·75
		First Day Cover		6·00
		Presentation Pack	5·25	

Nos. 618/24 also commemorate the 50th anniversary of the Royal Air Force Association and the 40th anniversary of the first air display on Jersey.

Plate Nos.: 17p, 23p 1A, 1B, 1C, 1D (each ×4); 28p, 33p, 39p, 57p 1A, 1B (each ×4)

Sheets: 20 (5×4)

Imprint: Central, left-hand margin

Quantities sold: 17p, 578,871; 23p 581,661; 28p 184,066; 33p 140,430; 39p 144,522; 57p 159,447; miniature sheet 113,236

Withdrawn: 30.4.94

595 'Jersey's Opera House' (Ian Rolls)

596 'The Ham and Tomato Bap' (Jonathan Hubbard)

597 'Vase of Flowers' (Neil Mackenzie)

Europa. Contemporary Art

(Litho Cartor)

1993 (1 APR). Perf 13½×14 (C)

625	**595**	23p multicoloured	60	60
626	**596**	28p multicoloured	70	70
627	**597**	39p multicoloured	1·10	1·10
625/7		Set of 3	2·25	2·25
		First Day Cover		2·75
		Presentation Pack	2·75	

Plate Nos.: All values 1A, 1B, 1C, 1D (each ×4)

Sheets: 20 (5×4)

Imprint: Central, left-hand margin

Quantities sold: 23p 422,536; 28p 340,206; 39p 230,510

Withdrawn: 30.4.94

598 1943 Occupation ½d Stamp

599 1943 1d Stamp

600 1943 1½d Stamp

601 1943 2d Stamp

602 1943 2½d Stamp

603 1943 3d Stamp

50th Anniversary of Edmund Blampied's Occupation Stamps

(Des G. Drummond. Litho Cartor)

1993 (2 JUNE). Perf 13½ (C)

628	**598**	17p myrtle-green, pale grn & blk	35	35
629	**599**	23p vermilion, salmon-pink & blk	50	50
630	**600**	28p chocolate, cinnamon & black	70	70
631	**601**	33p reddish orge, salmon & blk .	85	85
632	**602**	39p royal blue, cobalt and black .	1·25	1·25
633	**603**	50p bright magenta, pale mauve and black	1·40	1·40
628/33		Set of 6	4·50	4·50
		First Day Cover		4·75
		Presentation Pack	5·25	

Plate Nos.: All values 1A, 1B, 1C, 1D (each ×3)

Sheets: 20 (4×5)

Imprint: Central, left-hand margin

Quantities sold: 17p 549,708; 23p 565,711; 28p 174,159; 33p 120,570; 39p 93,502; 50p 99,135

Withdrawn: 30.6.94

604 Queen Elizabeth II (from painting by Marca McGregor)

40th Anniversary of Coronation

(Litho Questa)

1993 (2 JUNE). Perf 14½ (C)

634	**604**	£1 multicoloured (*ab*)	2·75	2·75
		First Day Cover		3·00
		Presentation Pack	3·50	

No. 634 was retained in use as part of the current definitive series until replaced by No. 804.

Printings: (*a*) 2.6.93; (*b*) 1.9.95

Plate Nos.: 1A, 1B, 1C, 1D (each ×4)

Sheets: 20 (5×4)

Imprint: Central, left-hand margin

Withdrawn: 31.3.99

605 Short-toed Treecreeper

606 Dartford Warbler

607 Northern Wheatear

608 Cirl Bunting

609 Jay

Summer Birds

(Des W. Oliver. Litho Cartor)

1993 (7 SEPT). Perf 13½×14 (C)

635	**605**	17p multicoloured	45	50
636	**606**	23p multicoloured	70	75
637	**607**	28p multicoloured	80	85
638	**608**	39p multicoloured	1·25	1·25
639	**609**	57p multicoloured	1·75	1·75
635/9		*Set of 5*	4·50	4·50
		First Day Cover		4·75
		Presentation Pack	5·00	

Plate Nos.: All values 1A, 1B, 1C, 1D (each ×4)

Sheets: 20 (5×4)

Imprint: Central, left-hand margin

Quantities sold: 17p 495,975; 23p 496,942; 28p 170,135; 39p 139,630; 57p 138,994

Withdrawn: 30.9.94

610 Two Angels holding 'Hark the Herald Angels Sing' Banner

611 Two Angels playing Harps

612 Two Angels playing Violins

613 Two Angels holding 'Once in Royal David's City' Banner

Christmas. Stained Glass Windows by Henry Bosdet from St. Aubin on the Hill Church

(Des N. Mackenzie. Litho Enschedé)

1993 (2 NOV). Perf 14×13 (C)

640	**610**	17p multicoloured	40	35
641	**611**	23p multicoloured	60	60
642	**612**	39p multicoloured	1·10	1·25
643	**613**	57p multicoloured	1·75	1·90
640/3		*Set of 4*	3·50	3·75
		First Day Cover		4·00
		Presentation Pack	4·25	

Plate Nos.: All values 1A, 1B, 1C (each ×4)

Sheets: 20 (5×4)

Imprint: Central, left-hand margin

Quantities sold: 17p 877,806; 23p 744,661; 39p 110,131; 57p 108,703

Withdrawn: 30.11.94

Post Office Yearbook

1993 (2 NOV). *Comprises Nos. 601/43*

	Yearbook	32·00

Sold out: By 9.97

614 *Coprinus comatus*

615 *Amanita muscaria*

616 *Cantharellus cibarius*

617 *Macrolepiota procera*

618 *Clathrus ruber*

Fungi

(Des W. Oliver. Litho Questa)

1994 (11 JAN). Perf 14½ (C)

644	**614**	18p multicoloured	45	40
645	**615**	23p multicoloured	65	70
646	**616**	30p multicoloured	80	85
647	**617**	41p multicoloured	1·25	1·25
648	**618**	60p multicoloured	1·60	1·60
644/8		Set of 5	4·25	4·25
		First Day Cover		4·50
		Presentation Pack	4·75	

Plate Nos.: 18p 1A (×4); 23p 1B (×4); 30p 1C (×4); 41p 1D (×4); 60p 1E (×4)

Sheets: 20 (5×4)

Imprint: Central, left-hand margin

Quantities sold: 18p 735,158; 23p 482,461; 30p 188,095; 41p 184,418; 60p 137,309

Withdrawn: 30.1.95

619a Pekingese (*illustration reduced. Actual size* 110×75 *mm*)

'Hong Kong '94' International Stamp Exhibition. 'Chinese Year of the Dog'

(Des P. Layton, adapted A. Copp. Litho Questa)

1994 (18 FEB). Sheet 110×75 mm. Perf 15×14½ (C)

MS649	**619a**	£1 multicoloured	2·50	2·75
		First Day Cover		3·00
		Presentation Pack	3·50	

Quantity sold: 120,029

Withdrawn: 28.2.95

620 Maine Coon

621 British Shorthair

622 Persian

623 Siamese

624 Non-pedigree

308

21st Anniversary of Jersey Cat Club

(Des P. Layton. Litho B.D.T.)

1994 (5 APR). Perf 14 (C)

650	**620**	18p multicoloured	40	30
651	**621**	23p multicoloured	60	50
652	**622**	35p multicoloured	80	80
653	**623**	41p multicoloured	1·10	1·25
654	**624**	60p multicoloured	1·60	1·75
650/4		Set of 5	4·00	4·25
		First Day Cover		4·50
		Presentation Pack	4·50	

Plate Nos.: 35p 1A, 1B, 1C, 1D (each ×4); others 1A, 1B (each ×4)

Sheets: 20 (5×4) 18p, 35p, 60p; (4×5) 23p, 41p

Imprint: Central, left-hand margin

Quantities sold: 18p 491,500; 23p 490,820; 35p 221,769; 41p 185,206; 60p 132,276

Withdrawn: 29.4.95

625 Mammoth Hunt, La Cotte de St. Brelade

626 Stone Age Hunters pulling Mammoth into Cave

627 Chambered Passage, La Hougue Bie

628 Transporting Stones

Europa. Archaeological Discoveries

(Des A. Copp. Litho Enschedé)

1994 (5 APR). Perf 13½×14 (C)

655	**625**	23p multicoloured	50	55
		a. Horiz pair. Nos. 655/6	1·00	1·10
656	**626**	23p multicoloured	50	55
657	**627**	30p multicoloured	75	85
		a. Horiz pair. Nos. 657/8	1·50	1·75
658	**628**	30p multicoloured	75	85
655/8		Set of 4	2·25	2·50
		First Day Cover		3·00
		Presentation Pack	3·00	

Plate Nos.: Both values 1A, 1B (each ×4)

Sheets: 20 (4×5) the two horizontal designs for each value printed together, se-tenant, in horizontal pairs throughout the sheets

Imprint: Central, left-hand margin

Quantities sold: No. 655, 371,149; No. 656, 373,190; No. 657, 273,889; No. 658, 275,833

Withdrawn: 29.4.95

629 Gliders and Towing Aircraft approaching France

630 Landing Craft approaching Beaches

631 Disembarking from Landing Craft on Gold Beach

632 British Troops on Sword Beach

633 Spitfires over Beaches

634 Invasion Map

50th Anniversary of D-Day

(Des A. Theobald. Litho B.D.T.)

1994 (6 JUNE). Perf 13½×14 (C)

659	**629**	18p multicoloured	55	50
		a. Booklet pane. Nos. 659/60, each ×3, with margins all round	3·00	
		b. Booklet pane. Nos. 659/64, with margins all round	4·50	
660	**630**	18p multicoloured	55	50
661	**631**	23p multicoloured	75	70
		a. Booklet pane. Nos. 661/2, each ×3, with margins all round	5·00	
662	**632**	23p multicoloured	75	70

663	**633**	30p multicoloured	80	75
		a. Booklet pane. Nos. 663/4, each ×3, with margins all round	6·00	
664	**634**	30p multicoloured	80	75
659/64		Set of 6	3·75	3·50
		First Day Cover		4·25
		Presentation Pack	4·50	

No. 659b was also available as a loose pane from the Philatelic Bureau.

Plate Nos.: All values 1A, 1B (each ×4)

Sheets: 20 (4×5)

Imprint: Central, left-hand margin

Quantities sold: No. 659, 361,667; No. 660, 365,169; No. 661, 377,546; No. 662, 367,033; No. 663, 229,455; No. 664, 226,520

Withdrawn: 30.6.95

635 Sailing

636 Rifle Shooting

637 Hurdling

638 Swimming

639 Hockey

Centenary of International Olympic Committee

(Des A. Theobald. Litho Questa)

1994 (6 JUNE). Perf 14 (C)

665	**635**	18p multicoloured	40	35
666	**636**	23p multicoloured	55	55
667	**637**	30p multicoloured	75	75
668	**638**	41p multicoloured	1·10	1·10
669	**639**	60p multicoloured	1·50	1·60
665/9		Set of 5	4·00	4·00
		First Day Cover		4·50
		Presentation Pack	4·50	

Plate Nos.: All values 1A (×4)

Sheets: 20 (5×4)

Imprint: Central, left-hand margin

Quantities sold: 18p 279,183; 23p 270,430; 30p 178,234; 41p 183,875; 60p 133,357

Withdrawn: 30.6.95

640 Strawberry Anemone

641 Hermit Crab and Parasitic Anemone

642 Velvet Swimming Crab

643 Common Jellyfish

Marine Life

(Des W. Oliver. Litho Cartor)

1994 (2 AUG). Perf 13½ (C)

670	**640**	18p multicoloured	40	45
671	**641**	23p multicoloured	60	65
672	**642**	41p multicoloured	1·25	1·40
673	**643**	60p multicoloured	1·60	1·60
670/3		Set of 4	3·50	3·75
		First Day Cover		4·25
		Presentation Pack	4·50	

Plate Nos.: All values 1A, 1B, 1C, 1D (each ×4)

Sheets: 20 (4×5)

Imprint: Central, left-hand margin

Quantities sold: 18p 465,890; 23p 453,750; 41p 171,459; 60p 175,656

Withdrawn: 31.8.95

644 Condor 10 (catamaran)

645 Map of Jersey and Pillar Box

646 Vicker's Type 953 Vanguard of B.E.A.

647 Shorts 360 of Aurigny Air Services

648 *Caesarea* (Sealink ferry)

651 'While Shepherds watched'

652 'We Three Kings of Orient Are'

Christmas. Carols

(Des A. Copp. Litho Questa)

1994 (8 NOV). Perf 14 (C)

680	**649**	18p multicoloured	40	40
681	**650**	23p multicoloured	50	50
682	**651**	41p multicoloured	1·25	1·25
683	**652**	60p multicoloured	1·50	1·50
680/3		*Set of 4*	3·25	3·25
		First Day Cover		4·25
		Presentation Pack	4·25	

Plate Nos.: All values 1A, 1B (each ×4)

Sheets: 20 (5×4)

Imprint: Central, left-hand margin

Quantities sold: 18p 981,010; 23p 883,715; 41p 174,413; 60p 179,888

Withdrawn: 30.11.95

Post Office Yearbook

1994 (8 NOV). *Comprises Nos.* **MS**248 *and* 644/83

Yearbook . . . . 32·00

Sold out: By 2.2000

653 Dog and 'GOOD LUCK'

654 Rose and 'WITH LOVE'

655 Chick and 'CONGRAT-ULATIONS'

656 Bouquet of Flowers and 'THANK YOU'

657 Dove with Letter and 'WITH LOVE'

658 Cat with 'GOOD LUCK'

25th Anniversary of Jersey Postal Administration

(Des A. Copp. Litho Questa)

1994 (1 OCT). Perf 14 (C)

674	**644**	18p multicoloured	50	45
675	**645**	23p multicoloured	60	50
676	**646**	35p multicoloured	85	85
677	**647**	41p multicoloured	1·10	1·00
678	**648**	60p multicoloured	1·60	1·50
674/8		*Set of 5*	4·25	3·75
		First Day Cover		4·50
		Presentation Pack	5·00	
MS679		150×100 mm. Nos. 674/8	4·50	4·50
		First Day Cover		5·25
		Presentation Pack	4·75	

Plate Nos.: All values 1A (×5)

Sheets: 20 (5×4)

Imprint: Central, left-hand margin

Quantities sold: 18p 473,837; 23p 472,468; 35p 184,871; 41p 186,653; 60p 182,108; miniature sheet 76,623

Withdrawn: 31.10.95

649 'Away in a Manger'

650 'Hark! the Herald Angels Sing'

659 Carnations and 'THANK YOU'

660 Parrot and 'CONGRATU-LATIONS'

661 Pig and 'HAPPY NEW YEAR'

Greetings Stamps

(Des A. Copp. Litho B.D.T.)

1995 (24 JAN). Perf 13 (C)

684	**653**	18p multicoloured	50	40
		a. Horiz strip of 4. Nos. 684/7 .	2·00	
		b. Booklet pane of 9. Nos. 684/92	6·00	
685	**654**	18p multicoloured	50	40
686	**655**	18p multicoloured	50	40
687	**656**	18p multicoloured	50	40
688	**657**	23p multicoloured	60	55
		a. Horiz strip of 4. Nos. 688/91	2·40	
689	**658**	23p multicoloured	60	55
690	**659**	23p multicoloured	60	55
691	**660**	23p multicoloured	60	55
692	**661**	60p multicoloured	1·50	1·50
684/92		Set of 9	5·50	4·75
		First Day Cover (Nos. 684/91)	6·00	
		First Day Cover (No. 692) . .	2·40	
		Presentation Pack	5·75	

No. 692 commemorates the Chinese New Year of the Pig

Plate Nos.: All values 1A, 1B, 1C, 1D (each ×4)

Sheets: 60p 10 (5×2); others 20 (4×5) the four designs for each value printed together, se-tenant, in horizontal strips of 4 throughout the sheets

Imprint: Central, left-hand margin

Quantities sold: 18p 369,217; 23p 338,047; 60p 101,753

Withdrawn: 31.1.96 (sheets)

662 'Captain Rawes'

663 'Brigadoon'

664 'Elsie Jury'

665 'Augusto L'Gouveia Pinto'

666 'Bella Romana'

Camellias

(Des and litho Questa)

1995 (21 MAR). Perf 14½ (C)

693	**662**	18p multicoloured	55	50
694	**663**	23p multicoloured	80	70
695	**664**	30p multicoloured	90	85
696	**665**	35p multicoloured	1·10	1·00
697	**666**	41p multicoloured	1·25	1·10
693/7		Set of 5	4·25	3·75
		First Day Cover		4·50
		Presentation Pack	4·50	

Plate Nos.: All values 1A (×5)

Sheets: 20 (5×4)

Imprint: Central, left-hand margin

Quantities sold: 18p 398,810; 23p 480,040; 30p 187,651; 35p 160,765; 41p 133,208

Withdrawn: 31.3.96

667 'Liberation' (sculpture, Philip Jackson)

Europa. Peace and Freedom

(Des A. Theobald. Litho Cartor)

1995 (9 MAY). Perf 13½ (C)

698	**667**	23p black and dull violet-blue . . .	55	55
699		30p black and rose-pink	70	95
698/9		Set of 2	1·25	1·50
		First Day Cover		2·25
		Presentation Pack	2·00	

Plate Nos.: Both values 1A, 1B, 1C (each ×4)

Sheets: 10 (5×2)

Imprint: Bottom margin

Quantities sold: 19p 251,352; 30p 278,162

Withdrawn: 31.5.96

668 Baliff and Crown Officers in Launch

669 *Vega* (Red Cross supply ship)

670 H.M.S. *Beagle* (destroyer)

671 British Troops in Ordnance Yard, St. Helier

672 King George VI and Queen Elizabeth in Jersey

673 Unloading Supplies from Landing Craft, St. Aubin's

674a Royal Family with Winston Churchill on Buckingham Palace Balcony, V.E. Day (*illustration reduced. Actual size* 110×75 *mm*)

50th Anniversary of Liberation

(Des A. Theobald. Litho B.D.T.)

1995 (9 MAY). Perf 15×14 (C)

700	**668**	18p multicoloured	40	40
		a. Booklet pane. Nos. 700/1, each ×3, with margins all round	2·00	
701	**669**	18p multicoloured	40	40
702	**670**	23p multicoloured	60	60
		a. Booklet pane. Nos. 702/3, each ×3, with margins all round	2·75	
703	**671**	23p multicoloured	60	60
704	**672**	60p multicoloured	1·50	1·50
		a. Booklet pane. Nos. 704/5, each ×3, with margins all round	7·50	
705	**673**	60p multicoloured	1·50	1·50
700/5		Set of 6	4·50	4·50
		First Day Cover		5·25
		Presentation Pack	5·50	
MS706		110×75 mm. **674a** £1 multicoloured	2·75	2·75
		a. Booklet pane. As No. **MS**706 with additional margins all round showing arms, mace and inscriptions	2·50	
		First Day Cover		3·50
		Presentation Pack	3·50	

Plate Nos.: All values 1A, 1B (each ×4)

Sheets: 20 (4×5)

Imprint: Central, left-hand margin

Quantities sold: 18p (No. 700) 207,666; 18p (No. 701) 214,869; 23p (No. 702) 279,930; 23p (No. 703) 274,379; 60p (No. 704) 131,342; 60p (No. 705) 136,508; £1 122,855

Withdrawn: 31.5.96 (sheets)

675 Bell Heather

676 Sea Campion

677 Spotted Rock-rose

678 Thrift

679 Sheep's-bit
Scabious

680 Field Bind-weed

681 Common Bird's-
foot Trefoil

682 Sea-holly

683 Common
Centaury

684 Dwarf Pansy

European Nature Conservation Year. Wild Flowers

(Des N. Parlett. Litho B.D.T.)

1995 (4 JULY). Perf 13 (C)

707	**675**	19p multicoloured	60	55
		a. *Horiz strip of 5. Nos. 707/11*	3·00	
708	**676**	19p multicoloured	60	55
709	**677**	19p multicoloured	60	55
710	**678**	19p multicoloured	60	55
711	**679**	19p multicoloured	60	55
712	**680**	23p multicoloured	70	65
		a. *Horiz strip of 5. Nos. 712/16*	3·50	
713	**681**	23p multicoloured	70	65
714	**682**	23p multicoloured	70	65
715	**683**	23p multicoloured	70	65
716	**684**	23p multicoloured	70	65
707/16		Set of 10	6·00	5·50
		First Day Cover		6·00
		Presentation Pack	6·50	

Plate Nos.: Both values 1A, 1B (each ×4)

Sheets: 20 (5×4) the five designs for each value printed together, *se-tenant*, in horizontal strips of 5 throughout the sheets the backgrounds forming composite designs

Imprint: Central, left-hand margin

Quantities sold: 19p 454,143; 23p 554,070

Withdrawn: 31.7.96

685 *Precis almana*

686 *Papilio palinurus*

687 *Caropsilia scylla*

688 *Papilio rumanzovia*

689 *Troides helena*

Butterflies

(Des W. Oliver. Litho Questa)

1995 (1 SEPT). Perf 14 (C)

717	**685**	19p multicoloured	50	55
718	**686**	23p multicoloured	55	60
719	**687**	30p multicoloured	80	85
720	**688**	41p multicoloured	1·00	1·10
721	**689**	60p multicoloured	1·60	1·75
717/21		Set of 5	4·00	4·25
		First Day Cover		4·75
		Presentation Pack	4·50	
MS722		150×100 mm. Nos. 720/1	2·40	2·50
		a. *41p value imperforate*		
		First Day Cover		3·25
		Presentation Pack	3·25	

No. **MS**722 includes the 'Singapore '95' International Stamp Exhibition logo on the sheet margin and shows the two stamp designs without frames.

Plate Nos.: All values 1A (×4)

Sheets: 20 (5×4)

Imprint: Central, left-hand margin

Quantities sold: 19p 475,496; 23p 466,880; 30p 246,270; 41p 117,354; 60p 133,026; miniature sheet 76,062

Withdrawn: 30.9.96

690 Peace Doves and
United Nations
Anniversary Emblem

691 Symbolic Wheat and
Anniversary Emblem

50th Anniversary of United Nations

(Des A. Copp. Litho Enschedé)

1995 (24 OCT). Perf 13×14½ (C)

723	**690**	19p cobalt and royal blue	60	50
724	**691**	23p turq-green & dp blue-green .	70	70
725		41p dp blue-green & turq-green .	1·25	1·25
726	**690**	60p royal blue and cobalt	1·50	1·50
723/6		Set of 4	3·50	3·50
		First Day Cover		4·50
		Presentation Pack	4·50	

Plate Nos.: 19p, 23p 1A, 1B (each ×2); others 1A (×2)

Sheets: 20 (5×4)

Imprint: Central, left-hand margin

Quantities sold: 19p 152,550; 23p 201,977; 41p 75,032; 60p 73,943

Withdrawn: 31.10.96

692 'Puss in Boots'

693 'Cinderella'

694 'Sleeping Beauty'

695 'Aladdin'

Christmas. Pantomimes

(Des V. Ambrus. Litho Cartor)

1995 (24 OCT). Perf 13½ (C)

727	**692**	19p multicoloured	50	40
728	**693**	23p multicoloured	55	45
729	**694**	41p multicoloured	1·00	1·00
730	**695**	60p multicoloured	1·60	1·50
727/30		Set of 4	3·25	3·00
		First Day Cover		4·25
		Presentation Pack	4·50	

Plate Nos.: All values 1A, 1B, 1C, 1D (each ×4)

Sheets: 20 (5×4)

Imprint: Central, left-hand margin

Quantities sold: 19p 986,299; 23p 716,510; 41p 118,699; 60p
131,497

Withdrawn: 31.10.96

Post Office Yearbook

1995 (24 OCT). Comprises Nos. 491c and 684/730
Yearbook . . . . 35·00

Sold out: 12.99

696a Rat with Top Hat
(illustration reduced. Actual size 110×75 mm)

Chinese New Year ('Year of the Rat')

(Des V. Ambrus. Litho Questa)

1996 (19 FEB). Sheet 110×75 mm. Perf 13½×14 (C)

MS731	**696a**	£1 multicoloured	2·50	2·50
		First Day Cover		3·25
		Presentation Pack	3·50	

Withdrawn: 28.2.97

697 African Child and Map

698 Children and Globe

699 European Child and
Map

700 South American Child
and Map

701 Asian Child and Map

702 South Pacific Child and Map

704 Elizabeth Garrett (first British woman doctor)

705 Emmeline Pankhurst (suffragette)

50th Anniversary of U.N.I.C.E.F.

(Des A. Copp. Litho Questa)

1996 (19 FEB). Perf 14½ (C)

732	**697**	19p multicoloured	45	40
733	**698**	23p multicoloured	55	45
734	**699**	30p multicoloured	70	65
735	**700**	35p multicoloured	90	80
736	**701**	41p multicoloured	1·00	1·00
737	**702**	60p multicoloured	1·50	1·40
732/7		*Set of 6*	4·50	4·25
		First Day Cover		5·25
		Presentation Pack	5·25	

Plate Nos.: All values 1A (×4)

Sheets: 20 (4×5)

Imprint: Central, left-hand margin

Quantities sold: 19p 464,379; 23p 413,906; 30p 152,043; 35p 84,359; 41p 86,886; 60p 90,074

Withdrawn: 28.2.97

703 Queen Elizabeth II (from photo by T. O.'Neill)

70th Birthday of Queen Elizabeth II

(Litho Questa)

1996 (21 APR). Perf 14×15 (C)

738	**703**	£5 multicoloured	10·00	9·00
		First Day Cover		12·00
		Presentation Pack	11·00	

No. 738 was retained as part of the current definitive series.

Plate Nos.: 1A (×5)

Sheets: 10 (2×5)

Imprint: Central, left-hand margin

Europa. Famous Women

(Des Jennifer Toombs. Litho B.D.T.)

1996 (25 APR). Perf 13½×14 (C)

739	**704**	23p multicoloured	60	60
740	**705**	30p multicoloured	90	90
739/40		*Set of 2*	1·50	1·50
		First Day Cover		2·00
		Presentation Pack	2·00	

Plate Nos.: 23p 1A, 1B, 1C (each ×4); 30p 1A, 1B, 1C, 1D, 1E (each ×4)

Sheets: 10 (5×2)

Imprint: Bottom margin

Quantities sold: 23p 245,907; 30p 432,935

Withdrawn: 30.4.97

706 Player shooting at Goal

707 Two Players chasing Ball

708 Player avoiding Tackle

709 Two players competing for Ball

710 Players heading Ball

(Des A. Theobald. Litho B.D.T.)

1996 (25 APR). Perf 13½×14 (C)

741	**706**	19p multicoloured	50	40
742	**707**	23p multicoloured	60	50
743	**708**	35p multicoloured	95	90
744	**709**	41p multicoloured	1·00	1·00
745	**710**	60p multicoloured	1·60	1·60
741/5		Set of 5	4·25	4·00
		First Day Cover		4·50
		Presentation Pack	4·75	

Plate Nos.: 19p, 23p 1A, 1B (each ×4); others 1A (×4)

Sheets: 20 (5×4)

Imprint: Central, left-hand margin

Quantities sold: 19p 450,588; 23p 458,412; 35p 105,519; 41p 106,826; 60p 109,092

Withdrawn: 30.4.97

Sporting Anniversaries

(Des A. Theobald. Litho Questa)

1996 (8 JUNE). Perf 13½ (No. **MS**751) or 14 (others), both comb

746	**711**	19p multicoloured	50	40
747	**712**	23p multicoloured	60	50
748	**713**	35p multicoloured	95	95
749	**714**	41p multicoloured	1·00	1·00
750	**715**	60p multicoloured	1·60	1·60
746/50		Set of 5	4·25	4·25
		First Day Cover		4·75
		Presentation Pack	5·00	
MS751		150×100 mm. **716a** £1 mult	2·50	2·50
		First Day Cover		3·50
		Presentation Pack	3·50	

Anniversaries:—Nos. 746/8, 750/1, Centenary of Modern Olympic Games; No. 749, 50th anniversary of International Amateur Boxing Association.

No. **MS**751 also includes the 'CAPEX '96' International Stamp Exhibition logo.

Plate Nos.: All values 1A (×4)

Sheets: 20 (5×4)

Imprint: Central, left-hand margin

Withdrawn: 30.6.97

711 Rowing

712 Judo

713 Fencing

714 Boxing

715 Basketball

716a Olympic Torch and Stadium
(*illustration reduced. Actual size 150×100 mm*)

717 Bay on North Coast

718 Portelet Bay

719 Greve de Lecq Bay

720 Beauport Beach

721 Plemont Bay

722 St. Brelade's Bay

Tourism. Beaches

(Des A. Copp. Litho B.D.T.)

1996 (8 JUNE), Perf 14 (C)

752	**717**	19p multicoloured	50	50
		a. Booklet pane. Nos. 752/3, each ×3, with margins all round	2·50	
		b. Booklet pane. Nos. 752/7, with margins all round	4·25	
753	**718**	23p multicoloured	60	60
754	**719**	30p multicoloured	80	80
		a. Booklet pane. Nos. 754/5, each ×3, with margins all round	4·00	
755	**720**	35p multicoloured	95	95
756	**721**	41p multicoloured	1·10	1·10
		a. Booklet pane. Nos. 756/7, each ×3, with margins all round	6·00	
757	**722**	60p multicoloured	1·60	1·60
752/7		Set of 6	5·00	5·00
		First Day Cover		5·25
		Presentation Pack	5·25	
		Postcards (set of 6)	3·00	8·50

Plate Nos.: 19p, 23p 1A, 1B (each ×4); others 1A (×4)

Sheets: 20 (5×4)

Imprint: Central, left-hand margin

Withdrawn: 30.6.97 (sheets)

723 Drag Hunt

724 Pony and Trap

725 Training Racehorses on Beach

726 Show-jumping

727 Pony Club Event

728 Shire Mare and Foal

Horses

(Des P. Layton. Litho Enschedé)

1996 (13 SEPT). Perf 13½×14 (C)

758	**723**	19p multicoloured	50	50
759	**724**	23p multicoloured	60	60
760	**725**	30p multicoloured	80	80
761	**726**	35p multicoloured	95	95
762	**727**	41p multicoloured	1·10	1·10
763	**728**	60p multicoloured	1·60	1·60
758/63		Set of 6	5·00	5·00
		First Day Cover		5·25
		Presentation Pack	5·25	
		Postcards (set of 6)	3·00	8·50

Plate Nos.: All values 1A, 1B (each ×4)

Sheets: 20 (4×5)

Imprint: Central, left-hand margin

Withdrawn: 30.9.97

729 The Journey to Bethlehem

730 The Shepherds

731 The Nativity

732 The Three Kings

Christmas

(Des V. Ambrus. Litho Cartor)

1996 (12 NOV). Perf 13×13½ (C)

764	**729**	19p multicoloured	50	50
765	**730**	23p multicoloured	60	70
766	**731**	30p multicoloured	90	95
767	**732**	60p multicoloured	1·40	1·50
764/7		Set of 4	3·00	3·25
		First Day Cover		4·25
		Presentation Pack	4·25	

Plate Nos.: All values 1A, 1B, 1C (each ×4)

Sheets: 20 (4×5)

Imprint: Central, left-hand margin

Withdrawn: 28.11.97

Post Office Yearbook

1996 (12 NOV). Comprises Nos. **MS**731/63

Yearbook .... 40·00

Sold out: 12.99

733a Jersey Cow wearing Scarf
(*illustration reduced. Actual size 110×75 mm*)

Chinese New Year ('Year of the Ox')

(Des V. Ambrus. Litho Questa)

1997 (7 FEB). *Sheet 110×74 mm. Perf 14×13½* (C)
MS768 **733a** £1 multicoloured . . . . 3·25   3·75
     First Day Cover . . . .   4·50
     Presentation Pack . . . . 4·50

Withdrawn: 28.2.98

'HONG KONG '97' International Stamp Exhibition

1997 (7 FEB). *No. **MS**768 optd with exhibition emblem in black and 'JERSEY AT HONG KONG '97' in red, both on sheet margin*
MS769 **733a** £1 multicoloured . . . . 3·25   3·75
     First Day Cover . . . .   4·50
     Presentation Pack . . . . 4·50

Withdrawn: 28.2.98

734 Lillie the Cow on the Beach

735 Lillie taking Photograph

736 Carrying Bucket and Spade

737 Eating Meal at Mont Orgueil

Tourism. 'Lillie the Cow'

(Des A. Copp. Litho B.D.T.)

1997 (12 FEB)–**99**. *Self-adhesive. Perf 9½* (C)
770 **734** (23p) multicoloured (*a*) 80   85
    a. With copyright symbol after date (*bc*) 70   75

771 **735** (23p) multicoloured (*a*) 80   85
    a. With copyright symbol after date (*bc*) 70   75
772 **736** (23p) multicoloured (*a*) 80   85
    a. With copyright symbol after date (*bc*) 70   75
773 **737** (23p) multicoloured (*a*) 80   85
    a. With copyright symbol after date (*bc*) 70   75
770/3   *Set of 4* . . . . 2·75   3·00
770a/3a   *Set of 4* . . . . 2·50   2·75
     First Day Cover . . . .   4·50
     Presentation Pack . . . . 4·00

Nos. 770/3, which are inscribed 'UK MINIMUM POSTAGE PAID', come, *se-tenant*, in strips of 4 or rolls of 100 with the surplus self-adhesive paper around each stamp removed. Nos. 770/3 were initially sold at 23p each; this was increased to 24p on 10 March 1997.

Printings: (*a*) 12.2.97. Inscr '1997'; (*b*) 2.7.99. Inscr '1999'; (*c*) 16.12.00. Inscr '2000'

Sold out: By 5.2001

738 Red-breasted Merganser

739 Sanderling

740 Northern Gannet

741 Great Crested Grebe

742 Common Tern

743 Black-headed Gull

744 Dunlin

745 Sandwich Tern

746 Ringed Plover

747 Bar-tailed Godwit

758 Great Cormorant

759 Curlew

748 Atlantic Puffin

749 Brent Goose

760 Oystercatcher

761 Ruddy Turnstone

750 Grey Plover

751 Black Scoter

762 Herring Gull

763 Rock Pipit

752 Lesser Black-
backed Gull

753 Little Egret

764 Greater Black-
backed Gull

765 Pied Avocet

754 Fulmar

755 Golden Plover

766 Grey Heron

767 Common
Redshank

756 Common Greenshank

757 Little Grebe

768 Razorbill

769 Shag

Seabirds and Waders

(Des N. Parlett. Litho Questa)

1997 (12 Feb)–**99**. Perf 14½ (C)

774	**738**	1p multicoloured (a)	....	10	10
775	**739**	2p multicoloured (b)	....	10	10
776	**740**	4p multicoloured (d)	....	10	10
777	**741**	5p multicoloured (b)	....	10	15
778	**742**	10p multicoloured (a)	....	20	25
779	**743**	15p multicoloured (a)	....	30	35
780	**744**	20p multicoloured (a)	....	60	45
		a. With copyright symbol after date (c)	....	40	45
781	**745**	21p multicoloured (b)	....	40	45
782	**746**	22p multicoloured (d)	....	45	50
783	**747**	23p multicoloured (e)	....	45	50
784	**748**	24p multicoloured (a)	....	70	50
		a. With copyright symbol after date (c)	....	45	50
785	**749**	25p multicoloured (b)	....	50	55
786	**750**	26p multicoloured (d)	....	50	55
787	**751**	27p multicoloured (e)	....	55	60
788	**752**	28p multicoloured (e)	....	60	65
789	**753**	29p multicoloured (e)	....	60	65
790	**754**	30p multicoloured (b)	....	60	65
791	**755**	31p multicoloured (d)	....	60	65
792	**756**	32p multicoloured (d)	....	65	70
793	**757**	33p multicoloured (e)	....	65	70
794	**758**	34p multicoloured (e)	....	70	75
795	**759**	35p multicoloured (e)	....	70	75
796	**760**	37p multicoloured (a)	....	75	80
797	**761**	40p multicoloured (d)	....	80	85
798	**762**	44p multicoloured (e)	....	90	95
799	**763**	45p multicoloured (e)	....	90	95
800	**764**	50p multicoloured (d)	....	1·00	1·10
801	**765**	60p multicoloured (b)	....	1·25	1·40
802	**766**	65p multicoloured (d)	....	1·25	1·40
803	**767**	75p multicoloured (a)	....	1·50	1·60
804	**768**	£1 multicoloured (b)	....	2·00	2·10
805	**769**	£2 multicoloured (a)	....	4·00	4·25
774/805		Set of 32	....	22·00	24·00
		First Day Covers (4)	....		28·00
		Presentation Packs (4)	.....	26·00	
		Postcards (set of 32)	......	13·00	40·00

MS806 Four sheets, each 136×130 mm. (a) Nos. 774, 778/80, 784, 796, 803 and 805 (a). (b) Nos. 775, 777, 781, 785, 790, 797, 801 and 804 (b). (c) Nos. 776, 782, 786, 791/2, 795, 798 and 800 (d). (d) Nos. 783, 787/9, 793/4, 799 and 802 (e)

Set of 4 sheets	....	24·00	24·00
First Day Covers (4)	....		40·00
Souvenir Folders (4)	......	32·00	
Complete series Souvenir Folder	....	28·00	

Printings: (a) 12.2.97. Inscr '1997' without copyright symbol; (b) 28.1.98. Inscr '1998' with copyright symbol; (c) 2.4.98. Inscr '1998' with copyright symbol; (d) 11.8.98. Inscr '1998' with copyright symbol; (e) 21.8.99. Inscr '1999' with copyright symbol

Plate Nos.: 1p, 2p, 22p, 25p, 26p, £2 1A, 1B, 1C, 1D (each ×4); 20p, 24p 1A, 1B, 1C, 1D (each ×4), 2A, 2B, 2C, 2D (each ×4) (Nos. 780a, 784a); 4p, 21p, 50p, 60p 1A, 1B, 1C, 1D, 1E, 1F, 1G, 1H (each ×4); **MS**806 1A (×4); others 1A, 1B (each ×4)

Sheets: 20 (4×5)

Imprint: Central, left-hand margin

770 De Havilland D.H.95 Flamingo

771 Handley Page H.P.R. Marathon

772 De Havilland D.H.114 Heron

773 Boeing 737-236

774 Britten Norman Trislander

775 BAe 146-200

60th Anniversary of Jersey Airport

(Des A. Theobald. Litho Enschedé)

1997 (10 MAR). Perf 13½×14 (C)

807	**770**	20p multicoloured	....	45	40
808	**771**	24p multicoloured	....	55	40
809	**772**	31p multicoloured	....	65	65
810	**773**	37p multicoloured	....	95	90
811	**774**	43p multicoloured	....	1·10	1·00
812	**775**	63p multicoloured	....	1·75	1·60
807/12		Set of 6	....	5·00	4·50
		First Day Cover	....		5·25
		Presentation Pack	....	5·50	

Plate Nos.: All values 1A, 1B, 1C (each ×4)

Sheets: 20 (4×5)

Imprint: Central, left-hand margin

Withdrawn: 31.3.98

776 The Bull of St. Clement

777 The Black Horse of St. Ouen

778 The Black Dog of Bouley Bay

779 Les Fontaines des Mittes

Europa. Tales and Legends

(Des Jennifer Toombs. Litho B.D.T.)

1997 (15 APR). Perf 15×14 (C)

813	**776**	20p multicoloured	65	60
814	**777**	24p multicoloured	75	70
815	**778**	31p multicoloured	1·10	1·00
816	**779**	63p multicoloured	1·75	1·60
813/16		*Set of 4*	3·75	3·50
		First Day Cover		4·50
		Presentation Pack	4·50	

Nos. 814/15 include the 'EUROPA' emblem.

Plate Nos.: All values 1A, 1B (each ×5)

Sheets: 10 (5×2)

Imprint: Bottom margin

Withdrawn: 30.4.98

'Pacific 97' International Stamp Exhibition, San Francisco

1997 (29 May). *No.* **MS**806a *optd with exhibition emblem on sheet margin*

MS817	136×130 mm. Nos. 774, 778/80, 784, 796, 803 and 805	7·50	8·50
	Souvenir Folder	9·50

780 Cycling

781 Archery

782 Windsurfing

783 Gymnastics

784 Volleyball

785 Running

7th Island Games, Jersey

(Des A. Theobald. Litho B.D.T.)

1997 (28 JUNE). Perf 13½ (C)

818	**780**	20p multicoloured	55	55
		a. Booklet pane. Nos. 818/19, each ×3, with margins all round	2·50	
		b. Booklet pane. Nos. 818/23, with margins all round	5·25	
819	**781**	24p multicoloured	65	65
820	**782**	31p multicoloured	80	80
		a. Booklet pane. Nos. 820/1, each ×3, with margins all round	4·00	
821	**783**	37p multicoloured	1·00	1·00
822	**784**	43p multicoloured	1·10	1·10
		a. Booklet pane. Nos. 822/3, each ×3, with margins all round	6·25	
823	**785**	63p multicoloured	1·75	1·75
818/23		*Set of 6*	5·25	5·25
		First Day Cover		5·75
		Presentation Pack	6·00	

Plate Nos.: 20p, 24p 1A, 1B (each ×4); others 1A (×4)

Sheets: 20 (5×4)

Imprint: Central, left-hand margin

Withdrawn: 30.6.98 (sheets)

786 Mallorcan Midwife Toad

787 Aye-Aye

788 Mauritius Parakeet

789 Pigmy Hog

794 Beech

795 Sweet Chestnut

790 St. Lucia Whip-tail

791 Madagascar Teal

796 Hawthorn

797 Common Oak

Wildlife Preservation Trust (Sixth Series)

(Des W. Oliver. Litho Cartor)

1997 (2 SEPT). Perf 13 (C)

824	**786**	20p multicoloured	. . . .	50	45
825	**787**	24p multicoloured	. . . .	60	50
826	**788**	31p multicoloured	. . . .	90	80
827	**789**	37p multicoloured	. . . .	1·00	1·00
828	**790**	43p multicoloured	. . . .	1·10	1·10
829	**791**	63p multicoloured	. . . .	1·75	1·75
824/9		Set of 6		5·25	5·00
		First Day Cover			5·50
		Presentation Pack	6·00		

Plate Nos.: All values 1A, 1B (each ×4)

Sheets: 20 (5×4)

Imprint: Central, left-hand margin

Withdrawn: 30.9.98

Trees

(Des Norah Bryan. Litho Questa)

1997 (2 SEPT). Perf 14½ (C)

830	**792**	20p multicoloured	. . . .	50	45
831	**793**	24p multicoloured	. . . .	60	45
832	**794**	31p multicoloured	. . . .	90	80
833	**795**	37p multicoloured	. . . .	1·00	1·00
834	**796**	43p multicoloured	. . . .	1·10	1·10
835	**797**	63p multicoloured	. . . .	1·75	1·75
830/5		Set of 6		5·25	5·00
		First Day Cover			5·50
		Presentation Pack	6·00		

Plate Nos.: 20p, 24p 1A, 1B (each ×4); others 1A (×4)

Sheets: 20 (5×4)

Imprint: 30.9.98

792 Ash

793 Elder

798 Father Christmas and Reindeer outside Jersey Airport

799 Father Christmas with Presents, St. Aubin's Harbour

800 Father Christmas in Sleigh, Mont Orgueil Castle

801 Father Christmas with Children, Royal Square, St. Helier

Christmas

(Des Colleen Corlett. Litho B.D.T.)

1997 (11 NOV). Perf 14 (C)

836	**798**	20p multicoloured	60	60
837	**799**	24p multicoloured	70	70
838	**800**	31p multicoloured	1·00	1·00
839	**801**	63p multicoloured	1·90	1·90
836/9		Set of 4	3·75	3·75
		First Day Cover		4·50
		Presentation Pack	4·50	

Plate Nos.: 20p, 31p 1A, 1B (each ×5); others 1A, 1B (each ×4)

Sheets: 20 (4×5)

Imprint: Central, left-hand margin

Withdrawn: 30.11.98

802 Wedding Photograph, 1947

803 Queen Elizabeth and Prince Philip, 1997

804a Full-length Wedding Photograph, 1947
(illustration reduced. Actual size 150×100 mm)

Golden Wedding of Queen Elizabeth and Prince Philip

(Des G. Drummond. Litho Questa)

1997 (20 Nov). Porf 13½ (**MS**842) or 14½ (others), both comb

840	**802**	50p multicoloured	1·50	1·50
		a. Horiz pair. Nos. 840/1	3·00	3·00
841	**803**	50p multicoloured	1·50	1·50
840/1		Set of 2	3·00	3·00
		First Day Cover		3·75
		Presentation Pack	3·75	
MS842		150×100 mm. **804a** £1.50, mult	4·50	4·50
		First Day Cover		5·00
		Presentation Pack	4·75	

Plate Nos.: 1A, 1B, 1C, 1D (each ×5)

Sheets: 20 (4×5). The two designs were printed together, se-tenant, in horizontal pairs throughout the sheets

Imprint: Central, left-hand margin

Withdrawn: 30.11.98

Year Pack 1997

1997 (20 NOV). Comprises Nos. **MS**768, 770/4, 778/80, 784, 796, 803, 805, 807/16 and 818/42
Year Pack .... 45·00

Post Office Yearbook

1997 (20 NOV). Comprises Nos. **MS**768, 770/4, 778/80, 784, 796, 803, 805, 807/16 and 818/42
Yearbook .... 50·00

805a Tiger wearing Scarf
(illustration reduced. Actual size 110×75 mm)

Chinese New Year ('Year of the Tiger')

(Des V. Ambrus. Litho Questa)

1998 (28 JAN). Sheet 110×75 mm. Perf 14×13½ (C)

MS843	**805a**	£1 multicoloured	2·50	2·75
		First Day Cover		3·75
		Presentation Pack	4·25	

Withdrawn: 30.1.99

806 J.M.T. Bristol 4 Tonner, 1923

807 Safety Coach Service Regent Double Decker, 1934

808 Slade's Dennis Lancet, *circa* 1943

809 Tantivy Leyland PLSC, Lion, 1947

810 J.B.S. Morris, *circa* 1958

811 J.M.T. Titan TD4 Double Decker, *circa* 1961

75th Anniversary of Jersey Motor Transport Company. Buses

(Des A. Copp. Litho B.D.T.)

1998 (2 APR). Perf 14 (C)

844	**806**	20p multicoloured	55	50
		a. Booklet pane. Nos. 844/5, each ×3, with margins all round	2·50	
		b. Booklet pane. Nos. 844/9, with margins all round	4·50	
845	**807**	24p multicoloured	65	50
846	**808**	31p multicoloured	75	70
		a. Booklet pane. Nos. 846/7, each ×3, with margins all round	4·00	
847	**809**	37p multicoloured	1·00	1·00
848	**810**	43p multicoloured	1·10	1·10
		a. Booklet pane. Nos. 848/9, each ×3, with margins all round	6·50	
849	**811**	63p multicoloured	1·50	1·40
844/9		Set of 6	5·00	4·75
		First Day Cover		5·75
		Presentation Pack	5·75	

Plate Nos.: 20p, 24p 1A, 1B (each ×4); others 1A (×4)

Sheets: 20 (4×5)

Imprint: Central, left-hand margin

Withdrawn: 30.4.99 (sheets)

812 Creative Arts Festival

813 Jazz Festival

814 Good Food Festival

815 Floral Festival

Europa. National Festivals

(Des A. Copp. Litho Enschedé)

1998 (2 APR). Perf 14×13½ (C)

850	**812**	20p multicoloured	65	45
851	**813**	24p multicoloured	70	55
852	**814**	31p multicoloured	90	90
853	**815**	63p multicoloured	1·75	1·75
850/3		Set of 4	3·50	3·25
		First Day Cover		4·00
		Presentation Pack	4·00	

Nos. 851/2 include the 'EUROPA' emblem.

Plate Nos.: All values 1A, 1B (each ×4)

Sheets: 10 (5×2)

Imprint: Bottom, left-hand corner margin

Withdrawn: 30.4.99

816 Hobie Cat and *Duke of Normandy* (launch)

817 Hobie Cat with White, Yellow, Red and Green Sails

818 Hobie Cats with Pink, Purple and Orange Sails

819 Bow of Hobie Cat with Yellow, Blue and Purple Sail

820 Hobie Cat Heeling

821 Yacht with Red, White and Blue Spinnaker

822 Yacht with Pink Spinnaker

823 Yacht with Two White Sails

824 Trimaran

825 Yacht with Blue, White and Yellow Spinnaker in Foreground

Opening of Elizabeth Marina, St. Helier

(Des A. Theobald. Litho Cartor)

1990 (15 MAY). Perf 13 (C)

854	**816**	20p multicoloured	50	60
		a. Horiz strip of 5. Nos. 854/8 . 2·50		
855	**817**	20p multicoloured	50	50
856	**818**	20p multicoloured	50	50
857	**819**	20p multicoloured	50	50
858	**820**	20p multicoloured	50	50
859	**821**	24p multicoloured	60	55
		a. Horiz strip of 5. Nos. 859/63 3·00		
860	**822**	24p multicoloured	60	55
861	**823**	24p multicoloured	60	55
862	**824**	24p multicoloured	60	55
863	**825**	24p multicoloured	60	55
854/63		Set of 10	5·00	4·75
		First Day Cover		5·50
		Presentation Pack	6·00	

Plate Nos.: Both values 1A (×4)

Sheets: 20 (5×4), the designs were each printed together, *se-tenant*, in horizontal strips of five throughout the sheets, each strip forming a composite design

Imprint: Central, left-hand margin

Withdrawn: 31.5.99

826 Bass

827 Red Gurnard

828 Skate

829 Mackerel

830 Tope

831 Cuckoo Wrasse

International Year of the Ocean

(Des W. Oliver. Litho B.D.T.)

1998 (11 AUG). Perf 15×14 (C)

864	**826**	20p multicoloured	50	50
865	**827**	24p multicoloured	65	65
866	**828**	31p multicoloured	80	80
867	**829**	37p multicoloured	1·00	1·00
868	**830**	43p multicoloured	1·10	1·10
869	**831**	63p multicoloured	1·50	1·50
864/9		Set of 6	5·00	5·00
		First Day Cover		5·50
		Presentation Pack	6·00	

Plate Nos.: 20p, 24p 1A, 1B (each ×4); others 1A (×4)

Sheets: 20 (4×5)

Imprint: Central, left-hand margin

Withdrawn: 31.8.99

832 Cider-making

833 Potato Barrels on Cart

834 Collecting Seaweed for Fertiliser

835 Milking Jersey Cows

Days Gone By

(Des A. Copp. Litho SNP Cambec, Melbourne)

1998 (11 AUG). *Self-adhesive. With copyright symbol after date.* Perf 11½×11 (Die-cut)

870	**832**	(20p) multicoloured (*abcd*)	90	90
871	**833**	(20p) multicoloured (*abcd*)	90	90
872	**834**	(20p) multicoloured (*abcd*)	90	90
873	**835**	(20p) multicoloure (*abcd*)	90	90
870/3		Set of 4	3·25	3·25
		First Day Cover		3·00
		Presentation Pack	2·50	

Nos. 870/3, which are inscribed 'BAILIWICK MINIMUM POSTAGE PAID' and were initially sold at 20p each, come, *se-tenant*, in strips of 4 or rolls of 100 with the surplus self-adhesive paper around each stamp removed.

Printings: (*a*) 11.8.98. Inscr '1998'; (*b*) 2.7.99. Inscr '1999'; (*c*) 3.11.2000. Inscr '2000'; (*d*) 19.11.2001. Inscr '2001'; (*e*) 4.4.2003. Inscr '2003'

836 Irises

837 Carnations

838 Chrysanthemums

839 Pinks

840 Roses

841 Lilies

842a *Lilium* 'Star Gazer'
(*illustration reduced. Actual size* 150×100 *mm*)

Flowers

(Des Wendy Tait. Litho Questa)

1998 (23 OCT). Perf 14×13½ (No. **MS**880) or 14½ (others), both comb

874	**836**	20p multicoloured	50	40
875	**837**	24p multicoloured	60	50
876	**838**	31p multicoloured	75	70
877	**839**	37p multicoloured	90	90

878	**840**	43p multicoloured	. . . .	1·00	1·00
879	**841**	63p multicoloured	. . . .	1·40	1·40
874/9		Set of 6		4·75	4·50
		First Day Cover	. . . . .		6·50
		Presentation Pack	. . . .	5·50	
MS880		150×100 mm. **842a** £1.50, mult	. . .	3·00	3·75
		First Day Cover	. . . .		4·50
		Presentation Pack	. . . .	4·50	

No. **MS**880 includes the 'ITALIA '98' stamp exhibition emblem on the margin.

Plate Nos.: 20p, 24p 1A, 1B (each ×4); 31p, 37p 1A (×4); 43p, 63p 1A, 1B, 1C (each ×4)

Sheets: 20 (4×5)

Imprint: Central, left-hand margin

Withdrawn: 30.10.99

843 Central Market Crib

844 St. Thomas's Church Crib

845 Trinity Parish Church Crib

846 Royal Square Crib

Christmas. Cribs

(Des Colleen Corlett. Litho Cartor)

1998 (10 NOV). Perf 13 (C)

881	**843**	20p multicoloured	. . . .	40	40
882	**844**	24p multicoloured	. . . .	50	55
883	**845**	31p multicoloured	. . . .	65	65
884	**846**	63p multicoloured	. . . .	1·50	1·60
881/4		Set of 4		2·75	3·00
		First Day Cover	. . . .		4·00
		Presentation Pack	. . . .	4·00	

Plate Nos.: All values 1A (×4)

Sheets: 20 (4×5)

Imprint: Central, left-hand margin

Withdrawn: 30.11.99

Year Pack 1998

1998 (10 NOV). Comprises Nos. 775/7, 781/2, 785/6, 790/2, 795, 797/8, 800/1, 804 and **MS**843/84

Year Pack . . . . 15·00

Post Office Yearbook

1998 (10 NOV). Comprises Nos. 775/7, 781/2, 785/6, 790/2, 795, 797/8, 800/1, 804 and **MS**843/84

Yearbook . . . . 50·00

847a Rabbit
(illustration reduced. Actual size 110×75 mm)

Chinese New Year ('Year of the Rabbit')

(Des V. Ambrus. Litho Questa)

1999 (16 FEB). Sheet 110×75 mm. Perf 14×13½ (C)

MS885	**847a**	£1 multicoloured	. . . .	2·50	2·75
		First Day Cover	. . . .		4·00
		Presentation Pack	. . . .	3·75	

Withdrawn: 29.2.2000

848 Jersey Eastern Railway Mail Train

849 Brighton (paddle-steamer)

850 De Havilland D.H.86 Dragon Express at Jersey Airport

851 Jersey Postal Service Morris Minor Van

125th Anniversary of Universal Postal Union

(Des A. Theobald. Litho B.D.T.)

1999 (16 FEB). Perf 14 (C)

886	**848**	20p multicoloured	. . . .	55	50
887	**849**	24p multicoloured	. . . .	65	60
888	**850**	43p multicoloured	. . . .	95	90
889	**851**	63p multicoloured	. . . .	1·40	1·40
886/9		Set of 4	. . . .	3·25	3·00
		First Day Cover	. . . .		4·50
		Presentation Pack	. . . .	4·50	

Plate Nos.: All values 1A (×4)

Sheets: 20 (4×5)

Imprint: Central, left-hand margin

Withdrawn: 29.2.2000

852 *Jessie Eliza*, St. Catherine

853 *Alexander Coutanche*, St. Helier

175th Anniversary of Royal National Lifeboat Institution

(Litho Questa)

1999 (16 FEB). Perf 14½ (C)

890	**852**	75p multicoloured	. . . .	2·00	2·00
		a. Horiz pair. Nos. 890/1	. . . . .	4·50	
891	**853**	£1 multicoloured	. . . .	2·50	2·50
890/1		Set of 2	. . . .	4·50	4·50
		First Day Cover	. . . .		5·00
		Presentation Pack	. . . .	5·00	

Plate Nos.: 1A, 1B (each ×7)

Sheets: 20 (4×5), the two values printed together, *se-tenant*, in horizontal pairs throughout the sheet

Imprint: Central, left-hand margin

Withdrawn: 29.2.2000

854 *Cymbidium Maufant 'Jersey'*

855 *Miltonia Millbrook 'Jersey'*

856 *Paphiopedilum Transvaal*

857 *Paphiopedilum Elizabeth Castle*

858 *Calanthe* Five Oaks

859 *Cymbidium Icho Tower 'Trinity'*

860a *Miltonia* Portelet
(*illustration reduced. Actual size* 150×100 *mm*)

Jersey Orchids (4th series)

(Litho Enschedé)

1999 (19 MAR). Perf 13½ (No. **MS**898) or 14×13, both comb

892	**854**	21p multicoloured	. . . .	55	50
893	**855**	25p multicoloured	. . . .	55	50
894	**856**	31p multicoloured	. . . .	75	70
895	**857**	37p multicoloured	. . . .	85	80
896	**858**	43p multicoloured	. . . .	90	90
897	**859**	63p multicoloured	. . . .	2·00	2·00
892/7		Set of 6	. . . .	5·00	5·00
		First Day Cover	. . . .		5·50
		Presentation Pack	. . . .	5·50	

MS898 150×100 mm. **860a** £1.50, mult . . . . . 4·00   4·50
First Day Cover . . . .   6·00
Presentation Pack . . . . 4·50

No. **MS**898 also includes the 'Australia '99' World Stamp Exhibition, Melbourne, emblem on the margin at top left.

Plate Nos.: 21p, 25p 1A, 1B (each ×5); others 1A (×5)

Sheets: 20 (5×4)

Imprint: Central, left-hand margin

Withdrawn: 31.3.2000

861 Howard Davis Park

862 Sir Winston Churchill Memorial Park

863 Coronation Park

864 La Collette Gardens

Europa. Parks and Gardens

(Des Ariel Luke. Litho Cartor)

1999 (27 APR). Perf 13×13½ (C)

899	**861**	21p multicoloured	50	50
900	**862**	25p multicoloured	70	70
901	**863**	31p multicoloured	1·00	1·00
902	**864**	63p multicoloured	2·00	2·00
899/902		Set of 4	4·00	4·00
		First Day Cover		4·50
		Presentation Pack	4·50	

Nos. 900/1 include the 'EUROPA' logo at top left and all four values show the 'ibra '99' International Stamp Exhibition, Nuremberg, emblem at top right.

Plate Nos.: All values 1A (×4)

Sheets: 10 (2×5)

Imprint: Central, left-hand margin

Withdrawn: 29.4.2000

865 Prince Edward and Miss Sophie Rhys-Jones

Royal Wedding

(Des A. Copp. Litho Questa)

1999 (19 JUNE) Perf 14½ (C)

903	**865**	35p mult (yellow background) . .	1·00	1·00
		a. Pair. Nos. 903/4	2·00	2·00
904		35p mult (blue background)	1·00	1·00
903/4		Set of 2	2·00	2·00
		First Day Cover		2·50
		Presentation Pack	2·50	

Plate Nos.: 1A, 1B, 1C, 1D (each ×4)

Sheets: 20 (4×5) with the two designs printed together, *se-tenant*, in horizontal or vertical pairs throughout the sheet

Imprint: Central, left-hand margin

Withdrawn: 30.6.2000

866 Jersey-built Benz, 1899

867 Star Tourer, 1910

868 Citroen 'Traction Avant', 1938

869 Talbot BG110 Tourer, 1937

870 Morris Cowley Six Special Coupé, 1934

871 Ford Anglia Saloon, 1946

Vintage Cars (3rd series). Centenary of Motoring in Jersey

(Des A. Copp. Litho B.D.T.)

1999 (2 JULY). Perf 14 (C)

905	**866**	21p multicoloured	45	45
		a. Booklet pane. Nos. 905/6, each ×3, with margins all round	2·75	
		b. Booklet pane. Nos. 905/10, with margins all round	4·25	

906	**867**	25p multicoloured	55	55
907	**868**	31p multicoloured	65	65
		a. Booklet pane. Nos. 907/8, each ×3, with margins all round	4·00	
908	**869**	37p multicoloured	80	80
909	**870**	43p multicoloured	90	90
		a. Booklet pane. Nos. 909/10, each ×3, with margins all round	6·25	
910	**871**	63p multicoloured	1·50	1·50
905/10		Set of 6	4·50	4·50
		First Day Cover		5·50
		Presentation Pack	5·50	

Nos. 905a/b, 906a and 909a also include the 'PhilexFrance 99' International Stamp Exhibition emblem on the margins at top right.

Plate Nos.: 21p, 25p 1A, 1B (each ×4); others 1A (×4)

Sheets: 20 (4×5)

Imprint: Central, left-hand margin

Withdrawn: 31.7.2000 (sheets)

872 West European Hedgehog

873 Eurasian Red Squirrel

874 Nathusius Pipistrelle

875 Jersey Bank Vole

876 Lesser White-toothed Shrew

877 Common Mole

Small Mammals

(Des W. Oliver. Litho Cartor)

1999 (21 AUG). Perf 13½×13 (C)

911	**872**	21p multicoloured	45	45
912	**873**	25p multicoloured	55	55
913	**874**	31p multicoloured	65	65
914	**875**	37p multicoloured	80	80
915	**876**	43p multicoloured	90	90
916	**877**	63p multicoloured	1·50	1·50
911/16		Set of 6	4·50	4·50
		First Day Cover		5·50
		Presentation Pack	5·50	

No. 913 is inscribed 'Pipestrelle' in error.

Plate Nos.: All values 1A (×4)

Sheets: 20 (4×5)

Imprint: Central, left-hand margin

Withdrawn: 31.8.2000

878 Gorey Pierhead Light

879 La Corbiere

880 Noirmont Point

881 Demie de Pas

882 Greve d'Azette

883 Sorel Point

150th Anniversary of First Lighthouse on Jersey

(Des A. Copp. Litho Walsall)

1999 (5 OCT). Perf 14 (C)

917	**878**	21p multicoloured	45	45
918	**879**	25p multicoloured	55	55
919	**880**	34p multicoloured	75	75
920	**881**	38p multicoloured	1·00	1·00
921	**882**	44p multicoloured	1·25	1·25
922	**883**	64p multicoloured	2·00	2·00
917/22		Set of 6	5·50	5·50
		First Day Cover		6·00
		Presentation Pack	6·00	

Plate Nos.: All values 1A, 1B (each ×4)

Sheets: 20 (5×4)

Imprint: Central, left-hand margin

Withdrawn: 31.10.2000

884 Mistletoe   **885** Holly

886 Ivy   **887** Christmas Rose

Christmas. Festive Foliage

(Des Colleen Corlett. Litho B.D.T.)

1999 (9 NOV). Perf 14 (C)

923	**884**	21p multicoloured	45	45
924	**885**	25p multicoloured	55	55
925	**886**	34p multicoloured	1·10	75
926	**887**	64p multicoloured	1·60	1·50
923/6		Set of 4	3·50	3·00
		First Day Cover		4·50
		Presentation Pack	4·50	

Plate Nos.: All values 1A, 1B (each ×4)

Sheets: 20 (5×4)

Imprint: Central, left-hand margin

Withdrawn: 30.11.2000

Year Pack 1999

1999 (1 DEC). Comprises Nos. 783, 787/9, 793/4, 799, 802 and **MS**885/926

Year Pack . . . . 48·00

Post Office Yearbook

1999 (1 DEC). Comprises Nos. 783, 787/9, 793/4, 799, 802 and **MS**885/926

Yearbook . . . . 55·00

888 Jersey Crest

New Millennium

(Des A. Copp. Litho, die-stamped and embossed Cartor)

2000 (1 JAN). Perf 13½ (C)

927	**888**	£10 gold, bright red and deep carmine	20·00	20·00
		First Day Cover		22·00
		Presentation Pack	21·00	

The printing of No. 927 incorporates metallic die-stamping and embossing using 22 carat gold.

Plate Nos.: 1A (×3)

Sheets: 10 (5×2)

Imprint: Upper left-hand margin

889a Dragon
(illustration reduced. Actual size 110×75 mm)

Chinese New Year ('Year of the Dragon')

(Des V. Ambrus. Litho Questa)

2000 (5 FEB). *Sheet* 110×75 *mm.* Perf 14½×13½ (C)

MS928	**889a**	£1 multicoloured	2·50	2·50
		First Day Cover		4·00
		Presentation Pack	3·75	

Withdrawn: 29.2.2001

890 'Ocean Adventure' (Gemma Carré) **891** 'Solar Power' (Chantal Varley-Best)

892 'Floating City and Space Cars' (Nicola Singleton) **893** 'Conservation' (Carly Logan)

'Stampin' the Future' (children's stamp design competition) Winners

(Litho Questa)

2000 (9 MAY). Perf 14 (C)

929	**890**	22p multicoloured	55	55
930	**891**	22p multicoloured	55	55
931	**892**	22p multicoloured	55	55
932	**893**	22p multicoloured	55	55
929/32		*Set of 4*	2·00	2·00
		First Day Cover		3·00
		Presentation Pack	3·00	
MS933		150×100 mm. Nos. 929/32	3·00	3·50
		First Day Cover		5·00
		Presentation Pack	4·00	

Plate Nos.: All designs 1A (×4)

Sheets: 10 (2×5)

Imprint: Central, left-hand margin

Withdrawn: 31.5.2001

894 'Jersey in Europe'

895 'Building Europe'

Europa

(Des A. Copp (26p), J.-P. Cousin (34p). Litho Cartor)

2000 (9 MAY). Perf 13½×13 (C)

934	**894**	26p multicoloured	90	90
935	**895**	34p multicoloured	1·25	1·25
934/5		*Set of 2*	2·00	2·00
		First Day Cover		3·00
		Presentation Pack	2·50	

Plate Nos.: Both values 1A (×4)

Sheets: 10 (2×5) 26p; (5×2) 34p

Imprint: Central, left-hand margin (26p); upper left-hand margin (34p)

Withdrawn: 31.5.2001

896 Roman Merchant Ship **897** Viking Longship

898 13th-century Warship **899** 14th–15th century Merchant Ship

900 Tudor Warship

901 17th-century Warship

902 18th-century Naval Cutter

903 19th-century Barque

904 19th-century Oyster Cutter

905 20th-century Ketch

'The Stamp Show 2000' International Stamp Exhibition, London. Maritime Heritage

(Des A. Theobald. Litho B.D.T.)

2000 (22 MAY). Perf 14×13½ (C)

936	**896**	22p multicoloured		60	60
		a. Horiz strip of 5. Nos. 936/40	3·00		
		b. Booklet pane. Nos. 936/9 and 941/4	4·50		
		c. Booklet pane. Nos. 936/7, 939/41 and 943/5	4·50		
		d. Booklet pane. Nos. 936, 938/42 and 944/5	4·50		
		e. Booklet pane. Nos. 936/8, 940/3 and 945	4·50		
937	**897**	22p multicoloured		60	60
		a. Booklet pane. Nos. 937/40 and 942/5	4·50		
938	**898**	22p multicoloured		60	60
939	**899**	22p multicoloured		60	60
940	**900**	22p multicoloured		60	60
941	**901**	26p multicoloured		65	65
		a. Horiz strip of 5. Nos. 941/5 .	3·25		
942	**902**	26p multicoloured		65	65

943	**903**	26p multicoloured		65	65
944	**904**	26p multicoloured		65	65
945	**905**	26p multicoloured		65	65
936/45		Set of 10		6·00	6·00
		First Day Cover			6·50
		First Day Covers (set of 5 booklet panes)			31·00
		Presentation Pack		6·50	
		Souvenir Folder		13·00	
MS946		174×104 mm. Nos. 936/45		6·00	6·00
		First Day Cover			7·00
		Presentation Pack		6·50	
		a. With 'The Stamp Show 2000' logo added to top margin		6·00	6·00
		First Day Cover			7·00
		Presentation Pack		6·50	

Plate Nos.: Both values and miniature sheet 1A (×5)

Sheet: 10 (5×2). The five designs for each value printed together, *se-tenant*, in horizontal strips of 5 throughout the sheets, with 'The Stamp Show 2000' logo on the bottom sheet margin

Withdrawn: 31.5.2001 (sheets)

906 Bottle-nosed Dolphins

907 Long-finned Pilot Whales

908 Common Porpoises

909 Grey Seals

910 Risso's Dolphins

911 White-beaked Dolphin

912a Common Dolphins
(*illustration reduced. Actual size* 150×100 *mm*)

World Environment Day. Marine Mammals

(Des W. Oliver. Litho B.D.T.)

2000 (5 JUNE). Perf 15×14 (C)

947	**906**	22p multicoloured	50	55
948	**907**	26p multicoloured	55	60
949	**908**	34p multicoloured	80	85
950	**909**	38p multicoloured	1·00	1·10
951	**910**	44p multicoloured	1·10	1·25
952	**911**	64p multicoloured	1·50	1·75
947/52		*Set of 6*	5·00	5·50
		First Day Cover		6·00
		Presentation Pack	6·00	
MS953		150×100 mm. **912a** £1·50, multi-		
		coloured	4·00	4·50
		First Day Cover		6·00
		Presentation Pack	4·50	

Plate Nos.: All values 1A, 1B, 1C (each ×4)

Sheets: 10 (2×5)

Imprint: Central, left-hand margin

Withdrawn: 30.6.2001

913 Prince William and Alps

914 Prince William and Polo Player

915 Prince William and Beaumaris Castle

916 Prince William and Fireworks

18th Birthday of Prince William

(Des W. Wall. Litho Questa)

2000 (21 JUNE). Perf 14½ (C)

954	**913**	75p multicoloured	1·50	1·50
955	**914**	75p multicoloured	1·50	1·50
956	**915**	75p multicoloured	1·50	1·50
957	**916**	75p multicoloured	1·50	1·50
954/7		*Set of 4*	6·00	6·00
		First Day Cover		6·75
		Presentation Pack	6·75	

Plate Nos.: All designs 1A (×4)

Sheets: 10 (2×5)

Imprint: Central, left-hand margin

Withdrawn: 30.6.2001

'World Stamp Expo 2000', Anaheim, U.S.A.

(Litho B.D.T.)

2000 (7 JULY). As No. MS953, *but with multicoloured exhibition logo added to top left corner of sheet margin.* Perf 15×14 (C)

MS958	150×100 mm. **912a** £1.50, multi-		
	coloured	3·50	4·00
	First Day Cover		6·00

Withdrawn: 31.7.2001

917 Queen Elizabeth the Queen Mother with Roses

918 Queen Elizabeth the Queen Mother with Daisies

Queen Elizabeth the Queen Mother's 100th Birthday

(Des Colleen Corlett. Litho and die-stamped Questa)

2000 (4 AUG). Perf 14½ (C)

959	**917**	50p multicoloured	1·25	1·25
960	**918**	50p multicoloured	1·25	1·25
959/60		*Set of 2*	2·50	2·50
		First Day Cover		3·25
		Presentation Pack	3·25	
MS961		150×100 mm. Nos. 959/60	2·25	3·00
		First Day Cover		4·00
		Presentation Pack	3·50	
		Souvenir Folder (*containing*		
		MS961, *first day cover and*		
		presentation pack)	16·00	

Plate Nos.: Both designs 1A (×6)

Sheets: 10 (5×2)

Imprint: Bottom margin

Withdrawn: 31.8.2001

919 Supermarine Spitfire
Mk la

920 Hawker Hurricane
MK I

921 Bristol Blenheim
Mk IV

922 Vickers Wellington
Mk Ic

923 Boulton Paul Defiant
Mk I

924 Short Sunderland
MK I

60th Anniversary of Battle of Britain

(Des A. Theobald. Litho Questa B.D.T.)

2000 (15 SEPT). Perf 14 (C)

962	**919**	22p multicoloured	. . . .	50	55
963	**920**	26p multicoloured	. . . .	60	65
964	**921**	36p multicoloured	. . . .	80	85
965	**922**	40p multicoloured	. . . .	90	95
966	**923**	45p multicoloured	. . . .	1·00	1·10
967	**924**	65p multicoloured	. . . .	1·50	1·60
962/7		Set of 6	. . . .	4·75	5·00
		First Day Cover	. . . .		5·50
		Presentation Pack	. . . .	5·50	

Plate Nos.: All values 1A

Sheets: 10 (2×5)

Imprint: Bottom margin

Withdrawn: 29.9.2001

925 Virgin Mary

926 Shepherd

927 Angel

928 Magi with Gift

Christmas. Children's Nativity Play

(Des F. Venton. Litho Cartor)

2000 (7 NOV). Perf 13 (C)

968	**925**	22p multicoloured	. . . .	55	55
969	**926**	26p multicoloured	. . . .	70	70
970	**927**	36p multicoloured	. . . .	1·00	1·00
971	**928**	65p multicoloured	. . . .	1·60	1·60
968/71		Set of 4	. . . .	3·50	3·50
		First Day Cover	. . . .		4·50
		Presentation Pack	. . . .	4·50	

Plate Nos.: All values 1A (each ×4)

Sheets: 10 (5×2)

Imprint: Bottom margin

Withdrawn: 30.11.2001

Year Pack 2000

2000 (1 DEC). Comprises Nos. 927/71
Year Pack . . . . 59·00

Post Office Yearbook

2000 (1 DEC). Comprises Nos. 927/71
Yearbook . . . . 60·00

929a Snake
(illustration reduced. Actual size 110×75 mm)

Chinese New Year ('Year of the Snake')

(Des V. Ambrus. Litho Questa)

2001 (24 JAN). *Sheet* 110×75 mm. *Perf* 14×13½ (C)

MS972	**929a**	£1 multicoloured	2·25	2·50
		First Day Cover		4·50
		Presentation Pack	3·25	

Withdrawn: 31.1.2002

930 *Rose* (1851–61)

931 *Comete* (1856–67)

932 *Cygne* (1894–1912)

933 *Victoria* (1896–1918)

934 *Attala* (1920–25)

935 *Brittany* (1933–62)

Maritime Links with France. Mail Packet Ships

(Des I. Boyd. Litho Cartor)

2001 (24 JAN). Perf 13×13½ (C)

973	**930**	22p multicoloured	. . . .	50	55
974	**931**	26p multicoloured	. . . .	60	65
975	**932**	36p multicoloured	. . . .	80	85
976	**933**	40p multicoloured	. . . .	90	95
977	**934**	45p multicoloured	. . . .	1·00	1·10
978	**935**	65p multicoloured	. . . .	1·50	1·60
973/8		Set of 6		4·75	5·00
		First Day Cover			5·50
		Presentation Pack		5·50	

Plate Nos.: All values 1A (×4)

Sheets: 10 (2×5)

Imprint: Central, left-hand margin

Withdrawn: 31.1.2002

936 H.H.S. *Jersey* (4th Rate), 1654–91

937 H.M.S. *Jersey* (6th Rate), 1694–98

938 H.M.S. *Jersey* (4th Rate), 1698–1731

939 H.M.S. *Jersey* (4th Rate), 1736–83

940 H.M.S. *Jersey* (cutter), 1860–73

941 H.M.S. *Jersey* (destroyer), 1938–41

Royal Navy Ships named after Jersey

(Des A. Theobald. Litho B.D.T.)

2001 (3 APR). Perf 14 (C)

979	**936**	23p multicoloured	. . . .	50	55
980	**937**	26p multicoloured	. . . .	60	65
981	**938**	37p multicoloured	. . . .	80	85

982	**939**	41p multicoloured	. . . .	1·00	95
983	**940**	46p multicoloured	. . . .	1·20	1·10
984	**941**	66p multicoloured	. . . .	1·50	1·60
979/84		*Set of 6*		5·00	5·00
		First Day Cover			5·50
		Presentation Pack		5·50	

Plate Nos.: 23p, 26p 1A, 1B (each ×4); others 1A (×4)

Sheets: 10 (2×5)

Imprint: Bottom, left-hand corner margin

Withdrawn: 30.4.2002

942 Jersey Cows

943 Potatoes

944 Tomatoes

945 Cauliflower and Purple-sprouting Broccoli

946 Peppers and Courgettes

Jersey Agriculture

(Des Colleen Corlett. Litho SNP Ausprint, Melbourne)

2001 (3 APR). *Self-adhesive.* Perf 11½×11 (C)

985	**942**	(26p) multicoloured (*ab*)	. . . .	65	70
986	**943**	(26p) multicoloured (*ab*)	. . . .	65	70
987	**944**	(26p) multicoloured (*ab*)	. . . .	65	70
988	**945**	(26p) multicoloured (*ab*)	. . . .	65	70
989	**946**	(26p) multicoloured (*ab*)	. . . .	65	70
985/9		*Set of 5*		3·00	3·50
		First Day Cover			5·00
		Presentation Pack		3·50	

Nos. 985/9, which are inscribed 'UK MINIMUM POSTAGE PAID' and were initially sold at 26p each, come, *se-tenant*, in strips of 5 or rolls of 100 with the surplus self-adhesive paper around each stamp removed.

Printings: (*a*) 3.4.2001. Inscr '2001'; (*b*) 5.10.2002. Inscr '2002'

947 Queen Elizabeth II

75th Birthday of Queen Elizabeth II

(Des W. Wall. Litho Questa)

2001 (21 APR). Perf 14×15 (C)

990	**947**	£3 multicoloured	. . . .	6·00	6·50
		First Day Cover			7·00
		Presentation Pack		7·00	

No. 990 will be retained in use as part of the current definitive series.

Plate Nos.: 1A, 1B, 1C, 1D, 1E, 1F (each ×4)

Sheets: 10 (2×5)

Imprint: Bottom margin

948 Agile Frog

949 Trout

950 White Water-Lily

951 Common Blue Damselfly

952 Palmate Newt

953 Tufted Duck

954a Common Kingfisher
(*illustration reduced. Actual size* 150×100 *mm*)

Europa. Pond Life

(Des N. Parlett. Litho B.D.T.)

2001 (22 MAY). Perf 14 (No. **MS**997) or 14½×14 (others), both comb

991	**948**	23p multicoloured	60	65
992	**949**	26p multicoloured	70	75
993	**950**	37p multicoloured	1·00	1·10
994	**951**	41p multicoloured	1·10	1·25
995	**952**	46p multicoloured	1·25	1·40
996	**953**	66p multicoloured	2·00	2·25
991/6		*Set of 6*	6·00	6·50
		First Day Cover		7·00
		Presentation Pack	7·00	

MS997 150×100 mm. **954a** £1.50, multicoloured . . . . 5·00 5·00
     First Day Cover . . . . 5·50
     Presentation Pack . . . . 5·25

The 26p and 37p values include the 'EUROPA' emblem.

Plate Nos.: All values 1A, 1B (each ×4)

Sheets: 10 (2×5)

Imprint: Central, left-hand margin

Withdrawn: 31.5.2002

'Belgica 2001' International Stamp Exhibition, Brussels

(Litho B.D.T.)

2001 (9 JUNE). *No.* **MS**997 *optd* 'JERSEY AT BELGICA 2001'
on sheet margin. Perf 14 (C)
MS998 **954a** £1.50, multicoloured . . . . . . 5·00 4·50
     First Day Cover . . . . 5·00
     Presentation Pack . . . . 5·50

Withdrawn: 29.6.2002

955 Long-eared
Owl

956 Peregrine
Falcon

957 Short-eared
Owl

958 Western
Marsh Harrier

959 Northern
Sparrow Hawk

960 Tawny Owl

961a Barn Owl
(*illustration reduced. Actual size* 110×75 *mm*)

Birds of Prey

(Des M. Chester. Litho Cartor)

2001 (3 JULY). Perf 13½×13 (C)

999	**955**	23p multicoloured	50	55
		a. Booklet pane. Nos. 999/ 1004	3·75	
		b. Booklet pane. Nos. 999, 1001 and 1004, each ×2 ..	4·25	
		c. Booklet pane. Nos. 999 ×2, 1000/1 and 1003 ×2	3·25	
		d. Booklet pane. Nos. 999/ 1001, 1002 ×2 and 1004 .	4·00	
1000	**956**	26p multicoloured	60	65
1001	**957**	37p multicoloured	80	85
1002	**958**	41p multicoloured	1·00	95
1003	**959**	46p multicoloured	1·20	1·10
1004	**960**	66p multicoloured	1·50	1·60
999/1004		Set of 6	5·00	5·00
		First Day Cover		6·00
		Presentation Pack	5·75	
MS1005		110×75 mm. **961a** £1.50, multicoloured	5·00	5·00
		a. Booklet pane. As No. **MS**1005, but 153×100 mm with line of roulettes at left	9·00	9·50
		First Day Cover		6·50
		Presentation Pack	6·00	

Nos. 999a/d each have margins all round and a bird illustration on the tab at left.

No. **MS**1005a also differs from the normal miniature sheet by the owl on the post being centred on the stamp. No. **MS**1005 shows the '£1.5' of the face value across the post, but on the booklet pane the figures are to the right of the post.

Plate Nos.: All values 1A (×4)

Sheets: 10 (5×2)

Imprint: Bottom margin

Withdrawn: 31.7.2002 (sheets)

962a Jersey Clipper (yacht)
(illustration reduced. Actual size 150×100 mm)

The Times Clipper 2000 Round the World Yacht Race

(Des B. Ozard. Litho Questa)

2001 (17 SEPT). Sheet 150×100 mm. Perf 13½×14 (C)

MS1006	**962a**	£1.50, multicoloured	4·00	5·00
		First Day Cover		6·00
		Presentation Pack	5·50	

Withdrawn: 30.9.2002

963 Tilley 26 Manual Fire Engine, circa 1845

964 Albion Merryweather, circa 1935

965 Dennis Ace, circa 1940

966 Dennis F8 Pump Escape, circa 1952

967 Landrover Merryweather, circa 1968

968 Dennis Carmichael, circa 1989

Centenary of Jersey Fire and Rescue Service. Fire Engines

(Des A. Copp. Litho Cartor)

2001 (25 SEPT). Perf 13×13½ (C)

1007	**963**	23p multicoloured	50	55
1008	**964**	26p multicoloured	60	65
1009	**965**	37p multicoloured	80	85
1010	**966**	41p multicoloured	90	95
1011	**967**	46p multicoloured	1·00	1·10
1012	**968**	66p multicoloured	1·50	1·60
1007/12		Set of 6	4·75	5·00
		First Day Cover		5·50
		Presentation Pack	5·50	

Plate Nos.: All values 1A (×4)

Sheets: 10 (2×5)

Imprint: Central, left-hand margin

Withdrawn: 30.9.2002

(Litho Cartor)

2001 (16 OCT). *As No.* **MS**1005, *but with brown-red exhibition logo added to bottom left corner of sheet margin and additionally inscr* 'Jersey visits Hafnia 01 Denmark'. Perf 13½×13 (C)

MS1013	**961a**	£1.50, multicoloured	3·75	3·50
		First Day Cover		4·50
		Presentation Pack	4·50	

Withdrawn: 31.10.2002

969 Nativity

970 Street Decorations

971 Carol Singers with Hand Bells

972 Father Christmas

973 Christmas Tree Decorations

974 Adoration of the Shepherds

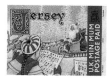

975 Carol Singers and Father Christmas in Sleigh

976 Paper Bell, Chains and Christmas Tree

977 Church Bells ringing

978 Christmas Cracker

Christmas. Bells

(Des M. Pollard. Litho SNP Ausprint, Melbourne)

2001 (6 NOV). *Self-adhesive.* Perf 11×11½ (die-cut)

1014	**969**	(23p) multicoloured (*abc*)		45	50
		a. Booklet pane. Nos. 1014, 1016/18, 1019/20 *and* 1022/3, each ×2 (*a*)	7·75		
1015	**970**	(23p) multicoloured (*abc*)		45	50
1016	**971**	(23p) multicoloured (*abc*)		45	50
1017	**972**	(23p) multicoloured (*abc*)		45	50
1018	**973**	(23p) multicoloured (*abc*)		45	50
1019	**974**	(26p) multicoloured (*ab*)		50	55
1020	**975**	(26p) multicoloured (*ab*)		50	55
1021	**976**	(26p) multicoloured (*ab*)		50	55
1022	**977**	(26p) multicoloured (*ab*)		50	55
1023	**978**	(26p) multicoloured (*ab*)		50	55
1014/23		Set of 10	4·75	5·25	
		First Day Cover		7·00	
		Presentation Pack	6·00		

Nos. 1014/18 are inscribed 'JERSEY MINIMUM POSTAGE PAID' and were initially sold for 23p, and Nos. 1019/23 are inscribed 'U.K. MINIMUM POSTAGE PAID' and were initially sold for 26p. The 5 designs for each value were printed together, *se-tenant*, in strips of 5 or rolls of 100. Nos. 1014, 1016/20 and 1022/3 also come from £3.92 booklets, containing pane No. 1014*a* on which the surplus self-adhesive paper was retained.

Printings: (*a*) 6.11.2001. Inscr '2001'; (*b*) 23.11.2002. Inscr '2002'; (*c*) 10.11.2003. Inscr '2003'

Post Office Yearbook

2001 (1 DEC). *Comprises Nos.* **MS**972/97, 999/1012 *and* 1014/23

Yearbook . . . . 60·00

979 *Duchess of Normandy* (launch)

980 *Duke of Normandy* (tug)

981 *Challenger* (customs patrol boat)

982 *Le Fret* (pilot boat)

983 *Norman le Brocq* (fisheries protection vessel)

States Vessels

(Des A. Theobald. Litho Cartor)

2002 (22 JAN). Perf 13×13½ (C)

1024	**979**	23p multicoloured	50	55
1025	**980**	29p multicoloured	65	70
1026	**981**	38p multicoloured	80	85
1027	**982**	47p multicoloured	1·00	1·10
1028	**983**	68p multicoloured	1·50	1·60
1024/8		Set of 5	4·00	4·25
		First Day Cover		5·25
		Presentation Pack	5·25	

Plate Nos.: All values 1A (×4)

Sheets: 10 (2×5)

Imprint: Bottom, left-hand margin

Withdrawn: 31.1.2003

984 Queen Elizabeth in Coronation Robes (after Cecil Beaton)

Golden Jubilee

(Litho with gold and silver embossing Cartor)

2002 (6 FEB). Perf 13½ (C)

1029	**984**	£3 multicoloured	6·25	6·50
		First Day Cover		7·50
		Presentation Pack	6·75	

Plate Nos.: 1A (×5)

Sheets: 4 (2×2)

Imprint: Upper left-hand margin

Withdrawn: 28.2.2003

985a Horse
(*illustration reduced. Actual size* 110×75 *mm*)

Chinese New Year ('Year of the Horse')

(Des V. Ambrus. Litho Questa)

2002 (12 FEB). *Sheet* 110×75 *mm. Perf* 14×13½ (C)

MS1030	**985a**	£1 multicoloured	2·25	2·50
		First Day Cover		4·50
		Presentation Pack	4·50	

Withdrawn: 28.2.2003

986 Elephant Float, Parish of St. John, 1980

987 Clown with Red Hair, Grouville, 1996

988 Clown with White Hat, Optimists, 1988

989 Performing Seal, Grouville, 1996

Europa. Circus. Carnival Floats

(Des N. Shewring. Litho B.D.T.)

2002 (12 MAR). Perf 14 (C)

1031	**986**	23p multicoloured	50	55
1032	**987**	29p multicoloured	65	70

1033	**988**	38p multicoloured	80	85
1034	**989**	68p multicoloured	1·50	1·75
1031/4		Set of 4	3·00	3·50
		First Day Cover		4·25
		Presentation Pack	4·25	

The 29p and 38p values include the 'EUROPA' emblem.

Plate Nos.: All values 1A, 1B (each ×4)

Sheets: 10 (5×2)

Imprint: Bottom margin, right-hand side

Withdrawn: 31.3.2003

990 Aubrey Boomer

991 Harry Vardon

992 Sir Henry Cotton

993 Diagram of Golf Swing

994 Putting

Centenary of La Moye Golf Club

(Des Jennifer Toombs. Litho Questa)

2002 (16 APR). Perf 14 (C)

1035	**990**	23p multicoloured	50	55
1036	**991**	29p multicoloured	65	70
1037	**992**	38p multicoloured	80	85
1038	**993**	47p multicoloured	1·00	1·10
1039	**994**	68p multicoloured	1·50	1·75
1035/9		Set of 5	4·00	4·50
		First Day Cover		5·50
		Presentation Pack	5·25	

Plate Nos.: 23p, 29p 1A, 1B, 1C, 1D, 1E, 1F (each ×7); 38p 1A, 1B, 1C, 1D, 1E, 1F, 1G, 1H, 1J (each ×7); 47p, 68p 1A, 1B, 1C (each ×7)

Sheets: 10 (2×5) with enlarged illustrated right margins

Imprint: Lower left-hand margin

Withdrawn: 30.4.2003

995 Vauxhall 12, 1952

996 Jaguar 2.4 MkII, 1959–60

997 Austin 1800 1972–73

998 Ford Cortina MKIV, 1978

999 Honda ST 1100 Motorcycle, 1995–2000

1000 Vauxhall Vectra, 1998–2000

50th Anniversary of States of Jersey Police. Patrol Vehicles

(Des A. Copp. Litho Cartor)

2002 (24 MAY). Perf 13 (C)

1040	**995**	23p multicoloured	50	55
1041	**996**	29p multicoloured	65	70
1042	**997**	38p multicoloured	80	85
1043	**998**	40p multicoloured	85	90
1044	**999**	47p multicoloured	1·00	1·10
1045	**1000**	68p multicoloured	1·50	1·75
1040/5		Set of 6	4·75	5·25
		First Day Cover		6·00
		Presentation Pack	6·00	

Plate Nos.: All values 1A (each ×4)

Sheets: 10 (2×5)

Imprint: Bottom, left-hand margin

Withdrawn: 31.5.2003

1001 Honey Bee

1002 Seven-spot Ladybird

1003 Great Green Bush-cricket

1004 Greater Horn-tail

1005 Emperor Dragonfly

1006 Hawthorn Shield Bug

Insects

(Des W. Oliver. Litho B.D.T.)

2002 (18 JUNE). Perf 15×14 (C)

1046	**1001**	23p multicoloured	50	55
1047	**1002**	29p multicoloured	65	70
1048	**1003**	38p multicoloured	80	85
1049	**1004**	40p multicoloured	85	90
1050	**1005**	47p multicoloured	1·10	1·25
1051	**1006**	68p multicoloured	1·50	1·75
1046/51		Set of 6	4·75	5·50
		First Day Cover		6·50
		Presentation Pack	6·00	

Plate Nos.: All values 1A, 1B (each ×4)

Sheets: 10 (2×5)

Imprint: Bottom margin, left-hand corner

Withdrawn: 30.6.2003

1007 Queen Elizabeth the Queen Mother in 1910, 1923 and 2002

Queen Elizabeth the Queen Mother Commemoration

(Des W. Wall. Litho Questa)

2002 (4 AUG). Perf 14×15 (C)

1052	**1007**	£2 multicoloured	4·25	4·50
		First Day Cover		5·50
		Presentation Pack	5·50	

Plate Nos.: 1A, 1B, 1C, 1D, 1E, 1F (each ×4)

Sheets: 10 (2×5)

Imprint: Lower left-hand margin

Withdrawn: 30.8.2003

1008 Hydrangeas

1009 Chrysanthemums

1010 Hare's Tails and Pampas Grasses

1011 Asters

1012 Carnations

1013 Gladiolo

1014a 'Zanzibar' Float (winner of Prix d'Honneur, 1999)
(illustration reduced. Actual size 150×100 mm)

Centenary of 'Battle of Flowers' Parade

(Des M. Pollard. Litho Cartor)

2002 (8 AUG). Perf 13 (C)

1053	**1008**	23p multicoloured	50	55
		a. Booklet pane. Nos. 1053/8, with margins all round . . .	5·25	
1054	**1009**	29p multicoloured	65	70
1055	**1010**	38p multicoloured	80	85
1056	**1011**	40p multicoloured	85	90
1057	**1012**	47p multicoloured	1·00	1·10

1058	**1013**	68p multicoloured	. . . .	1·50	1·75
1053/8		Set of 6	. . . .	4·75	5·25
		First Day Cover	. . . .		6·00
		Presentation Pack	. . . .	6·00	
MS1059		150×100 mm. **1014a** £2 multi-coloured	. . . .	4·25	4·50
		First Day Cover	. . . .		5·00
		Presentation Pack	. . . .	5·00	

Booklet pane No. 1053a exists in three versions which differ in the order of the stamps within the block of six.

Plate Nos.: All values 1A (×4)

Sheets: 10 (2×5)

Imprint: Central, left-hand margin

Withdrawn: 30.8.2003 (sheets)

1015 British Dilute Tortoiseshell

1016 Cream Persian

1017 Blue Exotic Shorthair

1018 Black Smoke Devon Rex

1019 British Silver Tabby

1020 Usual Abyssinian

1021a British Cream/White Bi-colour Cross
(*illustration reduced. Actual size* 110×75 *mm*)

25th Anniversary of Caesarea Cat Club

(Des G. Vasarhelyi. Litho B.D.T.)

2002 (12 OCT). Perf 14 (No. **MS**1066) or 15×14 (others), both comb

1060	**1015**	23p multicoloured	. . . .	50	55
1061	**1016**	29p multicoloured	. . . .	65	70
1062	**1017**	38p multicoloured	. . . .	80	85
1063	**1018**	40p multicoloured	. . . .	85	90
1064	**1019**	47p multicoloured	. . . .	1·00	1·10
1065	**1020**	68p multicoloured	. . . .	1·50	1·75
1060/5		Set of 6	. . . .	4·75	5·25
		First Day Cover	. . . .		5·75
		Presentation Pack	. . . . . .	5·75	
MS1066		110×75 mm. **1021a** £2 multi-coloured	. . . .	4·25	4·50
		First Day Cover	. . . .		5·50
		Presentation Pack	. . . . . .	5·50	

Plate Nos.: All values 1A, 1B (each ×4)

Sheets: 10 (2×5)

Imprint: Lower left-hand margin

Withdrawn: 31.10.2003

1022 Victorian Pillar Box in Central Market

1023 Edward VII Wall Box, Colomberie

1024 George V Wall Box, St. Clement's Inner Road

1025 George V 'Boite Mobile' Ship Box

1026 Elizabeth II Pillar Box, Parade

1027 Modern Pillar Boxes, La Collette

1028a Posting Letter in First Pillar Box, David Place
(*illustration reduced. Actual size* 150×100 *mm*)

150th Anniversary of the First Pillar Box

(Des Colleen Corlett. Litho Questa)

2002 (23 NOV). Perf 14½ (No. **MS**1073) or 14½×14 (others), both comb

1067	**1022**	23p multicoloured	50	55
1068	**1023**	29p multicoloured	65	70
1069	**1024**	38p multicoloured	80	85
1070	**1025**	40p multicoloured	85	90
1071	**1026**	47p multicoloured	1·00	1·10
1072	**1027**	68p multicoloured	1·50	1·60
1067/72		*Set of 6*	4·75	5·25
		First Day Cover		5·75
		Presentation Pack	5·75	
MS1073	150×100 mm. **1028a** £2 multicoloured		4·25	4·50
		First Day Cover		5·50
		Presentation Pack	5·50	

Plate Nos.: All values 1A (×5)

Sheets: 10 (5×2)

Imprint: Bottom, right-hand corner margin

Withdrawn: 31.10.2003

Post Office Yearbook

2002 (2 DEC). *Comprises Nos.* 1024/73
Yearbook . . . . 65·00

1029 Sanchez-Besa Hydroplane

1030 Supermarine S.6B Seaplane

1031 De Havilland DH84 Dragon

1032 De Havilland DH89a Rapide

1033 Vickers 701 Viscount

1034 BAC One Eleven

1035a Jacob Ellehammer's *Biplane*, 1906
(*illustration reduced. Actual size* 112×76 *mm*)

Centenary of Powered Flight

(Des T. Theobald. Litho Cartor)

2003 (21 JAN). Perf 13½×13 (No. **MS**1080) or 13×13½ (others), both comb

1074	**1029**	23p multicoloured	50	55
		a. Booklet pane. Nos. 1074/9 *with margins all round* . . .	4·75	
1075	**1030**	29p multicoloured	65	70
1076	**1031**	38p multicoloured	80	85
1077	**1032**	40p multicoloured	85	90
1078	**1033**	47p multicoloured	1·00	1·10
1079	**1034**	68p multicoloured	1·50	1·60
1074/9		*Set of 6*	4·75	5·25
		First Day Cover		6·75
		Presentation Pack	6·75	

MS1080   112×76 mm. **1035a** £2 multicoloured .... 4·25   4·50
   a. Booklet pane. As No.
   MS1080, *but* 153×100 *mm*
   with line of roulettes at left 4·25
   First Day Cover ....   4·75
   Presentation Pack ...... 4·75

No. 1074*a* comes with three different illustrations on the
margins.
   The stamp in booklet pane No. **MS**1080*a* differs from that
in the normal miniature sheet by having the imprint date
centred, rather than ranged to the left.

Plate Nos.: All values 1A (×4)

Sheets: 10 (2×5)

Imprint: Bottom, right-hand corner margin

Withdrawn: 31.1.2004

1036 Ram
   (*Illustration reduced. Actual size* 110×75 *mm*)

Chinese New Year ('Year of the Ram')

(Des V. Ambrus. Litho Questa)
2003 (1 FEB). *Sheet* 110×75 *mm. Perf* 14×13½ (C)
MS1081   **1036**   £1 multicoloured .... 2·25   2·40
   First Day Cover ....   3·25
   Presentation Pack ...... 3·25

Withdrawn: 28.2.2004

1037 'Portelet' (Adrian
   Allinson)

1038 'Jersey'
   (Lander)

1039 'Channel
   Islands Map'

1040 'Jersey, the Sunny
   Channel Island' (A.
   Allinson)

Europa. Travel Posters

(Des N. Shewring. Litho Cartor)
2003 (11 MAR). Perf 13½ (C)
1082	**1037**	23p multicoloured	50	55
1083	**1038**	29p multicoloured	65	70
1084	**1039**	38p multicoloured	80	85
1085	**1040**	68p multicoloured	1·50	1·60
1082/5		Set of 4	3·00	3·25
		First Day Cover		4·50
		Presentation Pack	4·50	

The 29p and 38p values include the 'EUROPA' emblem.

Plate Nos.: All values 1A (×4)

Sheets: 10 (2×5) 23p, 68p; (5×2) 29p, 38p

Imprint: Lower left-hand margin

Withdrawn: 31.3.2004

1041 Violet
   Channel Light
   Buoy

1042 St. Catherine's
   Breakwater
   Light

1043 Frouquie
   Aubert Light
   Buoy

1044 Mont Ube
   Lighthouse

1045 Banc des
Ormes Light
Buoy

1046 Gronez Point
Lighthouse

Jersey Lighthouses (2nd series)

(Des A. Copp. Litho B.D.T.)

2003 (15 APR). Perf 13½ (C)

1086	**1041**	29p multicoloured	65	70
		a. Pair. Nos. 1086/7	1·25	1·30
1087	**1042**	29p multicoloured	65	70
1088	**1043**	30p multicoloured	65	70
		a. Pair. Nos. 1088/9	1·25	1·30
1089	**1044**	30p multicoloured	65	70
1090	**1045**	48p multicoloured	1·00	1·10
		a. Pair. Nos. 1090/1	1·90	2·10
1091	**1046**	48p multicoloured	1·00	1·10
1086/91		Set of 6	4·25	4·50
		First Day Cover		5·50
		Presentation Pack	5·50	

The two designs for each value were printed together, *se-tenant*, both horizontally and vertically in sheets of ten stamps.

Plate Nos.: All values 1A (×4)

Sheets: 10 (5×2)

Imprint: Lower left-hand margin

Withdrawn: 30.4.2004

1047 Southern-marsh
Orchid

1048 Loose-flowered
Orchid

1049 Spotted
Orchid

1050 Autumn Ladies
Tresses

1051 Green-winged
Orchid

1052 Pyramidal
Orchid

1053a Loose-flowered Orchid
(*illustration reduced. Actual size* 110×75 mm)

Wild Orchids

(Des B. Ozard. Litho Cartor)

2003 (13 MAY). Perf 13 (C)

1092	**1047**	29p multicoloured	60	65
1093	**1048**	30p multicoloured	60	65
1094	**1049**	39p multicoloured	80	85
1095	**1050**	50p multicoloured	1·00	1·10
1096	**1051**	53p multicoloured	1·00	1·10
1097	**1052**	69p multicoloured	1·40	1·50
1092/7		Set of 6	5·25	5·75
		First Day Cover		6·50
		Presentation Pack	6·50	
MS1098		110×75 mm. **1053a** £2 multi-coloured	4·00	4·25
		First Day Cover		5·25
		Presentation Pack	5·25	

Plate Nos.: All values 1A (×4)

Sheets: 10 (5×2)

Imprint: Lower left-hand margin

Withdrawn: 31.5.2004

1054 Sovereign's Orb

1055 St. Edward's Crown

1056 Sceptre with Cross

1057 Ampulla and Spoon

1058 Sovereign's Ring

1059 Armills

50th Anniversary of Coronation. Coronation Regalia

(Des Jennifer Toombs. Litho and die-stamped B.D.T.)

2003 (2 JUNE). Perf 15×14 (C)

1099	**1054**	29p multicoloured	60	65
1100	**1055**	30p multicoloured	60	65
1101	**1056**	39p multicoloured	80	85
1102	**1057**	50p multicoloured	1·00	1·10
1103	**1058**	53p multicoloured	1·00	1·10
1104	**1059**	69p multicoloured	1·40	1·50
1099/1104		Set of 6	5·25	5·75
		First Day Cover		6·50
		Presentation Pack	6·50	
MS1105		150×100 mm. Nos. 1099/1104 ...	5·25	5·75
		First Day Cover		6·50
		Presentation Pack	6·50	

Nos. 1099/1104 were each printed in sheets of 10 (2×5) with enlarged illustrated right-hand margins.

Plate Nos.: All values 1A (×6)

Sheets: 10 (2×5) with enlarged illustrated right-hand margins

Imprint: Lower left-hand margin

Withdrawn: 30.6.2004

1060a Prince William, Prince Charles and Queen Elizabeth
(*illustration reduced. Actual size* 110×75 *mm*)

Royal Links

(Des The Partnership. Litho Questa)

2003 (21 JUNE). *Sheet* 110×75 *mm. Perf* 14×13½ (C)

MS1106	**1060a**	£2 multicoloured	4·00	4·25
		First Day Cover		5·25
		Presentation Pack	5·25	

Withdrawn: 30.6.2004

1061 Rock Samphire and Paternosters

1062 Bluebells and Les Ecrehous

1063 Tree-mallow and Les Ecrehous

1064 Smooth Sow-thistle and Les Minquiers

1065 Thrift and Les Minquiers

Offshore Reefs

(Des Colleen Corlett. Photo Questa)

2003 (5 AUG). *Self-adhesive.* Perf 11 (die cut)

1107	**1061**	(29p) multicoloured		60	65
1108	**1062**	(29p) multicoloured		60	65
1109	**1063**	(29p) multicoloured		60	65
1110	**1064**	(29p) multicoloured		60	65
1111	**1065**	(29p) multicoloured		60	65
1107/11		*Set of 5*		3·00	3·25
		First Day Cover			4·25
		Presentation Pack		4·25	

Nos. 1107/11, which are inscribed 'JERSEY MINIMUM POSTAGE PAID' and were initially sold at 29p each, come *se-tenant* in strips of 5 or rolls of 100 with the surplus self-adhesive paper around each stamp removed.

Nos. 1107/11 are inscr '2003' with copyright symbol before date.

For designs as Nos. 1107/11 printed in lithography by Sprintpak see Nos. 1180/4.

1066 Albino Rex Rabbit

1067 Black Labrador Puppy

1068 Canary and Budgerigar

1069 Hamster

1070 Guinea Pig

1071a Border Collie (*illustration reduced. Actual size 150×100 mm*)

Pets

(Des N. Parlett. Litho B.D.T.)

2003 (9 SEPT). Perf 13×13½ (No. **MS**1117) or 13½ (others), both comb

1112	**1066**	29p multicoloured		95	95
1113	**1067**	30p multicoloured		95	95
1114	**1068**	38p multicoloured		1·20	1·20
1115	**1069**	53p multicoloured		1·70	1·70
1116	**1070**	69p multicoloured		2·20	2·20
1112/16		*Set of 5*		7·00	7·00
		First Day Cover			9·25
		Presentation Pack		9·25	

MS1117   150×100 mm. **1071a** £2 Border collie . . . .   6·50   6·50

First Day Cover . . . .   8·50
Presentation Pack . . . .   8·50

Plate Nos.: All values 1A (×4)

Sheets: 10 (2×5)

Imprint: Central, bottom margin

Withdrawn: 30.9.2004

'Bangkok 2003' International Stamp Exhibition

2003 (4 OCT). No. **MS**1098 optd with 'Jersey at Bangkok 2003' and emblem on sheet margin. Perf 13 (C)

MS1118   110×75 mm. £2 multicoloured . . .   6·50   6·50

First Day Cover . . . .   8·50
Presentation Pack . . . .   8·50

Withdrawn: 31.10.2004

1072 Japanese Quince

1073 Winter Jasmine

1074 Snowdrop

1075 Winter Heath

1076 Chinese Witch-
hazel

1077 Winter Daphne

Winter Flowers

(Des Wendy Tait. Litho Questa)

2003 (10 NOV). Perf 14½ (C)

1119	**1072**	29p multicoloured	60	65
1120	**1073**	30p multicoloured	60	65
1121	**1074**	39p multicoloured	80	85
1122	**1075**	48p multicoloured	95	1·00
1123	**1076**	53p multicoloured	1·00	1·10
1124	**1077**	69p multicoloured	1·40	1·50
1119/24		Set of 6	5·25	5·75
		First Day Cover		6·75
		Presentation Pack	6·75	

Plate Nos.: 29p 1A, 1B, 1C, 1D; 30p 1A, 1B, 1C, 1D, 1E, 1F; others
1A, 1B (each ×5)

Sheets: 10 (5×2)

Imprint: Right-hand side, bottom margin

Withdrawn: 30.11.2004

Post Office Yearbook

2003 (1 DEC). *Comprises Nos.* 1074/1104 *and* **MS**1106/17
and 1119/24

Yearbook . . . . 65·00

1078 Rook

1079 Knight

1080 Bishop

1081 Pawn

1082 Queen

1083 King

Jersey Festivals (1st issue). Festival of Chess

(Des Jennifer Toombs. Litho BDT)

2004 (22 JAN). Perf 14×13½ (C)

1125	**1078**	29p multicoloured	95	95
1126	**1079**	30p multicoloured	1·00	1·00
1127	**1080**	39p multicoloured	1·30	1·30
1128	**1081**	48p multicoloured	1·60	1·60
1129	**1082**	53p multicoloured	1·70	1·70
1130	**1083**	69p multicoloured	2·20	2·20
1125/30		Set of 6	8·75	8·75
		First Day Cover		11·00
		Presentation Pack	11·00	

Plate Nos.: All values 1A (×5)

Sheets: 10 (5×2)

Imprint: Bottom margin

Withdrawn: 31.1.2005

1084a Monkey
(*illustration reduced. Actual size* 110×75 *mm*)

Chinese New Year ('Year of the Monkey')

(Des V. Ambrus. Litho Questa)

2004 (22 JAN). Sheet 110×75 mm. Perf 14½×13½ (C)
MS1131 **1084a** £1 multicoloured . . . . 3·25 3·25
First Day Cover . . . . 5·25
Presentation Pack . . . . . . 5·25

1085 St. Aubin's Harbour   **1086** Mont Orgueil Castle

1087 Corbiere Lighthouse   **1088** Rozel Harbour

Europa. Holidays

(Des A. Copp. Litho Cartor)

2004 (9 MAR). Perf 13×13½ (C)
1132 **1085** 29p multicoloured 95 95
1133 **1086** 30p multicoloured 95 95
1134 **1087** 39p multicoloured . . . . 1·30 1·30
1135 **1088** 69p multicoloured . . . . 2·30 2·30
1132/5 Set of 4 . . . . 5·50 5·50
First Day Cover . . . . 7·50
Presentation Pack . . . . 7·50

The 30p and 39p values include the 'EUROPA' emblem.

Plate Nos.: All values 1A (×4)

Sheets: 10 (2×5)

Imprint: Upper left-hand margin

1089 Green-winged Teal   **1090** Mute Swan
('Eurasian Teal')

1091 Northern Shoveler   **1092** Common Pochard

1093 Black Swan   **1094** European Wigeon
('Eurasian Wigeon')

1095a Mallard
(*illustration reduced. Actual size 150×100 mm*)

Ducks and Swans

(Des N. Parlett. Litho BDT)

2004 (6 APR). Perf 15×14 (C)
1136 **1089** 32p multicoloured . . . . 1·00 1·00
1137 **1090** 33p multicoloured . . . . 1·10 1·10
1138 **1091** 40p multicoloured . . . . 1·30 1·30
1139 **1092** 49p multicoloured . . . . 1·60 1·60
1140 **1093** 62p multicoloured . . . . 2·00 2·00
1141 **1094** 70p multicoloured . . . . 2·30 2·30
1136/41 Set of 6 . . . . 9·25 9·25
First Day Cover . . . . 11·25
Presentation Pack . . . . . . 11·25
MS1142 150×100 mm. **1095a** £2 multi-
coloured. Perf 14 . . . . 6·50 6·50
First Day Cover . . . . 8·50
Presentation Pack . . . . . . 8·50

Plate Nos.: All values 1A (×4)

Sheets: 10 (2×5)

Imprint: Central, left-hand margin

1096 *Cymbidium lowianum 'Concolor'*

1097 *Phragmipedium besseae* var. *flavum*

1098 *Peristeria elata*

1099 *Cymbidium tracyanum*

1100 *Paphiopedilum* Victoria Village 'Isle of Jersey'

1101 *Paphiopedilum hirsutissimum*

1102a *Phragmipedium* 'Jason Fischer'
 (illustration reduced. Actual size 110×75 mm)

Jersey Orchids (5th series)

(Des S. Giovinazzi. Litho Cartor)

2004 (25 MAY). Perf 13×13½ (C)

1143	**1096**	32p multicoloured	1·00	1·00
		a. Booklet pane. Nos. 1143/8 with margins all round . . .	9·50	
1144	**1097**	33p multicoloured	1·10	1·10
1145	**1098**	40p multicoloured	1·30	1·30

1146	**1099**	54p multicoloured	1·80	1·80
1147	**1100**	62p multicoloured	2·00	2·00
1148	**1101**	70p multicoloured	2·30	2·30
1143/8		Set of 6	9·50	9·50
		First Day Cover		11·75
		Presentation Pack	11·75	
MS1149		110×75 mm. **1102a** £2 multicoloured	6·50	6·50
		a. Booklet pane. No. **MS**1149, but 151×100 mm with line of roulettes at left	6·50	
		First Day Cover		8·75
		Presentation Pack	8·75	

Booklet pane No. 1143a exists in three versions which differ in the order of the stamps within the block of six.

Plate Nos.: All values 1A (×5)
Sheets: 10 (2×5)
Imprint: Lower left-hand margin

1103a Invasion Map
 (illustration reduced. Actual size 110×75 mm)

60th Anniversary of D-Day

(Des A. Theobald. Litho Cartor)

2004 (6 JUNE). *Sheet* 110×75 mm. Perf 13 (C)

MS1150	**1103a**	£2 multicoloured	6·50	6·50
		First Day Cover		8·75
		Presentation Pack	8·75	

1104 Mont Orgueil Castle in 13th Century

1105 King John, *c.* 1204

JERSEY

1106 Mont Orgueil Castle in 17th Century

1107 King Charles II, *c.* 1684

JERSEY

1108 Mont Orgueil Castle Castle, 2004

1109 Queen Elizabeth II, 2002

(Des V. Ambrus. Litho Questa)

Jersey—'A Peculiar of the Crown'

2004 (25 JUNE). Perf 14½×15 (C)

1151	**1104**	32p multicoloured	1·00	1·00
		a. Horiz pair. Nos. 1151/2 . . .	2·00	2·00
1152	**1105**	32p multicoloured	1·00	1·00
1153	**1106**	33p multicoloured	1·00	1·00
		a. Horiz pair. Nos. 1153/4 . . .	2·00	2·00
1154	**1107**	33p multicoloured	1·00	1·00
1155	**1108**	40p multicoloured	1·30	1·30
		a. Horiz pair. Nos. 1155/6 . . .	2·50	2·50
1156	**1109**	40p multicoloured	1·30	1·30
1151/6		Set of 6	6·50	6·50
		First Day Cover		8·75
		Presentation Pack	8·75	

Plate Nos.: All values 1A (×4)

Sheets: 10 (2×5). Nos. 1151/2, 1153/4 and 1155/6 were each printed together, *se-tenant*, in horizontal pairs

Imprint: Upper left-hand margin (32p, 33p) or central, left-hand margin (40p)

Salon du Timbre Stamp Exhibition, Paris

2004 (26 JUNE). As No. **MS**1149, *but optd with* "Jersey at Le Salon du Timbre 2004" *at top left corner of sheet margin.* Perf 13×13½ (C)

MS1157	110×75 mm. **1102a** £2 multi-coloured	6·50	6·50
	First Day Cover		8·75
	Presentation Pack	8·75	

1110 Wall Lizard

1111 Ant Lion

1112 Field Cricket

1113 Dartford Warbler

Endangered Species of Jersey

(Des W. Oliver. Litho BDT)

2004 (27 JULY). Perf 15×14 (C)

1158	**1110**	32p multicoloured	1·00	1·00
1159	**1111**	33p multicoloured	1·10	1·10
1160	**1112**	49p multicoloured	1·60	1·60
1161	**1113**	70p multicoloured	2·30	2·30
1158/61		Set of 4	6·00	6·00
		First Day Cover		8·25
		Presentation Pack	8·25	
MS1162		141×174 mm. Nos. 1158/61 each ×2	12·00	12·00

Plate Nos.: All values 1A (×4)

Sheets: 10 (2×5)

Imprint: Bottom margin

1114 Dead Man's Fingers

1115 Devonshire Cup

1116 White Sea Fan

1117 Pink Sea Fan

1118 Sunset Cup

1119 Red Fingers

Corals

(Des Colleen Corlett. Litho Cartor)

2004 (28 SEPT). Perf 13×13½ (C)

1163	**1114**	32p multicoloured	1·00	1·00
1164	**1115**	33p multicoloured	1·10	1·10
1165	**1116**	40p multicoloured	1·30	1·30
1166	**1117**	54p multicoloured	1·80	1·80
1167	**1118**	62p multicoloured	2·00	2·00
1168	**1119**	70p multicoloured	2·30	2·30
1163/8		*Set of 6*	9·50	9·50
		First Day Cover		11·50
		Presentation Pack	11·50	
MS1169	150×100 mm. Nos. 1166/8		6·00	6·00
		First Day Cover		8·25
		Presentation Pack	8·25	

Plate Nos.: All values 1A (×4)

Sheets: 10 (2×5)

Imprint: Lower left-hand margin

1120 Nativity Scene

1121 Fairy Lights over Busy Street

1122 Santa Claus, Children and Christmas Tree

1123 Candles in Church

1124 Three Candles and Holly

1125 Mary and Jesus

1126 Stockings and Candle on Mantlepiece

1127 Five Candles

1128 Angel and Candle

1129 Candles in Window

Christmas Illuminations

(Des M. Pollard. Litho SNP Sprint)

2004 (2 NOV). *Self-adhesive.* Perf 11×11½ (die-cut)

1170	**1120**	(32p) multicoloured	1·00	1·00
1171	**1121**	(32p) multicoloured	1·00	1·00
1172	**1122**	(32p) multicoloured	1·00	1·00
1173	**1123**	(32p) multicoloured	1·00	1·00
1174	**1124**	(32p) multicoloured	1·00	1·00
1175	**1125**	(33p) multicoloured	1·10	1·10
1176	**1126**	(33p) multicoloured	1·10	1·10
1177	**1127**	(33p) multicoloured	1·10	1·10
1178	**1128**	(33p) multicoloured	1·10	1·10
1179	**1129**	(33p) multicoloured	1·10	1·10
1170/9		*Set of 10*	10·50	10·50
		First Day Cover		12·75
		Presentation Pack	12·75	

Nos. 1170/4, which are inscribed 'JERSEY MINIMUM POSTAGE PAID' and Nos. 1175/9, inscribed 'U.K. MINIMUM POSTAGE PAID' were sold at 32p and 33p respectively and were available in strips of 5 and rolls of 100 with the surplus self-adhesive paper around each stamp removed.

(Litho SNP Sprint, Australia)

2004 (3 NOV). *Designs as Nos* 1107/11. *Self-adhesive.* Perf 11 (die-cut)

1180	**1061**	(32p) multicoloured	65	70
1181	**1062**	(32p) multicoloured	65	70
1182	**1063**	(32p) multicoloured	65	70
1183	**1064**	(32p) multicoloured	65	70
1184	**1065**	(32p) multicoloured	65	70
1180/4		*Set of 5*	3·25	3·50

Nos. 1180/4, which are inscribed 'JERSEY MINIMUM POSTAGE PAID' and were initially sold at 32p each, come *se-tenant* in strips of 5 or rolls of 100 with the surplus self-adhesive paper around each stamp removed.

Nos. 1180/4 are inscr '2004' with copyright symbol after date.

Post Office Yearbook

2004 (1 DEC). *Comprises Nos.* 1125/56 and 1158/79

	Yearbook	65·00

COMMEMORATIVE POSTAL STATIONERY ENVELOPE

40th Anniversary of Liberation

1985 (7 MAY). *Cover showing imprinted stamp design as No. 36. Sold at* 25p

PS1   13p multicoloured   . . . .   1·00   2·00

Quantity sold: 79,744

Sold out: 6.85

POSTAGE DUE STAMPS

D **1**

D **2** Map

D **3** Map

(Des F. Guenier. Litho Bradbury, Wilkinson)

1969 (1 OCT). Perf 14×13½ (C)

D1	D **1**	1d bluish violet (ab)		
D2		2d sepia (ad)	65	1·10
D3		3d magenta (ad)	90	1·10
D4	D **2**	1s bright emerald (acd)	1·00	1·10
D5		2s6d olive-grey (acd)	5·50	5·00
D6		5s vermilion (ad)	13·00	14·00
D1/6		Set of 6	15·00	16·00
		Set of 6 Gutter Pairs	32·00	35·00

Sheets: 120 (2 panes 6×10)

Imprint: Central, bottom margin

Printings: (a) 1.10.69; (b) 16.12.69; (c) 18.2.70; (d) 6.6.70

Quantities sold: 1d 98,535; 2d 181,601; 3d 155,832; 1s 174,599; 2s6d 205,962; 5s 200,698

Withdrawn and Invalidated: 14.2.72

Decimal Currency

(Des F. Guenier. Litho Bradbury, Wilkinson)

1971 (15 FEB)–**75**. Perf 14×13½ (C)

D7	D **3**	½p black (a)	10	10
D8		1p violet-blue (a)	10	10
D9		2p olive-grey (a)	10	10
D10		3p reddish purple (a)	10	10
D11		4p pale red (a)	10	10
D12		5p bright emerald (a)	10	10
D13		6p yellow-orange (b)	10	10
D14		7p bistre-yellow (b)	10	10
D15		8p light greenish blue (c)	15	20
D16		10p pale olive-grey (a)	15	20
D17		11p ochre (c)	20	20
D18		14p violet (a)	30	30
D19		25p myrtle-green (b)	35	40
D20		50p dull purple (c)	90	90
D7/20		Set of 14	2·50	2·75
		Presentation Pack	3·50	

Printings: (a) 15.2.71; (b) 12.8.74; (c) 1.5.75

Plate Nos.: 3p 1a, 1d; 8, 25p 1b 1c 1d 11p 1a, 1b, 1d; others 1a, 1b, 1c, 1d

Sheets: 50 (5×10)

Quantities sold: ½p 313,604; 1p 281,598; 2p 205,263; 3p 183,353; 4p 180,948; 5p 199,771; 6p 161,580; 7p 156,534; 8p 154,904; 10p 198,530; 11p 151,638; 14p 147,075; 25p 158,663; 50p 146,602

Imprint: Central, bottom margin

Withdrawn: 31.1.79

D **4** Arms of St. Clement and Dovecote at Samares

D **5** Arms of St. Lawrence and Handois Reservoir

D **6** Arms of St. John and Sorel Point

D **7** Arms of St. Ouen and Pinnacle Rock

D **8** Arms of St. Peter and Quetivel Mill

D **9** Arms of St. Martin and St. Catherine's Breakwater

D **10** Arms and Harbour of St. Helier

D **11** Arms of St. Saviour and Highlands College

D **12** Arms of St. Brelade and Beauport Bay

D **13** Arms of Grouville and La Hougue Bie

D **14** Arms of St. Mary and Perry Farm

D **15** Arms of Trinity and Bouley Bay

(Des G. Drummond. Litho Questa)

1978 (17 JAN). Perf 14 (C)

D21	D **4**	1p blue-green and black	10	10
D22	D **5**	2p orange-yellow and black ...	10	10
D23	D **6**	3p lake-brown and black	10	10
D24	D **7**	4p orange-vermilion and black .	10	10
D25	D **8**	5p ultramarine and black	10	10
D26	D **9**	10p brown-olive and black	10	10
D27	D **10**	12p greenish blue and black ...	15	10
D28	D **11**	14p red-orange and black	20	15
D29	D **12**	15p bright magenta and black ..	25	25
D30	D **13**	20p yellow-green and black	30	30
D31	D **14**	50p deep brown and black	90	55
D32	D **15**	£1 chalky blue and black	1·40	1·00
D21/32		*Set of* 12	3·25	2·50
		Presentation Pack	3·75	

Plate Nos.: All values 1A–1A, 1B–1B, 1C–1C, 1D–1D, 1E–1E, 1F–1F

Sheets: 50 (10×5)

Imprint: Right-hand corner, bottom margin

Withdrawn: 30.9.83

D **16** St. Brelade   D **17** St. Aubin   D **18** Rozel

D **19** Greve de Lecq   D **20** Bouley Bay   D **21** St. Catherine

D **22** Gorey   D **23** Bonne Nuit   D **24** La Rocque

D **25** St. Helier   D **26** Ronez   D **27** La Collette

D **28** Elizabeth Castle   D **29** Upper Harbour Marina

(Des G. Drummond. Litho Questa)

1982 (7 SEPT). Perf 14 (C)

D33	D **16**	1p brt turquoise-green & black .	10	10
D34	D **17**	2p chrome yellow and black ..	10	10
D35	D **18**	3p lake-brown and black	10	10
D36	D **19**	4p red and black	10	10
D37	D **20**	5p bright blue and black	10	10
D38	D **21**	6p yellow-olive and black	10	15
D39	D **22**	7p reddish mauve and black ..	15	20
D40	D **23**	8p bright orange-red and black .	15	20
D41	D **24**	9p bright green and black	20	20
D42	D **25**	10p turquoise-blue and black ...	20	15
D43	D **26**	20p apple-green and black	40	30
D44	D **27**	30p bright purple and black	60	40
D45	D **28**	40p dull orange and black	80	45
D46	D **29**	£1 bright reddish violet & black	2·00	75
D33/46		*Set of* 14	4·50	3·00
		Presentation Pack	4·75	

Plate Nos.: All values 1A, 1B, 1C, 1D, 1E, 1F, 1G, 1H (each ×2)

Sheets: 50 (10×5)

Imprint: Right-hand corner, bottom margin

357

STAMP BOOKLETS

PRICES given are for complete booklets. All booklets are stitched unless otherwise stated.

B **1** Map

1969 (1 OCT)–**70**.

2s Booklet. Blue cover as Type B **1**
SB1   Containing 5×4d (No. 19a), 4×1d (No. 16a),
       all in panes of one with wide margins . . . . .   2·00

B **2** Arms and
      Royal Mace

7s Booklet. Yellow cover as Type B **2**
SB2   Containing 12×4d (No. 19), 6×5d (No. 20),
       6×1d (No. 16b). all in vertical pairs . . . .   13·00
SB2a   Containing 12×4d (No. 19b). 6×5d (No. 20a),
       6×1d (No. 16), all in vertical pairs (5.5.70) . . .   £130

10s Booklet. Pink cover as Type B **2** showing Mont Orgueil
    Castle
SB3   Containing 14×4d (No. 19), 12×5d (No. 20),
       4×1d (No. 16b), all in vertical pairs . . . .   10·00
SB3a   Containing 14×4d (No. 19b). 12×5d (No. 20a),
       4×1d (No. 16), all in vertical pairs (5.5.70) . . .   35·00

Special printings in sheets of 48 were made for manufacturing the 2s. booklets, but the 7s. and 10s. booklets were made up from ordinary sheets, using vertical pairs with stitching through the side margins. Stamps from both sides of the sheet were utilised so that the panes come inverted.

Decimal Currency

1971 (15 FEB).

10p Booklet. Blue cover as Type B **1** showing Martello Tower
SB4   Containing 2×½p (No. 42a), 2×2p (No. 45a)
       and 2×2½p (No. 46a). Each stamp with wide
       margin at bottom   70
SB4a   Containing 2×½p (No. 42a), 2×2p (No. 45a)
       and 2×2½p (No. 46a). Each stamp with wide
       margin at top . . . .   2·75

35p Booklet. Yellow cover as Type B **2** showing The Royal
    Court
SB5   Containing 10×2p (No. 45) and 6×2½p (No.
       46)   95

50p Booklet. Pink cover as Type B **2** showing Elizabeth Castle
SB6   Containing 10×2p (No. 45) and 12×2½p (No.
       46) . . . .   1·75

The panes for Nos. SB4/a were produced in sheets of 48, of which half were *tête-bêche*. In consequence, half the booklets have the blank margin at the bottom (SB4), and the other half at the top (SB4a).

Owing to the postal information printed in the booklets being out of date, supplies of Nos. SB4/a dispensed from machines between 10 July and early September 1972 bore an adhesive label on the front with the words 'RATE TO UNITED KINGDOM LETTERS up to 4 ozs. and postcards 3p' in two lines. They were primarily to warn holiday-makers of the new rate and were issued only through the machines. Of these about 52,000 were sold.

Quantities sold: SB4/a 244,544; SB5 20,875; SB6 17,638

1972 (15 MAY).

20p Booklet. Green cover as Type B **2** showing Jersey Cow
SB7   Containing 8×2½p (No. 46), all in vertical pairs   2·25

30p Booklet. Yellow cover as Type B **2** showing Portelet Bay
SB8   Containing 10×3p (No. 47), all in vertical pairs   25·00

50p Booklet. Pink cover as Type B **2** showing La Corbière
    Lighthouse
SB9   Containing 8×2½p (No. 46) and 10×3p (No.
       47), all in vertical pairs . . . .   1·25

1972 (1 DEC).

10p Booklet. Orange cover as Type B **1** showing Legislative
    Chamber
SB10   Containing 3×½p (No. 42a), 1×2½p (No. 45a)
       and 2×3p (No. 47a). Each stamp with wide
       margin *at bottom*   90
SB10a As SB10 but with margin *at top*   90

Quantity sold: 126,877

1973 (1 JUNE).

10p Booklet. Green cover as Type B **1** *showing Mont Orgueil
by night*
SB11 Contents as No. SB10. Each stamp with wide
          margin *at bottom*   90
SB11*a* As SB11 but with margin *at top*   90

   Quantity sold: 109,129

1973 (10 SEPT).

20p Booklet. Green cover as Type B **2** *showing Jersey Wildlife
Preservation Trust species*
SB12   Containing 8×2½p (No. 46) . . . .   3·00

30p Booklet. Buff cover as Type B **2** *showing Jersey Wild
Flowers*
SB13   Containing 10×3p (No. 47) . . . .   2·00

50p Booklet. Blue cover as Type B **2** *showing 'English Fleet
in the Channel' by Peter Monamy*
SB14   Containing 8×2½p (No. 46) and 10×3p (No. 47)   1·50

   Quantites sold: SB12 8,790; SB13 11,450; SB14 14,145

1974 (7 JAN). *Jersey Wildlife Preservation Trust*

20p Booklet. Green cover as Type B **2** *showing Spectacled
Bear*
SB15   Containing 8×2½p (No. 46) . . . .   1·50

30p Booklet. Yellow cover as Type B **2** *showing White Eared-
Pheasant*
SB16   Containing 10×3p (No. 47) . . . .   1·00

50p Booklet. Red cover as Type B **2** *showing Thick-billed
Parrot*
SB17   Containing 8×2½p (No. 46) and 10×3p (No. 47)   2·25

   Quantities sold: SB15 14,283; SB16 14,049; SB17 15,976

1974 (1 JULY).

10p Booklet. Orange cover as Type B **1** *showing Jersey
Airport*
SB18   Containing 1×3p (No. 47*a*) and 2×3½p (No.
          48*a*). Each stamp with wide margin *at bottom* . .   60
SB18*a* As SB18 but with margin *at top*   60

   Quantity sold: 129,235

1974 (1 JULY). *Jersey Wildlife Preservation Trust*

60p Booklet. Pink cover as Type B **2** *showing Ring-tailed
Lemur*
SB19   Containing 6×3p (No. 47) and 12×3½p (No. 48)   1·60

   Quantity sold: 22,274

1974 (1 OCT). *Jersey Wildlife Preservation Trust*

60p Booklet. Green cover as Type B **2** *showing Tuatara Lizard*
SB20   Contents as No. SB19 . . . .   1·75

   Quantity sold: 20,984

B **3** Artillery Shako

1975 (25 FEB). *Military Headgear*

10p Booklet. Grey cover as Type B **3**
SB21   Containing 1×½p (No. 42*a*), 2×3p (No. 47*a*)
          and 1×3½p (No. 48*a*). Each stamp with wide
          margin *at bottom*   50
SB21*a* As SB21 but with margin *at top*   50

20p Booklet. Rose cover as Type B **3** *showing Shako, 2nd
North Regt*
SB22   Containnig 2×3p (No. 47*a*) and 4×3½p (No.
          48*a*). Each stamp with wide margin *at
          bottom*   60
SB22*a* As SB22 but with margin *at top*   50

   Quantities sold: SB21/*a* 37,849; SB22/*a* 38,854

STAMP SACHETS These are booklet covers with the stamps
loose inside and contained in clear plastic sachets. They are
noted but not priced as such items are outside the scope of
this checklist.

B **4** Post Office Crest

1975 (1 APR). *20p Stamp Sachet. Red cover as Type* B **4**
Containing 2×1p (No. 43), 2×4p (No. 49) and 2×5p (No. 50)

£1 Contents 8 at 1p 8 at 4p 12 at 5p

B **5** Astra Biplane
(*illustration reduced. Actual size 94×56 mm*)

1975 (21 APR). *Aviation History. Pale blue cover* (SB23) *or yellow cover* (SB24)

50p *Booklet as Type* B **2** *showing Supermarine Sea Eagle*
SB23   Containing 6×1p (No. 43), 6×4p (No. 49) and
4×5p (No. 50) .... 1·25

£1 *Booklet as Type* B **5**
SB24   Containing 8×1p (No. 43), 8×4p (No. 49) and
12×5p (No. 50) .... 2·00

Quantites sold: SB23 29,872; SB24 29,608

1976 (29 JAN). *20p Stamp Sachet. Blue cover as Type* B **4**
Containing 3×1p (No. 138), 2×5p (No. 139) and 1×7p (No. 141)

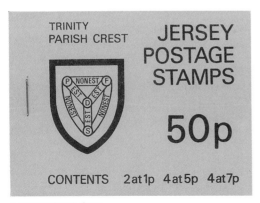

B **6** Trinity Parish Crest

1976 (5 APR). *Green cover* (SB25) *or magenta cover* (SB26) *as Type* B **6**

50p *Booklet. Trinity Parish Crest*
SB25   Containing booklet panes Nos. 138a, 139a
and 141a .... 1·50

£1 *Booklet. St. Ouen's Parish Crest*
SB26   Containing booklet panes Nos. 138b, 139a×2
and 141a×2 .... 2·50

Quantities sold: SB25 85,210; SB26 64,609

1976 (2 NOV). *20p Stamp Sachet. Green cover as Type* B **4**
Containing 3×1p, 2×5p and 1×7p (Nos. 138/9 and 141)

1977 (29 SEPT). *20p Stamp Sachet. Brown cover as Type* B **4**
Containing 3×1p, 2×5p and 1×7p (Nos. 138/9 and 141)

1978 (28 FEB). *Orange-red cover* (SB27) *or pale blue cover* (SB28) *as Type* B **6**

£1 *Booklet. Grouville Parish Arms*
SB27   Containing booklet panes Nos. 138b and 140a
×4 .... 2·50

£1 *Booklet. St. Saviour Parish Arms*
SB28   Containing booklet panes Nos. 138b and 142a
×3 .... 3·00

Quantities sold: SB27 43,446; SB28 45,015

1978 (1 MAY). *30p Stamp Sachet. Violet cover as Type* B **4**
Containing 2×1p, 2×6p and 2×8p (Nos. 138, 140 and 142)

1979 (13 AUG). *30p Stamp Sachet. Purple cover as Type* B **4**
Containing 2×1p, 2×6p and 2×8p (Nos. 138, 140 and 142)

B **7** Jersey Post Office Headquarters, Mont Millais, St. Helier
(*illustration reduced. Actual size 90×65 mm*)

1979 (1 OCT). *Bistre-brown on buff cover as Type* B **7**. *Stapled*
SB29   £1.20 booklet containing Nos. 138b, 140a and
142a each ×2 .... 4·00

Quantity sold: 82,738

1980 (6 MAY). *Black on red cover as Type* B **6** *showing St. Helier Parish Arms. Stapled*
SB30 £1.40 booklet containing Nos. 138b×3, 141a×2 and 143a×2 . . . . 4·50

Quantity sold: 29,900

1980 (6 MAY). *20p Stamp Sachet. Black on red cover as Type* B **4**
Containing 4×1p, 1×7p and 1×9p (Nos. 138, 141 and 143)

1981 (24 FEB). *Black on blue cover as Type* B **6**, *but* 82×65 *mm, showing De Bagot crest. Stapled*
SB31 £1.32 booklet containing Nos. 250a×2, 252a, 256a and 259a . . . . 4·50

Quantity sold: 49,486

1981 (24 FEB). *20p Stamp Sachet. Black on blue cover as Type* B **4** Containing 2×3p and 2×7p (Nos. 252 and 256)

1981 (1 DEC). *Black on green cover as Type* B **6**, *but* 82×65 *mm, showing Poingdestre Arms. Stapled*
SB32 £1.20 booklet containing Nos. 250a, 251a, 256a and 259a . . . . 4·00

Quantity sold: 43,434

B **8** Jean Martell
(*illustration reduced. Actual size* 155×80 *mm*)

Martell Cognac

1982 (7 SEPT). *Multicoloured cover as Type* B **8**. *Booklet contains text and illustrations on labels attached to panes and on interleaving pages*
SB33 £3.08 booklet containing Nos. 293b, 295b and 297b each ×2 . . . . 9·00

Quantity sold: 54,654

1983 (19 APR). *Black on orange-red cover as Type* B **6**, *but* 82×65 *mm, showing Bisson crest. Stapled*
SB34 £1.32 booklet containing Nos. 250a, 251a, 257a and 260a . . . . 4·00

Quantity sold: 29,393

1983 (19 APR). *20p Stamp Sachet. Black on turquoise-green as Type* B **4** Containing 2×½p, 1×8p and 1×11p (Nos. 249, 257 and 260)

1984 (3 JAN). *30p Stamp Sachet. Black in pink cover as Type* B **4** Containing 2×9p and 1×12p (Nos. 258 and 261)

1984 (27 APR). *Black on rose-lilac cover as Type* B **6**, *but* 80×65 *mm, showing Robin crest. Stapled*
SB35 £2.16 booklet containing Nos. 252ba×2, 258ab×2 and 261ab . . . . 8·00

Quantity sold: 38,782

1985 (15 APR). *50p Stamp Sachet. Black on light green cover as Type* B **4** Containing 1×1p, 3×3p and 4×10p (Nos. 250, 252b and 259)

B **9** Cross of Lorraine
(*illustration reduced. Actual size* 155×80 *mm*)

300th Anniversary of Huguenot Immigration

1985 (10 SEPT). *Multicoloured cover as Type* B **9**
SB36 £3.60 booklet containing Nos. 370a/5a . . . . . 10·00

Quantity sold: 31,042

1986 (1 APR). *Black on carmine cover as Type* B **6**, *but* 81×65 *mm, showing Messervy crest. Stapled*
SB37 £3.12 booklet containing Nos. 251ba, 259ba and 263ab, each ×2 . . . . 9·50

Quantity sold 23,729
Withdrawn: 31.3.91

B **10** Post Office Emblem

1986 (1 APR). 50p *Stamp Sachet. Black and orange-vermilion cover as Type B* **10** *Containing* 1×2p, 2×4p and 4×10p (Nos. 251b, 253a and 255)

1987 (6 APR). *Black on blue cover as Type B* **6**, *but* 81×65 *mm, showing Fiott crest. Stapled*
SB38   £3.60 booklet containing Nos. 253ab, 260ba
              and 264ab, each ×2 . . . .   8·00

Quantity sold: 23,647
Withdrawn: 31.3.91

1987 (6 APR). 50p *Stamp Sachet. Black and orange-vermilion cover as Type B* **10** *Containing* 1×2p, 1×3p, 3×4p and 3×11p (Nos. 251b, 252b, 253a and 260)

B **11** Vikings
    (*illustration reduced. Actual size* 168×80 *mm*)

900th Death Anniversary of William the Conqueror

1987 (16 OCT). *Multicoloured cover as Type B* **11**. *Booklet contains text and illustrations on labels attached to panes and on interleaving pages*
SB39   £5.50 booklet containing Nos. 422a/7a . . . . .   15·00

Quantity sold: 30,107
Sold out: 4.88

1988 (17 MAY). *Black on bright green cover as Type B* **6**, *but* 81×56 *mm, showing Malet crest. Stapled*
SB40   £3.84 booklet containing Nos. 253ab, 261ab
              and 265a, each ×2 . . . .   11·00

Quantity sold: 16,566
Withdrawn: 31.3.91

1988 (17 MAY). 50p *Stamp Sachet. Black and orange-vermilion cover as Type B* **10** *Containing* 1×2p, 3×4p and 3×12p (Nos. 251b, 253a and 261)

B **12** Chouan Rebels
    (*illustration reduced. Actual size* 155×80 *mm*)

Bicentenary of the French Revolution. Philippe D'Auvergne

1989 (7 JULY). *Multicoloured cover as Type B* **12**. *Booklet contains text on labels attached to panes and on interleaving pages*
SB41   £6 booklet containing Nos. 501a/6a . . . .   17·00

Quantity sold: 31,052
Sold out: 7.8.99

B **13** Flags of Jersey and Great Britain
    (*illustration reduced. Actual size* 108×63 *mm*)

'Stamp World London 90' International Stamp Exhibition

1990 (3 MAY). *Multicoloured cover as Type B* **13**
SB42   £4.20 booklet containing Nos. 470a, 474a and
              478a, each ×2 . . . .   9·50

Withdrawn: 30.6.96

POSTAGE STAMPS 50p

B **14**

1990 (3 MAY). *50p Stamp Sachet. Multicoloured cover as Type B* **14** *showing* 18p *stamp* (No. 478) *Containing* 2×4p *and* 3×14p (Nos. 470 *and* 474)

B **15** Elizabeth Castle
  (*illustration reduced. Actual size* 108×63 *mm*)

1991 (12 FEB). *Jersey Scenes. Multicoloured cover as Type* B **15**
SB43   £4.80 booklet containing Nos. 471*a*, 475*a* and
  480*a*, each ×2 . . . .   10·50

Withdrawn: 30.6.96

1992 (25 FEB). £1 *Stamp Sachet. Multicoloured cover as Type* B **14** *showing design of* 22p *stamp* (No. 480) *Containing* 1×2p, 2×16p, 3×22p (Nos. 467, 474 *and* 480)

B **16** William Mesny on Horseback
  (*illustration reduced. Actual size* 155×80 *mm*)

Jersey Adventures (3rd series). 150th Birth Anniversary of William Mesny

1992 (25 FEB). *Multicoloured cover as Type* B **16**. *Booklet contains text on labels attached to panes and on interleaving pages*
SB44   £5.50 booklet containing Nos. 573*b*/8*a* . . . . .   12·00

Withdrawn: 30.6.96

B **17** Jersey Post Logo

1992 (25 MAY). *Covers as Type* B **17**. *Panes attached by selvedge*
SB45   £1.12 booklet (scarlet on white cover)
  containing No. 474*b* . . . .   2·75
SB46   £1.28 booklet (bright yellow on scarlet cover)
  containing No. 476*a* . . . .   3·50
SB47   £1.76 booklet (scarlet on bright yellow cover)
  containing No. 482*a* . . . .   4·50

Withdrawn: 30.6.96

1993 (26 JAN). *Covers as Type* B **17**. *Panes attached by selvedge*
SB48   (£1.36) booklet (bright yellow on green cover)
  containing pane No. 601*a* . . . .   5·00
SB49   (£1.84) booklet (scarlet on flesh cover)
  containing pane No. 605*a* . . . .   5·50
SB50   (£2.24) booklet (white on bright new blue
  cover) containing pane No. 609*a* . . . .   7·00

Face values quoted for each booklet are those at which they were initially sold. The price of No. SB48 was increased to £1.44 and that of No. SB50 to £2.40 on 10 January 1994. No. SB48 was sold at £1.52 from 4 July 1995. On 10 March 1997. No. SB48 was increased to £1.60, No. SB49 to £1.92 and No. SB50 to £2.48.

Withdrawn: 30.9.99

B **18** Invasion Map
  (*illustration reduced. Actual size* 162×98 *mm*)

50th Anniversary of D-Day

1994 (6 JUNE). *Multicoloured cover as Type D 18. Booklet contains text and illustrations on panes and interleaving pages*

SB51   £5.68 booklet containing Nos. 659a/b, 661a
and 663a . . . .   17·00

Sold out: 12.94

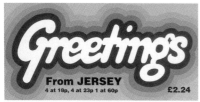

B **19** 'Greetings From JERSEY'
(*illustration reduced. Actual size 152×75 mm*)

Greetings Stamps

1995 (24 JAN). *Multicoloured cover as Type B 19. Pane attached by selvedge*

SB52   £2.24 booklet containing pane No. 684b . . . .   6·00

Quantity sold: 65,810

Withdrawn: 30.9.99

B **20** Crowd Celebrating
(*illustration reduced. Actual size 162×97 mm*)

50th Anniversary of Liberation

1995 (9 MAY). *Multicoloured cover as Type B 20. Booklet contains text and illustrations on panes and interleaving pages*

SB53   £7.06 booklet containing Nos. 700a, 702a,
704a and **MS**706a . . . .   14·00

B **21** Mont Orgueil Castle, Gorey
(*illustration reduced. Actual size 164×97 mm*)

Tourism

1996 (8 JUNE). *Multicoloured cover as Type B 21. Booklet contains text and illustrations on panes and interleaving pages*

SB54   £8.32 booklet containing Nos. 752a/b, 754a
and 756a . . . .   16·00

B **22** Island Sports
(*illustration reduced. Actual size 163×98 mm*)

7th Island Games, Jersey

1997 (28 JUNE). *Multicoloured cover as Type B 22. Booklet contains text and illustrations on panes and interleaving pages*

SB55   £8.72 booklet containing Nos. 818a/b, 820a
and 822a . . . .   17·00

B **23** Buses in Royal Square, St. Helier
(*illustration reduced. Actual size 164×98 mm*)

75th Anniversary of Jersey Motor Transport Company. Buses

1998 (2 APR). *Multicoloured cover as Type B* **23**. *Booklet contains text and illustrations on panes and interleaving pages*
SB56   £8.72 booklet containing Nos. 844a/b, 846a
and 848a . . . .   17·00

B **24** Four Vintage Humbers at the Weighbridge, 1905
(*illustration reduced. Actual size* 164×98 *mm*)

Centenary of Motoring in Jersey

1999 (2 JULY). *Multicoloured cover as Type B* **24**. *Booklet contains text and illustrations on panes and interleaving pages*
SB57   £8.80 booklet containing Nos. 905a/b, 907a
and 909a . . . .   17·00

B **25** Full-rigged Sailing Ship
(*illustration reduced. Actual size* 164×100 *mm*)

'The Stamp Show 2000' International Stamp Exhibition, London. Maritime Heritage

2000 (22 MAY). *Multicoloured cover as Type B* **25**. *Booklet contains text and illustrations on interleaving pages. Stitched*
SB58   £9.60 booklet containing Nos. 936b/e and
937a . . . .   19·00

B **26** Two Tawny Owls on Gate
(*illustration reduced. Actual size* 164×101 *mm*)

Birds of Prey

2001 (3 JULY). *Multicoloured cover as Type B* **26**. *Booklet contains text and illustrations on panes and interleaving pages. Stitched*
SB59   £10.76 booklet containing Nos. 999a/d and
MS1005a . . . .   21·00

B **27** Bells

Christmas

2001 (6 NOV). *Multicoloured cover as Type B* **27**. *Self-adhesive*
SB60   £3.92 booklet containing No. 1014a . . . .   7·75

B **28** Mickey Mouse Float
(*illustration reduced. Actual size* 165×100 *mm*)

Centenary of 'Battle of Flowers' Parade

2002 (8 AUG). *Multicoloured cover as Type B* **20**. *Booklet contains text and illustrations on panes and interleaving pages. Stitched.*

SB61 £9.35 booklet containing Nos. 1053a×3 and
  MS1059 . . . . 19·00

B **29** Ellehammer's *Biplane* and Space Shuttle
  (*illustration reduced. Actual size* 164×100 *mm*)

Centenary of Powered Flight

2003 (21 JAN). *Multicoloured cover as Type B* **29**. *Booklet contains text and illustrations on panes and interleaving pages. Stitched.*

SB62 £7.35 booklet containing No. 1074a×3, with
  different marginal illustrations, and **MS**1080a 15·00

B **30** *Paphiopedilum chamberlainianum*
  (*illustration reduced. Actual size* 165×100 *mm*)

Jersey Orchids (5th series)

2004 (25 MAY). *Multicoloured cover as Type B* **30**. *Booklet contains text and illustrations on panes and interleaving pages. Stitched.*

SB63 £10.73 booklet containing No. 1143a×3 and
  MS1149a . . . . 35·00

STANLEY GIBBONS

Certificate

Insurance valuations

Stanley Gibbons can provide a realistic, up-to-date valuation of your collection, essential when trying to decide on suitable insurance cover. Whether you need a valuation to cover replacement value, reimbursement in the event of total loss, or a valuation for probate purposes, Stanley Gibbons can assist you. With reasonable charges and over 140 years experience, you can be sure that a Stanley Gibbons valuation will provide you with the most accurate information available.

For further information, please contact the   Valuation Department

on 0207 836 8444,
email: valuations@stanleygibbons.co.uk,
or in writing to
Stanley Gibbons Ltd,
399 Strand,
London, WC2R 0LX

Davo Albums

With a space for each stamp and with crystal-clear protective mounts already affixed for immediate insertion of your stamps, these Luxury albums really are the albums for the collector who wants to give his collection a touch of class.

The leaves, which are of finest quality paper, have been expertly arranged and include selected illustrations and descriptions for your guidance.

Handsomely bound in navy blue leatherette, the deeply padded binders are richly embossed with the national crest of the country on the cover and spine, and each is presented in its own matching slipcase to keep both binder and collection in pristine condition. An album of this quality and craftmanship will lend an air of distinction to every collection and at the same time offer the security and protection that your stamps demand.

Davo Luxury

Country	Volume	Description	Item No	Price
Alderney	I	1983-2003	5292	£59.95
Guernsey	I	1969-1999	5549	£104.95
	II	2000-2003	5559	£52.95
Alderney	I, I & II	1969-2003	5549(SO)	£191.95

Guernsey Set

Jersey	I	1969-1999	5550	£104.95
	II	2000-2003	5560	£52.95
	I & II		1969-2003 5550(SO)	£142.95
Isle of Man	I	1973-1999	5286	£104.95
	II	2000-2003	5294	£49.95
	I & II	1973-2003	5286(SO)	£138.95

The Davo Standard binder is covered in finely woven navy canvas with the brass screw heads of the peg fittings easily accessible on either side of the spine. This album offers all the advantages of high capacity (all countries fit into either one or two binders), superb quality, handmade to the highest specifications, attractive cover design, selected stamp illustrations, professional layout, a luxury slipcase and, above all, superlative value for money.

Davo Standard

Country	Volume	Description	Item No	Price
Alderney, Guernsey, Jersey & Isle of Man				
	I	1969-1990	5287ST	£69.95
	II	1991-1999	5292ST	£69.95
	III	2000-2003	5294ST	£59.95
	I,II & III	1969-2003	5287ST(SO)	£160.95

Yearly supplements, accessories and many more country albums are also available, please phone for your free DAVO brochure.

Freephone: 0800 611 622

Source code PUBCGMAD05

STANLEY GIBBONS

First Day Cover Albums

Albums tailor-made for cover collectors

Stanley Gibbon's cover albums are designed to meet the needs of today's first day cover collectors and postal historians alike. All feature high-capacity padded PVC binders, each gold blocked on the spine and polypropylene leaves which do not crease, degrade or tear easily, protect against UV light and contain black insert cards.

1. New Pioneer

A great value single cover album available in red, green or black with 20 leaves to hold 40 covers up to 5.125 x 9.25 inches. Capacity 30 leaves.

- ■ **3510 New Pioneer Album (20 leaves)**   **£11.95**
- ■ **3511 Extra leaves (per 10)**   **£3.50**

2. New Classic

A compact deluxe single cover album available in deep blue or maroon with 20 reinforced, easy-access leaves to hold 40 covers up to 5 x 9 inches plus two matching index leaves and a leaf compression clip.

- ■ **3525 New Classic Album (20 leaves)**   **£15.95**
- ■ **3526 Extra leaves (per 10)**   **£5.50**

3. Malvern

An excellent fully-padded 4-ring double cover album in blue, green or red. Contains 19 double leaves to hold 5 x 8.75 inch covers and one single pocket leaf measuring 10.25 x 8.75 inches. A matching slipcase is now also available.

- ■ **3588 Malvern Album (20 leaves)**   **£13.95**
- ■ **3593 Extra double leaves (per 10)**   **£4.95**
- ■ **3594 Extra single leaves (per 10)**   **£4.95**
- ■ **3590 Malvern Slipbox**   **£7.95**
- ■ **3588(SC) Malvern Album with Slipbox**   **£19.95**

4. SG Major

The top-of-the-range album for that really special collection. Features a luxury padded maroon or deep blue peg-fitting binder, 15 reinforced double pocket and 5 single pocket leaves to hold 70 covers and two matching index leaves.

- ■ **3550 SG Major Album (20 leaves)**   **£21.95**
- ■ **3551 Extra double leaves (per 10)**   **£7.50**
- ■ **3552 Extra single leaves (per 10)**   **£7.50**

Order on FREEPHONE 0800 611 622 (UK only)

Stanley Gibbons Publications, 7 Parkside, Christchurch Road, Ringwood, Hampshire BH24 3SH
www.stanleygibbons.com   +44 (0)1425 472 363

Stanley Gibbons
One Country Albums

These albums have something the others do not...

Ideal for the straightforward single country collection and the only Commonwealth one-country albums that feature **Stanley Gibbons catalogue numbers throughout**.

Available as separate volumes or in a great value set, all albums accommodate high-quality printed leaves featuring illustrations, Stanley Gibbons catalogue numbers and dates of issue. Supplements are produced annually to keep your collection up to date. Each volume is housed in a padded 4 or 22-ring maroon PVC binder, gold blocked on the spine and supplied with a self-adhesive title sheet.

British Islands Albums (with 22-Ring binders)

■	5524	Guernsey Volume 1 (1941-1994)	**£34.95**
■	5526	Guernsey Volume 2 (1995-2004)	**£34.95**
■	5525	Jersey Volume 1 (1941-1994)	**£34.95**
■	5527	Jersey Volume 2 (1995-2004)	**£34.95**
■	5256	Isle of Man Volume 1 (1958-1994)	**£34.95**
■	5257	Isle of Man Volume. 2 (1995-2004)	**£34.95**
■		Guernsey, Jersey OR Isle of Man	
		2-Volume Set Offer Save £7.95	**£61.95**

Many more albums and accessories are available, please contact us for your FREE Lighthouse brochure.

Freephone: 0800 611 622

Source code PUBPSAD04

STANLEY GIBBONS

The most famous name in philately

S erving collectors for over 100 years, our showroom at 399 Strand is the world's largest stamp shop, covering everything philatelic from the highest quality Penny Blacks to the latest in watermark detection technology. Whether you are an experienced collector or just starting out, our friendly team of staff is happy to help with any query you may have.

With millions of stamps in stock at any time, we cater for the requirements of all collectors - from beginner to connoisseur

- **Over 1200 stockbooks containing stamps from 1840 to the latest issues**

- **Catalogues, albums and accessories from Stanley Gibbons and other leading names**

- **Our bookshelf section contains hundreds of rare philatelic titles from around the world**

- **Valuations available by appointment from our dedicated team of experts**

We cannot begin to do 399 Strand any justice in print so please take the time to visit our shop to judge for yourself, you will not be disappointed.

A collectors' paradise

The world famous philatelic counter

COLLECT CHANNEL ISLANDS AND ISLE OF MAN STAMPS

Priority order form
Four easy ways to order

Phone:
020 7836 8444
Overseas: +44 (0)20 7836 8444

Fax:
020 7557 4499
Overseas: +44 (0)20 7557 4499

Email:
stampsales@stanleygibbons.co.uk

Post:
Lesley Mourne,
Stamp Mail Order Department
Stanley Gibbons Ltd, 399 Strand
London, WC2R 0LX, England

Customer details

Account Number_____

Name_____

Address _____

_____ Postcode_____

Country _____ Email _____

Tel no _____ Fax no _____

Payment details

Registered Postage & Packing   £3.60

I enclose my cheque/postal order for
£............. in full payment. Please make
cheques/postal orders payable to Stanley
Gibbons Ltd.

Please debit my credit card for £.............
in full payment. I have completed the
Credit Card section below.

Card Number

☐☐☐☐☐☐☐☐☐☐☐☐☐☐☐☐☐☐

Start Date (Switch & Amex) Expiry Date   Issue No (switch)

☐☐☐☐   ☐☐☐☐   ☐☐

Signature _____ Date _____

COLLECT CHANNEL ISLANDS AND ISLE OF MAN STAMPS

Priority order form
Four easy ways to order

Condition (mint/UM/used)	Country	SG No.	Description	Price	Office use only
			SUB TOTAL	£	
			POSTAGE & PACKAGING	£3.60	
			GRAND TOTAL	£	

Please complete payment, name and address details overleaf